WHOLE
GRAIN
CEREAL
ENRICHED

FOOD
for the
FAMILY

FOOD *for the* FAMILY

FIFTH EDITION

An Elementary College Text

JENNIE S. WILMOT
Associate Professor Emeritus of Home Economics
The University of Texas

MARGARET Q. BATJER
Associate Professor of Foods and Nutrition
The Pennsylvania State University

Artistic Drawings by Mitsu Nakayama

J. B. LIPPINCOTT COMPANY
Chicago · Philadelphia · New York

LIBRARY OF CONGRESS CATALOG CARD NUMBER: 60–11508

5.644.4

This text is a revised volume, based on the authors' earlier works of the same title, copyrights 1938, 1944, 1950, and 1955 by J. B. Lippincott Company

PRINTED IN THE UNITED STATES OF AMERICA

To college students and homemakers interested
in improving food habits and standards
for families throughout the world
and to friends who have given
generously of their time and
talents in helping to
make this a useful
volume

PREFACE TO FIFTH EDITION

It has been more than two decades since the first edition of *Food for the Family* was published. During this time, there have been many changes in all areas of family living, but none more significant than those surrounding the multiple aspects of food for the family. Today's supermarkets are symbolic of these changes. They are largely responsible for alterations in buying habits and for greater variety in food served. Families have also made other adjustments because of new findings in nutrition research and continuing progress in the areas of equipment and all phases of food technology. As our standard of living has continued to rise, more family members, especially mothers, have become wage earners in order to purchase desired consumer goods and services. All of these factors have affected food for the family.

As drastic changes in family living have occurred, educational programs designed to benefit families have also undergone change. The approach to teaching foods has had to be continuously altered in order to keep pace with our fast-moving age.

The fifth edition of *Food for the Family* gives consideration to both the new requirements of families and the changed approach to teaching. Some major revisions have been made, including the *new* nutrition unit which introduces the text and the re-organization of the food preparation or laboratory section. Newer knowledge along many lines has been incorporated to bring material up to date. The food preservation unit has been extended considerably. Many illustrations are new and all have been selected to increase the effectiveness of the text.

Both students and instructors will find new "dimensions" in all areas. Nutrition has been given increased emphasis throughout the book. It is stressed as the various familiar foods are discussed and in the family meals section the scientific information presented in Unit 1 is applied in planning meals.

The laboratory projects are presented in a more challenging manner, with the hope that instructor and students will plan together, using the suggestions given as a basis for further exploration in broadening both knowledge and appreciations.

Many of the recipes are adapted from traditional regional classics of the United States. These are included because of the increasing interest in the preservation of American traditions. Food, like music and other forms of folklore, is a cherished part of these traditions. A number of adaptations of recipes from other countries are scattered through the food preparation unit. They are in the interest of helping students to understand and appreciate different cultures. Such recipes become more and more significant as increasing numbers of students from other countries enroll in American universities and as more college students and graduates travel abroad or go to other countries to live for a time.

The new glossary and several additional appendices are among the fifth edition features.

THE AUTHORS

CONTENTS

SECTION 3—THE FAMILY'S MEALS

SECTION 4—FOOD PREPARATION

SECTION II

Good Health

UNIT

I

Food and Nutrition

The title of a worthy book by a well-known nutrition authority is *Food Becomes You*.[1] In the past this has been interpreted in ways that seem ridiculous to present-day students. One prevalent idea was "part strengthens part"; i.e., in case of heart difficulty, that organ may be strengthened by eating the heart of an animal. Another belief was that a high percentage of cereal supposedly caused laziness or fear, while a person preparing for battle increased his vigor and bravery by eating a large portion of meat. The past fad for eating fish—preferably live goldfish—prior to an examination was a "descendent" from such notions, fish being considered "brain-food." In a very real sense, food *does* become those who eat it and dependence upon food for life is universally known. While water is not always considered a food, without it, life ends more quickly than if food is withheld. Food of primitive folk or of those living in remote parts of the earth may be distinctly limited. Whatever is native or can be provided readily is the food supply. Such a supply is considered satisfactory because no other is known. The people may have a fair degree of health and they acquire characteristics, such as average size, which seems satisfactory. If they have an opportunity for more and better food, they may change markedly, both in average size and in vigor. The food in the new pattern, like the old, has "become" them. The gradual change in physique is well-illustrated if a person has an opportunity to see armour worn by the knights of old. Few men of today could get into it. One of the main reasons for this change is that eating food of greater nutritive value has become customary.

Simply because an abundance of food is available, it does not follow that people are well-nourished. Not only must the food contain enough of certain nutrients to be potentially adequate, but also people must eat it in suitable

[1] Ruth Leverton, *Food Becomes You,* University of Nebraska Press, Lincoln, Nebraska, 1952.

TABLE 1. ENERGY EXPENDITURE FOR VARIOUS ACTIVITIES—CALORIES PER POUND PER HOUR

Activity	*Calories*	*Activity*	*Calories*
Sleeping	0.43	Dancing (slow)	1.59
Awake, lying still	0.50	Walking (moderate speed)	1.95
Sitting quietly	0.65	Dancing (fast)	2.18
Eating	0.72	Walking downstairs	2.36
Sewing (hand or motor machine)	0.72	Horseback riding (trot)	2.40
Lab. work (standing)	0.74	Swimming	3.25
Dressing and undressing	0.77	Walking upstairs	4.22
Driving automobile	0.86	Running a race	10.2

Adapted from Sherma, H. C. and Lanford, C. S., Essentials of Nutrition, 4th ed., 1957. By permission of the MacMillan Co., Publishers.

quantities. Ideally, food must supply energy for all necessary and desired activities, material for building and maintaining the body tissues, and for regulating body processes—in other words, the food is the means whereby people may be adequately nourished and enjoy both work and recreation.

Food for energy. Energy is needed for:

1) *Basal metabolism.* Metabolism involves all the chemical changes that occur in the body after food has been digested and absorbed and is being used by the cells for the activities of the body. Basal metabolism is the energy needed for the processes of the body when lying down, relaxed, after no food has been taken for at least twelve hours. Included is energy for breathing, beating of the heart, circulation of the blood, all cell activities, and other involuntary movements.

2) *Activity.* Energy required for muscular activity varies with the vigor of exercise, from very little needed for sitting still to a great deal for running a race. It also varies with a person's weight.

3) *Effect of food.* As food is digested, absorbed, and metabolized, energy is expended. This energy cannot be measured exactly; one authority suggested adding ten per cent to that required for basal metabolism and activity.

Energy is measured in terms of calories. In the sense in which the word is used in nutrition, a calorie is the amount of heat required to raise the temperature of one pound of water through four degrees Fahrenheit (or one kilogram of water through one degree Centigrade). The total calories needed by a person for a day may be determined by multiplying calories required for various activities by the time spent in each, and multiplying the sum by the person's weight. In the above table a number of typical activities and the calories per pound per hour required for each are presented. Other activities may be compared with these in estimating calories required.

In Appendix B nutrients in average servings of a number of foods are listed. In order to determine the calorie intake during a day, a list of the amount of all foods eaten both at meals and as snacks must be made and calories computed by reference to the table in this appendix. Comparing calories needed with those in food eaten indicates caloric "adequacy" for the day. If that day is representative of regular eating habits, the one sampling is an approximation of dietary adequacy in terms of calories. The same sort of check may be made with respect to other nutrients.

Foods that supply calories are carbohydrates, fats, and proteins. Four calories are available from one gram of both carbohydrates and proteins; nine from fats, or 113.4 per ounce of the first two; 255.2 per ounce of the third. Authorities differ as to the approximate distribution among these nutrients that is most desirable. One suggests the following percentages from:

Carbohydrates	Fat	Protein
50–60	25–35	10–15

In the following discussion frequent reference will be made to daily dietary allowances recommended by the Food and Nutrition Board, National Research Council. Figures are for girls and boys sixteen to nineteen years of age and for men and women aged twenty-five.

Food for building and maintaining body tissues. The fact that large quantities of food are needed for growth is apparent in any home where there are rapidly growing children. When growth has been attained, protein is needed to maintain the tissues of the body in a healthy condition. This relationship is reflected in the protein included in the Recommended Daily Dietary Allowances. For example, a boy sixteen to nineteen years of age may need 3,600 calories and 100 grams of protein; a man twenty-five years old, only 3,200 and 70, respectively. For a girl of the same age, the calorie allowance is 2,400; the protein, 75 gms., while those for a twenty-five-year-old woman are 2,300 and 58.[1]

While protein is the outstanding nutrient which serves the body in this capacity, others are also essential. Minerals insure healthful structure of the framework, proper functioning of glands, and formation of blood cells. Water, too, is necessary. The surprising percentages of water in tissues, body fluids, and even bones equal approximately two-thirds of the composition of the body. This must be maintained by sufficient intake.

Food for regulating body processes. Just as any mechanical device, such as a clock or a motor, requires lubrication to run smoothly, the intricate "mechanisms" of the body must have foods which act, directly or indirectly, in this capacity. Concerned are protein, water, cellulose, minerals, and vitamins.

Protein combines with either acid or alkali, so is important in maintaining the acid-base balance in the body. The activity of cells and enzymes is carried on most effectively in an approximately neutral medium.

---

[1] For other figures, see Appendix A.

TABLE 2. SOME GOOD SOURCES OF NUTRIENTS

Carbohydrates		*Fats* [1]	*Proteins* [1,2,3]	*Water* [2,3]	*Minerals* [2,3]	
Starches [1]	Alimentary pastes, breads, breakfast cereals, corn, potatoes, rice, tapioca.	Butter, cooking fats and oils, Cream, margarine, meat (fat), nuts, salad oils and dressings.	Cheese, dry legumes, eggs, fish, meat, milk, nuts, poultry.	Beverages, juices, fruits, vegetables.	Calcium	Broccoli, cheese, greens, milk, molasses (dark), salmon, sardines.
Sugars [1]	Candy, honey, syrups, sugars, sweet desserts.				Phosphorus	Dry legumes, egg yolk, fish, liver, meat (lean), milk, whole grain cereals.
Cellulose [3]	Celery, fruit (with skins), green legumes, leafy vegetables, whole grain cereals.				Iron	Dry legumes, egg yolk, greens, liver, meat (lean), molasses (dark), shellfish, whole grain and enriched cereals.
					Iodine	Iodized salt, seafood, vegetables grown near salt water.

Vitamins [2,3]

A	Butter, cream, egg yolk, fortified margarine, liver, greens, milk, parsley, yellow fruit, vegetables.	Thiamin	Bran, glandular meats, greens, lean meat (especially pork), whole grain, enriched cereals.	Panthotenate	Broccoli, eggs, liver, milk, potatoes, tomatoes.
D	Butter, cream, fortified margarine, liver, milk.	Riboflavin	Broccoli, eggs, glandular meats, green leaves, milk, poultry (dark meat), whole grain and enriched cereals.	Folacin	Glandular meats, green vegetables, legumes, nuts, whole grain cereals.
E	Leafy vegetables, vegetable oils, whole grain cereals.	Niacin	Fish, liver, meat (lean), milk, peanuts, poultry, whole grain and enriched cereals.	B12	Eggs, fish, oysters, liver, meat (lean), milk, poultry.
K	Egg yolk, green vegetables, liver.	B6	Egg yolk, fish, fresh vegetables.	Ascorbic acid	Broccoli, cabbage, cantaloupe, citrus, green leaves, guavas, mangoes, strawberries, tomatoes.

[1] For energy
[2] For building and repairing body tissues
[3] For regulating body processes

Water regulates evaporation of moisture through the lungs and the pores of the skin. It is also important in other regular excretion of waste materials. Substances needed in the blood, digestive juices, and tissues are held in solution in water. Body temperature is regulated by means of water.

Cellulose is subject to very little digestion. It helps to maintain normal mechanics along the digestive tract and to prevent constipation.

Minerals affect the acid-base balance. In general, they are needed for proper muscle contraction, nerve response, and blood coagulation. They influence the functioning of the thyroid gland and regulate activities of enzymes throughout the body.

Vitamins are necessary for normal health, growth and vigor. Formation of many enzymes and protection against a number of specific diseases are among the contributions of these regulating nutrients.

On the pages that follow the functions and effectiveness of these essential nutrients are presented in more detail. References will be guides to further reading.

CARBOHYDRATES

Among foods available to man in abundance and at relatively low cost are those whose nutritive value is largely carbohydrate. Carbohydrates are composed of carbon, hydrogen, and oxygen, the ratio between the hydrogen and oxygen being two to one. In numerous ways these elements are combined so that they become starches, sugars, and celluloses, which differ widely in texture, flavor, and uses in cookery.

Among the excellent sources of starches are potatoes and corn, native to America. Cereals, native grains found plentifully in many places, but most of them used widely since they have been brought to lands where they were not native, are the basis for breads. Tapioca, a carbohydrate food from South America, comes from the roots of the manioc or cassava. Poi is a dish found in Hawaii, the source of which is the taro root.

Sugars from canes, palm, beets, the sap of the sugar maple, and honey are all excellent carbohydrate foods. They differ widely in flavor and other characteristics.

Cellulose is plentiful in edible form in such vegetables as lettuce and celery. Fruits and whole grain cereals also provide cellulose. The carbohydrates are classified as monosaccharides (one sugar), disaccharides (two sugars), and polysaccharides (three or more sugars). Monosaccharides in foods, for example, levulose in fruits and honey and glucose in syrups, are directly absorbable through the walls of the stomach and intestinal tract. Another monosaccharide, galactose, is a product of the digestion of lactose.

The disaccharides are split to monosaccharides, each molecule becoming two, by enzymes in the pancreatic and intestinal juices, chiefly the latter.

Sucrase changes sucrose to glucose and levulose, lactase splits lactose (the sugar in milk) to glucose and galactose, and maltase changes maltose to two molecules of glucose.

There is a maltase enzyme in the saliva which accounts for a slight amount of conversion of maltose to glucose, but salivary digestion ceases as soon as the food material in the stomach is acidified by the gastric juice.

The polysaccharides (starches), are first converted to maltose by the amylases of the salivary and pancreatic juices. Maltose is then digested as indicated above.

The end products of carbohydrate digestion are absorbed and stored in the liver as glycogen, which is reconverted to glucose as needed.

Certain carbohydrates have other desirable effects. Lactose is a favorable medium for development in the intestinal tract of bacteria, especially *bacillus acidophilus,* which lessens any tendency toward indigestion of putrefactive order. Cellulose remains undigested in large measure. It is important in maintaining normal muscle tonus in the intestine for regular elimination.

Since the carbohydrate foods, as they are served in daily meals, are often very appealing, there is a tendency to eat too liberally of them—delicious rolls and desserts that are hard to resist, for instance. Carbohydrate not needed for energy is eventually stored in the body as fat. To some extent this is desirable but in excess it may lead to real trouble. Thus "self-rationing" of concentrated carbohydrates should be kept in mind, accompanied by emphasis on foods in which there are other essential nutrients.

FATS

The elements from which all the fats used as food are made are carbon, hydrogen, and oxygen. These combine to form the fatty acids and glycerol (glycerine) from which the various fats and oils are composed. There are a number of fatty acids and they are combined in many ways so that the products used for food vary considerably. The ratio of hydrogen to carbon is responsible for the difference between two distinct types of fatty acids—saturated and unsaturated (see p. 165).

When fat is eaten, no change occurs as a result of salivary digestion. The enzymes (lipases) which act upon fats are in the gastric and pancreatic juices. Gastric lipase converts emulsified fats, such as that in milk, to fatty acids and glycerol, the end products of fat digestion. Bile from the gall bladder and pancreatic juice from the pancreas are introduced together into the duodenum. Bile is not an enzyme, but it emulsifies fat. In this form, the pancreatic lipase changes it to fatty acids and glycerol. It is carried by the lymphatic vessels to the liver and other parts of the body for transformation to energy.

Some of the sources of fat are butter, shortenings, cooking and salad oils, and meats. While the chief function of fat in the diet is as a source of energy, certain fats are carriers of fat-soluble vitamins. Some of the unsaturated fatty acids, notably linoleic and arachidonic, are essential—that is, they must be provided by the food eaten. Fat also has satiety value. It does not leave the stomach as readily as some of the other nutrients and therefore a person is not conscious of hunger as quickly after a meal in which there is some fat as after one in which there is practically none. This may be carried to the extreme—too much fat in a meal may be a distinct hindrance to normal rate of digestion. Fats act as lubricants along the digestive tract. In a number of cases, fat has been helpful in the treatment of eczema, so there seems to be a connection between a reasonable intake of fat and healthy skin.

Many people are inclined to eat more fat than is desirable—note the French fries that accompany steaks, fried chicken, and fried fish in many commercial food-service places as well as the popularity of pastry, whipped cream and other fat-rich foods in home meals. In the opinion of Sherman,[1] "the same question arises with respect to fat as to sugar, whether it is wisest to take so much of our food energy in forms so poor in protein, mineral elements, and some of the vitamins." However, since they are necessary in a well-balanced diet, moderate use of them is important.

In addition to fats, as ordinarily recognized, there are fat-like substances, including lecithin and sterols. The former is found in the cells of the body as well as in the blood, the nervous tissues, and the liver. The latter are precursors of certain hormones as well as the fat-soluble vitamin D. Cholesterol is a sterol which has received much attention of late. It is found in connection with certain heart and arterial difficulties and this fact has lead to some extreme reactions. Since it is a constituent of both milk and egg yolk, people have prescribed diets for themselves eliminating both of these highly nutritious foods. Much research in connection with cholesterol continues to be done. Unless curtailment of fat, especially from such foods as milk and eggs, is suggested after a physician's diagnosis, there is no need for such measures. Concerning this reaction King[2] urges ". . . a balanced perspective . . . premature conclusions about the role of fat in relation to health tend to encourage extreme dietary measures that border on faddism and hence lead to greater risks to health than would be accomplished by following the types of diets that are now recommended as good or excellent."

PROTEINS

When, about a century ago, a substance essential to the well-being of the body was isolated, the name chosen was "protein"—word derived from Greek meaning "of first importance." This "substance" is really complex.

---

[1] Henry C. Sherman, *Chemistry of Food and Nutrition,* 8th Edition, The Macmillan Company, New York, 1952, p. 30.

[2] Charles G. King, *Fats Make Good Foods—Where and Why the Margins?,* Food Technology, 13.1:66–68, 1959.

There are many proteins, all composed of the elements carbon, hydrogen, oxygen, and nitrogen, and usually with the addition of one or more of the minerals, sulphur, phosphorus, and iron. These elements are combined to form about twenty-two amino acids which in turn make up proteins. Ten amino acids are known to be "essential," that is, they must be included in the food which we eat; the others may be synthesized in the body. Proteins vary, because of their amino acid content, in effectiveness. Some will maintain life and support normal growth; these are called "complete" proteins. Others maintain life but do not support growth adequately and are called "partially complete" proteins. Still others do not even maintain life and are referred to as "incomplete." Isolated proteins that illustrate these classes are casein of milk (complete), gliadin of wheat (partially complete), and zein of corn (incomplete). Proteins are necessary for all forms of plant and animal life.

Foods which provide protein from animal sources include milk, cheese, lean meats of all sorts, and eggs. Many nuts and legumes are valuable for protein. Whole grain cereals are superior to refined cereals; for example, rolled oats contain fourteen per cent protein as against seven and six-tenths per cent in polished rice. The rather extensive use of potatoes and green vegetables makes them valuable contributors to the total protein requirement, despite the fact that the percentages of protein are only two for potatoes and two to six for green vegetables.

The principal function of protein is to supply material for the building and maintenance of body tissue. It is also necessary for the formation of certain hormones and enzymes and it is a source of energy. With insufficient protein in the food of children, growth is stunted. Anyone whose diet lacks protein may have poor musculature and low resistance to disease. A diet high in proteins is important in the treatment of a number of diseases.

Like most nutrients, protein must be digested and assimilated to be available for use by the body. There is no enzyme in the saliva that acts on proteins. Rennin in the gastric juice coagulates milk, thus retaining it in the stomach so that other enzymes may play their part in the total process of digestion. Pepsinogen combines with hydrochloric acid to form pepsin, the gastric protease which splits protein to such simpler forms as proteoses and peptones. Proteases in the pancreatic juice continue the gradual change to simpler forms, including peptids and polypeptids. Others, formerly grouped as "erepsin," complete the digestion, the end products of which are amino acids. These are absorbed by the capillaries from the walls of the intestine. Sufficient "non-essential" amino acids, if not supplied by food, are synthesized. Given an adequate supply, the body can and does make use of protein foods to maintain itself in a splendid state of health.

An important responsibility of everyone in choosing food is to include sufficient protein in the daily meals. It is not enough to omit this type of food at breakfast and lunch and "make up" by eating a big steak for dinner. A good source of protein should be included in all meals. One result of a low-protein breakfast is what has been aptly called "midmorning lag"—insufficient "pep" to last until the next meal, with lowered ability to give attention to the task at hand. Amino acids from different sources supplement each other, so that several sources included in a day's food are doubtless preferable to few. People who refuse meat as part of their food may compensate with milk, cheese and eggs. Those who refuse all these find it difficult to maintain anything like "abundant" health, and, as a matter of fact, frequently fail. While it is possible to have an adequate diet when proteins are all from vegetable sources, the addition of those from animal sources makes such a diet easier and less likely to lead to protein deficiency. —"when grains and milk are fed together in favorable proportions, their proteins so supplement each other in furnishing the nutritionally essential amino acids that the combination may be practically as efficient as the milk proteins alone. This supplementary relation between proteins is of great importance both nutritionally and economically, since it makes possible the full utilization of the low-cost proteins of grains and other vegetable foods, provided only that they are fed in combination with sufficient amounts of those foods which reinforce their content of certain essential amino acids."[1]

The recommended daily allowance for protein is given on page 5.

MINERALS

When, in the recommended allowances for a good diet, only one and three-tenths grams of calcium are listed for girls, one and four-tenths for boys, and eight-tenths for both men and women, it seems that they must be of little consequence. Similarly, for iron the corresponding figures are fifteen for both girls and boys, twelve for women, and ten for men. Yet these small amounts, and even smaller quantities of several other minerals, are requisites for good nutritional status. Their functions have to do with building and maintaining the body and with the regulation of its many intricate processes.

Calcium and phosphorus. Perhaps the two minerals that might have "first place" are calcium and phosphorus. They are necessary for development of bones and teeth of proper formation and rigidity. In this they are assisted by Vitamin D. In addition, calcium has to do with proper coagulation of the blood, normal muscle contraction, and heartbeat. Adequate calcium throughout life is important, as is apparent in many cases of bone decalcification in older people.

The principal source of calcium in the usual diet is milk, with green vegetables—especially green leaves and broccoli—in second place. Those persons who are allergic to milk need to be sure of sufficient calcium from other sources.

[1] Henry C. Sherman and Carolyn S. Lanford, *Essentials of Nutrition*, 4th Edition, The Macmillan Company, New York, 1957, p. 108.

Phosphorus is a component of all the cells of the body and it is helpful in maintaining body neutrality. It is present in milk, meats, (particularly fish) and whole grain cereals.

The allowance for calcium has been mentioned. None has been suggested for phosphorus. While about one and a half times as much phosphorus as calcium is needed, if the protein and calcium requirements are met, there is plenty of phosphorus.

Iron and copper. Another "pair" of minerals is iron and copper. Iron is well known as a component of the hemoglobin of blood. This is also true of the myoglobin (muscle hemoglobin), certain enzymes, and all cells. Copper too, is needful (perhaps as a catalyst) for hemoglobin formation and for the activity of some of the enzymes.

One of the best sources of iron is liver, with meat, eggs, and green vegetables contributing to an important degree. Liver is an excellent source of copper, as are most foods containing iron. Unrefined cereals are also important. The requirement for iron has been stated above. None is suggested for copper. Iron deficiency is present in anemias, both so-called "iron deficiency anemia" and pernicious anemia.

Iodine. Iodine is another mineral of great importance. Without it as a regulator, the thyroid gland does not function normally. Lack of iodine is largely a matter of geographic location. Since the chief food sources are sea foods and vegetables grown near salt water, it follows that some inland regions would not provide iodine-containing foods. People in such areas are particularly likely to develop goiter—an enlargement of the thyroid gland. Since potassium iodide has been added to table salt, goiter due to lack of iodine has declined and no requirement has been suggested by the Food and Nutrition Board.

Fluorine. "What to do about fluorine" has become a controversial subject. Like iodine, it is not distributed evenly. In the water of some localities there is so much that, in time, the enamel of teeth becomes mottled. In other places there is practically no fluorine in the water. In the first instance the teeth are remarkably free from caries; in the latter, caries are numerous. From carefully controlled studies, the beneficial effects of fluorine on incidence of tooth decay has been reported. There is often strong opposition to water fluoridation in communities, much of it on the part of people who do not want to add the expense of the program to accepted costs and of those who want no change in whatever is provided by nature. No recommendation is included by the Food and Nutrition Board for a suitable allowance.

Other minerals. A number of other minerals, in small quantities, are needed by the body. Obviously, sodium and chlorine are among them, since the need for salt (sodium chloride) is universal. That used in food is sufficient in most instances. "Trace" minerals include potassium, magnesium, sulphur, manganese, zinc, cobalt, and molybdenum.

Minerals have an important role in maintaining the acid-base balance, some of those discussed above being among them. Acid-forming minerals are phosphorus, sulphur, and chlorine; base-forming, calcium, iron, sodium, potassium, and magnesium. Several are involved in enzyme activity. In a varied diet the "trace" minerals are doubtless supplied in satisfactory quantities. There is no suggested standard requirement.

VITAMINS

In addition to the above nutrients, an unknown number of chemical compounds are present in foods. Those identified have been proven to be required for the maintenance of good health. Experiments with several have demonstrated that animals deprived of them develop different diseases and die. These compounds are the vitamins. Before any scientific study, it was known that sailors on long ocean voyages need not have scurvy if plenty of raw cabbage or the juice of lemons or limes was included in sufficient quantity in the diet. Nor would they develop beri beri if whole wheat and milk was added to the food served.

In general, vitamins are essential for normal growth, healthy offspring, good general health, prevention and/or cure of certain diseases, and resistance to infections. Before their chemical structure was known they were identified by letters of the alphabet; and in some cases these are still commonly used. They may be divided into two groups—those soluble in fat, and those soluble in water.

FAT-SOLUBLE VITAMINS

Vitamin A (Axerophtol). Vitamin A must be present if the eyes are to adjust quickly to changes in intensity of light, and for vision to be clear when light is dim. The difficulty is especially noticeable at night if light is suddenly increased; hence the term "night-blindness." The danger from this condition if a person is driving an automobile after dark is obvious. When Vitamin A is lacking, or withheld for a long time, a more serious condition develops (xerophthalmia) and may finally lead to blindness. The vitamin is also important for growth, vigorous health, and longevity.

As such, Vitamin A is present in animal foods, particularly liver, butter and egg yolk. In the form of its precursor, carotene, it is available from vegetables and fruits that are yellow or green in color.

Vitamin A is measured in International Units (see glossary). The daily requirement suggested is 5000 I.U.

Vitamins D. (Calciferol). Three Vitamins D are recognized at present. The first was known as the "antirachitic vitamin" because of its association with healthy bone structure (see p. 11). A sterol, ergosterol, is converted to

Vitamin D_2 and another, 7-dehydrocholesterol, can be formed in the body by sunlight or ultraviolet light because provitamin D is present in the skin.

Extreme deficiency, as indicated above, results in bow legs, narrow chest, and enlarged joints that are the evidence of rickets.

Butter, egg yolk, milk, and fish oil are a few of the foods containing vitamin D. Milk is often fortified with Vitamin D in the amount of 400 I.U. per quart. Since this is the daily allowance recommended for people up to twenty years of age, a quart of milk would provide the entire suggested allowance. For adults other than women during pregnancy and lactation, no recommendation has been made.

Vitamins E (Tocopherols). Four Vitamins E are known. They influence growth and reproduction in experimental animals and deficiency results in muscular degeneration. They serve as antioxidants for Vitamin A and carotene both in foods and in the body. The vitamins are rather widely scattered, vegetable oils, whole grains, and leafy vegetables being among the food sources. The human requirement is not known.

Vitamins K (Phylloquinones). Vitamin K exists in at least two forms and a similar substance has been synthesized. It is essential for the formation of the enzyme prothrombin, without which blood does not coagulate properly and a slight wound bleeds excessively. If a test prior to surgery indicates slow blood coagulation, Vitamin K is administered. The vitamin is formed, probably from precursors in food, in the intestinal tract. Liver, egg yolk, and green vegetables are good sources. The probability that there is no deficiency makes it unnecessary to list a daily requirement.

WATER-SOLUBLE VITAMINS

Ascorbic acid (Vitamin C). The first vitamin to be identified chemically was ascorbic acid. Its connection with prevention and treatment of scurvy had been known for some time. While scurvy is no longer common, less than an optimal intake of ascorbic acid is responsible for a number of the early symptoms of the disease. The vitamin maintains capillary strength, hence is an aid in healing wounds or severe burns, also in preventing bleeding gums and slight hemorrhages beneath the skin. If deficiency is greater or more prolonged, the teeth become loose, joints stiffen, fleeting pains are felt in arms and legs, and strength wanes. Ascorbic acid helps to protect the body from infection and bacteriological toxins.

Indirectly, this vitamin is associated with anemia. If the cells in the bone marrow do not function normally, hemoglobin is not formed in sufficient amounts. Also the tendency toward hemorrhage due to weakened capillaries may lead to loss of blood.

Ascorbic acid is oxidized easily. It is retained in an acid medium and destroyed by alkali. While raw fruits and vegetables are better sources than those cooked or processed, correct techniques result in retention of a high percentage in the latter. Among the foods that are excellent sources of ascorbic acid are citrus fruits, tomatoes, dark green leaves, broccoli, and raw cabbage. Difference in the content of several fruit juices is presented on p. 40. The recommended allowance for girls is eighty milligrams; for boys, one hundred; for women, seventy, and for men, seventy-five.

Thiamin (Vitamin B_1). Thiamin is important for growth, a good appetite, vigor, sound nerves, good digestion, and healthy muscle tonus. Volunteers for a low-thiamin diet became nervous, irritable, easily tired, and their appetites and ability to concentrate decreased. With the vitamin added, they soon regained their usual state of health. Such instances have led to the term "Morale vitamin" being applied to thiamin. This vitamin is the active part of the coenzyme necessary for the final oxidation of carbohydrates. Thus the requirement cannot be stated explicitly because people require or consume different amounts of carbohydrate. However, the requirement suggested by the Food and Nutrition Board is one and two-tenths milligrams for both girls and women, one and eight-tenths for boys and one and six-tenths for men. Perhaps whole grain and enriched cereal products are the best over-all source of thiamin. Greens and lean pork are also very valuable sources of thiamin.

Riboflavin (Vitamin B_2 or G). Riboflavin, in combination with protein and phosphoric acid, forms enzymes which are important to all body tissues. It is needed for normal vision. Continued deficiency in experimental animals results in dim vision and, finally, cataract. This condition can be corrected if riboflavin is added to the diet soon enough. It is helpful in making the body resist infections. Symptoms of deficiency are inflammation and cracking at the corners of the mouth (cheilosis), unnaturally red lips, purplish-red tongue, inflamed and cloudy eyes, and a greasy, scaly skin.

Riboflavin is found in milk, eggs, glandular meat, and numerous other foods. In milk Vitamin B may be lost from ten to twenty per cent during the pasteurization and irradiation processes, but far more—up to two-thirds—if milk is allowed to stand in bright sunlight for several hours.

The recommended daily allowance is one and nine-tenths milligrams for girls, two and five-tenths for boys, one and five-tenths for women, and one and eight-tenths for men. A pint of milk supplies more than the requirement.

Niacin (nicotinic acid). Niacin is a coenzyme necessary for effective metabolism of carbohydrates. It can be formed in the intestinal tract from tryptophane, one of the essential amino acids.

Deficiency is indicated by rough skin with a reddish rash (dermatitis), abnormal functioning of nerve tissue of the gastro-intestinal tract (diarrhea), and of the general nerve tissue (depression). Such are the symptoms of pellagra. While it is a multiple-vitamin deficiency disease, the "key" vitamin in prevention and cure appears to be niacin. Pellagra is likely to be common in areas where corn or some refined cereal is a major food and where milk and vegetables are used sparingly, if at all. Concerted effort, including a convincing program of education concerning food habits, has been effective in ridding communities—in fact, regions—of the disease. One such instance is the southern part of the United States, where the work of Dr. Tom Spies and many others has been so effective as to practically eradicate the disease.

In foods, niacin is abundant in fish, glandular meats, milk, and whole grain cereals. The recommended daily allowance for girls is sixteen milligrams; for boys, twenty-five; for women, seventeen; and for men, twenty-one. This includes niacin equivalents from tryptophane.

Vitamin B_6 (*pyridoxine, pyridoxamine, pyridoxal*). The three substances in parentheses, taken together, comprise Vitamin B_6. It is a coenzyme connected with the metabolism of amino acids and essential fatty acids and is necessary for normal cell activity. It is related to growth and is one of the factors which, if not provided, leads to pellagra.

Symptoms of deficiency include insomnia, irritability, abdominal pains, weakness, and convulsive seizures. In experimental animals deficiency has been associated with anemia and sclerotic lesions in the arteries.

Vitamin B_6 is present in many foods, especially fish, egg yolk, whole wheat, and lettuce. In a varied diet there is little likelihood of deficiency and no allowance is included in the Food and Nutrition Board's recommendations.

Pantothenate (*Pantothenic Acid*). Pantothenate is a component of coenzyme A, important in the metabolism of carbohydrates, fats, and proteins. Few instances of effects of deficiency in man have been cited, but the "burning feet syndrome" of Japanese prisoners of war was relieved by administration of the vitamin.

Some of the foods which contain this vitamin are liver, egg yolk, and fresh vegetables.

In laboratory animals, graying hair (black rats), bald spots, loss of appetite, constipation, dizziness, and low blood pressure have been noted. With a varied diet, deficiency is not likely to occur and no allowance has, to date, been listed in the recommendations of the Food and Nutrition Board.

Folacin (*Folic Acid*). Folacin is necessary for normal red blood cell formation and is connected with the metabolism of several amino acids. Perhaps it has served most convincingly in the treatment of one type of anemia—sprue. This disease is one from which large numbers of people in some areas suffer.

Folacin is available from green vegetables, especially leaves, whole grain cereals, and glandular meats. While no specific standard has been set, it is considered probable that five-tenths milligram daily is sufficient.

Cobalamin (*Vitamin B_{12}*). This vitamin promotes growth and is necessary for the formation of red blood cells. Isolated from liver, the molecule has both cobalt and phosphorus in its chemical structure. It is the latest of the Vitamin B complex to be recognized, but its importance is great because of its effectiveness in the treatment of anemia, including pernicious anemia. In fact, it is called the "antipernicious anemia vitamin."

Cobalamin is formed by bacteria in the intestinal tract. Animal foods are its dietary source and liver, meats, and milk supply the necessary material for its formation. It is abundant in seaweeds.

It has been observed that symptoms of deficiency are rather common among vegetarians. Among the symptoms are sore tongues, pains in the spine, and "poker" backs.

No standard has been set for inclusion of cobalamin in the diet.

Biotin. Biotin is important for normal cell functioning and metabolism of carbohydrates, fats, and proteins. Deficiency is accompanied by a fine, scaly skin, nausea, muscular pains, weariness, and depression. The vitamin is found in milk, eggs, and fresh vegetables and is formed by bacteria in the intestinal tract. Very little of this substance is needed, perhaps only 150 to 300 micrograms daily.

Choline. Choline is important in fat metabolism. In experimental animals it has prevented accumulation of fat in the liver. Among food sources are egg yolk and glandular meats. It is probable that only very restricted diets fail to provide enough of this vitamin.

Inositol. Inositol is also effective in preventing fatty liver in experimental animals and in curing skin lesions. As yet, its role in human nutrition is not understood thoroughly. Grains and meat contain inositol. No recommendation for its inclusion in the diet has been made by the Food and Nutrition Board.

WATER

The contributions made by water to the building and regulation of the body have been discussed (see p. 7). From six to eight glasses daily should suffice except in cases of unusual moisture loss from the body, such as perspiration during very warm weather.

NUTRITIONAL STATUS

The nutritional status of a person is due to both quantity and quality of the food eaten. An adequate diet is necessary for good health, which is recognized in many ways, including:

1) Normal growth
2) Weight that is right for height, frame, and age
3) Good appetite
4) Freedom from digestive disturbance
5) Clear skin of good color
6) Clear, sparkling eyes

7) Smooth, glossy hair
8) Happy outlook on life.

While these conditions may be present with a good diet, there are improvements if the diet is made better.

Weight and nutritional status. Based on height and body frame, "ideal" weights have been suggested for people of different ages (see Appendix C). These are helpful guides for adjusting the food pattern. Temporary fluctuations occur, but the "ideal" is the point of reference. If weight is increased ten per cent, "overweight" is the term usually applied; if twenty per cent or more, "obese." "Underweight" is approximately ten per cent below the ideal weight.

There are definite disadvantages of both over- and under-weight. Increased weight is associated with a tendency to heart difficulties, poor circulation, high blood pressure, and burden on the liver, kidneys, and pancreas. Marked underweight may be accompanied by nervous tension, susceptibility to infections, including tuberculosis, and lack of endurance. Both are related to "Food Becomes You" in a different sense. Neither obesity nor extreme leanness is as "becoming" as "ideal" weight. Both carry an economic penalty. Clothing may be reduced or increased in size within a narrow limit and at some cost in money or time. Beyond that limit the cost is greater.

Schemes for quick weight reduction are usually ineffective and may be dangerous. The only way to reduce and stay reduced is to decrease caloric intake under guidance of a physician or nutritionist and hold it at the level which matches energy needs. In other words, "put both hands on the edge of the table and *push.*" One suggestion is a decrease of 500 calories daily. Gradual reduction is safer than quick reduction. The opposite would be the "program" for the underweight person.

Undernutrition. Of great concern is the large number of people whose difficulty, often unnoticed, is undernutrition. An abundance of food in homes where "the table groans" may be lacking in one or more of the important nutrients, particularly minerals and vitamins. The consequence is a state of health that is anywhere from slightly below par to specific disease. The faulty food patterns are doubtless due to ignorance—certainly not to financial problems.

Insufficient income in terms of food prices often leads to undernutrition, although sufficient knowledge of the nutritive value of foods would enable many to provide a good diet within the limited income.

Perhaps the principal causes of undernutrition are the entrenched personal, family, and national food habits and prejudices that make people accept faulty diets complacently, even refusing to change permanently when a better pattern has been proved to be superior. Following fads or "boosting" advertisements may introduce foods which, in themselves, are good, but which ignore other, even better, foods. For children, the "easy way" may not be the best way. Children do *not* inevitably select the foods that are best for them any more than adults do. Their unguided selections sometimes result in very poor eating habits and consequent undernourishment.

Influence of good appetite. The healthy person is hungry at regular intervals, finds his meals acceptable, and his appetite a fairly safe guide as to the amount of food needed. The appetite may, on the other hand, be an indication of illness rather than of health. An abnormally large appetite may indicate a habit of eating more food than is needed, a nervous condition which should be corrected, or an oversecretion of thyroxin from the thyroid gland. Loss of appetite may indicate an insufficient amount of some factor in the food which influences appetite, or it may be a symptom of some illness.

There are several regulatory centers in the brain near the pituitary gland. Dr. Joliffe, Director of the Bureau of Nutrition in the New York City Department of Health, suggested the name "appestat" for the one in the hypothalamus which regulates the appetite. It seems to operate rather like a thermostat. When blood sugar is low, the appestat "registers hunger"; when replenished, the hunger has been satisfied. The center is amenable to "training" to different amounts of food and different meal hours. The food eaten influences the blood sugar level. Protein raises the level more slowly than carbohydrate but the level is maintained longer.

Nutritional status and emotional stability. Under stress, appetite may be temporarily poor—fortunately, for food may be followed by digestive discomfort. Persistent dissatisfaction, frustration, unhappiness, feeling of inadequacy, insecurity, etc. may lead to attempts to "make up" by over-eating as well as over-drinking or over-smoking. The nutritional status suffers and, in case of over-eating, over-weight results. The others may result in undernutrition.

The interplay between excellent eating habits and healthy mental attitudes is very real. Lack of a nutrient or group of nutrients has been mentioned as leading to depression; depression may result in almost insatiable appetite or loss of appetite. The mature person will return to normal attitudes and food habits quickly after temporary strain. Stable mental attitudes are a prerequisite to superior nutritional status.

Nutritional status and eating habits. There have been—and are—numerous fads that have to do with eating habits. For example, one suggested that carbohydrate foods should be eaten at one meal; protein, at another. A superficial study of the nutrients in foods (see Appendix B) is sufficient to convince a person that very few foods consist of one nutrient only. Examined carefully, other fads are equally misleading. Knowledge of what the nutrients are and why they are necessary, applied, must result in eating well-planned meals regularly.

This involves starting the day with a good breakfast. Unfortunately, omitting breakfast or letting orange juice and coffee or coffee and a doughnut suf-

TABLE 3. RECOMMENDED FOOD ALLOWANCE OF AN AVERAGE COLLEGE GIRL AND AMOUNTS PROVIDED BY THE ABOVE BREAKFAST[1]

Food constituent	*Recommended allowance*	*Breakfast*
Calories	2400	452
Protein (grams)	75	18.7
Calcium (grams)	1.3	.383
Iron (milligrams)	15	2.5
Vitamin A (International Units)	5000	1620
Thiamin (milligrams)	1.2	0.37
Riboflavin (milligrams)	1.9	0.63
Niacin (milligrams)	1.2	1.6
Ascorbic acid (milligrams)	80	64
Vitamin D (International Units)	400	About 100

[1] This fulfills the recommendation of nutritional scientists that from one-fourth to one-third of the daily requirement be included in the breakfast. The above breakfast provides about one-fourth of the daily requirement.

fice, are all too common practices. Excuses include "I overslept," "I am not hungry in the morning," "Nobody prepared breakfast for me," and "I'm trying to lose weight!" There is an obvious answer to refute such excuses. The last is defeating the purpose. After the longest period without food during a twenty-four-hour day, breakfast prevents over-eating later because of increased hunger. Ability to work or play without lag declines and if there is a morning snack, it seldom provides real nourishment.

Numerous studies of breakfast habits have been made. In the Iowa study[1] it was found that, in general, fruit, milk, eggs, and meat were not eaten regularly. "From half to two-thirds of the breakfasts of the children were predominantly poor . . . the breakfast habits of girls, particularly with reference to milk and eggs, apparently became worse as they grew older." The studies also revealed that "The good breakfasts seemed to fortify the children against poor daily diets. The poor breakfasts remained uncompensated throughout the day . . . only one in five made up the deficit in the other meals."

An "average" college girl five feet four inches tall and weighing 120 pounds might eat the following breakfast:

Orange juice .... ½ cup   Whole wheat toast .... 1 slice
Poached egg 1   Butter or Margarine .... ½ tb.
Milk .... 1 cup

The contribution to the food requirement for the day is presented in Table 3.

[1] Virginia D. Sidwell and Ercel S. Eppright, *Food Habits of Iowa Children—Breakfast,* Jnl. of Home Economics, 45.6:401–405, 1953.

In the interest of better nutrition for all people, a number of plans for daily food have been compiled. One of these includes four groups.[1]

Milk group: Some milk daily—

Children	3 to 4 cups
Teenagers	4 or more cups
Adults	2 or more cups
Pregnant women	4 or more cups
Nursing mothers	6 or more cups

Cheese and ice cream can replace part of the milk. For example, the calcium requirement for the group of girls and women used throughout this unit is 1,300 and 800 milligrams, respectively. One ounce of cheddar cheese contains 206 milligrams; one cup of ice cream, 176.

Meat group: two or more servings—Beef, veal, pork, lamb, poultry, fish, with dry beans, peas, and nuts as alternates.

Vegetable-fruit group: four or more servings, including—a dark-green or deep-yellow vegetable important for vitamin A—at least every other day; a citrus fruit or other fruit or vegetable important for vitamin C—daily; other fruits and vegetables, including potatoes.

Bread-cereals group: four or more servings—whole grain, enriched, restored.

With these foods as a foundation, others may be chosen, knowing that the nutrients essential for a good diet have been included. As has been pointed out, fat in moderation that supplies both vitamin A (and perhaps vitamin D) and essential fatty acids is important and would, in all probability, be included in a day's menu. That sweets should be used sparingly has been suggested. As desserts, they do not lessen the appetite and so replace more important nutrients. Often, too, the sugar is a minor ingredient, as is true of such desserts as custards and ice creams.

Making a good food better. This is the title of a moving picture[2] showing how corn meal is enriched. Enrichment of corn meal and rice followed the enrichment of wheat flour and bread (see pp. 189 and 190). Some of the important nutrients removed in the interest of keeping quality under conditions prevailing in our marketing system are replaced to make refined cereal products more comparable with whole grain products.

Margarine was originally the answer to a need for a spread for bread for which low-income families could pay. Later, Vitamin A was added—15,000 International Units per pound. Vitamin D is often added—2000 International Units per pound. Vitamin D is also sometimes added to milk.

[1] Essentials for an Adequate Diet, *Agricultural Information Bulletin No. 160,* Agricultural Research Service, U.S.D.A.

[2] Clemson Agricultural College, Clemson, S. C.

From labels, it is found that other foods have nutrients added, such as ascorbic acid in gelatin desserts and some fruit beverages. These efforts to increase the nutritive value of foods are helpful in the attempt of people in many parts of the world to improve nutritional status—to provide good diets for everyone. An idea advanced against cereal enrichment is that the added substances are "chemicals" and therefore harmful, while the whole grain food is healthful. To this, and similar arguments, the answer of the Food and Nutrition Board is, "there can be no possible difference between thiamin prepared synthetically and that which is extracted from a natural source of thiamin such as wheat or meat (or yeast). The same is true of riboflavin or of other vitamins that thus far have been synthesized. A vitamin is a chemical compound whether it is made by nature or by man." [1]

In Brief. Reviewing the foregoing brief summary of nutrients needed and of how these needs are met, the complicated, yet smooth-running ways by which the food we eat "becomes us" is impressive. It is not difficult to understand how the body functions so well despite frequent abuses—unintentional or otherwise. It *is* difficult to understand continuance of abuses against the background of this knowledge. Good eating habits are the basis for a healthy body.

REFERENCES

Bogert, L. Jean, *Nutrition and Physical Fitness.* 6th Ed. W. B. Saunders Co., Philadelphia, 1954.

Boorsook, H., *Vitamins. What They Are and How They Can Benefit You.* Viking Press, 1945.

Byrd, Oliver E., *Nutrition Sourcebook.* Stanford University Press, Stanford, California, 1955.

Chaney, Margaret S. and M. Ahlborn, *Nutrition.* 4th Ed. Houghton Mifflin Co., Boston, 1949.

Leverton, Ruth M., *Food Becomes You.* University of Nebraska Press, Lincoln, Nebraska, 1952.

Pattison, Mattie, Helen Barbour, and Ercel Eppright, *Teaching Nutrition.* The Iowa State College Press, Ames, Iowa, 1957.

Sherman, Henry C. and Carolyn S. Lanford, *Essentials of Nutrition.* 4th Edition, The Macmillan Company, New York, 1957.

Stevenson, Gladys T. and Cora Miller, *Introduction to Foods and Nutrition.* John Wiley and Sons, Inc., New York, 1960.

Taylor, Clara Mae, Grace McLeod, and the late Mary Swartz Rose, *Foundation of Nutrition.* 5th Edition. The Macmillan Company, New York, 1956.

---

[1] Oliver E. Byrd, *Nutrition Sourcebook.* Stanford University Press, Stanford, Calif., 1955, p. 60.

U.S.D.A., Agricultural Handbook Number 8—*Composition of Foods—Raw, Processed, Prepared*. Bureau of Human Nutrition and Home Economics, Washington, 1950.

U.S.D.A., *Food. The 1959 Yearbook of Agriculture*. Government Printing Office, Washington, D. C.

Wilson, Eva D., Katherine H. Fisher, and Mary E. Fuqua, *Principles of Nutrition*. John Wiley and Sons, Inc., New York, 1959.

UNIT 2

Food Habits

A great deal of serious research has been done in an effort to understand the food habits of men, and to influence or change them in the direction of better health. If everyone ate what was good for him rather than what he liked there would be no need for such research. However, eating is a highly personal matter and for many people it furnishes important values other than providing food for the biological need for growth and energy. To some individuals food is a means of relieving worry or tension; to others food is a measure of social or financial success; and in certain cases food becomes compensation for lack of security or love. While such attitudes are only a few of the emotional uses to which food may be put, they serve to illustrate the complexities involved in evaluating food habits and changing them where adequate nutrition is not provided. Even when individuals, families, or whole nations become aware of inefficiency and ill health due to faulty diets, improvements are difficult to make because of the reluctance on the part of many to change fixed food habits.

A dramatic example of how food habits win out over knowledge is illustrated by this case: A student, enrolled in a university foods and nutrition course, developed an acute case of scurvy which kept her away from classes for two weeks. When she returned to school her instructor, on learning of the doctor's diagnosis, expressed surprise that the student had been so shortsighted as not to apply her knowledge of food values to her own daily diet, particularly since the ascorbic acid needed to prevent scurvy was available in such plentiful and palatable forms in the locality. The explanation by the student presented an all too familiar story—at home the family diet consisted of meat, potatoes and bread, and because she liked these things the student continued to eat them at her university boarding house, omitting the variety of foods served. As for her newer knowledge of nutrition—she had simply used it to earn a high grade in the course! It is probable that no habits are stronger than those relating to food. Perhaps all of us know people who have changed either their political or religious beliefs but who adhere to food habits that were formed in early childhood.

Most of us are not conscious of the facts surrounding our own food habits, but if we delve into family background and observe the patterns of eating of parents and grandparents, at least some of these habits will be partially understood. It is sometimes easier to understand food habits of others than it is to comprehend our own. From casual observation it can be seen that a young child will choose foods he likes, and naturally the foods with which a child is familiar are those that he is used to eating at home. From this simple chain of events family patterns of eating are developed that are handed down from generation to generation. Fortunately, many of these patterns are conducive to good nutrition. Often we see *good* food habits being discarded for less desirable ones. An example of this is the mistake made by many Mexicans in the United States who have changed the principal ingredient in their tortillas from whole corn to refined wheat flour. We see other instances where families discard iron-rich turnip greens for spinach, which is, by comparison, a mediocre source of this mineral. In the sugar cane country, molasses was at one time considered to be the "standard" table sweetening but today we will find that the less nutritious white sugar is usually preferred. "Prove all things; cleave to that which is good" is sound advice before substituting one food for another in the diet.

Any attempt to alter family food patterns must take into consideration existing customs with respect to eating. If alterations are to be successful it is basic that they blend, rather than clash, with the habits of the family, region or nation concerned. A study[1] sponsored by the United Nations Educational, Scientific, and Cultural Organization points out that modern food technology can create havoc rather than alleviate suffering unless improvements are superimposed on age-old customs with the greatest caution. The study gives specific examples showing how disrupting the change of a single food can be, and cites as an illustration the adverse effect on Greek family life, of adding raisins, which a nutritionist for a child care service persuaded mothers to try in raisin bread and other unacceptable forms as a part of the children's diet at family meals. This practice stimulated friction because of the divergence in diet of the fathers and the children. The anthropologists making the study suggested that the friction might have been avoided if the raisins had been included in the frequent snacks in which all Greek families indulge instead of at mealtime.

Even though there is general agreement that the factors determining just what foods will be served at the family table are many and varied, there is some difference of opinion as to the significance of the various factors. Ac-

[1] Margaret Mead, *Cultural Patterns and Technical Changes* (New York: Columbia University Press, 1953).

cording to a recent book [1] by two research sociologists, the psychological and cultural factors determine the choice of food more than do education and economic factors.

Granting that the study of food habits is a highly complex subject, still there is no doubt that anyone who wanted to do so could find out more about what governed his own choice of food. Such information would not only be interesting but would in all probability be of positive assistance in altering food habits for general health improvement. Some of the areas in which pertinent and revealing information can be discovered are: regional food habits, national traditions, seasonal influences, religious beliefs, psychological implications, socio-economic backgrounds, superstitions, taboos, and food fads.

Regional food habits. At one time in our history foods that were favorites in certain parts of the United States were unknown in other localities, but now that many American families go "visiting" at least once a year and service men travel from one section of the country to another, Americans are becoming acquainted with more and more regional favorites. Visiting need not be to faraway places to reveal interesting and new dishes. They may be found in the next county or in a neighboring state, and when we start traveling across the country we can, if we do not choose to ignore them, encounter many deliciously different things to eat. Even before we became a nation of travelers certain dishes gained national popularity through trade and travel and the exchange of recipes. "Boston brown bread," the name suggesting its origin, belongs in this category.

Other factors beside travel have contributed to interest in regional foods and cookery. The influence of national magazines on American food has been significant. These magazines, with their huge circulations, carrying recipes and menus, and food advertisements, have, for example, made chili con carne as popular in New Haven as it is in San Antonio, and Manhattan clam chowder a standard soup recipe from coast to coast.

In many sections of the country local restaurants fail to capitalize on regional dishes, and unless a traveler is privileged to eat in homes he may have some difficulty in finding the distinctive cuisine of the region. The menus presented to diners in numerous restaurants, from the Atlantic to the Pacific, list as specialties of the house "steaks and chops." This would indicate that favorite foods of many Americans have become more or less standardized. If regional foods were commonly available at restaurants, one would see many interesting items listed on menu cards throughout the country. A few of the dishes which might appear are "hush puppies" (a fried cornbread popular in several Southern States); "bubble and squeak" (a fried beef and cabbage concoction often prepared in some New England homes); "Hoppin' John"

[1] Margaret Cussler and Mary DeGine, *"Twixt The Cup and The Lip* (New York: Twayne, 1951).

(black-eyed peas and rice, a traditional dish of South Carolina); "syllabub" (a type of eggnog probably originating in Virginia); and "shoo-fly pie" (a molasses pie of Pennsylvania Dutch origin).

In many instances food habits remain stubbornly sectional and there is little or no appreciation of the goodness of food common to other places. It is not very likely that a person will accept or become enthusiastic about all regional foods to which he is introduced. A breakfast of hot biscuit and Southern fried ham may be relished by an Easterner traveling in the South, but he may reject the hominy grits, a traditional accompaniment to the ham. On the other hand, many Southerners visiting in any one of the Northeastern states will anticipate with pleasure a lobster or other "seafood" dinner, but these same people may not even be willing to try a New England boiled dinner, Philadelphia scrapple, or some of the other regional favorites.

The food habits of the people of a given state or region naturally stem from the cultures of the early settlers of the area. Many of the states have unusually colorful history in this respect. Wisconsin serves to illustrate the point. While some people think of it as being largely populated by citizens of German and Swedish descent, the state is a mixture of nearly all European nationalities. This means that in addition to sauerkraut and smörgåsbord there is a great diversity in food tastes. Cornish pasty, saffron bread and other English delicacies will be found in the portion of the state settled by English immigrants. Polish sausage, Italian pizza, Bohemian poppyseed cake and Norwegian lutfisk are among other interesting dishes which can be savored in other Wisconsin communities.

National traditions. More and more we are experiencing universality of interests within the wide range of human living. Because food is a common denominator to people all over the world, it ranks high in this field of interest. In many countries we have the same basic materials for our meals. Not only do these materials vary in quantity and quality; but climate, tradition, and the mode of living all enter the picture to produce an interesting variety both in the specific foods produced and in the methods of preparing them.

Cereal grains are a basic food of all nations. Certain grains are frequently considered as "belonging" to the countries to which they are native. Rye bread is connected with Germans, barley and oats with the Scots, and the Chinese are frequently referred to as "rice eaters." Today these and other grains are produced over wide areas in the world and many countries have learned to include several cereal grains in their diet rather than the one or more which is native. In the case of rice, a recent book on rice cookery[1] describes this grain as the basic food of more than half the world. According to the author, rice is eaten "all around the world, all around the clock, by

[1] Marion Tracy, *The East-West Book of Rice Cookery* (New York: Viking, 1952).

the rich and the poor, the young and the old, on feast days and on fast days." This theme is carried out by the more than one hundred international rice recipes contained in the volume. While less basic than cereal grains, certain foods or combinations of foods have an almost universal appeal. Apples with pastry is a dish enjoyed in varying forms in many countries. Some Americans argue that the apple and pastry combination known in all parts of the United States as "apple pie" is peculiarly our own. However, the English make an apple custard tart, in Hungary and Germany apple strudel is a favorite, and France prefers an apple tart similar to our turnovers.

Increasing our knowledge of how people in other countries eat can be both interesting and beneficial. The Chinese method of "undercooking" vegetables is one which is scorned by many Americans who traditionally overcook their vegetables, while others accept the Chinese method as superior in producing vegetables which are highly palatable and more nutritious. The Mediterranean custom of serving fresh fruit and cheese for dessert would be a good health measure to adopt in situations where overly rich desserts usually follow hearty meals. There are many other interesting examples which might be listed.

Seasonal influences. Before suitable storage facilities for perishable foods, refrigeration, and rapid transportation made a variety of fresh foods available during the entire year, meals were of necessity planned from the foods which were in season and those which could be stored easily. An abundance of fresh fruits and vegetables was at hand during the warm months, but in winter, meats, foods from grain, and such vegetables as would keep in cellars or pits were the principal articles of food. In most localities this condition no longer prevails. Salad plants are on the market all the year; strawberries may be served at the Christmas dinner. The numerous quick-frozen foods have done a great deal to overcome mere seasonal availability of fresh fruits and vegetables. A varied diet is becoming available everywhere throughout the entire year.

Another aspect of seasonal foods is concerned with customs which suggest certain festival seasons. The Cratchit family could not properly celebrate Christmas without a goose. The American wild turkey was made a symbol of Thanksgiving very early in the history of New England. Fish prepared in a special way is a definite part of the Christmas festival among Scandinavian people, and particular kinds of cakes figure in the same celebration in many lands. No less important is the association of eggs with Easter, hot-cross buns with Good Friday, and unleavened bread with the Passover.

Religious influences. As has been shown, many foods have religious as well as seasonal significance, the festivals at which they are used being religious in character.

Early in the history of almost any group, specific foods were prescribed or forbidden by the religious leaders. A health measure may have been the basis for the prohibition of the use of swine for food by the old Mosaic law, but it was made effective through the people's religion. The ancient Egyptians, among whom beef was a favorite food, assured their meat supply by making the female of the species sacred, thus prohibiting their slaughter. The prohibitions were not the same for all groups. The Hebrews might not use the camel as food, but that animal furnished a large part of the meat supply for the Arabs. "Thou shalt not seethe a kid in his mother's milk," said the early Hebrews. Precisely that method of cooking is the basis of one of the favorite stews of the Armenians.

Among primitive tribes many taboos are enforced by the religious leaders. "The head chief of the Masai may eat nothing but milk, honey, and the roasted livers of goats; for if he partook of any other food he would lose his power of sooth-saying and of compounding charms." [1]

Other religious influences, both ancient and modern, are numerous. Currently, the series of holidays marking the beginning of the Jewish Calendar year, Rosh Hashonah, followed by Yom Kippur (a day of fasting), and Sukkoth (the Jewish Thanksgiving) is one of the most elaborately celebrated religious festivals in this country. Symbolism is an important factor, particularly where food is concerned. Traditionally, no bitter or sour food is served during this season. Fruits, honey, sweet wine, and nuts are widely used to betoken a "good" "sweet" and "fruitful" year. Certain foods having special symbolic significance are always served. Some of these are: new fruits of the season to denote gratitude for having lived to see a new season, carrots in some form to symbolize prosperity, and "challah," the traditional holiday Sabbath loaf of bread which is round in form to signify life without end. Other Jewish favorites which are a part of this festival fare are gefillte fish, honey cake, and tzimmes of various kinds.

Psychological implications. As has already been pointed out, there are many psychological factors which have bearing on what individuals or families eat. Most food dislikes probably stem from such causes. The memory of having eaten too much of a rich food sometimes results in permanent dislike for that food. The loss of appetite at the sight of large quantities of food has a similar cause. Perhaps we enjoy eating rabbit meat, but cannot think of eating squirrel, or vice versa, because we think of one or the other animal as a pet. Steaks from cattle are eaten with relish by people in the United States who would scorn the steaks from horses that are not uncommon in Russia. This difference in preference is due primarily to the fact that United States citizens have, in their thinking, associated cattle with food and horses with racing and working.

Socio-economic background. The socio-economic status has a definite bearing on the kind and amount of food that people eat. An example of this is in evidence in certain parts of the rural South, where share-crop farming is practiced. Here social levels of eating are quite clearly defined. White farm

[1] Sir James George Frazer, *The Golden Bough* (New York: Macmillan, 1942), p. 238.

owners eat more food and a greater variety of food than do their white and Negro sharecropper neighbors. These owners occupy an enviable position in the eyes of others in the community who are not so fortunate economically and who are considered as "lower" class. The standard of living of the white landowner is a model for other social levels, particularly insofar as food is concerned, and whenever possible the food habits of the "privileged" class are emulated by "lower class" groups.

Regardless of social class there are, within many family patterns of eating, several different levels of diet. Sometimes these are developed unconsciously, such as a weekday and Sunday level, and a company and holiday level. However, where family income is spasmodic or seasonal, the plentiful and scarcity levels are more likely to be deliberately established.

Cultural differences in the diet are often the result of economic conditions of long standing. As economic circumstances improve, traditional food habits are likely to be shifted. As stated above, in a number of instances the "new" standard is less nutritionally desirable than the old. The prestige value of food cannot be denied. No matter how low the income and regardless of their nutritive value, certain foods will always be purchased that give the purchaser a feeling of well-being. Prestige foods vary with social and economic class. Canned pink salmon may be such a food to the sharecropper farmer mentioned above but to a wealthy city dweller it would be purchased only for the cat. On the other hand, white sugar might be considered by both of the above purchasers as a prestige food under *different* circumstances. To the farmer, who traditionally has used dark molasses as his sweetening, white sugar represents a step up in dietary level. The city-dweller considers white sugar as an ordinary staple item, except in time of scarcity, when it is likely to become a commodity of great significance to him.

The effect of income on the family food supply is specifically discussed on pages 309–311.

Superstitions and taboos. From the earliest days of which we have a record, superstition has played an important part in food habits. Among numerous tribes, the king may not be seen eating or drinking, those seeing him, even by accident, being put to death.[1] Food which is not eaten must be buried or thrown into the sea, lest an enemy find it and devise a charm against the one who left it.[2] These superstitions are laughable to us, but some of our own modern ones have no more real basis. Many people still think fish is a brain food and that celery is quieting to the nerves. These ideas are very much like one expressed by Brillat-Savarin:[3] "Starch is the basis of bread, of pastry, and of purées of all kinds, and thus to a great degree enters into the nourishment of nearly every nation. It has been remarked that such nourishment softens the fibre and diminishes the courage. We may refer to the Hindus, who live

[1] Frazer, *op. cit.*, p. 199.

[2] *Ibid.*, p. 201.

[3] Jean Anthelme Brillat-Savarin, *The Physiology of Taste* (New York: Liveright, 1926).

almost exclusively on rice, and who have become subjugated by any one who chose to conquer them."

Taboos about certain foods and combinations of foods abound in all cultures. Milk seems to be one of the chief items causing concern in this area. Many people are found who have an aversion to eating fish and drinking milk at the same meal; yet these same people will relish oyster stew or creamed tuna fish. In such cases it appears that milk in its *natural* state is suspect, but when changed by cooking it meets with approval. Certain individuals claim that they are "allergic" to sweet milk but that buttermilk or yogurt "agrees" with them. The facts behind such taboos and aversions provide the bases for interesting study.

There is an old superstition that when salt is spilled at the table a quarrel will ensue unless the person spilling it throws some over his shoulder. There are people in all social classes who still faithfully respect this and many other superstitions.

Food fads. The realm of foods and nutrition has always offered a fertile field for the operation of faddists, who seem to be extremely adept at perverting scientific findings to their own advantage. In the last few years the American public has been subjected to an unusual number of pseudo-nutritionists. Their essentially faddish propaganda has been spread through means of lectures, radio and television broadcasts, magazine articles, books, and by many manufacturers of so-called "health" foods and vitamin products. Because these faddists are good showmen, and glib users of scientific terms who are likely to appeal to such emotions as fear, they have inspired the confidence of a large segment of the gullible public. In such instances the high drama and hysteria of the propagandist overshadows the teachings of the authoritative person who has no axe to grind and nothing to sell. The selling of "special" foods, equipment, or concentrates is usually one of the identifying marks of quack "nutritionists." Because of this tendency toward commercial exploitation, it is well to bear in mind that behind every dietary cult there is always one or more persons who receives substantial financial profits from the "scheme." One of the most recent waves of food faddism has been the promotion of "wonder foods." The promoters promise so much for so little that it is understandable how uninformed people who are seeking the best health and welfare for themselves and their families find this propaganda irresistible. Some of the foods which have been labeled by the faddists as "cure-alls" or "youth rejuvenators," are blackstrap molasses, brewers' yeast, yogurt, nonfat dry milk solids, and wheat germ. The suggestion that such foods be used as a way of attaining health is, of course, inconsistent with research findings. If we seek information on this particular group of foods from reliable sources, some of the pertinent facts are as follows:

1) Blackstrap molasses is a waste product from manufacturing sugar. The manufacturers of molasses have never considered it as an *edible* product

since it is chiefly used as an ingredient in industrial alcohol. Its black, bitter, burnt, unpleasant flavor is due to the fact that it results from the third boiling of sugar. The iron present is in unavailable form.

2) Brewers' yeast is an excellent source of the B vitamins, but since its flavor and texture are unpleasant, and since it is not effective unless there is a real need, it should only be taken when prescribed by a physician as a vitamin B supplement.

3) Yogurt, as manufactured in the United States, is cultured whole milk. This means that its nutritional value is the same as the fresh fluid milk from which it is made. Since yogurt is much more expensive than milk in other forms, its only advantage may be one of palatability. Some people may prefer the acid flavor and custard-like texture of yogurt to that of fluid milk.

4) Nonfat dry milk solids (powdered skim milk) are a highly nutritious and economical food. They are a particularly good source of protein, calcium and the B vitamins. Their food value, like that of yogurt, is not magical but depends on the other foods included in the diet.

5) Wheat germ is rich in B-complex vitamins, which any normal diet containing enriched cereals and breads will supply. In fact, wheat germ is part of the enrichment of many bread formulas. Besides being an expensive source of these vitamin values, wheat germ may, because of its coarseness, be a factor in causing intestinal disturbances. Dr. Glenn King, Director of the Nutrition Foundation, reports that there is nothing wrong with wheat germ except that it is not necessary.

Reliance on any one of the above or on any single food or group of foods as a cure for disease, or as a substitute for a well rounded diet is contrary to our present knowledge of nutrition. Today scientists are giving more and more attention to research which determines how foods function together to give maximum benefits to the body, rather than focusing their interests on single new nutrients which are discovered from time to time. In following the doctrines of the faddists some people are likely to ignore the need for medical attention. Other dangers may result in throwing body chemistry out of balance by adding unneeded and unreliable food concentrates to the blood stream.

A review of other health and dietetic cults reveals fads just as fanatical as the above-mentioned one. The craze for trick reducing diets and their resulting ill effects has been described on page 18. One of the most dangerous doctrines of the faddists is the recommendation by some that raw milk be included in the diet, even in infants' formulas, instead of pasteurized milk since, according to their "folklore," pasteurization destroys much of the food value. This statement distorts actual scientific facts. Another favorite theme is the crusade against white bread. In this case the faddists disregard the flour enrichment program which has been in effect since 1941. Through this program virtually all white flour and white bread are now enriched in compliance with standards recommended by government and industry. According to some leading nutritionists, there is no evidence to support the idea that enriched flours are inferior nutritionally to whole-wheat products.

The fad of excluding meat from the diet may have had its origin in abhorrence at the thought of eating an animal. It is not based on physiological facts, for the human digestive tract is so constructed that a diet including both animal and vegetable foods is not only appropriate, but highly beneficial. The experiences of Stefansson [1] show that people who are not accustomed to a diet made up principally of meat may nevertheless use such a diet over an extended period with no harmful results. While "vegetarians" exclude meat from their diets, they usually include other animal proteins such as eggs, cheese, and milk.

There is any number of unfounded notions about foods or combinations of foods. One that presents itself from time to time is that starch and protein should not be eaten at the same meal. We have only to consult tables showing composition of foods to see that these two constituents are combined in many of the foods we eat. Also, if digestive enzymes were not so specific in their action (see pp. 8–10), there might be some argument for separating the two constituents from the standpoint of ease of digestion. Since the enzymes are not only specific but simultaneously active, the idea fails to be convincing to a thoughtful person.

It is true that fads gain popularity because some people have tried them with consequent improvement in health. In their enthusiasm they often give the fad all the credit, rather than the accompanying changes in habits which may mean a decrease in certain rich foods, an increase in important protective foods, an alteration of cooking methods, greater regularity of meals, and other things which are routine practices to persons on normal balanced diets. Fads are doubtless of considerable value psychologically in that they develop confidence to replace fear.

Altering Cooking Habits. Recipes, like food habits, are frequently handed down from generation to generation. These are often for the rich, high calorie dishes, such as desserts, breads, etc., and no one along the line has dared to "tamper" with the proportion of, or the number of ingredients in, such family "treasures." As stated in Unit 1, there is a tendency to eat too liberally of such popular foods. It is highly desirable to evaluate or appraise *all* recipes in terms of individual and family needs.

Fear of a cooking failure is probably responsible for the rigid adherence to a printed or written recipe. Actually, many dishes can be improved by eliminating or substituting certain ingredients, cutting down on quantities of others, such as fat and sugar, and changing the cooking method.

---

[1] Stefansson, V., *Adventures in Diet,* Part II. Harper and Brothers, New York, 1935.

The following recipe taken from the food page of a metropolitan newspaper, is representative of popular "gourmet" recipes. An appraisal of this and other recipes of this type will show the desirability of altering them to fit circumstances:

Shrimp and Crab Poulette
Six Servings

Butter	1 Cup
Shallots, chopped	4
Shrimp, peeled and deveined	32
[1] Chicken stock	1 Cup
Flour	¾ Cup
Milk	2 Cups
Heavy cream	2 Cups
Lemon juice	1 Tablespoon
Egg yolks	3
Lump crab meat	2 Cups

[1] The original recipe specified wine.

The directions specify sautéing the shrimp and shallots in part of the butter, making a sauce of the other ingredients, and adding the shrimp mixture and crab to the sauce. At a glance, even an inexperienced cook will see that this is a luxury dish in terms of cost; but she may not analyze it from the standpoint of the composition of ingredients. The heavy cream and butter, alone, would provide more than 3,000 calories, the egg yolks and milk, another 500.

A likely adjustment for such a recipe would be: (1) reduce the butter by ½ cup; (2) reduce the total amount of liquid by 1 cup, since 5 cups for 6 servings is overly generous; (3) substitute light cream for heavy, using only 1 cup; (4) use skim milk instead of whole; (5) substitute one whole egg for the three yolks; and (6) reduce the flour by ¼ cup, since the liquid has been cut down.

The habit of using fats as a major seasoning is one employed by many homemakers. The flavor and crispness resulting from frying is responsible for such widespread use of this cookery method in the United States. Changing practices of food preparation are frequently recommended when someone in the family is put on a special diet. Such a recommendation need not lead to monotonous meals. In fact, it may open up avenues for more interesting meals through creativity.

SUGGESTIONS FOR LABORATORY

A "first" laboratory period might be devoted to the preparation of a few foods that are representative of the different backgrounds in the class. Food preparation in strange surroundings is a difficult hurdle for most people, especially students working in a laboratory. This situation can be relieved somewhat, if the instructor and students plan a project involving the preparation of dishes which are familiar to the students. A variety of recipes adapted from traditional dishes of different countries will be found in Section IV. These will serve as a guide in a "cultural background" laboratory.

In addition to dishes which are representative of family backgrounds, a first laboratory might also reflect new and interesting food which students have had introduced to them through travel experiences or associations with others. It is more feasible if such projects are carried out on a group basis, with four or five students participating in each group. In a pre-planning discussion students can get better acquainted in small groups and are more likely to discuss freely their experiences with food, both at home and away from home.

In one particular class four groups presented the following projects:

1) A dinner consisting of borsch, Hungarian goulash, Italian green salad, and Pennsylvania Dutch apple butter custard. The borsch was the contribution of a Jewish girl who described to the class the ceremony, in her particular home, that involved the preparation of the soup by her grandfather. The goulash represented the culinary skill of a student who had been schooled by her Hungarian grandmother in some of the classics of the old country. A first generation Italian girl fascinated the class by dressing the green salad at the table. For this she used olive oil, wine vinegar, fresh basil, salt, and freshly ground black pepper. The dessert for the dinner was created by one of the boys in the class who had often watched his mother make the Pennsylvania Dutch apple butter custard, a family favorite.

2) A Japanese dinner. This was the outgrowth of an "exchange" between the mother of one of the students and her Japanese-American neighbor. The two had visited periodically to get acquainted with and learn how to prepare some of the different foods of their respective families. An interested participant had been the student who delighted in instructing her class associates in the art of Japanese cooking.

3) Variations in apple desserts. For this project five students each prepared and described the favorite apple dessert of their families. The results were: apple pot-pie; apple crunch; apple dumplings; apple shortcake, and open-face apple pie.

4) A European classic dessert. Several students had spent the previous summer traveling in Europe and in their exchange of information found that all had enjoyed a dessert, similar to the baked custard of America, called flan. After checking references and discussing their project with the instructor, they prepared several different versions of flan, including the one on pp. 527–28.

REFERENCES

BOOKS

Beck, Neil and Fred, "Farmers Market Cook Book." Henry Holt & Co. New York, 1951.

Brillat-Savarin, Jean Anthelme, *The Physiology of Taste*. Liveright Publishing Corp., New York, 1926.

Brown, Cora, Rose and Bob, *The European Cook Book*. Prentice-Hall, New York, 1951.

Cussler, Margaret, and Mary DeGine, *'Twixt The Cup and The Lip*. Twayne Publishers, New York, 1951.

Frazer, Sir James George, *The Golden Bough*. The Macmillan Co., New York, 1942.

Mead, Margaret, *Cultural Patterns and Technical Changes*. Columbia University Press, New York, 1953.

Nichols, Nell B., *Good Home Cooking Across the United States*. Iowa State College Press, Ames, Iowa, December 1952.

Packard, Vance Oakly, *The Status Seekers*. D. McKay Company, 1959.

PERIODICALS AND BULLETINS

Babcock, Charlotte G., "Food and Its Emotional Significance," *Jour. Am. Diet. Assoc.* Vol. 24, No. 5, 1948.

Biester, Charlotte, "Why Not Start With a Unit on International Cookery," *Practical Home Economics,* Sept. 1953.

Huddleson, Mary P., "Youth, Beauty and Yogurt," *Jour. Am. Diet. Assoc.* Vol. 27, No. 7, July 1951.

Lewin, K., *Forces Behind Food Habits and Method of Change,* National Research Council, Washington, D. C. Bull. 108, 1943.

"Food Facts Talk Back," American Dietetics Assoc., 1957.

Stefansson, Vilhjalmur, *Adventures in Diet,* Part II. Harpers, Dec. 1935.

Sullivan, Lenore, "What to Cook for Company." Iowa State College Press, 1952.

SECTION 2

Familiar Foods

UNIT

3

Fruits

As long ago as anything is known of the food habits of people, records show that fruits have made an important contribution to the food supply. When the Israelites were nearing the Land of Canaan, spies, sent ahead to survey the situation, returned with reports and samples of the native fruits. "We came unto the land whither thou sentest us, and surely it floweth with milk and honey, and this is the fruit of it." [1] The ancient Egyptian frequently built his house in the corner of a garden in which figs and pomegranates were plentiful and grapes abundant.

Colonists in America found and used wild fruits as food. These fruits had been a part of the food supply of the Indians and in at least one instance figured in a treaty made between the natives and the new settlers. Along the North Atlantic coast, beach plums grow abundantly. They were cherished by the Indians. When Richard Hartshorne settled on land which included Sandy Hook, New Jersey, "The lands were purchased from the Indians who when they sold Sandy Hook to Hartshorne, reserved the liberty to go on Sandy Hook and get plumes." [2] These plums are still highly prized for making jelly and jam.

When people are accustomed to certain fruits, they are reluctant to omit them from their dietary when they move from one place to another. Consequently, fruits become common in vicinities and countries far removed from the original habitat of the plants. Peaches were probably native to Persia and were taken from there to other parts of Asia and Europe, where the climate was too severe for them unless they were raised very carefully. So highly were they esteemed that the trees were sometimes raised in greenhouses or trained against the southern walls of dwellings. In the garden of an English friend

[1] Numbers 13:27.

[2] *General History of Fort Hancock* (N. J.). Courtesy Lieut.-Col. R. S. Dodson and Colonel J. C. Johnson.

an esplanade is in the form of an arbor that provides apples and pears as well as shade.

In the early years of the settlement of the United States by Europeans, priests in the Southwest spent much time in raising fruits. Not all succeeded as well as those at the San Buenaventura Mission in California, where gardens, according to a visiting English captain, contained "apples, pears, plums, figs, oranges, grapes, peaches, and pomegranates, together with the plantain, banana, coconut, sugar cane, indigo, and a great variety of the necessary and useful kitchen herbs, plants, and roots." [1] When oranges were scarce and very expensive, many a garden of high-income families included an orangery—a house or otherwise protected spot in which oranges were grown. Sometimes bananas and pineapples were there also.

Fruit for health's sake. As a group, fruits are valuable for their vitamin, mineral, and cellulose content. Some have unusually large amounts of other nutrients. For example, bananas and watermelons contain a high percentage of carbohydrates; avocados, of fat. As part of a good daily food pattern, at least two fruits are desirable. Unless a vegetable that is chiefly important for ascorbic acid is included, one of the fruits should provide that essential nutrient (see p. 15).

Eating fruit for breakfast is an excellent habit because fruit is appealing and appetizing as well as a source of important vitamins and minerals. However, the fruit juice that may be the constant part of the breakfast menu is sometimes a misleading "good habit," because it may be expected to provide the essential ascorbic acid for the day. The capacity of the average fruit juice glass is ½ cup. Using this as a serving, and supposing that a person should include 70 to 75 mg. of ascorbic acid in a day's meals, the following amounts of ascorbic acid are provided by some of the commonly used fruit juices:

Orange		*Tomato*	19
Fresh	61	*Pineapple*	11
Canned (unsweetened)	52	*Apple*	1
Frozen (conc.)	48	*Grape*	tr.
Grapefruit			
Fresh	50		
Canned (unsweetened)	43		
Frozen (conc.)	45		

It is obvious that if one of the juices that is low in ascorbic acid is used for breakfast, some excellent source should be included in one of the other meals. If a whole (medium) orange or half of a grapefruit (medium) is included for breakfast, the total ascorbic acid requirement is met. Fruits that are eaten fresh are more valuable sources of ascorbic acid than cooked fruits. It is al-

[1] George Wharton James, *In and Out of the Old Missions* (Boston: Little, Brown, 1916), p. 183.

ways well to serve at least one of the two fruits recommended for each day raw. The tartness of fruits is due to the fruit acids present. These acids, chiefly citric and malic, are present as acid salts of the various minerals.

Fruits are alkaline in their reaction. They aid in digestion because they both stimulate the flow of digestive juices and furnish considerable bulk.

Production. Wild fruits of many kinds are still gathered for eating fresh. There are many instances of the use of these fruits for making jams and jellies, and of home industries that have expanded into larger industries. Many varieties of berries, wild plums, mayhaws, roselles, and grapes are highly prized in the regions where they grow. Cultivated varieties have been developed that make it possible for many of these fruits to be used widely. The efforts of independent horticulturists and of those connected with the United States Department of Agriculture and with state agricultural colleges and experiment stations have resulted in both new and improved varieties of fruit. Cantaloupes that are not affected by mildew, peaches that grow over a wide range of climatic conditions, others that can be ripened on the tree and still ship well, and new varieties of plums and cherries are among the results of these efforts. Comparatively new fruits include hybrids which combine the characteristics of two or more fruits, such as the tangelo, a cross between the grapefruit and a variety of tangerine; Monsteria Deliciosis, hybrid between banana and pineapple; and boysenberry, a hybrid including loganberry, raspberry, and blackberry. New fruits also result from mutations, such as the pink and ruby-red grapefruit. Buds from branches bearing fruit of the desired color are used in budding other trees. The nectarine is a smooth peach produced both as a bud sport and from the peach pit. Through agricultural research hormone sprays have been developed that strengthen the stems of some varieties of apples and other fruits, thus preventing preharvest drop and resulting in more tree-ripened fruit. Other sprays are used to lighten the fruit load of trees. The advantages of this technique are that the fruit is better in size and the quantity of fruit from year to year is more even.

Not only the introduction of new fruits and the increased production of many kinds, but also the development of rapid transportation and adequate refrigeration account for the quantity and variety of fresh fruits available on our markets throughout the year. Use of air transportation is responsible for bringing fresh fruit from many countries to our markets. Consumers take this variety for granted and when some unusual circumstance, such as a blizzard or a flood, interrupts the transportation schedule, they are annoyed.

Among farm families, fruit production to meet their needs is encouraged by the various agricultural and homemaking agencies. Preservation of fruits by canning, dehydrating, and quick freezing is also stressed. Fruits that require little space and that come into bearing within a short time, such as berries, are being recommended as a beginning. One village family that was interested in apples planted a tree and then had it grafted so that there were apples of different varieties ripe at different times over the whole apple season for that community. Dwarf trees are also practical for growing fruit if space is limited. Any effort at home production of fruit requires advice from local or regional horticultural authorities.

To the casual observer, the beauty of an apple orchard in full bloom, the bending boughs of trees when fruit is ready to gather, miles of grapevines or acres of berry bushes are easy to attain. It seems only a step from these sources of production to the fruit ready to be taken home by the city dweller. To appreciate the fruit supply, a careful observer must understand the toil required to plant an orchard, to cultivate fruit trees or plants so that their yield will be maximum, to hoe and pull weeds, to spray and remove pests that develop in the ground or on the trees or plants, and to gather, grade, pack, and find a satisfactory market for the fruit. The risks of the farmers insofar as weather conditions are concerned cannot be estimated, and the discouragements when a late frost or a hailstorm destroys the prospect of a good crop must be experienced to be fully appreciated.

Buying and storing fruit. On the market, choice in fruit varies greatly during the year, from one variety of a given fruit to several varieties and sizes from several states and abroad. Many distinctly seasonal fruits may be expected in abundance for brief periods each year. Modern transportation and storage have lengthened the season for most fruits, making many available for a considerable time, but with prices that vary with distance from production points as well as abundance. For example, berries are among the most perishable fruits, but these facilities, together with excellent market reporting, make it possible for wholesalers to obtain them from points where they mature early in the year to those where they mature late. The price is relatively high for both the early and late ones, and least when they are in season locally.

Strawberries at Christmas are not unusual if price is not a factor. Storage of the hardy fruits, such as most apples and citrus, makes it possible to have them in abundance the year around.

An example of up-to-date marketing is one used for the soft-fleshed apples which are taken from orchard to storehouse in field crates or lugs and stored in "controlled atmosphere" rooms. The regulated carbon dioxide in the air arrests the maturing of the apples, which are graded, packaged in ventilated pliofilm bags, and marketed. In the words of one packer, these are, "Sleeping beauties that are awakened for your eating pleasure"; another refers to the "Rip Van Winkle sleep." The extended time for availability of these apples is appreciated by consumers and enables producers to sell them to far greater advantage than was previously possible.

Both general and specific information are needed as guides in selecting fresh fruits. Among general considerations, the following may be noted:

1) Select fruit personally whenever possible.
2) Select fruit which is ripe but firm.

3) Whenever possible, judge fruit by appearance.

4) If the fruit must be handled, be gentle. Tender fruit which has been handled roughly spoils quickly, and buyers should consider the person who will visit the market later.

5) If possible, purchase fruit by weight.

6) Size and appearance do not always indicate flavor, but they usually influence price. For example, the rosiest apples may be inferior to less attractive ones, and small oranges may be more juicy than larger ones. Distinguish between blemishes that affect eating quality and those that do not.

7) Whenever it is possible, buy by grade. Choose the grade that is suited to the purpose for which it is to be used. For example, apples for making sauce or a pie need not be of as fine quality as apples to be served as fresh fruit.

8) Plan menus around fruits that are in season. They are not only less expensive, but also better in flavor.

9) Among the factors which determine the amount to purchase are:
   a) Size of the group.
   b) Amount of money to be spent for fruit.
   c) Popularity of various fruits with the group.
   d) Variety on the market.
   e) Keeping qualities of the fruit.
   f) Storage space.

There are many specific considerations which are helpful in selecting fruit. The following paragraphs will help in buying the most commonly used fruits:

Apples. The varieties of apples on the market differ greatly from place to place, because many are not shipped far from the production area. A few varieties find their way to all parts of the country. The consumer should become familiar with the varieties on the local market and select from them those best suited to her needs. As a rule, apples of medium size are cheaper than large apples and are of as good quality. Cooking apples are less expensive than dessert apples and are frequently firmer and more tart.

Early apples are often packed in baskets, while fall and winter varieties are marketed either in baskets, boxes, or barrels, depending largely upon the section in which the fruit is grown and the disposition that is to be made of it. Choice dessert apples are sometimes packed in two-pound boxes with a cellophane "window" top. This lessens bruising of the more tender varieties. Apples grown in the Northwest are packed exclusively in boxes. Eastern and Midwest apples are marketed largely in baskets, though the box as a package is becoming increasingly popular in this section. The use of barrels as an apple package has declined sharply in recent years, and at the present time only a limited amount of fruit is sent to market in this type of container.

Fruit that is overripe, bruised, shriveled, dull in color, or frosted should be avoided. Mealy apples are undesirable for eating purposes, but they are hard to detect unless a person is familiar with the fact that certain varieties, includ-

Courtesy Pennsylvania Agricultural Extension Service

Fig. 1. Strawberries rate high in beauty, palatability and vitamin C.

ing Tolman Sweet, Ben Davis, and Arkansas Black, are apt to be mealy. Early apples should be purchased for immediate use, since they do not keep well. Late apples should be purchased in as large quantity as the family's use will warrant—by the box, peck, bushel, or even barrel—and with regard to the best price available. In small quantities, buying by weight should be encouraged. Bruised or decaying fruit should be removed so that the decay will not spread to sound fruit. Storage space should be cool and dry.

Apples are graded on the basis of size, color, and absence of bruises and other defects. The grades are U. S. Fancy, U. S. No. 1, U. S. No. 2, and U. S. Utility.

Bananas. There are many varieties of bananas. The red one which was originally most commonly sold is now used occasionally as a change from the yellow variety so prevalent on the market. The development of modern banana production and world-wide distribution by special ships is one of the interesting stories of the food industries. The bananas of the tropics are harvested green and ripened wholly or in part in special storerooms by the wholesalers. The process of ripening is frequently completed by the retailer. The bunches usually consist of from seven to twelve clusters, called hands, each having ten to twenty bananas.

In self-service stores, bananas are usually cut from the main stem and are readily available in clusters of two to ten. The skin of the banana should not be broken. When fully ripe, the yellow skin of the banana is somewhat mottled with brown, but the fruit is not soft. Bananas should be bought by weight and stored outside a refrigerator. Some bananas are soft in spots before they are ripe. This is usually due to damage during shipping.

Berries. During a year's time many varieties of berries find their way to the market. Blackberries, dewberries, loganberries, raspberries, huckleberries, blueberries, cranberries, currants, and gooseberries are all more or less popular. In some communities, lingonberries, packed in barrels, are imported from Scandinavia, and are available at Christmas time. These berries are used traditionally as one of the special Christmas foods of Scandinavian people. Strawberries are more popular and plentiful than any of the others. Cranberries marketed by a cooperative organization have been made available over an extended time period. With the exception of cranberries, all berries are very perishable and should be purchased in small quantities, unless they are to be preserved. Berries should be fresh, clean, well colored, and free from leaves and twigs. They are packed in standard pint or quart baskets or in ventilated mesh baskets. Most are shipped in crates which hold from twelve to forty-eight baskets. Some are graded and the top is protected by a plastic cover. When they are not graded, the buyer may tip a basket enough to have an idea of the size and quality of all the berries without bruising them. Berries should be stored without washing in a cold place, preferably a refrigerator. A shallow container will prevent molding or packing.

Citrus fruits. The citrus fruits include lemons, limes, oranges, grapefruit (pomellos), tangerines, Temple oranges, tangelos, Satsumas, and kumquats. Most of them are graded as to size, and the size is stated as the number in a box. There are seven sizes of lemons—240's, 270's, 300's, 360's, 420's, 442's, and 490's. The sizes of oranges are 80's, 96's, 100's, 126's, 150's, 176's, 200's, 250's, 324's, and 350's. Grapefruit are packed in seven sizes—28's, 36's, 46's, 54's, 64's, 70's, and 96's. The larger fruits are usually higher in price than the smaller ones but are not always more juicy.

Citrus fruit that is heavy for its size is juicy. Thin skin is denoted by small pores, and is usually considered a desirable characteristic. Color is not necessarily an indication of ripeness because color is often increased by the use of ethylene gas in storage rooms or added by dipping the fruit in a vat of coloring. The latter fruit is stamped, "color added." Color is not necessarily related to quality. Most people associate a bright orange color with good oranges, but russet oranges are equally good and frequently less expensive. Rosy color on the skin identifies ruby-red grapefruit.

The riper citrus fruits are when they are picked, the better their flavor, but present marketing practice does not make it possible to provide a large quantity of tree-ripened fruit. Some of the recent methods should lead to shipping more ripe fruit. For example, the fruit may be sprayed with flavorless oil that seals the pores and aids in keeping ripe fruit over a longer period. Tangelos and Temple oranges do not have the keeping qualities of other oranges; thus their season is short. Oranges and grapefruit of different varieties and those that are grown in different states vary considerably in flavor. It is interesting to compare these.

Grapes. There are few areas in America where grapes of some kind do not grow. The eastern varieties, including Niagaras, Catawbas, Concords, and Delawares, are usually shipped in climax baskets which contain from two to twelve quarts. These varieties do not keep long, even in cold storage, and are not shipped so far as the hardier varieties. The Tokays, Black Ribiers, Cornichons, and Sultaninas (Thompson Seedless), mostly from California, are among the firmer varieties which may be shipped farther than eastern grapes because of their superior keeping qualities. Some grapes, including Malagas, are imported. The fruit should be plump and well colored, and should not shatter when the bunch is lifted. All varieties should be purchased for immediate use, and kept in a cool, dry place.

Melons. Melons are grown in nearly all parts of the United States, but thirteen states furnish most of those that are shipped an appreciable distance. Muskmelons are divided into three groups by the color of the flesh, which may be green, pink, or salmon. Indications of ripeness are heavy netting, a yellowish color under the netting, characteristic odor, pliability at the stem end, and, if they were ripened on the vine, a smooth, slightly sunken scar at the blossom end. They should be heavy for their size and free from soft spots, mold, and moisture at the stem end. They are packed in crates or baskets and are retailed by unit or by weight.

Watermelons are graded as to size, shape, variety, and freedom from blemishes. They are round or oval, green or greenish gray, and the flesh is red, pink, or yellow, depending upon the variety. Yellowish color where the melon touched the ground, easily scraped epidermis, and a dull rather than a sharp sound when the melon is thumped are the usual tests for ripeness. The better melons are symmetrical in shape. Watermelons vary greatly in size, from the recently developed small ones weighing from two to three pounds to specially "fed" melons weighing over a hundred pounds.

Peaches. Every state in the United States produces peaches, but many of the most delicious varieties are not firm enough to be shipped. The skin is creamy white to deep yellow, usually with a pronounced blush. The flesh is white or yellow, and loosely or closely attached to the stone, depending upon the variety. Peaches should be firm, plump, and show no spots of decay. They are marketed in baskets of several sizes, and usually vary in ripeness, so that it is possible to buy a reasonably large basket, select the ripe ones for immediate use, and store the others in a cool place where they will ripen slowly. Since all peaches bruise easily, they should be handled very gently, if at all, when selecting them. Those who have had the experience of growing peaches for their table know that the best peach is tree-ripened.

Pears. Unlike most fruits, many pears are best if ripened in cool, dry storage. Unless they are ripe, refrigeration is unnecessary. When pears are purchased in fairly large quantities, they should be sorted frequently to remove the spoiled ones. They are marketed in baskets, boxes, crates, and barrels, and are usually sold by the unit, dozen, or basket. The most popular market pear is the Bartlett; the Kieffer perhaps being second. The Kieffer is cooked for table use or canned. Bosc, Anjou, and Comice pears are popular. Anjou and Comice pears are found on the market most of the winter. The small Seckel pear, juicy and sweet, is often preserved or pickled, and is also used as a dessert fruit. When purchased, pears should be firm and free from decay or bruises.

Other fruits. The table on page 48 lists a number of fruits not so abundant or widely used as those discussed.

Special marketing practices. If a producer has fruit of good quality and in sufficient quantity, the buyer for a local food store or grocery chain may contract for the entire crop, just as a wholesaler may have the same arrangement with a large producer or production area. Considerable fruit is sold direct to the consumer from roadside stands or from producers operating in a farmers' or municipal market. Where cost of labor is high, consumers often go to an orchard, pick the fruit, and pay much less than they would even at a roadside market when the fruit has been gathered by pickers. Certain producers pack a fancy grade of fruit in attractive packages and ship them directly to the consumer, on order. These fruits are usually advertised especially at the holiday season.

Preparation of fresh fruit for storage and eating. After fruits are brought home from the market, they should be washed carefully to remove dust, microorganisms, and any spray that may cling to the fruit. The spray may be harmful because of its arsenic or lead content. In most cases, measures to reduce this danger are being taken. Most apples must be washed before they are shipped. However, all fruit is exposed to dust, bacteria, and soil due to handling and, as a health measure, should be washed before it is eaten or stored in the home. The exception is most berries. It is better to wash them just before they are eaten because they are so tender that their texture will be undesirable if they are allowed to stand after being washed.

If some fruits, including apples, pears, and peaches are prepared for eating fresh and allowed to stand, they darken because of oxidation of tannins and the flavone pigment (in apples). This may be prevented by sprinkling them with citrus, or pineapple juice.

TABLE 4. SELECTION OF LESS COMMON FRUITS

Fruit	*Characteristics and Suggestions for Selection*	*Market Units*	*Storage*
Apricot	Yellow, 8–12 or 12–16 per lb.; firm, not bruised; for immediate use	Unit, dozen, basket, weight	Cool, dry, well ventilated
Avocado (alligator pear)	Green to mahogany; varieties differ in size and shape; yield to slight pressure	Unit, weight	Refrigerator if ripe; room temperature to ripen
Cranberry	Usually bright red; clean, firm, plump	Weight, measure	Cold, well ventilated
Cherry	Color varies with kind; plump; free from decay; skin not broken; sweet and sour varieties	Weight, basket—quart or climax	Cool, dry, well ventilated; for short time only
Currant	White, red, or black; fresh, not falling from stems; plump	Pint or quart	Cool, dry; piled loosely
Fig	Greenish yellow to nearly black; mature, not bruised; buy for immediate use. Size differs with variety	Weight, dozen, quart	Cool, dry, for short time only
Gooseberry	Green to deep, dull red; firm, not wrinkled or decayed	Basket, usually quart	Cool, dry
Melons:			
Casaba	Yellow, flesh creamy white; rough, deeply wrinkled rind	Unit, weight	Cool; room temperature to ripen
Honeydew	Creamy yellow; delicate green flesh, smooth, oval	Unit, weight	Cool; room temperature to ripen
Santa Claus	Green, broad stripes; flesh white to yellowish green; oblong	Unit, weight	Cool; room temperature to ripen
Nectarine	Greenish with blush; skin smooth. Avoid handling	Unit, dozen, weight	Cool, dry, well ventilated
Papaya	Orange-yellow; melon shaped; buy for immediate use	Unit, weight	Cool; room temperature to ripen
Persimmon	Orange-red; sweet varieties firm; astringent varieties soft	Unit, weight	Cool, dry, well ventilated
Pineapple	Orange-yellow to greenish bronze; fragrant; heavy for size; "eyes" flat; spines readily pulled out	Unit, weight	Cold; room temperature to ripen
Plum and prune	Color differs with variety; clean; plump; skin unbroken; slightly soft. Avoid handling	Weight, basket—climax or bushel	Cold, free from decayed fruit
Pomegranate	Yellow to reddish; skin tough but thin	Unit	Dry
Quince	Yellowish; hard, free from bruises and discolored spots	Unit, weight, quart, peck, bushel	Cool, dry, free from decayed fruit
Rhubarb	Red stem which is used like a fruit; not wilted	Bunch, weight	Cool, dry

Cooking fruit. There are a number of reasons for cooking fruit. Some of these reasons follow:

1) Fruit may be cooked to improve its flavor and increase its digestibility. A pie made from unripe apples is very acceptable, while a green apple eaten raw is inferior and may digest with difficulty.

2) One way to add interest to the diet is to vary the method of preparing foods. Apples are cooked in a number of ways; bananas are baked or broiled; and other fruits are stewed or baked, partly to give variety.

3) Sometimes fruits ripen more quickly than it is possible to use them, and they are cooked to prevent spoilage.

4) Many fruits are cooked to preserve them for later use. These provide variety in the diet, especially in rural districts during the season when fresh fruits are not readily available. The use of many fruits is extended throughout the year by canning, drying, and freezing.

Fruits are cooked by several methods, the one chosen depending upon the fruit and the way it is to be used.

Cooking in water or sirup. Apples for sauce will usually be better if they are cooked in unsweetened water. If they are not pared, both color and flavor are usually better. The skin is removed by putting the cooked apples through a colander, food mill, or Sep-ro-siv. If sour apples are to be served sliced or as cinnamon or mint apples, they should be cooked in sirup rather than unsweetened water. The process of osmosis, by which liquid is transferred from the fruit to the more concentrated sirup, makes the apple firm. This does not apply to all fruits, but apricots, peaches, and plums may be cooked satisfactorily in sirup. Strawberries and pitted sour cherries are likely to collapse if cooked in sirup, especially if the sirup is concentrated and if the cooking is rapid. If they are allowed to stand with sugar sprinkled over them until some of the juice is removed and the sugar has melted and has been partially absorbed by the fruit, they retain their shape nicely when cooked.

In any case, the cell walls of the fruit tend to break during rapid boiling, while the shape of the fruit is retained far better by simmering or stewing. The concentration of the sirup or the quantity of sugar added after fruits are cooked depends upon both the sourness of the fruit and personal taste. The second influence is so variable that it is difficult to state amounts which would be of general value. The use of a quantity of sugar sufficient to detract from the flavor of the fruit should be discouraged.

Baking. Apples, firm winter pears, and bananas are frequently baked. The methods of baking may vary considerably, offering pleasing changes when the same fruit is used a great deal.

Sautéing. Apples and bananas are the fresh fruits most commonly cooked by sautéing.[1] Canned pineapple is frequently sautéed.

[1] Sautéing is cooking in a suitable container, using only enough fat to prevent sticking.

Broiling. Broiled bananas have many uses. Spiced, they may be served as an appetizer; with the meat course; or as a dessert. They are delicious with bacon, for breakfast or luncheon.

Cooking combinations of fruit. Some fruits are sufficiently bland to need added flavor, or are particularly pleasing when combined with another fruit. Pears take on added interest if a few quinces are cooked with them. Strawberries and pineapple, in a ratio of about half as much pineapple as berries, make an acceptable change. In many localities rhubarb is an inexpensive product which is sometimes used with more expensive fruits, such as strawberries.

SUGGESTIONS FOR LABORATORY

(SELECTED RECIPES ON PP. 490 THROUGH 498.)

Available fresh fruits naturally depend upon season and location. As wide a variety as possible gives an opportunity for instructor and students to show many ways to serve them. Supplemented by items selected from the processed fruits, these opportunities are multiplied. At best, those prepared will be only a sampling of the versatility of fruits for giving keen interest to the preparation and eating of meals. The nutritional importance of various fruits as served should be a definite part of the summarizing discussion of the laboratory activities. Using citrus as an example, points in selection, range in size and price, and introduction of less common varieties are a few of the ways in which the words of the text may be "brought to life." Preplanning by instructor and students might result in certain projects being a part of student participation that would prove more challenging than if the whole plan were made by the instructor. The following examples of such projects are cited for the student's information:

1) Comparative nutritional value of ½ c. of available fruit juices served for breakfast. (See p. 40.)

2) Cost, preparation time, and opinions of palatability of fresh, frozen, and canned citrus juice.

3) Versatility of fruit for breakfast, lunch, dinner and snacks. Any selected fruit might be chosen to illustrate its use in different parts of the meal.

4) Uses of fruits by different nationalities.

5) Table arrangements to show the decorative possibilities of fruits.

REFERENCES

Extension Service of State or County: *Bulletins concerning production, storage, and use of fruits.*

Stewart, Jean J., and Alice L. Edwards, *Foods: Production, Marketing, Consumption.* Prentice Hall, New York, 1948.

Todoroff, Alexander, *Food Buyer's Information Book*. The Grocery Trade Publishing House, Chicago, 1946.

Troelstrup, Arch W., *Consumer Problems and Personal Finance*. McGraw-Hill Book Co., Inc., New York, 1957.

United States Department of Agriculture, *A Fruit and Vegetable Buying Guide for Consumers,* Misc. Pub. No. 167, 1946.

The United States Department of Agriculture, *The Yearbook of Agriculture, 1959, Food*. Boswell, Victor R., *What Makes Fruit and Vegetables Good?*

The Wise Encyclopedia of Food. Wm. H. Wise and Co., New York, 1951.

UNIT

4

Vegetables

Vegetables are among the foods that have been in common use for ages. They have been cultivated, even under adverse circumstances, for so long that the accounts of such cultivation are legendary.

One of the world legends I have always found most fascinating is that of the nomadic truck gardeners, traces of whose fame you will find all over the globe—the legends of peoples incurably nomadic but just as incurably addicted to fresh vegetables. These peoples traveled always with carts loaded with good loam, leaf soil, alluvial earth, and composts. When they came to worthless land, the exposure of which suited them, they would dig little shallow trenches in the poor soil, pour out their good earth, prick out their seedlings, make sowings, and very soon have crops that would provide them with green things during their stay, and roots and fodder for themselves and their cattle during the dead months.[1]

Wild plants are popular to use as greens in the early spring. Among these, dandelion, marsh marigold (cowslip), chicory, sorrel, watercress, lamb's-quarters (pigweed), pokeweed, and mustard are commonly used. Sometimes a combination is more appetizing than one green; dandelion, lamb's-quarters, and a bit of sorrel are delicious when cooked together. In a bulletin prepared by Carver,[2] over forty wild plants are listed as edible. Some, such as dandelion and sorrel, are used rather commonly where they grow, but others, including evening primrose and alfalfa, are less commonly considered foods.

Edible roots of wild plants include arrowhead, sweet flag, jack-in-the-pulpit, and wild onion. Palmetto (cabbage palm) furnishes a delicacy sometimes found canned as "hearts of palm."

There are numerous edible mushrooms and puffballs[3] growing wild that

---

[1] Ford Madox Ford, "The Small Producer," *The American Mercury*, Aug., 1935. Reprinted by permission.

[2] George Washington Carver, *Nature's Garden for Victory and Peace*, Bul. No. 43, Tuskegee Institute, Ala., 1942.

[3] Nina Lane Faubion, *Some Edible Mushrooms and How to Know Them* (Binfords and Mort, Portland [Ore.], 1938).

Courtesy National Dairy Council

Fig. 2. A variety of vegetables which can be found in most markets.

supply not only interesting and delicious flavor but also calcium, iron, and thiamin.

Plants differ in the portion which is edible. In many instances only one part of the plant is edible; in others, more than one. Only the tuber of the potato plant is eaten; both root and leaf of beets; and stem, leaf, and flower buds of cauliflower. In Table 5, page 55, vegetables are listed under the commonly eaten part or parts. Of the sixty vegetables listed, nine are roots, five are bulbs, and two are tubers—the Irish potato and the Jerusalem artichoke, both native to the Americas, but one used very commonly and the other seldom seen on the market. More leaves are eaten than other parts of the plant—twenty, with fruits coming next—ten. There are five stems, six seeds, three flowers, and two fungi. The majority are not native to the Western Hemisphere.

Vegetables are important for good nutrition. Vegetables, like fruit, are chiefly important for their mineral, vitamin, and cellulose content. Yellow and green color indicates carotene (provitamin A), and the deeper the color, the more real vitamin A is available for conversion by the body. Tomatoes, greens, broccoli, cauliflower, and cabbage contain ascorbic acid in appreciable amounts. Greens, peas, and potatoes are important sources of the B vitamins. Green vegetables contribute calcium and iron.

Some vegetables, particularly Irish and sweet potatoes, are considered mainly as carbohydrate foods. However, they supply some of the minerals and vitamins in quantities that are important because of the frequency with which they are eaten. Dried legumes furnish protein, soybeans containing high quality protein. However, in the United States, soybeans are not readily available because they have not become a commonly-used food.

Against this background, a green or yellow vegetable and two others are highly desirable as part of the day's food. Interchange with fruit may be kept in mind; e.g., a vegetable rich in ascorbic acid if a comparable fruit is not served; a light colored yellow vegetable, such as summer squash, if cantaloupe is used; potatoes may be replaced by rice or one of the alimentary pastes, but deserve a prominent place among everyday foods. Since raw vegetables contain the maximum nutrients, at least one may well become a daily food habit.

Production and distribution. Vegetables are raised in varying quantities in all parts of the country. In cities, small plots in which a very few vegetables are grown may be found; in villages, larger plots which furnish from a few greens and salad plants to enough vegetables for the family for a considerable part of the year; in farming areas, many well planned gardens where sufficient vegetables for the year are produced. The planning is done against a background of the amount and type of vegetables needed; and freezing, canning, and sometimes drying are used to preserve the winter's supply. For city dwellers, large areas are devoted to truck gardening, often not far from the city markets. Winter garden areas are also extremely important for the constant supply of fresh vegetables throughout the country.

Newly developed vegetables appear on the market frequently, and seed companies encourage people to try these new foods. Extension Service bulletins are available containing information about soil, planting directions, varieties suitable for certain areas, cultivation, and means of coping with plant diseases and insect pests.

Given equal soil and climate conditions, fresh vegetables are more nutritious than those held in storage. Where the climate is sufficiently mild, fall as well as spring gardens are planted. Where wind and excessive heat discourage gardening, frame gardens have become popular. They are also used by many families who want a small, easily-cared-for plot in which quick-growing plants such as lettuce, greens, and some of the root vegetables can be provided. The gardens combine small space with very rich soil, effective subirrigation, and protection from unfavorable weather.

Families frequently plan a garden that will more than supply their needs, and sell the surplus. Roadside stands or markets, farmers' markets, and the usual marketing channels provide an outlet for this surplus.

Retail markets are provided with vegetables from a wide area in this country, and, as a rule, from a number of foreign countries. While a large propor-

TABLE 5. CLASSIFICATION OF VEGETABLES BY THE EDIBLE PART OF THE PLANT

Roots	*Bulbs*	*Tubers*	*Stalks or Stems*	*Leaves*	*Flowers*	*Fruits*	*Seeds*	*Fungi*
Beets	Chives	Artichokes (Jerusalem)	Asparagus	Beets	Artichoke (French)	Beans (snap)	Beans (dry)	Mushrooms
Carrots	Garlic	Potatoes (Irish)	Broccoli	Broccoli	Broccoli	Cucumber	Beans (shelled)	Puffballs
Celeriac	Leeks		Celery	Brussels sprouts	Cauliflower	Eggplant	Corn	
Parsnips	Onions		Celtuce	Cabbage		Okra	Lentils	
Potatoes (sweet)	Shallots		Kohlrabi	Carrots		Peppers	Peas	
Radishes				Celtuce		Pumpkin	Soybeans	
Rutabagas				Chard		Squash		
Salsify				Collard		Tomatoes		
Turnips				Cress (garden)		Vegetable marrow		
				Cress (water)		Vegetable pear		
				Endive				
				Escarole				
				Kale				
				Lettuce				
				Mustard				
				Parsley				
				Spinach				
				Romaine				
				Tampala				
				Tendergreen				

Courtesy Kraft Foods Company

Fig. 3. A salad tray with so much variety provides a choice of vegetables.

tion of the vegetables imported come from as nearby as Canada, Mexico, Cuba, and Puerto Rico, a considerable quantity are also received from Australia, Egypt, Italy, Argentina, and other countries.

For successful commercial crops of vegetables, the soil and climate must be well adapted. Thus, green beans in large quantities are raised in Western New York, tomatoes in New Jersey, onions and spinach in the Rio Grande Valley, and baking potatoes in Idaho. The same variety of vegetable produced in different parts of the country does not have the same characteristics, including food value. Research has shown the influence of soil on mineral content of vegetables, and has also resulted in better seed, superior varieties, and better means of controlling disease and insect pests. To appreciate the constant supply of vegetables, the consumer-buyer should be aware of the risks which producers must take which can seldom be foreseen or controlled, such as too much or insufficient rain, early or late frost, hail, and wind.

Among produce dealers and market experts vegetables are frequently classified as perishables, semiperishables, and "hardware" or staples. Perishables, including lettuce and spinach, require cold storage and need to be disposed of quickly when they reach the terminal market. Semiperishables, such as tomatoes and eggplant, require cold storage but can be held for a longer period of time. Staples, of which class Irish potatoes make up the greatest volume, may be kept in common storage. In all cases of cold storage, the temperature and degree of humidity of the storage rooms and frequent inspection are important. To maintain a satisfactory supply, the wholesalers must be in touch with various sources, and aware of the approximate amount of the different vegetables that will be needed by both wholesale and retail trade.

Buying vegetables. When buying vegetables some general suggestions may be helpful:

1) Choose them yourself whenever possible, and by grade when it is indicated.
2) Choose mature vegetables which show no signs of decay, frost, or worm injury.
3) Root vegetables and tubers should be firm, plump, and free from dirt. They become woody if they have been left in the ground too long.
4) Avoid wilted vegetables, especially leafy ones. However, in warm, humid weather edges of many lettuce leaves are brown. If the injury is slight, these spots may be removed with little waste.
5) Increasingly, vegetables are prepackaged for retailing. These may be compared with unpackaged ones as to price related to amount of waste, quality, and preparation time.
6) If it is necessary to handle vegetables, do so carefully. This applies especially to the perishable vegetables.
7) Choose a variety of vegetables, but be sure that the variety contains the types suggested for inclusion in well-planned menus.
8) Vegetables in season locally are usually cheaper, and may be better in flavor and nutritive value than stored vegetables.
9) While vegetables may be selected by number needed, they are nearly always sold by weight. This is an advantage over buying by unit for both buyer and seller. Large quantities of vegetables are purchased by measure, such as a bushel of potatoes, or by the crate, such as a crate of tomatoes.
10) Weigh nutritional values. Cabbage and cauliflower are the same flavor-type, the former being cheaper. Spinach may be replaced by turnip greens, which are less expensive and higher in calcium, phosphorus, and several vitamins. Green beans and peas have a similar use, but the latter require more preparation time, and there is much greater waste.

Characteristics of some of the vegetables need special attention:

Asparagus becomes tough soon after it is cut. It should be as fresh as possible and should not be purchased far in advance of the time it is to be used.

Beans (*snap*) are crisp and firm when young and fresh. These include both green and wax beans, most of which are stringless. They snap easily and the beans in the pods should be very small. If they are fairly even in size, they cook uniformly.

Broccoli should be gathered before the flower clusters have bloomed. Yellow color of flowers and woody stems denote overmaturity. It should be fresh, with crisp, rich, green leaves and tender stalks.

Brussels sprouts should be compact and the color should be green with no yellow spots.

Cabbage that is desirably firm is heavy for its size and free from decay and worm injury. Heads that are cracked should be avoided. There are several varieties, the early ones being less compact and more subject to cracking than the later ones. The early cabbage is likely to be green in color; late cabbage, white. Red cabbage is less common but is interesting as a means of getting a variety of vegetables. Savoy cabbage is also uncommon in comparison to the usual varieties. It has a dark-green, loose head with curly leaves and is mild in flavor.

Cauliflower should be compact and clearly white. The presence of dark spots and spreading of the flower clusters indicate overmaturity.

Corn is at its best if cooked very shortly after it is picked. Market corn is seldom strictly fresh, but the ears should be firm, the husks crisp and green, and there should be no evidence of earworm or corn borer.

Cucumbers should be smooth, even in shape and in color. Characteristics to be avoided are softness and a wrinkled skin.

Eggplants should be firm, smooth, and not over-size. They are a dark reddish-purple in color. Sometimes small eggplants are on the market—the Japanese variety, whose characteristics are the same as those of the larger ones.

Irish potatoes of several varieties are usually on the market. Early varieties are likely to be waxy and not desirable for baking. Mature potatoes are of two general types—the "waxy" which are chosen for salads or frying, and the "mealy" which are good for boiling, mashing, and baking. On any market, consumer-buyers need to know the varieties and how they may best be used. Potatoes are usually graded according to U. S. grades, but too frequently these do not appear in retail stores. They should be smooth, shallow-eyed, and fairly uniform in shape. They should be chosen with cookery method in mind and should be fairly even in size to insure uniform cooking. Indications of worm injury, scars, rotten spots, and wilting are qualities to avoid when choosing potatoes. If purchased in large quantities, they should be stored in a cool, dark place.

Okra must be young, with small, tender, pods. Large pods are usually tough and the seeds are hard.

Onions are of several varieties and sizes. Some types, especially Spanish and Bermuda onions, are milder in flavor than others. They are rather flat in shape; the stronger ones are round. The mild onions are preferred for eating raw; the stronger ones, for seasoning and serving cooked. Green onions, shallots, and leeks should be crisp with bright-green, unwilted tops. Chives are herbs whose leaves are used for seasoning when a very mild, onion-like flavor is desired.

Peas are best when the pods are plump and unwrinkled, free from dark spots, mildew, or yellowish color. The pods should be well filled with mature but tender peas. As storage time increases, the flavor becomes less sweet; therefore they, like corn, are best if they can be cooked very soon after they are gathered.

Spinach leaves should be fresh and crisp, and well colored. Yellow leaves, wilted leaves, and the presence of stems with seeds are to be avoided. Selected, washed leaves are commonly marketed in cellophane packages.

Sweet potatoes may be mealy or moist, depending upon the variety. They vary in color from pale yellow to deep orange. They should be smooth and firm. Care in digging, proper curing, and suitable storage are necessary if sweet potatoes of good quality are to be available on the market.

Tomatoes of good quality are firm, smooth, and evenly colored. They are free from decay, catfaces, scars, cracks, and worm injury. Flavor and texture of local tomatoes ripened in the sun are different from those that are harvested green and ripened in storage. They are often the most prized product of home gardeners, who believe there is no substitute. Tomatoes may be red or yellow, and vary in size from the "cherry" type to some weighing more than a pound.

Home storage. In a cool climate such vegetables as potatoes, carrots, and late cabbage may be purchased in fairly large quantity and stored in a cool part of the basement (or cellar) of the house, in a specially constructed cellar outside or even, in some cases, in well-made pits. In many homes a ventilated pantry is used to advantage. Directions for making storage room for all types of vegetables may be secured from state experiment stations or county agricultural and home demonstration agents. These directions are made to meet the requirements of the state.

Most urban families use the grocery store as "storage" for more than a week's supply of vegetables. A rack or bin is satisfactory for the hardy vegetables. The more perishable ones are stored in a refrigerator after being washed. Most refrigerators have one or two built-in hydrators, but the use of plastic bags is increasing. Special containers for left-over cooked vegetables may be purchased; bowls and jars, well covered, are excellent because the size is easily selected for the amount to be stored and jars are likely to occupy less space than purchased containers.

PREPARATION OF VEGETABLES TO USE RAW

It is obvious that the maximum nutritive value of vegetables is obtained if they are eaten raw. Many raw vegetables are well liked and others are being added to the list as usage changes habit. Leaves of plants used in salads are served raw. Carrots, turnips, cauliflower, onions, celery, cucumbers, tomatoes, peppers, radishes, and tender green beans are common ingredients of salads or appetizers.

It is important that these raw vegetables be clean. Dust, dirt, spray residue, and soil bacteria must be removed by thorough washing and, in the case of root vegetables and celery, by scrubbing with a brush before the vegetables are ready to eat. Although they may look clean when purchased, this thorough washing is necessary because dust and bacteria from the air and from handling need to be removed.

In addition to washing and scrubbing, other preparation processes may be desirable. Tomatoes are usually peeled. If they are vine-ripened, rubbing the skin with the back of a paring knife loosens it sufficiently so that it can be stripped off. Leaving them in boiling water for a few seconds or rotating them over a flame will loosen the skins that are more firmly attached to the pulp. In these cases, the tomatoes should be chilled after they are peeled. Cucumbers and turnips are often pared; carrots are frequently scraped; and cauliflower may be divided into pieces convenient for eating.

Crispness is a desirable quality in raw vegetables. Leaves that have been washed are made crisp, as well as cold, by storing them in the refrigerator for an hour or two. Celery curls and carrot and turnip slices are made crisp by leaving them standing in ice water for half an hour to an hour. Some food value is lost by this procedure, but the crisp texture may be more desirable than the slight loss of food constituents.

VEGETABLE COOKERY

Vegetables are cooked for several reasons:

1) To soften the cellulose and hemicellulose. *Example:* leafy vegetables.
2) To make them easier to eat. *Example:* dried legumes.
3) To modify the flavor. *Example:* onions.
4) To partially gelatinize starch. *Example:* potatoes.
5) To add variety.
6) To make the vegetables more desirable as food. *Example:* few persons would appreciate raw squash, corn, or potatoes.

A few general suggestions should be kept in mind when vegetables are being cooked:

1) Vegetables are cooked when they are tender but firm, not soft.
2) Vegetables should look attractive by being prepared in such a way that their form and their original color are retained as nearly as possible.
3) Cooked vegetables should retain as much of their nutritive value as possible. When money is very limited, attractive color should be sacrificed to nutritive value. Otherwise, the color may seem more important.

Retention of form. Nearly everyone is familiar with potatoes which have "cooked all to pieces," mushy green peas, and cabbage cooked until all semblance of crispness is gone and it is a grayish brown color. In none of these instances is the shape remotely like it was when the vegetable was put into the saucepan. That means it was overcooked. Habit is responsible for the cookery method that produces these unattractive vegetables, and it may be necessary to change such a habit gradually. Compliance with the rule, "cook only until tender" will usually result in vegetables that retain the form of the raw ones. There must, however, be an understanding of "tender," because to some people the word means "mushy." The water should boil steadily but not vigorously. Violent action of water on potatoes, for instance, helps to make them rough and also removes considerable food value. Boiling such vegetables as potatoes, carrots, and turnips "in the jacket" and peeling them after cooking helps to retain form.

It may not be desirable to retain the form of the whole vegetable in the cooked product. Carrot strips or slices and snapped or French-style beans are necessarily cut before cooking. Squash or eggplant to be sautéed or used in a casserole dish is cut before parboiling. Beets to be served sliced or diced may be cut before boiling when the right cooking method is used. The cooking time is reduced for these smaller pieces, but guarding against overcooking is perhaps even more necessary. Potatoes or turnips to be mashed are not necessarily cut before boiling.

Retention or modification of flavor. The flavor of vegetables is due to plant acids, sugar, tannins, and volatile oils. As a rule, the flavor of the vegetable is pleasing and should be retained. To this end, boiling in a small quantity of water in a covered or pressure pan, steaming, panning, or baking are satisfactory cookery methods.

Onions contain a volatile oil which is responsible for their so-called "strong" flavor. It may be desirable to modify the flavor during cooking. In some other vegetables, including cabbage, turnips, broccoli and kale, volatile oils are combined with a glucoside, one of whose components is sulphur. Upon hydrolysis during boiling, the sulphur-containing compound causes the strong flavor to which many people object, and a cookery method which modifies this flavor is desirable. The usual method is to boil the vegetables in a relatively large amount of water with no cover on the pan. The volatile substances are thus allowed to evaporate. The hydrolysis is hastened by both the plant acids and an enzyme contained in the plant. While the enzyme is not destroyed as quickly when a large amount of water is used, the plant acids are diluted and partially neutralized, because most tap water is slightly alkaline. The net result is less formation of the sulphur-containing compound.

If the vegetable is cut into small pieces, cooked in a small quantity of water and covered, the enzyme is destroyed rather quickly. However, the volatile substances do not have an opportunity to escape and the influence of the plant acids as catalyzers is greater than when a large amount of water is used. The vegetable will be less mild in flavor than a similar one cooked in more water. This flavor may or may not be objectionable, depending upon personal taste.

Retention of nutritive value. Food nutrients may be lost in four ways during preparation for cooking:

1) Volatile losses include plant acids, sulphur compounds, and other aromatic compounds.
2) Solubility losses include sugars, minerals, the water-soluble vitamins, and color pigments.
3) Oxidation destroys ascorbic acid, especially in the presence of heat and in an alkaline medium.
4) The losses may be mechanical, as occurs when vegetables are not pared thin, when they are soaked before cooking, when the water into which they are put is not boiling, when the water boils too vigorously, and when they stand in water after they are done.

The types of losses during preparation and cooking of vegetables are summarized in Table 6, p. 63, and suggestions for reducing them are given.

The old saying that "some women throw out more in a teaspoon than their husbands bring in on a shovel" might apply to inefficient methods of cooking vegetables. As has been stated, the best way to obtain the most food value is from raw vegetables. Baking is one way to conserve nutritive value. Steaming results in less loss than boiling, and boiling in a small amount of water, less than in a large amount. Boiling in the skin is also recommended. Potatoes, sweet potatoes, beets, carrots, turnips, rutabagas, and parsnips may all be boiled in the skin and peeled when done. Time is also saved. Cooking only until tender destroys less food value than overcooking, and the short time needed to cook vegetables in a pressure pan results in better food conservation than the longer time in a saucepan. Care must be taken, however, to follow directions carefully to avoid overcooking.

Vegetables cooked whole retain more of their food constituents than the same vegetables cut, and vegetables such as carrots and parsnips sliced lengthwise retain more food value than when sliced crosswise. If, however, they are steamed, cooked in a waterless cooker, or in a very small amount of water, and if whatever water remains in the saucepan is used in soup stock or a sauce, practically all the food value becomes a part of the diet anyway, and the manner of cutting is of little importance, since a large percentage of the loss in cooking is due to the solubility of food nutrients.

Vegetables having a high percentage of water may be panned successfully —that is, cooked in a covered frying pan with a small amount of fat. Vegetables are sometimes cooked a very few minutes in water and then baked.

Cushaw, squash, and eggplant are frequently cooked this way, and may be stuffed before the baking begins.

Retention of color. As they appear on the market, vegetables are beautiful in color. It is desirable to retain as much as possible of this color in the cooked products. They owe their color to certain pigments and the behavior of these pigments in the presence of water, metals, acid, and alkali leads to suggestions for ways of cooking that retain the color.

TABLE 6. NUTRITIVE LOSSES DURING PREPARATION AND COOKING OF VEGETABLES

Type of Loss	*Nutritive Loss*	*Methods which Prevent or Decrease Loss*	*Remarks*
Volatile losses	Plant acids, volatile oils	Use raw Bake unpared Cover while cooking Cook only until tender	Losses may be desirable, e.g. in onions and sulphur-containing vegetables
Solubility losses	Sugars, minerals, water-soluble vitamins, especially ascorbic acid	Use raw Bake Steam Use pressure pan Boil with very little water Start cooking in boiling water Cook only until tender Cook whole or in large pieces Cut lengthwise rather than crosswise	If water remaining is used in sauces, soups, etc., these losses are of little importance
Oxidation	Ascorbic acid, thiamin	Use raw Steam Start cooking in boiling water and heat rapidly during first part of cooking period Cook only until tender Retain acidity of vegetable	The enzyme that is connected with oxidation should be destroyed quickly
Mechanical losses	Minerals, especially those just under the skin; starch	Cook in skins Scrape or peel Pare thinly Start cooking in boiling water Boil steadily but not vigorously Do not soak before cooking or leave in water after cooking	A knife with rotating blade is an aid to thin paring

Carotenoids (pro-vitamin A) are the color pigments in yellow, orange, and some red vegetables. There are several carotenoids, the most common of which is carotene. The color of yellow corn is due to the carotenoid xanthophyll; lycopene is the pigment in tomatoes; and capsanthin in red peppers. These pigments are not readily soluble in water and are stable to heat, metals, acid, and alkali. Vegetables containing carotenoids are therefore easily cooked from the point of view of color retention, so that in most instances a method that retains nutritive value would be chosen without question.

Flavones are found in white vegetables. When isolated, they are actually yellow in color. They are soluble in water and become brownish-gray if subjected to heat for a long time. Acid makes them almost colorless and alkali intensifies the yellow. This color change is reversible. *Example:* Very hard water gives the vegetables a yellowish color, especially if they are overcooked. Iron produces a greenish color which may become brown.

From the point of view of color only, white vegetables should be cooked in a glass or unchipped enamel utensil and an alkaline medium should be avoided. Usually the latter is not a problem, but in localities where there is a high mineral content in the water, the addition of a very small amount of vinegar may be desirable.

Anthocyanins, of which there are many, are responsible for the red, purple, and blue color in plants. These pigments are readily soluble in water but are stable to heat. The color is intensified in an acid medium and changed to purple or blue in alkali. This color change is reversible and may be illustrated by cooking a little red cabbage, adding vinegar, then soda, then vinegar again. Color change in red cabbage may illustrate another possibility. There are also flavones in the white portion of the cabbage. The yellow of the flavones, combining with the blue of the anthocyanins after alkali is added, makes the color green. Anthocyanins become blue when in contact with metal, particularly iron.

Color retention in red vegetables is best if a glass or unchipped enamel saucepan is used for cooking and if the medium is not alkaline. Beets retain color well if they are not pared and if the tiny root and some of the stem are not removed. However, in a pressure pan the cooking time is so short that sliced or diced beets are well colored. The variety of beet has much to do with the final color, some containing much more color pigment than others. As is true of white vegetables, in communities where there is a high mineral content in the water, the addition of a very small amount of vinegar to the cooking water will result in better color of the cooked vegetable.

Chlorophyll is the pigment responsible for green coloring. It is well known that sunlight is necessary for the formation of chlorophyll in plants and that chlorophyll is important for the development of carbohydrates in plants. Pure chlorophyll is not soluble in water, but changes produced during cooking make it slightly soluble. Unlike the flavones and anthocyanins, chlorophyll is found dissolved in the phospholipids (fat-like substances) of plants. Subjected to heat, the color becomes olive-green, the change depending upon the degree of heat and length of time heat is applied. Chlorophyll is stable to metals.

In an acid medium, chlorophyll fades to a pale olive green. An alkaline medium intensifies the color. As long ago as Roman times, soda was added to green vegetables to brighten the color.[1] In the quantity used soda destroys vitamins, but as little as 1/16 to 1/8 teaspoon per quart of water is advocated by some people. Most water used for cooking is slightly alkaline, so if water "to cover" or nearly cover is used, fading is lessened. Since the acid is volatile, in an uncovered utensil it will escape in the steam. Thus if green vegetables are boiled in water to cover in an open utensil and are not over-cooked, they will have a desirable color. A pressure pan is practical because, despite the cover and small quantity of water, the time is very short.

The effect of various treatments upon chlorophyll may be illustrated by comparing the color of fresh green peas with that of both frozen and most canned ones. The rather subdued green of the fresh peas is intensified in the frozen ones. Plant acids and chlorophyll are present in separate cells in the plant. Before vegetables are frozen, they are scalded and the cell walls expand, thus becoming thinner and making the green color more intense. Since the time for cooking frozen vegetables is less than that for fresh ones, the cooked frozen peas are also greener than cooked fresh ones.

In canning, vegetables are also scalded. But the vegetable, with very little water, is sealed in cans or jars before processing and the heat applied is 240° F. rather than 212° F. Thus the plant acid cannot escape and the chlorophyll is faded.

Choosing the cooking method. It is evident that one method of boiling does not necessarily give the best results with all vegetables in terms of color, flavor, and nutritive value. Fresh green peas are mild in flavor, but if they are cooked in a small amount of water in a covered pan, they will be faded in color. Cabbage is an excellent source of ascorbic acid, which is water-soluble, but if steamed or cooked in a covered utensil and in very little water, the flavor may be undesirable. Which, then, shall be kept—the color or the flavor; the flavor or the food value?

The appearance and texture of cooked vegetables are important. Pleasing flavor and attractive color have a real value in our food habits, and unless we are operating on such a limited budget that every calorie or every gram of mineral substance is important, it may be that nutritive value will seem less desirable than appearance. At least, there is a choice to be made.

In Table 7, p. 68, the effects of boiling upon flavor and color are summarized, and suggestions for boiling are made. Thus, the carotenoid pigments

[1] Apicius, *Cookery and Dining in Imperial Rome,* trans. Joseph Dommers Verling (Chicago: Hill, 1936).

in yellow and some red vegetables are very slightly soluble in water and stable to heat, acid, alkali, and metals. If the vegetable is mild in flavor, it is best boiled in a small quantity of water in a covered utensil. If, however, the vegetable contains sulphur, e.g., rutabagas, it is desirable to use a large amount of water and leave the utensil uncovered. The utensil may be made of any material, and the medium may be either acid or alkaline.

Cooking dried legumes.[1] Dried legumes include beans of several varieties: peas, split peas, and lentils. They should first be washed. Beans and whole peas need to be soaked, but split peas and lentils may be cooked without soaking. If hot water is used, three to four hours have been found to be sufficient time for soaking.

The latest recommendation is to cook the vegetables for 2 minutes in boiling water, then leave them in the water for an hour. The cooking is continued in the same water. If the water is very hard, it may be helpful to add about ⅛ tsp. of soda per cup of beans to shorten the cooking time. This destroys some of the thiamin and ascorbic acid, and the flavor is impaired if too much is used.

When cooking the larger beans, foaming may be a problem. It may be decreased by adding a little fat to the water. If the beans are cooked in a pressure pan, this precaution may be *especially* desirable.

The time element. Perhaps the main reason for the use of canned and frozen vegetables is the saving of time needed for food preparation. This is frequently a major consideration for the busy homemaker. There are, however, ways to prevent use of fresh vegetables from being burdensome and a little thought will enable a homemaker to take advantage of them. True, studies have indicated some loss of nutritive value as cooked vegetables are held over. It would seem that our varied diet would, in most instances, make time economy in vegetable cookery practical. A few examples of this time-saving follow:

1) Boiling potatoes for two meals, to be served mashed, and using those left over for making delicious vichyssoise.

2) Baking potatoes for three meals and stuffing enough for two. Half of these would be served at once; the others, wrapped in foil and frozen. The rest of the potatoes might be stored in the refrigerator and served in two or three days as creamed potatoes.

3) Making extra squash en casserole and freezing the "extra."

4) Cooking more broccoli than will be needed and using what is left over in a soufflé.

Variety in serving vegetables. Potatoes that always appear plain-boiled for dinner, mashed potatoes and peas served with chicken, or carrots and peas as an inevitable vegetable combination are tiresome from the point of view of

[1] *Dry Beans, Peas, Lentils . . . Modern Cookery.* U. S. Department of Agriculture, Leaflet No. 326, 1952.

Courtesy Kraft Foods Co.

Fig. 4. Chilled, fresh asparagus, crisp lettuce, and deviled eggs make a delicious summer salad.

both the person who prepares three meals a day and the people who eat them. Vegetables lend themselves to variety in methods of preparation to a greater degree than most foods. They may be cooked by boiling, steaming, panning, sautéing, frying, baking, and broiling. They may be served buttered or with any number of interesting and flavorsome sauces. Herbs cooked with them or used to flavor a sauce are surprisingly pleasing. Meats, nuts, and some fruits combine nicely with certain vegetables. They may be served scalloped or au gratin; as fritters, croquettes, or timbales; and in salads, soufflés, and omelets. Various combinations of vegetables are pleasing served buttered, creamed, or as a casserole dish.

Vegetable plates are popular, and they may be made attractive and pleasing in flavor. The combination of vegetables should be well considered, keeping

TABLE 7. EFFECTS OF VARIOUS FACTORS UPON COLOR OF BOILED VEGETABLES—MILD-FLAVORED AND SULPHUR-CONTAINING

<table>
<tr><th rowspan="2">Color</th><th rowspan="2">Pigment</th><th rowspan="2">Water</th><th rowspan="2">Heat</th><th rowspan="2">Metals</th><th rowspan="2">Acid</th><th rowspan="2">Alkali</th><th colspan="2">Recommendations for Boiling</th></tr>
<tr><th>Mild-flavored</th><th>Sulphur-containing</th></tr>
<tr><td rowspan="2">Yellow, orange, red</td><td rowspan="2">Carotenoid</td><td rowspan="2">Very slightly soluble</td><td rowspan="2">Stable</td><td rowspan="2">Stable</td><td rowspan="2">Stable</td><td rowspan="2">Stable</td><td colspan="2">Only until tender</td></tr>
<tr><td>Little water; cover on utensil</td><td>Water to cover; no cover on utensil</td></tr>
<tr><td rowspan="2">White</td><td rowspan="2">Flavones</td><td rowspan="2">Soluble</td><td rowspan="2">Brownish-gray if cooked long</td><td rowspan="2">Green to brown with iron</td><td rowspan="2">Bleached</td><td rowspan="2">Yellow</td><td colspan="2">Only until tender
Glass or unchipped enamel utensil</td></tr>
<tr><td>Little water; cover on utensil</td><td>Water to cover; no cover on utensil</td></tr>
<tr><td rowspan="2">Red</td><td rowspan="2">Anthocyanins</td><td rowspan="2">Very soluble</td><td rowspan="2">Stable</td><td rowspan="2">Blue with iron, tin, aluminum</td><td rowspan="2">Intensified</td><td rowspan="2">Purple,* blue</td><td colspan="2">Only until tender
Glass or unchipped enamel utensil
In very hard water, may add a little acid</td></tr>
<tr><td>Little water; cover on utensil; beets without paring</td><td>Water to cover; no cover on utensil</td></tr>
<tr><td>Green</td><td>Chlorophyll</td><td>Slightly soluble</td><td>Decomposed</td><td>Stable</td><td>Olive-green</td><td>Intensified</td><td colspan="2">Only until tender
Water to cover; no cover on utensil †</td></tr>
</table>

* Red cabbage contains flavones also; color with alkali, green.
† Spinach may be cooked in water adhering to leaves, utensil covered until leaves wilt.

in mind color, flavor, texture, food value, and the arrangement of the food on the plate. An odd number of vegetables is frequently used in an attempt to give a pleasing arrangement.

SUGGESTIONS FOR LABORATORY

(SELECTED RECIPES ON PP. 498 THROUGH 514.)

The general suggestions for a laboratory concerned with fruit are equally applicable to vegetables. Perhaps two main outcomes should be expected: 1) Appreciation of cookery methods that result in attractive, nutritious vegetables. 2) Extension of learning with regard to variety in ways to serve vegetables. This is likely to increase acceptability of unpopular vegetables and to give ideas for use of those left over from a meal.

Prior to the laboratory groups of students might go to the local market-wholesale and/or retail and prepare reports on subjects selected from the following and others suggested by students and instructor:

1) Vegetable varieties and their sources.

2) Marketing practices and storage facilities which insure a constant supply of fresh vegetables.

3) Some vegetables that are available fresh, frozen, canned, and dried, with prices.

4) The market offerings in ready-to-eat vegetables, e.g., potatoes and salads.

5) Retail market display that makes shopping for vegetables easy and pleasant.

6) Vegetables that might be substituted for those on the consumer-buyer's market list when these are either not available or too high in price, e.g., substitutes for cauliflower, green peas, and spinach.

7) What information is on packages of frozen vegetables and cans of vegetables.

REFERENCES

VEGETABLES

Extension Service of State or County: *Bulletins concerning production, storage, and use of vegetables.*

Halliday, Evelyn G. and Isabel T. Noble, *Hows and Whys of Cooking.* The University of Chicago Press, Chicago, 1946.

Lowe, Belle, *Experimental Cookery.* 4th Ed. John Wiley and Sons, New York, 1955.

The Wise Encyclopedia of Food, Wm. H. Wise and Co., New York, 1951.

Todoroff, Alexander, *Food Buyer's Information Book.* The Grocery Trade Publishing House, Chicago, 1946.

Troelstrup, Arch W., *Consumer Problems and Family Finance*. McGraw-Hill Book Co., Inc., New York, 1957.

United States Department of Agriculture, *A Fruit and Vegetable Buying Guide for Consumers*. Misc. Pub. No. 167, 1946.

The United States Department of Agriculture, *The Yearbook of Agriculture, 1959, Food*. Boswell, Victor R., *What Makes Fruit and Vegetables Good?*

Ward, Artemas, *Encyclopedia of Food*. Baker and Taylor Co., New York, 1929.

UNIT 5

Salads

The use of a wide variety of ingredients for making salads is a relatively new idea. However, certain leaves served with a dressing have been used as salads for centuries. Chicory and lettuce were grown for use as salad plants by the early Romans. During the fifteenth century, green vegetables and herbs were planted in the kitchen gardens of England. Most of them were cooked, usually with meat, but the idea of eating them raw gradually gained popularity. A writer of the time "observes that some were eaten raw, in spring and summer with olive oil and spices, but questions the propriety of the custom." [1]

Formerly, the salad was served at a definite time during a meal, and when this custom began to be changed, protests were made. Ellwanger writes,[2] "The salad belongs to the roast, and it should not be called upon to perform the services of a separate bridge between this and the sweets." Its position on the menu as a separate course has, however, won favor. It may be the first course for luncheon or dinner, the main course for luncheon or supper, or a combination of salad and dessert. Salads are also acceptable as a part of light afternoon refreshments or teas.

A salad plant and a dressing are the characteristic ingredients of a salad. The addition of many other ingredients has become common, particularly in America. Meat was doubtless first used in salads in England, where "the old English supper dish, salmagundi, was a meat salad, mixed and decorated with hard-boiled eggs, anchovy, pickles, and beet root." [3] To Germany we owe the use of both potatoes and cucumbers as salad ingredients, and the Spanish have made the flavor of green and red peppers, as well as garlic,

---

[1] Frederick W. Hackwood, *Good Cheer* (New York: Sturgis and Walton, 1911) pp. 140–141.

[2] George Herman Ellwanger, *Pleasures of the Table* (Garden City, New York: Copyright 1902, by Doubleday, Doran and Co.), p. 418.

[3] Hackwood, *op. cit.,* p. 183.

popular. In France a salad consisting of a fresh, crisp plant with a perfectly seasoned dressing is almost automatically a part of the dinner. A few salads are known internationally and may be found on menus in a number of countries. Waldorf salad, the ingredients of which, besides the plant and dressing, are apples, celery, and English walnut meats, is one of these.

Nutritional value. The nutritive quality of salads cannot be evaluated without considering the composition of the many and varied ingredients from which they are made. However, there is some basic information that is generally applicable to salads. They are considered significant nutritionally because most of them are made from fruits and vegetables, both raw and cooked, and from such foods as fish, poultry, cheese, eggs, meats and nuts. Because of the vitamin, mineral, and protein content of these ingredients they rank high as protective foods, giving the salads that are made from them an important role in the diet. Certain salad materials contribute more protective values than others; salad plants with *green* leaves and stalks contain about ten times more vitamin A than do those with bleached or pale leaves and stalks; carrots that have a bright, deep-yellow color furnish more vitamin A than the pale-yellow ones; cottage cheese is superior to cream cheese in contributing proteins and minerals; salads built around such foods as potatoes and macaroni will be more valuable nutritionally if leftover meats, hard-cooked eggs or cheese are added; and fruits and vegetables in the raw state are a better source of vitamins and minerals than when cooked.

Some salad dressings have greater nutritive value than others. Those having milk and eggs in them add protective value, while a French type, made of oil and vinegar, contributes chiefly energy. Naturally the former dressings are not suitable for all salads. Low-calorie salad dressings are of several types. Some of them have as their base tomato juice or buttermilk (see p. 522). It is not advisable to use mineral oil as a salad dressing. Mineral oil is not only a cathartic, but since it goes through the body unchanged it may pick up some of the fat-soluble vitamins, making them unavailable for the body's use.

The palatability of salads is a factor in measuring their nutritive contribution. Many times salads are not eaten because they lack crispness or proper seasonings. The best way to have salads perform their nutritional function is to have them taste good. This does not necessarily call for elaborate combinations of ingredients; in fact simple salads are frequently the most appealing.

Salad plants. The most commonly used salad plant is lettuce. It may be obtained on most markets, even in rural villages, throughout the year. Romaine, endive (both French and curly), escarole, chicory, and water cress are welcome changes from the use of lettuce. Shredded cabbage, Chinese cabbage, spinach, young leaves from mustard greens or tender-greens, nasturtium leaves, and the leaves from wild plants used as greens—such as the dandelion—lend pleasing variety to the list of salad plants. The use of more than one salad plant is often desirable. Pale green of lettuce and the darker green of a few leaves of spinach are interesting from the color point of view; the mild flavor of lettuce and the tang of a few leaves of nasturtium or sorrel make a pleasing contrast. The salad plant is not a mere background for the salad; it is a definite part of it, and should be eaten. When arranging salads, it is well to keep this in mind, and to use a sufficient amount of the salad plant to make an attractive serving, but not so much that a large portion will be wasted.

In many localities it is possible to have salad plants as well as some other fresh vegetables growing throughout the year. Protected southern exposures in sections of the country where frosts are not often severe make ideal garden spots. Such winter gardens are common among a group of Czechoslovakian farmers in Texas and are encouraged by both agricultural and home demonstration agents where this type of garden is likely to be successful.

Cold frames or frame gardens may be used to provide fresh vegetables which would otherwise not be available, either because they are not on the market, or because the price is prohibitive.

If possible, suburban and rural homemakers should acquaint themselves with wild greens, since many are delectable either as salad ingredients or as a cooked green vegetable. These include poke, lamb's quarters, sorrel, dandelion, and water cress. The library will have books on wild plants telling where they can be found and how to prepare them.

When salad plants are selected at a market, they should be fresh and crisp. Heads of lettuce should be heavy for their size and free from brown spots. The buyer should realize, however, that these spots cannot be avoided during damp, hot weather. Tomatoes should be firm, but not hard, and without soft spots. Often it is desirable to have tomatoes of uniform size for use in salads for their appearance.

Whatever their source, salad plants should be washed carefully before they are stored in a refrigerator. Clean salad plants should be wrapped in a damp cloth or waxed paper, or placed in a special storage bag or covered hydrator, and stored in a refrigerator. If the cloth is used, it must be kept damp. Salad plants that are stored properly are crisp and dry when it is time to use them. Several hours before using, the leaves of head lettuce may be separated easily by cutting out the stem and holding the lettuce, with the cut portion up, under running water. The action of the water separates the leaves without tearing them. The separated leaves should be dried with a clean towel and returned to the refrigerator to insure dryness and crispness when they are used. If salad greens are wet when the salad is combined with the dressing, the moisture on the greens will prevent dressing from coating the leaves.

Salad dressings. Both the proportion of the ingredients used and the way they are blended are important in making salad dressings. Referring to

French dressing, an old Spanish proverb "calls for a quartet to compose it—a spendthrift for oil, a miser for vinegar, a counselor for salt, and a madcap for mixing."[1]

Salad dressings are of three types: French, mayonnaise, and cooked. All dressings are emulsions, and these will be discussed in Unit 13 on page 170. True French dressing is a temporary emulsion made from oil, acid, and seasonings. The oil may be corn, peanut, olive, soybean or cottonseed. Since olive oil is expensive, and some prefer its flavor to the more bland oils, a good quality salad oil formula can be blended by using one part of olive oil to two parts of one of the more thrifty varieties, such as peanut oil. The acid is usually plain vinegar or lemon juice, but flavor may be enhanced by adding herb vinegars, lime juice, or spiced vinegar from pickles. Seasonings vary from salt and pepper to a variety of other ingredients such as sugar, dry mustard, paprika, tabasco, or one or more selected herbs. Both mustard and paprika not only add flavor, but they have a stabilizing effect on the emulsion. They are not soluble in either oil or vinegar but are dispersed by the vinegar and become a part of the film that surrounds the globules of oil.

Mayonnaise, according to the definition of the Food and Drug Administration, consists of vegetable oil, vinegar or lemon juice, egg yolk or whole egg, and seasonings, including salt, sugar, and spice. At least 50 per cent of oil is required and the combined per cent of oil and egg is not less than 78 per cent. The egg in mayonnaise acts as a stabilizer, causing a permanent emulsion (see p. 170). In addition to proportion of ingredients and methods for making mayonnaise (p. 519), there are other factors which influence the formation and permanency of mayonnaise as well as its thickness.

1) The utensil used for making mayonnaise should be one into which the beater fits well and in which it covers the beating area fairly completely.

2) The use of a whole egg or of egg white produces an emulsion more quickly than the use of egg yolk. Because of this, it is easier for an inexperienced person to make mayonnaise if the whole egg or egg white is used instead of the egg yolk. The latter produces a thick mayonnaise. Egg yolk results in a dressing which is usually considered more desirable in color than when either egg white or whole egg is used.

3) Seasonings may be beaten into the egg yolk before the other ingredients are added. Paprika and mustard, when used, help to stabilize the emulsion; and salt, if added at the beginning and in amounts desirable for good flavor, also acts as a stabilizer.

4) Either oil or acid may be added to the egg and seasonings first. It is better, however, to add the acid first, because it has a tendency to make the oil break into smaller globules, thus making the emulsion more stable.

5) The quantity of oil which is added at one time, particularly at the beginning, is important. If acid has been added first, the largest quantity of oil that may be added at one time is equal to the combined quantity of acid and egg

[1] Ellwanger, *op. cit.,* p. 419.

yolk. However, for many people good results will be more certain if not more than two teaspoonfuls of oil are added at one time when one egg yolk is used. This quantity may be increased after the emulsion is definitely formed. More oil may be added at a time if beating is rapid rather than slow, and if the ingredients are at room temperature rather than at refrigerator temperature. If oil is added first, not more than one-half teaspoonful should be added at a time until the emulsion is formed. Beating should be rapid and should be sufficient to emulsify each added amount of oil.

6) Fresh eggs are more satisfactory than storage eggs, although the idea that strictly fresh eggs are essential has been proved false. Eggs several days old are most satisfactory.

7) Ingredients at room temperature form an emulsion more readily than very cold ingredients. The decrease in the viscosity of the oil and in the interfacial tension [1] of the liquids accounts for this.

There are a number of reasons why mayonnaise may break. Too low temperature, especially if the oil used was not wintered (see p. 170), too high temperature, and surface drying cause separation. Broken mayonnaise may be re-formed quickly by beating it slowly into a bowl in which a tablespoon of vinegar has been placed. Vinegar or water cannot be added to the broken mayonnaise. Another method is to start again with egg, acid, seasonings, and sufficient oil to form an emulsion, then beat the broken mayonnaise into it slowly.

Cooked dressings are made with milk—fresh or canned—buttermilk, sour cream, or water. They are thickened with starch or egg, or both, and the acid used is usually either vinegar or lemon juice. Seasonings vary as in other dressings and fat in the form of butter, margarine or bacon fat may be added. Commercial cooked dressings are considerably cheaper than mayonnaise and regulations require that they be labeled "salad dressings."

There are many commercial salad dressings in food markets but they all fall into one of the above categories. In addition to those sold in stores a number of restaurants make a specialty of selling their own salad dressings. Such dressings are usually of French or mayonnaise type and may be varied with such ingredients as avocados, Roquefort cheese, chopped olives and pickles, chili sauce, capers, chutney, and poppy or celery seed.

Salad dressings made at home can be just as tasty and interesting as those that are purchased and certainly they can be made more economically. The goodness of the salad is due in large measure to the dressing and the goodness of the dressing is dependent on the seasoning used. Whatever the seasoning, it should be delicate, as suggested by two lines from Sydney Smith's recipe for a salad dressing:

Let onion atoms lurk within the bowl
And, scarce suspected, animate the whole.

[1] The reason that oil and water are immiscible is because of the high interfacial tension. This tension is less at high than at low temperature.

A French dressing that is obviously sweet may spoil a fruit salad, but if the dressing is sweetened sparingly with honey, sweet pickle juice, or sugar it gives the salad a distinctive flavor.

Fresh ground pepper or a dash of chili powder may make the difference between an interesting and uninteresting salad dressing. Too much garlic, either minced or in salt form, or similar types of seasoning will overshadow the bland, subtle flavor of certain salad ingredients.

Herbs and herb vinegars can contribute materially to the palatability of salads (see p. 74). Because of the many different herbs, vinegars, and other ingredients, there are many variations possible for salad dressings.

Choosing salad ingredients. As a rule, one salad ingredient is chosen as the basic one and others that enhance its flavor or lend contrast in texture are combined with it. Tuna fish by itself would make a compact, uninteresting salad, but when crisp celery and chopped pickles or capers are added, along with a dressing seasoned with tarragon, the resulting salad is both interesting and delicious. A mold of cherry gelatin served on a bed of salad greens and topped with a spoonful of whipped cream dressing would not be very appealing as an accompaniment to a meat course, but if raw cranberries and oranges are finely chopped and added to the basic gelatin ingredient, there is interest in flavor, texture, and color.

Sometimes the ingredients chosen to combine in a salad seem not to "belong" together, but the resulting dish is likely to be extremely appealing. Caesar salad (sometimes called California salad) has such ingredients (see recipe on page 515. In addition to the basic green of romaine, olive oil, lemon juice, and seasonings of garlic, salt and pepper, this salad also contains croutons, a raw egg, and grated cheese of the Parmesan type. Caesar salad became popular from coast to coast in a very short time. One large metropolitan daily newspaper with subscribers throughout the country reported that their readers requested this recipe more often than any other printed during a year's time.

Making and serving salads. Most salads are served cold. The German potato salad is one exception. A part of the distinctive flavor of this salad is due to the hot bacon fat which is used instead of oil in the dressing. If the salad were not served hot, the fat would solidify, making the salad unpalatable. Wilted lettuce, mustard greens, or other salad plants are also served hot.

The salad plant should be crisp, as should such vegetables as celery, cucumbers, and radishes. The ingredients should be pleasing in color, and their flavors should blend well. The seasoning supplied by the dressing should be subtle and appropriate. When a garnish is used, it should be edible, and should serve to enhance the attractiveness of the whole salad rather than to "steal the show" from the principal ingredients.

Leftover meats, vegetables, and fruits may be stored in covered jars or refrigerator dishes and used in salads. "The salad of the house," often seen on

Courtesy Kraft Foods Co.

Fig. 5. Top. *Pear, prune, and cottage cheese salad. A trite arrangement, often seen and popular with many.* Bottom. *A mixed green salad is attractively served here in a handsome glass bowl.*

menu cards in hotels and restaurants, is said to have had its origin in left-overs combined to produce a delicious salad.

Many vegetables are bland in flavor and need to stand in well-seasoned French dressing long enough to permit the dressing to permeate them. The dressing so used is called a marinade and the process is referred to as marinating. Just enough dressing to season the vegetables is needed. Excess dressing should be drained off before the ingredients are combined with another dressing. Each vegetable should be marinated separately and combined just before the salad is served. This assures retention of form and flavor of each ingredient, and the salad is better than where all ingredients are marinated together. Some ingredients, e.g., citrus sections, should not be marinated because they lose their shape. French dressing is often mixed at the table and added to the salad as it is served, or dressing ingredients are added to the salad ingredients, and the salad is "dressed" in the bowl.

A well-chosen combination of fruits, vegetables, or both, may be placed in a bowl with dressing of the French type, and the ingredients tossed, to combine them with the dressing, using forks or a salad-serving fork and spoon. The French refer to this process as "fatiguing" the salad. When this is done, the salad should be served immediately to be sure that the ingredients retain their crispness. Only enough dressing to season the salad should be used in combining the ingredients.

Garnishing materials include green or red pepper, chopped or cut into rings or strips, pimiento, hard-cooked eggs, pickles, olives, and leaves from water cress, garden cress, parsley, mint, and nasturtiums. A dark accent, made possible by the use of ripe olives, truffles, a stuffed prune, or a dark plum, is often desirable. Maraschino cherries are used pleasingly as a garnish for fruit salads, but they should not be considered the only appropriate garnish. When they are chopped fine or cut into rings and sprinkled over the top of the salad, they are often more attractive than when used whole or cut in half. A dash of paprika is frequently exactly the touch required, or a bit of grated cheese may add just the color and contrast needed. Pomegranate seeds are especially delightful as a garnish for citrus salads. A garnish should not be considered essential because in many instances skillfully arranged ingredients do not need a garnish.

Salads are sometimes "overdone." Definite shapes and attempts at realism should be avoided when arranging salads. There may be some excuse for making a poinsettia, a candle, or a jack-o'-lantern salad for a children's party, but even here it seems that the children might be amused in some other way. Another objection to realism in salads is that they appear to have required too much time on the part of the hostess and an undue amount of handling of ingredients.

Salads may be molded, but are usually more attractive when not so definitely shaped. Gelatin, either plain or flavored, is generally used

Courtesy American Can Company

Fig. 6. Cottage cheese with a tomato and egg aspic.

for molding salads. Gelatin added to mayonnaise and whipped cream may serve to mold fruit for a combination salad and dessert course. Chicken or fish as the basic ingredient may be used as a main-dish salad and molded similarly. They may be either in individual molds or in one large mold. For serving at the table as a separate course or as a part of a buffet meal, the large ones are especially attractive.

Some salads are frozen. The fruit salad-dessert referred to above is often frozen. Cans of fruit or of fruit mixtures are sometimes frozen to be served as salads. These thaw quickly and should be removed from the can and sliced just before serving.

The role of the salad is a versatile one. Whether served as the main course for a summer buffet or as accompaniment to a barbecued sandwich, salads add considerable relish to dining. Since a salad can be served as any part of the meal and can be simple or elaborate, light or substantial, zestful or bland, hot or cold, attention should be paid to choosing the right salad for the right time. If in doubt a simple salad is best. Overembellishing detracts from their appearence and often their palatability. First course salads should, as any other appetizer, *pique* the appetite and be light (see Fig. 5). Those accompanying or following the main course should also be light. Dessert salads

Courtesy American Can Company

Fig. 7. A luncheon salad plate made up of several favorites—tomato, tuna fish, potato chips and pickles.

need not be overly rich or sweet. A simple fruit and cottage cheese combination is appreciated by many in preference to one made with whipped cream or mayonnaise base. Main course salads are *protein* salads, using as a principal ingredient fish, meat, poultry, dried beans, cheese, etc. A starchy food such as potato or macaroni is sometimes used in combination with the protein ingredients. Figs. 6 and 7 show one type of salad appropriate for main dishes. Cottage cheese and aspic is a low calorie protein combination, while Fig. 7 shows a more substantial tuna fish salad.

SUGGESTIONS FOR LABORATORY

(SELECTED RECIPES ON PP. 515 THROUGH 523.)

A salad laboratory provides an excellent opportunity to correlate food and art since the ingredients used are especially notable for their beauty of form, color, and texture. It is a universally accepted fact that the enjoyment of food is in part due to its eye appeal. Stimulating experiences have been provided by inviting an interested staff member from the art department to give a demonstration on the arrangement of salads. After students have seen their own or a guest instructor arrange salads from the standpoint of design they will have a greater appreciation of their aesthetic qualities.

Also a demonstration highlighting the nutritional contribution of salads is an effective way to show their versatility. Since the preparation of ingredients and arrangement of salads is of importance in their acceptance, each student should have an opportunity to prepare one or more salads after the demonstration.

UNIT

6

Milk

In no instance has scientific research more clearly approved the habit of centuries than in the use of milk as an important part of the diet. From very early times, milk has been provided for man by the domestication of some animal—goat, sheep, reindeer, mare, camel, or cow. Goat's milk is used in many places in the world, and in Italian towns it is still a common sight to see herdsmen driving their flocks along the street, pausing to draw milk for the housewives who bring their own pails and designate the quantity needed. Such a practice would be considered a public health hazard in our country, where standards for milk production, processing, and distribution are a model for the world.

This unusual progress in the dairy industry has taken place in the United States within a little more than fifty years. At the turn of the century very little was known about scientific feeding and management and there were no pure breeds, as known today. Milk was largely consumed in fluid form or made into butter or cheese. The variety of milks described on pages 89–92 was unknown. At this time per capita consumption was far below what it is today, and consequently the market for fluid milk and cream was limited. Not only did farm families have their own cows, but many people living in towns and even cities kept a family cow which was pastured adjacent to the town. Most of the milk that was marketed was raw, and was delivered directly to the stores by individual producers in large cans, where it was measured out to customers. Butter and cheesemaking were still home industries in many areas. Both products varied greatly in quality, and were seasonal since refrigeration facilities for storage were extremely limited.

Even though milk consumption is heartening at present, it should be increased to meet the standards set by nutritionists. A peak level was reached in 1945 when it was slightly over a pint per day per person, but since that time per capita consumption has fallen off, to slightly less than a pint a day.

Trends in food consumption are directly traceable to education in better nutrition. Since federal, state, and local governments, the medical and teaching professions, social welfare agencies, public health officials, and the milk industry itself are all working toward realization of increased milk consumption, it is hoped that the goal of a quart or more a day for children, and at least a pint for adults, will soon be reached for *all* families, regardless of economic status.

At least a quart or a pint of milk daily. The role of milk in fulfilling the food needs of infants and children is well known. Likewise the value of milk during pregnancy and lactation, and in certain functional disorders and chronic ailments is unquestioned. The science of nutrition is giving increased attention to the nutritional needs of other groups, particularly adolescents and the aging. As progress in this area goes forward, the dietetic significance of milk continues unchallenged.

There are many mistaken ideas about the place of milk in the diet, particularly insofar as adult consumption is concerned. Milk and milk products are rejected by certain individuals for various reasons, one of the most common being fear of adding weight. To help offset inadequate fad diets, which exclude milk and milk products, an extensive piece of research in human nutrition was conducted at Michigan State College in collaboration with the National Dairy Council. Student and adult groups acted as human "guinea pigs" in carrying out the study. The test diets included recommended quotas of milk and milk products. Since physically active adults usually lose weight on an intake of 1400 to 1800 calories, the research staff developed two sets of menus; the 1400 calorie menus included approximately 16 oz. of whole milk plus limited amounts of butter, cheeese and ice cream, while the 1800 calorie diet had approximately 21 oz. of whole milk and more liberal amounts of butter and other milk products. The results of the study were recorded on a documentary film[1] which gives convincing evidence of the success of the project.

At Cornell University, Young[2] developed a successful low carbohydrate, moderate-fat reducing diet based on the above-mentioned research. This was a 1400 calorie diet and included 18 oz. of whole milk daily, in addition to limited amounts of butter and other fats. College students were used as subjects in this study.

Such studies as these help to counteract the over-emphasis that has been placed on the butterfat in milk, and direct attention to the other important nutrients—protein, minerals, and vitamins.

As the science of nutrition advances, milk takes on an increasingly important role in human nutrition. To understand why it is basic to the growth of

---

[1] *Weight Reduction Through Diet* (Chicago: National Dairy Council, 1953).

[2] Charlotte M. Young, "Weight Reduction Using a Moderate-fat Diet," *Journ. Am. Diet. Assoc.,* Vol. 28, No. 2 (May, 1952).

children and the health and well-being of people of all age groups, we need to consider each part of this important "whole" food. While it contains approximately 87 per cent water, it is the *quality* of the solids which makes milk "nature's most nearly perfect food." Milk contains on the average 3.8 per cent fat, 3.5 per cent protein, 4.8 per cent carbohydrate, and .7 per cent minerals. Variation in milk constituents occurs principally in respect to butterfat, where the range is from approximately 3.3 per cent to over 5 per cent. This is influenced by the breed of the cow, ration fed, and season of the year. The fat in milk, containing vitamin A in quantities dependent on the carotene content of the feed of the cow, is in emulsified form; hence it is easily digested.

The fat of milk, like other animal fats, contains cholesterol. Even though it has been determined that this substance is in some way related to certain types of arterio-vascular disease, it has not been established that cholesterol obtained from a good normal diet contributes to this disease.[1]

The principal proteins, casein and lactalbumin, are of the highest quality, containing all of the essential amino acids. If we compare milk with other complete proteins we find that a quart of milk contains the same amount of protein as 5¾ ounces of beef, 6½ ounces of fish, 5½ ounces of liver, 4 ounces of cheese or 5 large eggs. The carbohydrate in milk, lactose, is one of the least sweet sugars (about ⅙ as sweet as sucrose) and therefore it does not ferment readily. Lactose promotes the growth of lactic acid bacteria which tend to prevent digestive disturbances of a putrefactive nature. This sugar plays a role in calcium metabolism.

The mineral for which milk is particularly superior is calcium. In addition to the important function it performs in the development of the bones and teeth of children and their maintenance in adults, calcium is needed by *both* children and adults for other body functions, such as normal blood clotting, muscle contraction, and nerve stability. The surest and easiest way of providing calcium for all these body needs is the inclusion of the full quota of milk in the daily diet. In the case of teen-age boys there is some indication that the daily milk quota should be increased to 1½ quarts to provide needed calcium.[2] These needs will be safeguarded even further if the group has received a quart of milk daily during early years. This permits some storage of calcium prior to the sudden prepubertal spurt of growth when the increased amount of milk is necessary.

Milk is a very good source of phosphorus. It contains a small amount of iron which is utilized by the body easily. There may be a little iodine in milk, depending upon the feed of the cows.

With the exception of vitamin D, milk contains all of the known vitamins,

---

[1] William J. Darby, "Nutrition In Preventive Medicine and Public Health," *Nutrition News,* Vol. 17, No. 1 (Oct. 1953), National Dairy Council.

[2] Janice M. Smith, *Nutrition News,* Vol. 10, No. 4 (April 1947), National Dairy Council.

TABLE 8. QUANTITY OF SEVERAL FOODS NECESSARY TO GIVE THE QUANTITY OF CALCIUM IN ONE QUART OF MILK (1.169 GRAMS)

Food	*Quantity*	*Food*	*Quantity*
Oats, rolled	3.73 lb.	Beef round (E.P.)	20.88 lb.
Rice, brown or white	28.5 lb.	Beans, navy, dry	1.61 lb.
Eggs, medium	37 eggs	Cabbage (A.P.)	6.7 lb.
Halibut, boned (E.P.) *	12.7 lb.	Carrots (A.P.)	5.75 lb.
Oysters	4.95 lb.	Cauliflower (A.P.)	2.09 lb.
Apples (A.P.) †	48.73 lb.	Lettuce (A.P.)	7.0 lb.
Prunes, dry (A.P.)	4.77 lb.	Peas, green (A.P.)	16.7 lb.

* E.P. means edible portion.
† A.P. means as purchased.

but it is an especially good source of vitamin A and riboflavin. The vitamin A in milk and other animal foods is in active form and can be used at once by the body. This is in contrast to certain green and yellow vegetables which are also valuable for their vitamin A content, the carotene of which must be changed to vitamin A by the body before it can be used.

Milk is the outstanding source of riboflavin in American dietaries. As in the case of calcium, the full daily quota of milk assures sufficiency of this vitamin. Even though lean beef, eggs, and liver are also good sources of riboflavin, one quart of milk contains the same amount of this important vitamin as 2⅓ pounds of beef, 12 large eggs, or 3¼ ounces of liver. Milk should be protected from strong sunlight, since riboflavin is subject to some loss during such exposure. In certain areas amber colored milk bottles are used as a protection against this.

Thiamin, ascorbic acid, and niacin are present in lesser quantities, but because of the regular use of milk in the diet these small amounts become significant. Even though some losses of both thiamin and ascorbic acid during pasteurization have been reported, carefully controlled high-temperature, short-time pasteurization reduces these losses to a minimum.

Reports show that this method of pasteurization reduces the loss of thiamin from about 10 per cent to 3 per cent.[1] Because milk is an ideal food for dispensing vitamin D, which is very scarce in the average diet, vitamin D concentrate is being added to an increasing proportion of fluid whole milk on the present market. Requirements for vitamin D milk were established by the Council on Foods and Nutrition of the American Medical Association, which stipulates that the milk must contain not more than 400 U.S.P. units of vitamin D. Milk is the only food for which this council has approved fortification with vitamin D.

[1] A. D. Holmes, *et. al.*, "Effect of High-Temperature–Short-Time Pasteurization on the Ascorbic Acid, Riboflavin, and Thiamin Content of Milk," *Journal of Dairy Science,* 28:29 (Jan.), 1945.

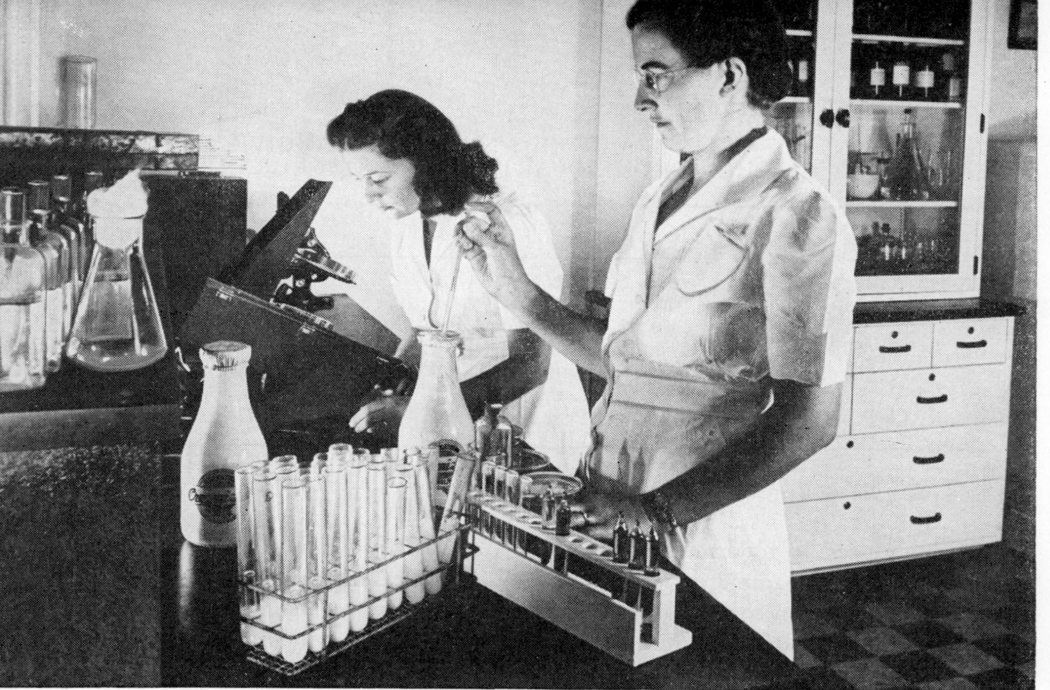

Courtesy Dellwood Dairy Company, Inc.

Fig. 8a. Laboratory testing helps to insure a safe milk supply.

Some of the more recently discovered vitamins known to be present in milk are B_{12}, pantothenic acid, and biotin.

A safe milk supply. Because of the value of milk as a food and its extreme perishability, the most rigid controls of production, processing, and distribution must be enforced to assure a safe supply. Fig. 8 shows two important steps included in milk processing. Modern science has demonstrated how safe milk can be produced, and many communities (mainly cities of 500,000 and over) have proven that it is economical to provide *only* safe milk. In order to encourage greater uniformity of milk-control practice, the U. S. Public Health Service formulated a Milk Ordinance and Code,[1] which is recommended for adoption by states and communities. The Ordinance and Code, which is kept up to date as improvements develop, sets forth in great detail the best information on milk control legislation. Certainly students of foods and nutrition should study this document and familiarize themselves with the many important links in the chain of producing safe milk.

In spite of the great progress that has been made in safeguarding milk, not only by the Public Health Service and the industry itself, but by state, county, and city governments, the hazards of milk-borne diseases still exist and will not be entirely eliminated as long as raw milk is sold in any community. Unfortunately, the majority of states and cities still permit the sale of raw milk.

---

[1] *Milk Ordinance and Code,* Public Health Bulletin No. 220 (1939) and Public Health Bulletin 229 (1953), (U. S. Public Health Service, Federal Security Agency).

Courtesy Dellwood Dairy Company, Inc.

Fig. 8b. Modern plant equipment is an essential step in maintaining high standards of milk processing.

A limited number of states, counties and cities now require that all market milk (except certified) be pasteurized.[1] Many families who leave their city residences (where pasteurization is compulsory) in the summer and go to resort areas, unwittingly submit their families to the dangers of the local milk supply, which, in numerous cases, is raw. Hazards are also present for those individuals who can not resist the propaganda of the food faddist who advocates the use of raw milk.

Limited space in a text of this type makes it impossible to present information on all of the important aspects of so highly complex an industry as the milk industry. However, the basic principles which govern a *safe* milk supply are briefly summarized below. The details regarding these principles can be found in the Milk Ordinance and Code mentioned above.

1) *Regular inspection and sanitary control of farms and milk plants.* This covers, among other things, water supply, construction and maintenance of buildings, choice and installation of equipment, and sterilization of *all* utensils, equipment, and bottles.

2) *Supervision of the physical examination and testing of cows.* Of the specific diseases of cattle communicable to man through milk, the best known are bovine tuberculosis and Bang's disease, that is, undulant fever. Through modern methods of disease control, excellent progress is being made in eliminating these diseases in animals by individual tests of all animals in a herd

[1] *Newer Knowledge of Milk* (Chicago: National Dairy Council, 1952).

and by slaughter of infected animals. According to the Milk Ordinance and Code, both tests are compulsory; but, since there are many communities which have not adopted the Code, the only sure protection against these diseases to consumers of milk is through pasteurization.

3) *Regular physical examination of all persons engaged in the production, processing, and distribution of milk.* Human diseases transmitted by milk constitute another type of milk-borne disease that must be controlled through periodic physical examinations of all handlers of milk, as well as through rigid controls of sanitary conditions at farm and plant. Some well-known diseases of this type are diphtheria, typhoid fever, scarlet fever, and septic sore throat.

4) *Proper pasteurization.* Pasteurization means heating every particle of milk to at least 143° F. (61.7° C.) and holding it at such temperature for 30 minutes, or heating it to at least 160° F. (71° C.) and holding at this temperature for 15 seconds. This treatment is followed by immediate cooling to 50° F. or less. "The public health value of pasteurization is unanimously agreed upon by health officials."[1] As stated above, it is the only measure known which will prevent all milk-borne diseases.

At the present time health officials in a number of cities are recommending the time-temperature combination of 160° F. (71° C.) for 15 seconds which is known as the high-temperature–short-time pasteurization method. This method has certain advantages in devitalizing milk-borne pathogens, and in reducing to a minimum the loss of ascorbic acid and thiamin. The latter advantage should not be construed to mean that the food value of milk is significantly impaired through pasteurization, since the increased safety far outweighs any slight difference there may be in food value.

Pasteurization should not be looked on as a substitute for rigid sanitary controls in the production of raw milk, but should be considered instead as an added safeguard.

5) *Laboratory examinations.* During the approximate 24-hour period from the time milk is drawn from the cow until it reaches the consumer it is subjected to many tests, all of which are basic in assuring its safety. In many cities, even after numerous tests have been made at farm, receiving station, and plant, wholesale or retail delivery trucks may be stopped by city health officials and samples taken for further testing. Laboratory tests are concerned largely with bacteria count, butterfat content, and checking of pasteurization methods. Because bacteria multiply rapidly in a temperature of above 50° F. (10° C.), temperature is also of prime importance (see Table 9). Since these factors are the principal ones in designating milk "grades," the laboratory tests should take on added significance to the consumer.

---

[1] *Milk Ordinance and Code,* U. S. Pub. Health Bul. No. 220, (Washington, D. C., 1939).

TABLE 9.* THE RELATION BETWEEN TEMPERATURE AND BACTERIAL DEVELOPMENT IN MILK DURING 12 HOURS

Temperature: Degrees Fahrenheit	*Bacteria per c.c. After 12 Hours*
40	4,000
45	9,000
50	18,000
55	38,000
60	453,000
70	8,800,000
80	55,300,000

* W. E. Petersen, *Dairy Science*, J. B. Lippincott Co., Chicago, 1950.

The number of grades and their meanings vary according to local regulations. For instance, in the New York Metropolitan area, only one grade of fluid whole milk can be sold legally. In Greater New York this is designated as "Approved Milk" while in outlying suburban areas the same milk is "Grade A." In both cases it is pasteurized with a permissive bacterial count of 30,000 and butterfat content of at least 3.3 per cent. In those communities where the U. S. Public Health Service Ordinance and Code is in effect, standards are uniform. According to this code the highest bacterial counts per c.c. allowed for various grades are, Grade A pasteurized—30,000; Grade A raw—50,000; Grade B pasteurized—50,000; and Grade B raw—1,000,000. While these counts may serve some purpose to the student of foods and nutrition, by themselves they are meaningless, since much more is involved in producing quality milk than keeping within permissive bacteria counts. Ethical milk dealers know that it is only good business to distribute milk which has a bacteria count far *below* that which is permissive, and by the same token they distribute milk with a butterfat content which *exceeds* the minimum requirements. But, for her own assurance, the homemaker should familiarize herself with the standards of milk processing and handling used in the dairy that supplies her with milk, and from these observations she can determine what sort of standards have been maintained all along the line. If she has seen exceptionally high standards of plant maintenance, processing, and bottling, she has good reason for assuming that like standards will have been upheld from the farm to the time the milk reached the processing plant. In no instance should consumers be satisfied with a milk supply that has not received the utmost in scientific and sanitary controls.

Kinds of milk. While, generally, the market milk sold in the United States may be divided into two classes—pasteurized and raw—in most areas consumers have their choice of fresh fluid milk in several different forms, including varieties of specially cultured and concentrated milks. Besides the various grades of regular pasteurized and raw milk, some or all of the following milks may be found on most marktes:

1) Homogenized milk. A second-grade schoolboy once explained homogenized milk simply as "milk with the cream all busted up in the inside of it." To be more technical, homogenization is a special mechanical process whereby whole milk is forced through a series of jets at several thousand pounds of pressure. This breaks the fat globules and redistributes the cream uniformly through the milk, eliminating the cream line. The food value of milk is not altered by this process; in fact it results in the formation of a softer curd during digestion. Physically, homogenized milk will show slight differences in color and viscosity from ordinary milk, and its uniformly "richer" taste accounts, no doubt, for the increasing demand for it. The uniformity of cream is also assured by homogenization, and on some markets all cream is homogenized.

2) Certified milk. This is a milk produced under standards of the American Association of Medical Commissions. The production and distribution of certified milk is also subject to the supervision of the state, county, and city officials. In spite of the exceptionally high standards and rigid controls in producing certified milk today, most of it is being pasteurized. This, after all, is the only way to assure its absolute safety.

3) Vitamin D milk. As mentioned on page 85, an increasing amount of market milk is being fortified with vitamin D concentrate. Two other methods of fortification, which have been accepted but are less frequently used, are exposure of milk to ultraviolet light, and feeding cows irradiated yeast. The concentrate is added by most processors to homogenized milk.

4) Skim milk. This is a nonfat milk which has all the milk nutrients of whole milk except fat and fat soluble vitamins. In many cities there is increasing demand for skim milk, both for dietary reasons and as a measure of cutting food costs. Physicians sometimes prescribe it for infants' formulas as well as for adult diets of low fat content. Within the last few years some milk companies have taken advantage of the public interest in low calorie foods, and have increased the sales value of skim milk by labeling it "Fat-free Milk."

5) Flavored Milks. The two most common flavored milks are eggnog and chocolate. The former, which is nonalcoholic, is a seasonal item appearing in most instances at Thanksgiving, Christmas, and New Year's. The butterfat content of eggnog must be at least 8 per cent,[1] and to this rich milk is added a mix consisting of egg yolks, a stabilizer, sugar, and flavoring. Chocolate milks are popular the year around for both hot and cold beverages. They are prepared by adding chocolate sirup or cocoa powder to either whole or skim

---

[1] New York State Standard.

milk. Local regulations govern the formulas and labeling of such beverages. For example, on the New York market a beverage sold under the label of "Chocolate Milk" must contain at least 3.3 per cent butterfat. Any product having less than this amount of butterfat must be labeled "Chocolate Drink." If whole milk is used in the making of the chocolate-flavored beverage, there is little difference in food value from the whole milk itself, except that the added sugar and chocolate or cocoa increases the caloric value. Likewise, when skim milk is used, the food value is practically the same as that for plain skim milk. There is considerable difference of opinion on the value of chocolate milk in the human diet, the principal point in question being the effect of the cocoa on the availability of milk calcium. However, recent research on a good grade of cocoa indicates that availability of milk calcium is not affected by the presence of cocoa.[1]

6) *Cultured milks.* The most common type of cultured milk is "buttermilk," which is prepared from sweet, skim milk by the addition of lactic acid bacteria. Among other types are acidophilus milk and yogurt, both being made from whole milk with special cultures added. Since yogurt has been termed by food faddists as a "magical" food, its consumption has greatly increased (see p. 31). In addition to plain yogurt, it is available on some markets in flavored form. Strawberry, vanilla and orange are the most common flavors. The therapeutic value of cultured milks is a subject of some debate. However, it is generally agreed that they have a tendency to lessen putrefaction during digestion in the intestine.

7) *Concentrated milks.* These include evaporated, condensed, and dried milks. Evaporated milk is made by placing fresh whole milk in vacuum pans and heating to 120–140° F. (49–60° C.) until more than half the water content is removed. The milk is then homogenized, cooled, placed in cans, and sterilized at 240° F. (116° C.) for 15 minutes. The sterilization process changes the flavor slightly by caramelizing some of the lactose. Most evaporated milk is fortified with vitamin D. It is frequently prescribed for infant feeding.

Condensed milk is somewhat more reduced in water content than is evaporated milk. Before the milk is placed in the vacuum pans sugar is added, about 18 pounds of sugar to 100 pounds of milk. The finished product has a sucrose content of about 42 per cent. After removing it from the pan, the milk is sealed in cans and, because the sugar acts as a preservative, no further heat treatment is necessary. This milk is used principally in cookery, being the chief ingredient in a number of foods, such as some ice cream, cookies, puddings, and other desserts.

Dried milks are widely manufactured from both whole and skim milk. In each case the water content is reduced to a fraction (5 per cent is the maxi-

[1] H. H. Mitchell and J. M. Smith, "The Effect of Cocoa on the Utilization of Dietary Calcium," *Journ. Am. Med. Assn.* 129–871 (Nov.), 1945.

mum allowance) of the original amount by concentration in vacuum pans. The drying of the milk concentrate is then done by spraying it either into a chamber containing hot air or on a slowly revolving heated drum. The former method produces a superior product. Law requires that the type of process be printed on the label.

The whole-milk powder contains all of the protein, fat, lactose, and minerals of the original milk. Ascorbic acid is the only vitamin lost in an appreciable amount. To prevent spoilage it is marketed in sealed containers. Four and one-half ounces of the dry product are equivalent in food value to about one quart of fresh milk. It is useful in many of the processes of cookery, and may be used as a beverage. The skim-milk powder contains very little fat and fat-soluble vitamins, A and D. As a source of other milk constituents, it is valuable. Both whole and skim-milk powder are convenient for home use, especially "instant" skim milk.

8) *Goat's milk.* This milk is available in scattered areas throughout the United States. There is an extremely limited demand for it, and since its cost is more than two and a half times that of cow's milk it is usually ordered only on a doctor's advice.

9) *Frozen milks.* Fresh fluid, pasteurized, homogenized, whole milk can be frozen successfully by using scientific methods of freezing foods. It should be frozen in the paraffined containers in which it is sold and should stay flavorful at 0° F. for about 30 days. Freezing fresh milk is of no particular advantage to families who have a source of supply very near by, but for those who have to travel considerable distance to the nearest grocery store such a plan has merit. Milk which has not been homogenized will, on thawing, separate into flaky particules and fat globules. Fresh concentrated milk may also be frozen successfully. In this case it is essentially the same as evaporated milk except that it is frozen after canning. This milk, like other frozen foods, should be used soon after thawing.

Even though milk is not changed chemically during freezing, the process seems to affect the fat fraction, which sometimes separates in thawing. Also, when stored for some time protein solubility is gradually decreased.[1]

In spite of the variety of milks that are found in our markets, some individuals find it difficult to make substitutes for fresh fluid milk during times of emergency. Some of these people base their objections on flavor, others are reluctant to accept the fact that nutritionally speaking, canned and dried milks are equivalent to fresh milk (see Table 10).

Changing concepts of milk. Even though milk is a "prestige" food to many individuals, especially fresh fluid, its nutritional importance is not always considered in relation to the cost. The psychological approach to "selling" milk in nutrition education programs should be given prime consideration. Milk, along with eggs, is one of the most healthful foods available and it should be included daily at one's meals.

TABLE 10. PERCENTAGE COMPOSITION OF MILK IN VARIOUS FORMS AND EQUIVALENTS IN TERMS OF FLUID WHOLE MILK

	Water	*Fat*	*Protein*	*Lactose*	*Ash*	*Amount for 1 qt. Milk*		
						Milk	*Water*	*Butter*
Fluid milk (Whole)..	87.0	4.0	3.3	5.0	0.7	1 qt.	.....	......
Fluid milk (Skim)....	90.4	0.15	3.7	4.98	0.8	1 qt.	......	......
Evaporated.	73.5	8.2	6.7	10.1	1.5	1 pt.	1 pt.	......
Powdered (Whole)..	1.5	28.0	26.7	38.0	5.8	1¼ c.	3¾ c.	......
Powdered (Skim)....	2.8	1.4	37.7	49.9	8.2	1¼ c.	3¾ c.	2½ tb.

A number of people associate "protein" with meat. Since red meat is also a great "prestige" food (and by far the most popular source of protein) and since it is something that is considered to be essential for health, it is included as a regular part of the diet. It seems logical to assume that constant association of milk with protein will help to relate it to meat, which in turn will help counteract the theory held by uninformed people that milk is a substitute *beverage* for coffee, tea, soda, or other drinks.

Numerous people including men, women and teen-agers have been given an "uncomfortable feeling" about milk by being reminded constantly of its butterfat content. However the consumption of skimmed milk is increasing greatly, and users of this nutritious milk are relying on green and yellow vegetables and other sources to supply the vitamin A of the deleted butterfat.

There is more and more evidence that the average consumer is broadening his horizons about what he eats. He no longer is satisfied with a meat and potato existence. Travel is partially responsible for this. Other factors are food advertising, a continuous stream of newly published cook books, more casual entertaining, interest in outdoor cooking, to say nothing of the influence of popular periodicals, TV programs, and a growing appreciation of better nutrition. "Gourmet" foods are regularly stocked supermarket items in many communities. The inexpensive magazines obtainable at supermarkets have articles on gourmet cooking from time to time. Well-known food writers, formerly known to only a limited number of readers of the more sophisticated magazines, come into the average homemaker's kitchen through their writings in these popular magazines.

Milk, too, is a gourmet food when considered in the light of its versatility as an ingredient in such dishes as vichyssoise, fish chowders, delicate custards, party punches, etc.

Cost of milk. Regardless of food prices milk generally has its full share of country-wide criticism. Delivery of milk to homes or stores involves the time and work of a number of people. Even though milk looks unchanged when it reaches the consumer, much processing has taken place. If *water* were processed and delivered to homes in quart bottles it would cost approximately two-thirds as much as milk. The cost of a bottle of milk must cover production, transportation, processing, and delivery. Profit in each of these steps is modest.

Even though home-delivered milk costs from two to five cents more per quart than milk purchased at a store there are many families who prefer to pay for the convenient and "automatic" service of milk on the door-step. In some sections of the country there is a trend to base the price of home-delivered milk on volume. Under this plan a householder pays the standard price for the first one or two units and receives a cut of several cents on each additional unit, thereby bringing the cost of home-delivered milk to only slightly more than that bought in a store. The increasing use of milk-vending machines in apartment houses in certain areas is another method of reducing milk-delivery costs.

Regardless of the price of milk, its scientifically supported position of high priority in the diets of children and adults should be considered before cutting food costs by cutting the milk supply. This is of great importance in the interest of our national health and efficiency.

Milk in cooking. Besides the use of fresh milk as a beverage, it lends itself in cookery to combination with practically all foods (meats, fish, poultry, eggs, cheese, vegetables, and fruits). It is the basic ingredient in many soups, main dishes, and desserts, as well as the liquid for a number of flour mixtures.

Milk is seldom boiled, although there are times when boiling is advisable. The flavor of boiled milk may be described as "flat," the change being due to the loss of the carbon dioxide and oxygen. Caramelization of lactose also alters the flavor.

Heating milk results in the formation of a scum on the surface—coagulated calcium-caseinate, together with other constituents entangled in it. Milk is scalded when bubbles appear around the edge of the container—before this scum starts to form. After scalded milk is turned out of the utensil, a film remains on the sides and bottom. This is chiefly lactalbumin, which is precipitated by heat. Some calcium phosphate is also present in the film, which is made more noticeable if milk is heated over a direct flame. As a rule, milk should be heated over water in a double boiler. To a slight degree, the same flavor changes occur in heated milk as when milk is boiled. The fat is broken into smaller globules by heating, and heated milk has less cream, if allowed to stand, than unheated milk. The curd formed in the stomach from heated milk is more tender and more easily digested than that from unheated milk.

The proteins of fresh milk require a high temperature for coagulation. As acidity increases in the souring of milk, the coagulation temperature is lowered until milk coagulates at "room" temperature because the acid precipitates casein. While the destruction of lactic acid bacteria during pasteurization retards souring, after a time the flavor will be altered because of increased bacteria count. However, reports show that when pasteurized milk is refrigerated at 45–50° F. (9–10° C.) this break in flavor does not come until after the fourth day during hot weather and the seventh day during fall and winter. Every-other-day deliveries, instituted during World War II, and found so successful that they have been continued, were responsible for extensive research on the keeping qualities of pasteurized milk.[1]

Milk or cream that is so slightly sour that acidity is scarcely detectable may separate or coagulate when added to coffee, used on hot cereals, or heated; even sweet cream or milk poured on acid fruits often curdles. The difficulty encountered in making caramel custard or candies as well as in making certain cream soups is due to the coagulation of milk by the acidity of some of the ingredients. With skillful preparation this can be avoided.

Coagulation of milk by rennet or junket—the commercial form in which the rennin enzyme is marketed—makes possible many varieties of cheese, as well as the dessert known as junket. High temperature destroys the activity of the enzyme, so that milk used in the preparation of junket should be heated to only 98° or 100° F. (37° or 38 °C.) or lukewarm, if no thermometer is available to measure the exact temperature. The action of this enzyme upon calcium caseinate may be represented as follows:

Calcium caseinate + rennin ⟶ paracasein
Paracasein + calcium salts ⟶ calcium paracaseinate

When milk is heated sufficiently to precipitate the calcium salts, rennin coagulation is impossible, as the second step in the reaction indicates. Slight acidity favors this type of coagulation, while strong acidity inhibits or prevents the action.

Homogenized milk used in cooking such foods as oatmeal and wheat cereals tends to have less stability than unhomogenized milk. Also, experiments in making white sauces with homogenized milk showed that the milk "behaved" differently from plain milk.[2] For example, the fat in the sauce seemed to be incapable of uniting with the fat of the milk, and less flour was needed for thickening than when unhomogenized milk was used. Indications are that increased information on the cooking qualities of this kind of milk is needed.

Cream. Since the specific gravity of fat is lower than that of water, the fat of milk rises to the surface in the form of cream as the milk stands. It is sep-

---

[1] A. C. Dahlberg, *The Keeping Qualities of Pasteurized Milk*, Cornell University Agricultural Experiment Station, Bul. 838, Dec. 1946.

[2] Alice M. Touson and G. M. Trout, "Some Cooking Qualities of Homogenized Milk in White Sauces," *Food Research*, Vol. II, No. 3 (1946), pp. 261–273.

arated from milk by means of separators which operate by centrifugal force, and which can be so regulated as to give cream of any desired fat content.

Two types of cream are generally available on all markets—light cream and heavy cream. In most instances the former contains not less than 18 per cent butterfat while the latter contains approximately 36 per cent. In both cases the fat content is determined by local and state health departments. Light cream is used mainly for coffee, cereals, and in cooking where richness is desired, while heavy cream is usually purchased for either whipping or making some frozen desserts.

In order to whip cream successfully it must have a butterfat content of at least 30 per cent, be "aged" for four hours or longer, have a temperature of 40–45° F. (4–7° C.) and be whipped in a cold bowl. A turbine beater is best suited for whipping cream and for large amounts, the cream is less likely to be overwhipped if it is divided into portions of approximately one cup each. Heavy cream sold by milk companies has in most instances more than sufficient fat for successful whipping, and the aging has been done before it is sold. Consequently the homemaker need be concerned only with the temperature of the cream and the type of utensils used to get good results.

Cultured sour cream is being manufactured increasingly and is available in many cities throughout the country. It is made from fresh sweet cream, of approximately 18 per cent butterfat, by adding a lactic acid culture. The resulting thick, creamy, slightly acid product contributes an inimitable quality to a number of dishes such as salad dressings, sauces for meats, poultry, and fish, and for certain desserts. Where cultured sour cream is not sold it is possible to make it at home by adding a small amount of cultured buttermilk to sweet cream.[1]

SUGGESTIONS FOR LABORATORY

(SELECTED RECIPES ON PP. 522 THROUGH 534.)

Laboratory experiences in connection with a study of milk logically fall into four categories:

1) Techniques concerned with cooking principles which involve the effect of heat on milk. In beginning classes these can best be learned by application to the preparation of milk dishes under various circumstances. The recipes on the above pages may be used as a guide in planning the laboratory projects. Since these include beverages, soups, main dishes, and desserts they will serve to illustrate the versatility of milk in family meals.

2) Nutritional importance of milk. Visual displays on this subject can be very dramatic. Examples are: arrangements showing the quantity of different foods needed to supply the amount of calcium in a quart of milk and an ex-

---

[1] *Sour Cream—How to Prepare It and Use It At Home,* U.S.D.A. Leaflet 213, Oct., 1941.

hibit showing the contribution a quart of milk makes to the daily food requirements as established by the Food and Nutrition Board of National Research Council. Food values of the various milks and creams—fresh, skimmed, and evaporated milk and heavy, light, and sour cream—when set up in a display are more meaningful than when studied from a table (see Appendix B).

3) Cost of milk in relation to food value. The number of possibilities to illustrate this are extensive, especially when the application is made to milk dishes using fresh fluid, evaporated, and dried milk. Any one of the recipes given on pp. 522 through 534 or those selected from the references may be used as the basis for interesting cost comparisons. In order to highlight the significance of *protein* in milk, laboratory assignments might include one in which a cost comparison is made of the protein in milk, eggs, round steak, Cheddar cheese, etc.

4) Production, processing, and distribution. Whenever feasible, laboratory time may be utilized to good advantage by field trips to observe first hand the handling of milk from producer to consumer. There is no better way to emphasize milk sanitation.

REFERENCES

Cooper, Lenna F., Edith M. Barber, Helen S. Mitchell, and Hendrika J. Rynebergen, *Nutrition in Health and Disease*. J. B. Lippincott, Philadelphia, 13th edition, 1959.

Eckles, C. H., J. B. Comba, and H. Macy, *Milk and Milk Products,* 3rd Ed. McGraw-Hill Book Co., N. Y., 1943.

Fitch, Natalie K., and Charlotte A. Francis, *Foods and Principles of Cookery*. Prentice-Hall, Inc., 1948.

Food—The Yearbook of Agriculture, 1959; U.S.D.A., Washington, D. C.

Hovey, Helen S., and Kay Reynolds, *The Practical Book of Food Shopping*. J. B. Lippincott Co., Chicago, 1950.

Stewart, Jean J., and Alice L. Edwards, *Foods: Production, Marketing, Consumption*. Prentice-Hall, New York, 1948.

The Composition of Milks, Bul. 119, Nat'l. Research Council, Washington, D. C., 1953.

Dahlberg, A. C., *The Keeping Qualities of Pasteurized Milk,* Cornell University Agri. Exp. Station Bul. 838, 1946.

Milk Regulations and Milk Quality, Bul. No. 250, Nat'l. Research Council, Washington, D. C., 1953.

Newer Knowledge of Milk, National Dairy Council, Chicago, 1956.

Sanitary Milk and Ice Cream Legislation in the United States, Bul. No. 121, Nat'l. Research Council, Washington, D. C., 1953.

UNIT

7

Cheese

"Reading descriptions of foreign cheeses has always made me want to pack my traveling bag and start for Europe," said a home economics teacher. It is interesting to watch local markets for novel cheeses—a pineapple cheese which, although it originated in Connecticut, is not uncommon on the market, or the red bread-loaf type from Holland or a new brand from Italy or France. It is even more interesting to purchase small samples of different cheeses from time to time and acquire a firsthand knowledge of them. A Pennsylvania "hand cheese" (a small pot cheese finished with a thick covering), a five-pound block of pimiento from one of the state agricultural colleges, a sage cheese from the Women's Agricultural College at Studley, England, and a fine Vermont cheese found in a small cheese factory at Healdville are treasured memories of one person who appreciates cheese.

The origin of cheese is unknown, although legend traces it to Arabia where it is supposed first to have been made accidentally. It is fairly certain that wandering Arabs introduced cheese into Europe. The early records of many nations mention cheese, and it can be definitely traced to 1400 B.C. The ancient Hebrews were well acquainted with it, the early Romans frequently served bread and cheese for breakfast, and cheese-making was developed in many of the medieval monasteries.

Dietary value of cheese. The nutritive value of cheese differs within as well as between varieties. Water and fat are the most variable constituents. Soft cheeses naturally have a higher water content than do the hard cheeses. Cottage cheese has both the highest water content (from 70 to 75 per cent) and the lowest fat content (4 to 8 per cent). The protein contained in cheese is variable but not to the extent of water and fat. Cream cheese has the lowest percentage of protein (13 to 16 per cent) and Swiss cheese contains the highest percentage (25 to 30 per cent). Cheese made with whole milk is an excellent source of vitamin A and all cheeses are rich in thiamin, riboflavin, and pantothenic acid. Some calcium is lost in cheese making, depending on whether or not acid coagulation of the curd is used. The calcium becomes more soluble in the acid and more of it remains in the whey. Calcium equivalents are interesting in this connection. To obtain the same amount of calcium as is present in 8 oz. of milk, 12 oz. of cottage cheese would be needed and 1½ oz. of Cheddar cheese. In the case of cottage cheese, acid coagulation is used, while in Cheddar cheese rennin is used. Because of the concentration of food values, cheese is, with the exception of cream cheese, an excellent alternate for meat, eggs, and other protein-rich foods. It is also very economical, and because of its versatility it lends itself to combination with a variety of other foods. Not only can cheese be introduced into breakfast, luncheon, and dinner dishes but it is also one of the favorite foods for snacks for many people.

Even though cheese is an excellent alternative to meat many people are reluctant to use it freely because of their mistaken notion that it is difficult to digest. This idea is not supported by research. In general, cheese is easily digested and well utilized by the body. It does not cause constipation. Since most cheeses are concentrated food with a high fat content, difficulty may follow the unwise use of it. It is a good nutritional practice to eat cheese with bread, crackers, fruit, or vegetables. The popularity of cheese sandwiches, crackers, and cheese with fruit, counteracts difficulties which may be connected with eating concentrated cheese.

Varieties of cheese. While there are only eighteen distinct types of cheese, there are more than 400 varieties. Many of these derive their names from the locality of their origin, others from their shape. Thus, Roquefort cheese originated in Roquefort, France; pineapple cheese has the shape of the fruit. The varieties differ in hardness and in the way they are made. With many from which to choose, a real spirit of adventure is needed, together with much tasting and testing, if the homemaker is to know which varieties are best suited to various purposes and whether imported cheese or the similar domestic variety would be more satisfactory.

Within the last few years a new cheese, "Nuworld," has been developed by the Universities of Wisconsin and Minnesota.[1] It is said to be the first new cheese in 500 years. "Nuworld," which was test-marketed for about a year during 1953–54 in the Midwest, is now available in other sections of the country. It is a mold-ripened, semi-soft product with a distinctive flavor half way between mild and sharp. The new flavor is due to a micro-organism developed with the use of ultra-violet light. The cheese is creamy in consistency, yet is crumbly. The interesting texture has been likened to overbeaten whipped cream, but is somewhat firmer. It is a pale yellow, natural cheese made from whole milk.

---

[1] Wisconsin Alumni Research Foundation, Madison, Wisconsin.

Courtesy National Dairy Council, Chicago

Fig. 9. Italian cheeses: Top, left to right, *Provolone, Salame, Provolette;* Bottom, left to right, *Parmesan, Gorgonzola* (*cut*), *Romano, Asiago* (*cut*).

Versatility of cheese. The consumption of cheese in America is on the increase. While some families confine their use of it to a few favorites such as macaroni and cheese, grilled sandwiches, and as an accompaniment to apple pie, many others are discovering (what Europeans have long known) that it has multitudinous possibilities in any course and in any meal.

The increased availability of a variety of American manufactured cheeses, comparable in many instances to those of Europe, has stimulated interest in wider use of this versatile food. If association with cheese is limited to the mild flavors of processed Cheddar types, cream, etc., it will require some adventuresome experimentation to cultivate a taste for the sharp and pungent varieties. Only in this way is it possible to discover that through this single food there is a wealth of interesting experiences in dining. The recipes in Section IV are suggestive of some of the diverse ways of including it in meals. Other recipes will be found throughout Section IV as well as in other references.

Cheese-making. Cheese-making used to be entirely a home industry. In 1851, Jesse Williams began making cheese in a factory in Oneida County, New York. This was the first cheese factory in the United States. The story of cheese-making, as related by those who still recall the home industry, is interesting. The homemaker was undoubtedly grateful, however, when that part of her work was taken to a factory. A great deal of cottage cheese is still made at home, as is some cheese very similar to, if not identical with, some of the commercial cheeses.

In certain Swedish communities in this country, at the Christmas season an announcement is made from the church pulpit and printed in the local paper that on a stated day cheese will be made at the parsonage for the parson and his family. The families of the congregation bring whatever milk they can spare and meet early in the morning—the women to make cheese, the men to chop wood for the parsonage or church, or to do repair work on the buildings. Lunch is brought, each family contributing a favorite dish, and the occasion takes on a distinct social air. Sometimes as many as a dozen cheeses, very much like American Cheddar, are made, the curd being pressed by hand. If they are available, baskets that are the cheese molds in Sweden are still used. A coffee can may be used as a mold. Each cheese must remain in the mold several days, being turned daily. It is ready to eat when three or more weeks old. The cheese may be plain, but sometimes anise or cardamon seed is added. This cheese is known as bandost (farmer cheese).

Modern cheese making is a science as well as an art. Both chemistry and bacteriology figure prominently in the control of every step, from choosing the milk to curing and packaging the cheese. United States cheese manufacture consists largely of hard cheeses—Cheddar and Swiss—and while Wisconsin and New York are the leading cheese producing states, a number of other states also produce considerable amounts. Broadly speaking there are two sets of processes involved in making Cheddar cheese (the principal one manufactured in the United States)—producing the coagulum, and ripening or curing the cheese. Within this broad framework there are a number of important steps to be considered.

Good cheese requires good milk. This means milk of high quality from the standpoint of flavor and micro-organism control. Bad flavors can come from the feed of the cows, or from careless handling of the milk. Any undesirable bacteria, yeasts, or molds will introduce "unknowns" which interfere with the ripening process, thereby producing inferior cheese. Pasteurization of low-quality milk before it is made into cheese is not a substitute for high-quality raw milk. Whether or not milk for cheese is pasteurized depends on the section of the country where it is made. In Wisconsin most Cheddar cheese is made from pasteurized milk while in New York raw milk is used almost exclusively. The dangers normally associated with raw milk are eliminated, (see p. 88) because by law the cheese must be cured a minimum of 60 days. During this curing or aging period the cheese not only develops a desirable flavor and texture, but through bacterial action all harmful micro-organisms are devitalized. The longer cheese is held or aged past the minimum 60-day period, the better the flavor and texture. There is a difference of opinion among cheese connoisseurs as to which of the above methods produces the better cheese. Since a considerable amount of New York State cheese is shipped to Wisconsin, and since Wisconsin cheese is popular with many Easterners, it appears that it is all a matter of taste. In general, cheese made from raw milk has a sharper flavor than it is possible to get in cheese made with pasteurized milk. While sharpness is something highly desired by some people, it is avoided by others.

Regardless of whether raw or pasteurized milk is used for cheese making, it is placed in steam-jacketed vats where it is ripened by adding a small amount of lactic acid culture to hasten the process. When the proper degree of acidity has developed the milk is heated to between 86 and 88° F. Higher temperatures produce a tough curd and lower temperatures, one that is too soft. If coloring is to be added it is done at this point, being carefully mixed in order to prevent streaking. The milk is coagulated by adding rennet.[1] Thorough blending is assured by diluting the rennet extract in 40 to 50 parts of water. When the curd has reached the proper firmness it is cut both horizontally and vertically into small cubes in order to hasten the separation of the curd from the whey. The curd is next toughened by heating it (in the whey) to between 100 and 103° F. for about 30 minutes. It must be stirred to

[1] Rennet, which contains the gastric enzyme rennin, is a commercial product made from the lining of the stomachs of calves. This enzyme, in the presence of calcium salts, acts on the caseinogen of milk, changing it to coagulated casein. With it most of the fat and many other constituents of milk which are not dissolved in water are enmeshed, and become part of the finished cheese.

prevent settling or matting. During this process the curd particles shrink to about half their original size and take on a tough, rubbery characteristic. The whey is then drained off and the cheddaring process begins. This consists of cutting the curd into slabs and stacking them in order that the particles will mat or form a solid mass. Additional whey is also forced out during this time. These slabs are then put through a mill which cuts the curd into small pieces. Salt is added at this point and the milled curd is then packed into cheesecloth-lined hoops—heavy steel cylinders of the desired diameter. There are several sizes of hoops for packing Cheddar cheese, each having a different name. In all cases the name of the cheese is designated by the name of the hoop—"Flats" weigh 35 to 40 pounds; "Daisy" 20 to 24 pounds; "longhorn" 10 to 15 pounds, "Young America" 10 pounds, etc. All of these molds are flat and circular with the exception of "longhorn," which tapers. "Pineapple" cheese is a hard Cheddar which is shaped by swinging the pressed curd in nets to give the characteristic shape of pineapple.

After the cheese is packed into the hoops it is put into a cheese press which presses the curd particles into one homogeneous mass. The length of time in the press varies from 48 to 72 hours. An exterior drying process of from three to five days follows the pressing, after which the cheese is paraffined by dipping it into a vat of paraffin which is heated to about 220° F. The last step is curing, which requires a minimum of two months but may last for one or more years.

The United States Department of Agriculture has established standards for American Cheddar Cheese,[1] but these standards are in effect only for cheese that is purchased by the government. The standards include, among other things, inspection, moisture content, size, and packaging.

There are a variety of semihard cheeses manufactured in America, but on a much smaller scale than American Cheddar. These include Roquefort types, Gorgonzola, Port du Salut, and brick. Roquefort cheese which is imported from France is made of sheep's milk but the Roquefort type of cheese manufactured in the United States is made from cow's milk with a culture added. Recently, caves that closely resemble those at Roquefort, France, used there for ripening the cheese of that name, have been made in the cliffs along the banks of the Mississippi River at St. Paul, Minnesota, and considerable Roquefort cheese is being ripened in them.

Most of the semi-hard cheeses made in the United States are of foreign origin, being made in areas where certain national groups have settled and continue to make cheese as they did in their native country.

Soft cheeses without mold (sometimes referred to as unripened soft cheeses) are manufactured widely in this country in the form of cottage cheese, cream cheese and, to a lesser degree, Neufchâtel cheese.

[1] U. S. Dept. of Agriculture, Production and Marketing Adm. Docket, UVP—982, Washington, D. C., April 1, 1953.

The origin of cottage cheese can be claimed by many countries since this type of soft cheese has been and still is a home industry of many people. The making of cottage cheese has not been standardized in the United States because in each section of the country consumers demand a product of somewhat different character. Basically, cottage cheese is made of skim milk with a pure culture added to sour the milk and cause a curd to form. The curd is cut, heated slightly, and the whey drained off. Salt may or may not be added and the same is true of cream.

The wide variation in types of cottage cheese is due to the degree of acidity, the softness of the curd, the moisture content, amount of salt, and the percentage of butterfat. Cottage cheese may be marketed as "Pot Cheese," "Dutch Cheese," "Farmer's Cheese," or Schmierkäse, and it is often labeled as different styles of cottage cheese, such as "Creamed," "California," "Country," etc. Some manufacturers use a basic formula to produce several types of cottage cheese. The nutritive value of the different types is exactly the same, but because of mechanics of making, the cheeses appear different. Such an example from one large manufacturer is cottage cheese (creamed style) made from skim milk, with ½ of 1 per cent salt, and 4 per cent butterfat added. The same formula is used for "Pot Cheese" which has a popcorn size curd, is less moist, and appears less creamy. Another variation of this formula is "California style" cottage cheese which has a medium-sized curd and is more liquid than either of the other cheeses. The butterfat content is kept consistent with the other two cheeses by using *more* of a lighter per cent cream.

There are a number of "flavored" cottage cheeses on the market. These include chive, caraway, and pineapple. Also, where certain national groups are concentrated, "soft" cheeses representative of their culture will be found, such as ricotta cheese which is the "cottage" cheese of the Italians.

To meet the demand for low calorie foods some dealers manufacture salt-free, fat-free cottage cheese. Other dealers make it available to customers on special order. Hospitals sometimes have a standing order with their milk dealer for this item.

Because of the popularity of cottage cheese it is often used in special sales promotion programs, particularly during the Lenten season. It lends itself to packaging in attractive containers that have household use, such as glasses, bowls, and refrigerator dishes.

In areas where pasteurization is not compulsory cottage cheese may be made of naturally soured raw milk. In such cases the dangers of raw milk are still present.

Cream cheese, which is American in origin, is manufactured similarly to cottage cheese, except that it is made from cream of varying fat content. As previously stated, it has a high percentage of butterfat, and has less protein than any other cheese. Some people consider cottage cheese and cream cheese as similar foods. In fact, cottage cheese is sometimes looked upon as the "poor man's cream cheese." In reality, cottage cheese is a high quality protein food having much of the same vitamin and mineral value as milk, while cream cheese, in addition to its high fat content, is valuable mostly for vitamin A. Cream cheese is available in a number of flavored "spreads." In addition to the popular chives, it may be purchased in pimiento, "tutti frutti," and several other flavors.

The packaging of cream cheese has changed considerably from the original three ounce foil-wrapped package. It is now available not only in larger foil packages but in plastic refrigerator dishes of varying size. It is packed for wholesale trade in three-pound, foil-wrapped loaves which are put in a light wooden box. The loaves are cut in slices of different weights by the retail stores and rewrapped for selling.

A number of ripened soft cheeses are manufactured in various parts of the United States. These include Camembert, Limburger, and Primost. The latter is a whey cheese and is made by evaporating the water from the whey. The remaining substance consists mainly of milk sugar. It is of a doughy consistency and is packed in brick-shaped packages.

Process cheese is the only cheese with which a large number of American consumers are familiar. Its popularity is probably due to the mildness of flavor, ease of slicing, and readiness of melting. The people who judge quality of cheese by whether it breaks in slicing, naturally frown on aged cheese, most of which, because of its dry, crumbly texture, usually breaks when sliced. Process cheese is made by shredding one or more types of natural cheese and blending and pasteurizing them to make a smooth, uniform texture. Flavors of this cheese are greatly varied by adding spices, relishes, and other seasonings. Some of the most popular varieties are smoked pimiento, Swiss Gruyère, and brick. Process cheese keeps well, and because there is no rind it has little waste. Cheese spreads are also made from process cheese. They are soft and creamy and come in a wide variety of flavors. In addition to the above-mentioned flavors, which are also used in spreads, some other varieties are pineapple, olive, bacon, and Roquefort.

Buying and storing cheese. Regardless of the kind of cheese a person prefers there is usually a wide choice of all types. Packaging and wrapping have done much to encourage cheese buying. Both natural and process cheeses are presented in today's market in packaged amounts to suit families of any size. For those who like a variety of cheese on hand, it is possible to purchase five or six varieties and still have less than a pound. If larger quantities are desired they are also available. The diversified package size is due largely to the fact that many different types of cheese are cut from wholesale-sized pieces and re-packaged in retail stores. This is a common practice of chain markets. In such cases many cheeses lose the identity of the manufacturer, and are simply labeled, "Domestic Swiss," "Sharp Cheddar," "Imported

Roquefort," etc. In repackaging, Wisconsin cheese is labeled as "made with pasteurized milk" while New York State cheese is not so labeled. The length of time aged usually appears on both Wisconsin and New York cheeses.

Labeling of all process cheese and cheese spreads is specific as to ingredients. In fact the homemaker will find that in most instances the information on cheese labels is adequate to help her make a choice from the wide selection. Imported cheeses are available in many stores along with their domestic counterparts and they are clearly labeled. Cheddar cheese is labeled "mellow," "mild," "nippy," "aged," "sharp" or "very sharp." Degree of hardness is frequently stated, such as "for grating." Also, added flavors or spices are clearly indicated on labels. With all of this information, the homemaker can buy different cheeses for different uses. However, variety in cheese is not desired by many consumers. In some households mild process cheese is an all-purpose cheese and is bought in quantities of from two- to five-pound loaves. Since this cheese keeps well, there is little danger of spoilage in buying the large amounts, which may be stored in the refrigerator in the original package. The family that likes sharp natural Cheddar cheese may choose to use such cheese for many different purposes, and to purchase as much as a five-pound wheel. Since natural cheese must have special care in storing in order not to mold, the larger cheeses are not an economical buy in households where cheese is not popular for a variety of purposes. If a "wheel" of Cheddar cheese is purchased it will be coated with paraffin which helps to preserve it. In such cases a wedge of the cheese can be cut out and wrapped in foil for immediate use while the larger piece will keep better if the cut surfaces are spread with softened butter or margarine before wrapping in aluminum foil. As in the case of all varieties, Cheddar cheese should be stored in a cool place, preferably the refrigerator. In addition to wrapping smaller pieces of Cheddar cheese in foil, they may also be wrapped in a cloth dampened with acidulated water and then wrapped in wax paper. Some people prefer to place wrapped cheese either in a hydrator or a special glass container in order to further insure that it does not absorb refrigerator odors. These containers permit placing the cheese on a rack and using salt and vinegar in the bottom of the container to prevent molding. Most of the semihard cheeses have a pronounced odor and should be well wrapped before storing in order that other foods in the refrigerator will not pick up the cheese flavor.

Cottage cheese and cream cheese are extremely perishable and if stored in the home refrigerator for longer than a week they develop an "off" flavor which characterizes them as "old." Cream cheese packaged in plastic containers will keep slightly longer than that wrapped in foil or other paper. Likewise cottage cheese in glass or plastic containers may not break in flavor as quickly as that in paper cartons. If soft cheeses are carelessly handled by leaving them out of the refrigerator for any length of time the keeping time is shortened even further.

The price of cheese varies considerably from time to time. Also, price varies with the kind of cheese and with its form. A number of interesting comparisons may be made by pricing cheese at a store that carries several varieties, or at several stores in a vicinity. For example, it is interesting to compare the price of aged and unaged American cheese made in the same locality, and to compare cheese made near by with similar cheese made in another state. The price of a pound of cheese, cut from a five-pound loaf, may be quite different from that for the same sort of cheese in a half-pound package. Where imported cheeses are available, the price of these may be compared with that of our most common American Cheddar cheese, and with a cheese like the imported one, made in the United States. Such a study heightens an awareness of the various factors that influence the price of this commodity, and should result in more thoughtful buying.

Uses. Cheese may be a part of any luncheon or dinner course. As its composition would indicate, cheese is often used in place of meat. There are many delicious cheese dishes, including soufflés, fondues, timbales, omelets, and sandwiches, which are suitable for the principal dish of the main course for luncheon. The flavor of cheese is frequently desired in other products, and cheese crackers, cheese straws, cheese sauces, and cheese used as a garnish for soups, salads, and sauces, is pleasing. Frequently rather highly flavored cheese is used for these purposes, or cheese with a rather distinct flavor. Well-ripened American Cheddar cheese is far better in a sauce than very mild cheese, and the popularity of Parmesan cheese with soups and spaghetti is well known.

In hors d'oeuvres or as an accompaniment for a salad used as a first course, cheese is popular. Cheese sauce enlivens bland vegetables; cheese dressing lends interest to many salads. A luncheon salad may well contain cheese as one of the ingredients. As an accompaniment for pie, particularly apple pie, cheese has long been favored. Roquefort or Camembert, Gruyère, Romano, or English Cheddar cheese, or a variety of cheeses, served with crackers and black coffee and perhaps fruit, bring a meal otherwise not high in protein to a very satisfying close. The flavor of these cheeses is distinctive and some prefer one, some another. Of Camembert cheese, Burdett says,[1] "None can complain of any want of flavour in a genuine, ripe Camembert cheese. It shows the heights of delicacy to which soft cheeses can aspire. Even the most mild palate cannot be offended by it."

Cooking. When cheese is heated, the temperature should be low to moderate. A high temperature produces a tough, rubbery mass, especially if the cheese is not well ripened. If cheese is added to a sauce, it will blend more quickly and easily with the other ingredients if it is grated or pressed through a coarse sieve.

---

[1] Osbert Burdett, *The Little Book of Cheese* (London: Gerald Howe, Ltd.; 1935), p. 55.

SUGGESTIONS FOR LABORATORY

Depending upon the geographic locality and the composition of the class group, the instructor and students will discover that the possibilities for laboratory projects in connection with the study of cheese are numerous and varied. The selected projects should reflect the international popularity of cheese; its nutritional and economic importance; the wide choice as to flavor and texture; the fundamental principles involved in cooking, and its versatility in meals. Additional projects might include aspects of production and marketing.

The choice of recipes to illustrate any of the above or other points will be more stimulating if they represent experiences which are entirely new for the students. There is little or no challenge in removing a slice of processed cheese from a package, placing it on a slice of bread, and grilling it for an open face sandwich. However, exploring other ways in which cheese and bread are used, either hot or cold, as sandwiches, appetizers, main dishes, or desserts, will open up new avenues of interest. The same type of exploration in connection with other *basic* ways of using cheese will be revealing. The recipes on pp. 534–542 and others throughout Section IV should be supplemented by those of the instructors' and students' choosing.

REFERENCES

BOOKS

Brown, Robert Carlton, "The Complete Book of Cheese," Random House, N. Y., 1955.

Burdett, Osbert, *The Little Book of Cheese.* Gerald Howe, Ltd., London, 1935.

Hovey, Helen S. and Kay Reynolds, *The Practical Book of Food Shopping.* J. B. Lippincott Company, Philadelphia, 1950.

Monroe, Day, Hazel Kyrk, and Ursula Batchelder Stone, *Food Buying and Our Markets.* M. Barrows and Co., New York, 1939.

Ripperger, Helmut, *Cheese Cookery.* George W. Stewart, New York, 1941.

Sherman, Henry C., *Food Products,* 4th Edition. The Macmillan Co., New York, 1937.

Thom, Charles, *The Book of Cheese.* The Macmillan Co., New York, 1921.

Todoroff, Alexander, *Food Buying Today.* The Grocery Trade Publishing House, Chicago, 1946.

von Loesecke, Harry W., *Outlines of Food Technology.* Reinhold Publishing Corp., New York, 1949.

Ward, Artemus, *Encyclopedia of Food.* Baker and Taylor Co., New York, 1929.

Wilster, G. H., *Practical Cheddar Cheese Manufacture and Cheese Technology,* 5th Edition. Oregon State College Co-operative Assn., Corvallis, 1947.

BULLETINS

Ayres, W. E., *Homemade Cheese: Unripened Varieties—Cottage, Cream, Neufchatel.* Extension Bul. 322, Cornell University, 1935.

Ayres, W. E., *Homemade Cheeses: Ripened Varieties, American-Type Cheese.* Extension Bul. 346, Cornell University, 1936.

Brewer, Lucile, "Use More Cheese," Reading Course for the Home, Lesson 133, Cornell University, 1920.

Doane, C. F., and H. W. Lawson, *Varieties of Cheese.* U.S.D.A. Bul. 608, 1932

National Dairy Council, *Newer Knowledge of Cheese.* Chicago, 1947.

Tenny, Lloyd S., *National Standards for Farm Products.* U.S.D.A. Cir. 8, 1930.

Van Slyke, L. L., and W. V. Price, *Cheese: A Treatise on the Manufacture of American Cheddar Cheese and Some Other Varieties,* Revised and enlarged. Orange Judd Co., New York, 1938.

Wilson, H. L., S. A. Hall, and L. A. Rogers, "The Manufacture of Cheddar Cheese from Pasteurized Milk," *Jour. of Dairy Science,* 28:201, March, 1945.

UNIT

8

Nuts

We usually think of nuts as accessory foods, but they have been used as staple foods by people in several parts of the world, and to some extent are still so used. Some of the American Indian tribes ground acorns for bread making and some of the chestnuts raised in Corsica, Italy, and other Mediterranean countries are ground for flour at present. Pine nuts were a part of the regular diet of the Indians of the southwest. Pioneer Americans found diversion in gathering nuts, and pleasure for long winter evenings in cracking and eating hickory nuts, chestnuts, butternuts, or black walnuts as the family, and perhaps neighbors, gathered around the open fire. Removing the shells from tiny beechnuts might have been considered a real task, but the cake in which they were used was sufficiently delicious to compensate for the work involved.

Nutritive value. From the nutritive point of view, nuts have considerable value. Their protein is similar in quality to that of meat, and their high fat content makes them valuable as energy foods. A few nuts, particularly chestnuts and lichi nuts, contain a high percentage of carbohydrate. In general, nuts furnish appreciable amounts of calcium, phosphorus, iron, copper, magnesium, and some of the B vitamins, especially thiamin. Table 11 lists some of the commonly used nuts, with their average composition.

Production. Many nuts are being produced as food crops. The varieties raised extensively in the United States include pecans, almonds, English walnuts, and peanuts. The latter are not true nuts, but legumes used as nuts. Chestnuts, beechnuts, hickory nuts, pine nuts, and both black and white walnuts [1] are used to a considerable extent where they are native and some are produced for sale. Imported nuts include Brazil nuts, Italian chestnuts, filberts, cashew nuts, pistachio nuts, coconuts, and lichi nuts. Marrons are chest-

[1] White walnuts are more commonly called butternuts.

TABLE 11. COMPOSITION OF SOME COMMONLY USED SHELLED NUTS

Variety	*Measure (Approx.)*	*Calories*	*Protein (Gm.)*	*Fat (Gm.)*	*Calcium (Mg.)*	*Iron (Mg.)*	*Vit. A (I.U.)*	*Thiamin (Mg.)*	*Riboflavin (Mg.)*	*Niacin (Mg.)*	*Ascorbic acid (Mg.)*
Almonds	1 tb.	53	1.6	4.8	23	6.2	0	.02	.06	.4	tr.
Brazil nuts	1 tb.	57	1.3	5.2	16	0.3	tr.	.07	0	0	0
Cashew (chopped)	1 tb.	65	2.1	5.5	5.2	5.6	...	.07	.02	.24	0
Coconut (dried)	1 tb.	22	0.2	1.5	1.7	0.2	0	tr.	tr.	tr.	0
Peanuts (Va.) (chop'd)	1 tb.	50	2.4	0.3	7	0.2	0	.03	.01	1.5	0
Pecans (chop'd)	1 tb.	52	0.7	0.3	6	0.2	tr.	.05	.01	0.1	tr.
Walnuts (Eng.) (chop'd)	1 tb.	49	1.1	0.3	6	0.2	tr.	.04	.01	0.1	tr.

nuts preserved by drying or by cooking in sirup. They are used in desserts, sauces, and salads.

During the War Between the States, peanuts were used extensively in many parts of the South and their use continued after the war. There are several kinds—Spanish and Valencia, which are small, and whose fat content is high; African, which are medium in size and high in fat; Virginia, which are large, and whose fat content is relatively low; and Runner, a cross between the Spanish and Virginia varieties. People not familiar with the growth of peanuts are always interested in seeing the plants. Their flower stalks curve downward and force themselves into the soil, where the legumes develop. Peanuts are used extensivly in candy and as salted nuts. Oil from peanuts is a common salad oil and is used in making margarine. In peanut butter, Spanish and Virginia peanuts are blended. It may be made at home by grinding the peanuts in a home-size mill. It is possible to vary the consistency by grinding from one to four times.

Flour has been made from peanuts and used as an ingredient in bread in the same way as soybean flour to give a loaf relatively high in protein.

Buying. Nuts of several kinds are available at most grocery stores throughout the year. The variety is usually increased for the Thanksgiving and Christmas trade because of the customary increased use of nuts at these seasons. Counters at which only nuts are sold are common in many large grocery stores and in some department stores, and nut shops which deal in this one commodity are common.

From a sanitary point of view it is often wise to buy unshelled nuts. The conditions under which many are shelled and packaged sometimes leave much to be desired in the way of cleanliness. When it is certain that sanitary methods have been used, time is saved and waste avoided by purchasing the shelled nuts.

The present trend is toward packaged, shelled nuts, either vacuum sealed in tin cans or packed in plastic or cellophane. Unshelled nuts are likely to be available in greater abundance at the Christmas season than at other times.

In order to decide whether shelled or unshelled nuts are a better buy from the economic point of view, it is necessary to know the approximate weight of nuts in the shell that will be required to yield a pound of nut meats. The resulting price comparison and the relative importance of time and money will determine which to buy. For example, suppose that walnuts in the shell cost $.49 per pound and shelled ones in 4-oz. cans cost $.35, or $1.40 per pound. The cost of 2½ pounds of walnuts needed for a pound of shelled nuts would be $1.23 and if time for shelling is available, the saving would be $.17. The approximate weight of some nuts in the shell needed to give one pound of nut meats is listed below:

Variety	*Pounds needed*
Almonds	3½
Brazil nuts	2
Filbert	2¼
Peanuts (Va.)	1½
Pecans	2½
Pistachio	2
Walnuts (Eng.)	2½

Storage. The principal reason for spoilage of nuts is their high fat content. They become rancid rather easily, particularly if they are shelled. They should be stored in a cool, dark place, and, if carried over for any appreciable time during warm weather, they require cold storage. Commercially, nuts may be stored satisfactorily for a period of a year, if the storage temperature is 31° to 32° F. (about −1° C.). In cool climates, the cellar is a satisfactory home storage place. Shelled nuts may be packed in sterilized jars, the air exhausted,[1] the jars semisealed and placed in boiling water that reaches to within two inches of the top. After they have been in the water for thirty minutes, the jars are removed and the seal is completed. When cool, they are stored in a cool, dark place.

Uses. Nuts may be used as part of a first course, as a substitute for meat, in sauces, salads, breads, and desserts—including cakes, cookies, and pies. Many candies contain nuts as an essential ingredient and others are made more decorative by their use. Increasing in popularity as accessory foods are two seeds imported from Mexico—pumpkin seeds and chick peas (garbazos). These are roasted in vegetable oil and salted. They are used in the same ways as salted nuts.

[1] Food is placed in cans or jars, in this case, without added liquid. They are placed in a hot water bath, the water reaching to within about two inches of the tops of the containers. The containers are then covered, and the water brought to a boil. Steaming time depends upon the product. Thus air is "exhausted" from the cans or jars.

SUGGESTIONS FOR LABORATORY

Laboratory projects dealing with nuts can best be introduced when studying other foods (see recipes pp. 542–547). However, some special techniques in shelling, grating, and grinding might well be demonstrated. Shelling and grating coconuts, salting nuts by oven-roasting, and making nut butters or spreads in an electric blender, are a few suggestions.

UNIT

9

Eggs

Many primitive people used the eggs from wild birds as food. Others, including some African tribes, used them in medicine but not as a food. The eggs of domesticated birds, including turkeys, ducks, and geese, are used to some extent, but practically all of the egg supply is from poultry farms where hens are raised for egg production. Because of the many ways of preparing them as an item in a meal and their important uses in cookery processes, eggs are among the foods that are considered essential.

Eggs in the diet. The several proteins in both white and yolk of eggs make them an important source of this nutrient. Most of the calcium is in the shell, but the yolk contains some. The yolk is a good source of iron and phosphorus. Most eggs are from hens so fed and exposed to the sun or irradiation that significant amounts of Vitamins A and D are present. They supply considerable thiamin and riboflavin, a trace of niacin, but no ascorbic acid. Eggs lend themselves to varied, attractive service in any meal. Their use in many foods extends their value from the point of view of good nutrition.

Production. As reported in *Agricultural Statistics* for 1957, the per capita consumption of eggs in the United States during 1956 was 369, or about the number recommended by those who use "an egg a day" as a standard. Not all were used for human food, however, nor were they evenly distributed among the population. Many flocks are kept on farms for the family's egg supply with some for sale, but most of the total comes from henneries where egg production is a specialty, and where there may be several thousand hens. They are kept under good sanitary conditions and fed to produce not only a large quantity of eggs, but also high quality eggs from a nutritive point of view. Another effect of modern methods of poultry raising is the extension of the season of relatively heavy production so that not so many eggs need to be held in storage to keep a stable supply on the market. Light-weight breeds, e.g., Leghorns, are usually raised for egg production.

TABLE 12. CONTRIBUTION OF ONE EGG TO DAILY FOOD REQUIREMENT OF "AVERAGE" COLLEGE GIRL

Nutrient	*Amount*	*Per cent of Requirement*	*Nutrient*	*Amount*	*Per cent of Requirement*
Calories	77	3.2	Vitamin D (I.U.)	400	12.5
Protein	6.1 (gm.)	8.1	Thiamin (mg.)	.05	4.2
Calcium	26 (mg.)	2.0	Riboflavin (mg.)	.14	7.4
Iron	1.3 (mg.)	8.7	Niacin	tr.	tr.
Vitamin A (I.U.)	550	11.0	Ascorbic acid	......	....

Ideally, eggs should not need to be cleaned. Clean surroundings and frequent gathering are important, but in spite of care, some cleaning is necessary. Hand washing is done by many small and some large producers and machine washing has been improved in recent years. However, in a careful study, washed eggs, even "under the best controlled conditions showed a much higher loss and quality decline in storage than clean eggs." [1] There are mechanical cleaners, both large and small, which are electrically operated and which clean eggs by abrasion.

Sometimes the fancy of consumers takes precedence over other factors in determining the sort of eggs produced. Many people think that an egg with a pale yolk is a fresh egg. There is some basis for this idea because the yolks darken somewhat as eggs age. The principal reason for variation in color, however, is difference in feed. Green feed produces highly colored yolks. In producing pale yolks of high vitamin A content, poultrymen add fish oil to the feed and omit green feed entirely. On some markets a premium is paid for eggs with a brown shell; on others, eggs with a white shell are preferred. However, there is no difference in food value or in cooking quality.

Storage and preservation. In the home, eggs are usually stored for a few days only. They should be refrigerated or, lacking that, kept in as cool a place as possible. In plastic egg containers, they are placed small end down in the separate compartments and covered. Where eggs are produced in considerable numbers, walk-in coolers are used for storage until the eggs are sold.

For home use, eggs may be preserved in a number of ways. Water glass is still used to some extent although it is not a very good method. Another method, used seldom, but of proven worth, is called the "flash heat" treatment.[2] Home application of the "flash heat treatment" has been shown to have

---

[1] Orme Kahlenberg, *et al., A Study of the Washing and Storage of Dirty-Shell Eggs,* Cir. No. 911, U.S.D.A. (1952), p. 2.

[2] A. L. Romanoff, and A. J. Romanoff, "Preservation of Eggs by Flash Heat Treatment," *Food Research,* 9:358–386, 1944.

Fig. 10. Label showing U.S.D.A. grade of eggs.

merit. Placed in a wire basket, the eggs are immersed in boiling water for five seconds and cooled in the air. Stored in a cool place—preferably refrigerated—they keep well for three or four months.[1]

More recently, eggs have been frozen for home storage (see pages 291–2). The whole eggs may be scrambled or used in French omelets, yolks may be used in custards or mayonnaise, and whites make excellent angel cakes. For general use in flour mixtures or to mix with other ingredients, frozen eggs are equal to fresh eggs.

Commercially, large numbers of eggs are held in cold storage. For storing, eggs should be produced under carefully controlled conditions, some of which follow:

1) Eggs to be kept in cold storage must be of high quality and preferably infertile.

2) They are gathered at least twice daily; oftener in warm weather.

3) They are cooled quickly and delivered to a central packing place soon after cooling.

4) They are graded, sometimes dipped into tasteless mineral oil to close the pores, packed, and placed in cold storage.

5) Cold-storage rooms are kept at about 29° F. (—2° C.) with the humidity from 82 to 85 per cent.

A recently developed treatment for large numbers of eggs is called "thermostabilization." Spraying the shells with oil at 134° F. (56.7° C.), for 16 minutes results in eggs which keep exceptionally well. "After 7½ months of storage the number of Grade A eggs remaining in the lots which had been thermostabilized averaged 84 per cent, while the number in the lots that were oiled but not heated averaged 37.8 per cent."[2]

The effects of storage, either at home or in warehouses, may be understood by considering the structure of a fresh egg (see Fig. 11). The shell is rather porous so that as the egg ages, water evaporates through it. As moisture decreases, the air cell (the space between the shell and egg membranes) enlarges. Viewed through a candle, the yolk is distinctly visible, mobile, and larger in size than that of a fresh egg. Such eggs are of course not of high quality.

The quality of eggs is easily distinguished when they are broken and placed on a flat surface. In fresh—Grade AA or A—eggs, the yolks stand high and the thick white is firm. They cover a small area. Not all hens produce equally thick white and this should be considered when judging freshness. As the

---

[1] Lillian B. Adamcik, "A Study of Eight Methods of Egg Storage and the Use of Eggs by Selected Farm Families" (Unpublished Thesis, University of Texas, 1948).

[2] Harry E. Gorseline, K. M. Hayes, and A. W. Otte, *Thermostabilization of Shell Eggs: Quality Retention in Storage,* Cir. No. 898, U.S.D.A. 1952, p. 1.

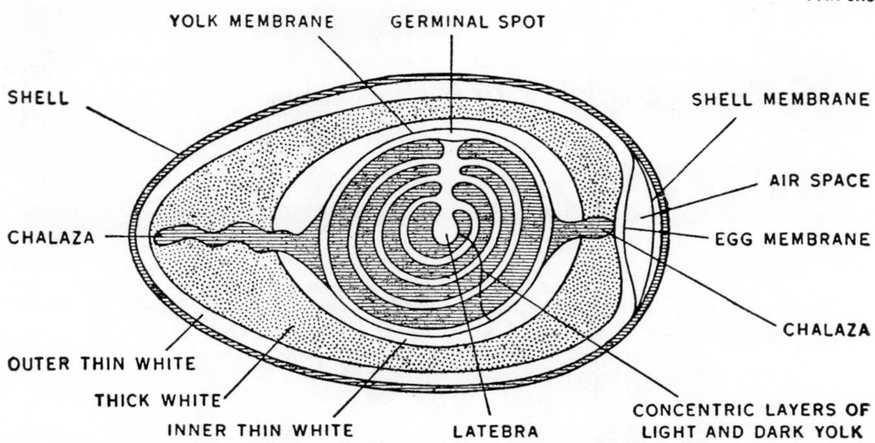

Courtesy U. S. Department of Agriculture, Poultry Branch, Production and Marketing Administration

Fig. 11. Parts of an egg.

quality decreases, the yolk becomes increasingly flattened, the white is thinner, and the egg covers a much larger area. Fig. 12 shows these characteristics and also the effect on the appearance of fried and poached eggs.

Eggs are frozen and dried (egg solids) commercially. The former are available to commercial concerns and institutions in 30-pound cans and may be whole eggs, egg whites, or egg yolks. The latter are advantageous for shipping for long distances and are used in cookery processes, such as flour mixtures and casserole dishes. (See new standards, p. 548; glossary, p. 692.)

Buying eggs. Whenever possible, it is important to buy eggs by grade. Standards of quality and for grades have been formulated by the United States Department of Agriculture. These are used on a voluntary basis and it is encouraging to note that grading is being done increasingly; the Poultry Division, Agricultural Marketing Service of the U. S. Department of Agriculture, is responsible for the grading program. Grades are U. S. Grade AA, U. S. Grade A, U. S. Grade B, and U. S. Grade C. If Grades AA or A are bought for eating and Grade B or C for cooking, money is saved and the grade is suited to the use.

The official weight classes, in terms of minimum weight per dozen, are: Jumbo, 30 oz., Extra Large, 27 oz., Large, 24 oz., Medium, 21 oz., Small, 18 oz., and Peewee, 15 oz. Jumbo eggs do not appear on the market often, and peewee eggs are found in the late summer and early fall when the pullets are beginning to lay. Both grade designation and size should be known to the buyer (see Fig. 12).

Since the size of eggs varies considerably, the result of using different sizes is sometimes evident in flour mixtures. Figure 13 illustrates the differences in

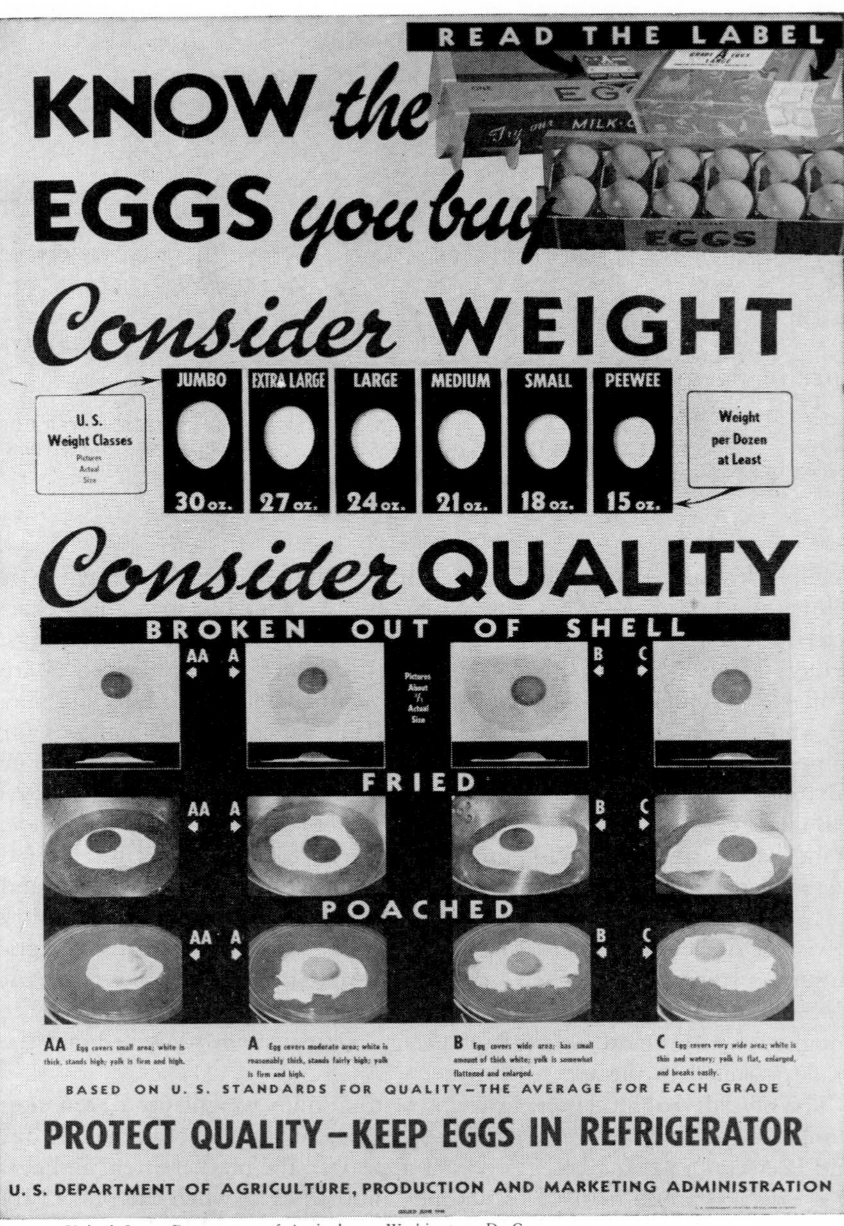

Courtesy United States Department of Agriculture, Washington, D. C.

Fig. 12. Considerations when buying eggs.

size and in volume of eggs, and in their effect upon cakes. The cakes in Figure 13, bottom, were made by the same recipe. All ingredients except the eggs were measured or weighed carefully, but the eggs were used by number. The first cake appeared to contain too much fat. The second was an excellent cake in every respect. The third was too moist, its volume was unusually large for a cake of its type, and it was spongy. If eggs purchased are not of approximately the same size, the medium to large-sized eggs should be used for most cookery processes.

Methods of serving eggs. Eggs may be used in many ways and at any meal. They are cooked in water by poaching or cooking in the shell, steamed, broiled, fried, or baked by themselves or with the addition of other ingredients. Properly prepared, scrambled eggs are delicious for either breakfast or lunch, as are the many interesting varieties of omelets. Once the art of making omelets is mastered, they are easy to prepare; yet a perfect omelet never fails to be considered an achievement.

Uses of eggs in cookery processes. For success in a number of widely diversified products, eggs are essential or desirable.

1) *Eggs as a leavening material.* As the white is beaten, it stretches and surrounds bubbles of air, i.e. foam is formed. The air is the chief or only leavening agent in such mixtures as omelets, soufflés, meringues, and sponge-type cakes. The white is responsible for tenacity of thin batter used for popovers and cream puffs, resulting in baked batter that surrounds one or more large air pockets.

Egg white may be beaten with either a flat whip or a rotary beater. The former results in greater volume, but the foam is coarse. The rotary beater produces a fine foam that is more stable. Stability is increased by the addition of salt, cream of tartar, or both during the beating. Desirable stiffness of foam before other ingredients are added varies with the product being made. This stiffness is indicated in recipes for meringue, sponge cakes, and other products.

2) *Eggs used for thickening.* Because heat coagulates the proteins of eggs and the proteins hold water, eggs are used for thickening custards, sauces, and some puddings. The temperature should be just above that at which the protein coagulates. High temperature results in separation of liquid.

3) *Eggs used in emulsions.* The use of eggs in stabilizing emulsions is discussed in the unit on fats and oils (see p. 170).

4) *Eggs for color and flavor.* The color resulting from the use of egg yolks has become a part of our standard for such products as mayonnaise, plain cakes, and some sauces. The variation which this factor alone gives is sometimes illustrated as a class makes cakes, the color of the finished products varying from rather light yellow to orange with the variation of the color of the egg yolk. The flavor of eggs adds materially to that of many foods.

5) *Eggs used as mixers.* Due to their viscosity, eggs are used to bind other

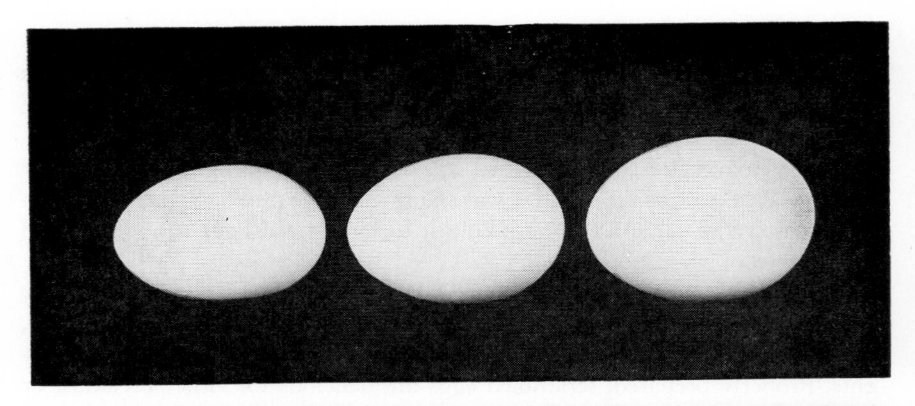

Photographs by Visual Instruction Bureau, University of Texas

Fig. 13. Top, *eggs graded as small, medium, and jumbo.* Center, *volume of eggs in above photo.* Bottom, *cakes made with small, medium, and jumbo eggs:* left, *small;* center, *large;* right, *jumbo.*

ingredients, as in croquettes, stuffings, or meat loaves. This quality of egg white also makes it useful for clearing consommé or boiled coffee.

Effects of cooking. A high temperature should always be avoided when eggs are being cooked. Egg white coagulates at 143° to 149° F. (62° to 65° C.) and egg yolk at 158° F. (70° C.). Thus, if a temperature as high as that of boiling water is used, the protein of the white becomes hard and tough and the yolk is dull in color and sometimes rubbery in texture. The coagulation is accelerated by acid; hence, when an egg which has a watery white is poached, vinegar or lemon juice—about one teaspoon per pint of water—aids in coagulating the white quickly so that it separates less. Salt also hastens coagulation but sometimes detracts from the appearance of the egg.

When beaten egg is used in a hot liquid or mixture, as in making ice cream or some puddings, a little of the mixture is usually added to the egg to increase the temperature gradually. The egg is then added to the rest of the hot mixture and the cooking time after this addition is short. If the egg is added directly to a hot mixture, it cooks at once and the mixture looks curdled. (See American ice cream, p. 528.)

In some cooked salad dressings, beaten egg, seasonings, and cold liquid are cooked together over low heat. This method is satisfactory for cornstarch puddings. Also, other cooked ingredients may be added to beaten egg, and the mixture beaten. The heat of the cooked mixture is sufficient to cook the egg and the mixture is very smooth. (See butterscotch pudding, p. 529.)

Egg white contains more sulphur than does the yolk; the yolk contains more iron. If eggs are cooked in boiling water or if they remain in hot water after they are cooked, hydrogen sulphide combines with iron to form iron sulphide. This is responsible for the green coating around the yolk. It tends to increase as eggs get older. Either soft- or hard-cooked eggs should therefore be cooked in water below boiling and cooled immediately in cold water. Preferably, fresh eggs should be used.

SUGGESTIONS FOR LABORATORY

In the laboratory the principles that apply to egg cookery and the ways in which eggs are used in cookery may be illustrated by definite application of these principles and uses. This may be done within the framework of interesting variety in products whose basis is eggs or in which eggs are a very important ingredient.

A display arranged ahead of time might include eggs of different sizes with prices, evidence showing how color of shell influences price on the local market (if it does), wall charts depicting egg sizes and qualities as determined by U.S.D.A., Production and Marketing Administration, Poultry Branch and by the Poultry and Egg National Board, and quality as shown by eggs broken out onto a flat surface.

REFERENCES

Brant, A. W., and H. L. Shrader, *How to Measure Egg I.Q. (Interior Quality)*. U.S.D.A. Animal Husbandry Division, Bureau of Animal Industry, PA202, 1952.

Carlin, A. F., and J. Foth. "Interior Quality and Functional Properties of Oiled and Thermostabilized Shell Eggs Before and After Commercial Storage." *Food Technol.* 6:443 (1952).

Hughes, Osee, *Introductory Foods*. 3rd Ed. The Macmillan Co., New York, 1955.

Miller, E. L., and G. E. Vail, "Angel Food Cakes Made from Fresh and Frozen Egg Whites." *Cereal Chem.* 20:528 (1943).

Poultry and Egg National Board, Chicago, Consumer Information Service:
Eggs—Selection, Grades, Care, Cookery, Nutrition.
The Magic of Egg Solids.

Troelstrup, Arch W., *Consumer Problems and Personal Finance*. 2nd Ed. McGraw-Hill Book Co., Inc., New York, 1957.

U.S.D.A., Production and Marketing Adm., Poultry Branch:
Know the Eggs You Buy.
U. S. Standards for Quality of Individual Shell Eggs, 1954.

UNIT

10

Meat

It is probable that food from animal sources was first obtained by robbing birds' nests, stealthily capturing birds at night, and catching fish by quietly waiting at the water's edge and quickly reaching for the unsuspecting prey. For many prehistoric centuries wild animals were used for food; in many cases, the only food. Crude weapons were devised, increasing man's ability to procure food, and the use of fire made meat more appealing to many. According to Hodge,[1] American Indians used their hands, various weapons, snares, traps, and pits for hunting game. They lured their prey by fires and torches and drugged it with potions made from the bark of walnut root, soap root, or buckeye.

As time went on, such animals as were easily domesticated became a dependable part of the food supply. Herds or flocks were the property of the tribe or clan and in some cases seasonal pilgrimages were made to find pasture and water.

The American colonists brought some animals from Europe, but at first they obtained much meat by hunting and by purchasing deer, turkeys, and other game from the Indians. As the frontier extended westward, the abundant wild game was always a source of food, both during the journey to a new settlement and after the new community was established.

The game which supplied food for the Indians was not conserved by the European settlers. In fact, the buffalo of the plains were practically exterminated by hunters bent on ridding the territory of the animals. Cattle, sheep, and hogs, brought by both Spanish and English settlers, became the animals of the plains, the cattle becoming as numerous and nearly as wild as the buffalo had been. In discussing the growth of "The Cattle Kingdom" Webb[2]

[1] F. W. Hodge, *Handbook of the Indians* (Washington, D. C.: Bureau of American Ethnology, 1906).

[2] W. P. Webb, *The Great Plains* (New York: Ginn & Co., 1931), Ch. 6.

says, ". . . it has conformed in its territorial delimitations very closely to the semi-arid portion of the Great Plains country." Exciting stories of cowboys and cattle thieves; of "wars" between cattlemen and sheepmen; of cattle drives along well-defined trails in search of a market where cattle brought good prices; of tremendous ranches—all are part of the story of the meat industry of the United States. Cattle raised for food, such as the rangy Longhorns, bore little resemblance to Aberdeen Angus, Hereford, and Shorthorn, some of the principal beef animals of today. Improved qualities have been developed by introducing Brahman characteristics, and cross-breeds known as "Braford" and "Brangus" are well known. At the King Ranch in South Texas "an acutely executed breeding program" resulted in the new breed, Santa Gertrudis, which has the beef qualities of the Shorthorn and the hardihood of the Brahman[1] (see Fig. 15). Another example of breeding domestic animals to exist under specific weather and forage conditions is the large, long-wooled sheep that abound on Exmoor, England.

Nutritive value of meat. As applied to nutrition, the term "meat" includes also poultry and fish. There is considerable difference of opinion on the part of individuals as to the place of meat in the diet. Some give it an important place by using large amounts; others omit it entirely. The "middle ground" would seem to be one serving daily, with other good sources of protein as a part of the other meals.

While body-building protein is the main nutrient, meat supplies energy both from whatever amount of fat is eaten and from the protein. Iron, phosphorus, and copper are found in meat, with glandular meats ranking highest. Liver and kidney are especially important; the association of liver with the diet of anemic persons is well known. These also rank high in Vitamin A, riboflavin, and niacin. Meat is a good source of thiamin, lean pork being most important.

Income may be the determining factor in amount of meat used by a family. Marked increase in price of meat led one person to ask, "Which would you prefer seeing me wear—feathers or fins?" Considering money to be spent for meat, waste, particularly the amount of bone, may be more important than price per pound, so that figuring should be in terms of price per pound of edible portion.

The meat supply in the United States. As new practices are introduced, old ones are not entirely discarded. Hunting is no longer the means by which most families acquire meat, but it is still a popular sport; and it is necessary to conserve the game supply by laws specifying the hunting season and by permitting only the male of many species to be killed.

On ranches or farms on which cattle, sheep, or hogs are raised, these animals usually furnish most of the meat used by the family. Local dealers, who purchase animals from the surrounding farms, furnish much meat to small

[1] Lea, Tom, *The King Ranch,* Vol. 2. Little, Brown and Co., Boston, 1957.

communities and to some markets in larger towns. In some localities there are still meat or "butcher" clubs whose members contribute proportionately to the meat needed by the families, process it, and divide it in such a way that all have a fair share of the various cuts. This custom is usually for a portion of the year only. Municipal abattoirs furnish processing facilities to individual families and to organized market units. However, the large packers supply the greater part of the supply of meat for the country. The locations of packers has not depended upon places of origin of animals processed. Traditionally packing houses have been located near final feeding areas where animals are fattened after being removed from the grasslands of their origin.

Increasing population means greater demand for meat. Increased supply is accomplished by raising more animals, by holding animals until they are relatively heavy, and by the introduction of new breeds which fatten more quickly than the older ones. Such a breed is the Santa Gertrudis, mentioned above. (See Fig. 15, p. 127.) Holding the animals for greater weight may depend upon a number of circumstances, including weather conditions which provide abundant feed, price fluctuation, and the demand for grain for human consumption rather than for feed for animals.

On farms where meat production is not a specialty, meat projects for 4-H Club boys and Future Farmers of America provide another way to increase both the number of meat animals produced and the quality of the meat. Boys who are feeding a calf for the fat-stock show frequently feed another for the family's meat supply.

Safety of the meat supply. When meat is produced for family consumption, healthy animals are usually rather carefully fattened, and the meat is, as a rule, safe. The farther the producer or processor is from the consumer, the more impersonal the relationship becomes. The demands of consumers are met by many qualities of meat, and greed or haste to supply demand sometimes leads to methods which would not be considered if the buyer of the meat were a neighbor.

To protect this distant and impersonal consumer, strict laws concerning the health of the animals, the sanitation of the packing houses, and the conditions of holding, processing, and transporting meat are enforced. All firms shipping meat in interstate commerce or to foreign countries are required to undergo constant inspection by federal inspectors who examine the premises, the live animals, and the carcasses of the slaughtered animals. The inspection stamp assures officials of foreign countries as well as our own that the meat is safe for food. Any meat unfit for food is tagged "Condemned," and is sent to rooms where it is sterilized and used in certain types of feed or in fertilizer, the fat being used by the soap-making industry. Carcasses which are accepted carry the stamp of approval, "U. S. Inspected and Passed," on each wholesale cut. The "little purple stamp" means that the meat is safe for food. (See Fig. 14). It does not indicate grade of the meat. Local abattoirs in which

Fig. 14. A federal inspection stamp.

meat is inspected use a stamp that is different in shape and size, but it, too, is a guarantee of safety of the meat. This meat may not be shipped in interstate commerce.

While the major portion (about 60 per cent) of the meat used in the country is inspected, there is still need for stricter local ordinances. Consumers should acquaint themselves with regulations pertaining to their supply of meat, and, if they find them insufficient, insist upon measures which will secure desirable meat.

By law, ready-to-eat meats and cured pork must be prepared in such a way that they are safe to eat. These regulations include heating pork during curing to at least 137° F. (58° C.), freezing it and holding it not higher than 5° F. (−15° C) for ten to twenty days, or curing it by specially prescribed methods.

Classes of meat. For marketing convenience meat animals are divided into groups by age and sex. Beef animals are steer, heifer, cow, stag, and bull; pork animals are barrow, gilt, sow, stag, and boar. Meat from sheep, based on age, is lamb or mutton; on sex, ewe, wether, and ram. "Veal" is from calves three to twelve weeks old; "calf" from those three to eight months old.

Grades of beef. Grading is permissive. The services of trained Federal graders are available for any large-scale meat dealer, upon request. Contrary to the arrangement for inspection, the party requesting the service pays for it. Grading is based upon conformation, finish, and quality.

Conformation is determined primarily by the breed of the animal. The rangy dairy type of animal never possesses the full round and loin of the beef type. The feed which an animal is given helps to determine its conformation because, if the feeding is right, the animal develops firm flesh, and the rangy appearance characteristic of a less compactly built animal is lessened. The conformation of an animal that has been fed corn is usually superior to that of a range-fed animal. The steer, a male that is castrated before sexual maturity, puts on flesh more desirably than any other class of beef animal, but steers differ in conformation. Some heifers are almost equal to steers in conformation. The amount of meat in relation to the bone is largely a matter of conformation.

Finish refers to the quality, quantity, and distribution of fat. Good finish includes a smooth covering of creamy, brittle fat over a large portion of the outside of the carcass. (See Fig. 16). Fat around the kidneys and along the ribs is plentiful and firm. The lean is marbled with fat. The fat adds to the appearance of both carcass and cuts and makes the meat more juicy and hence more palatable. The difference in covering and marbling in a rib cut from Choice and Utility carcasses is shown in Figure 17.

Quality refers to the firmness, texture, and color of the muscle and fat, and the character and color of the bones.

Courtesy King Ranch, Kingsville, Texas

Fig. 15. Top. *A dairy cow.* Bottom. *A pen of Santa Gertrudis steers, representative of fine beef animals.*

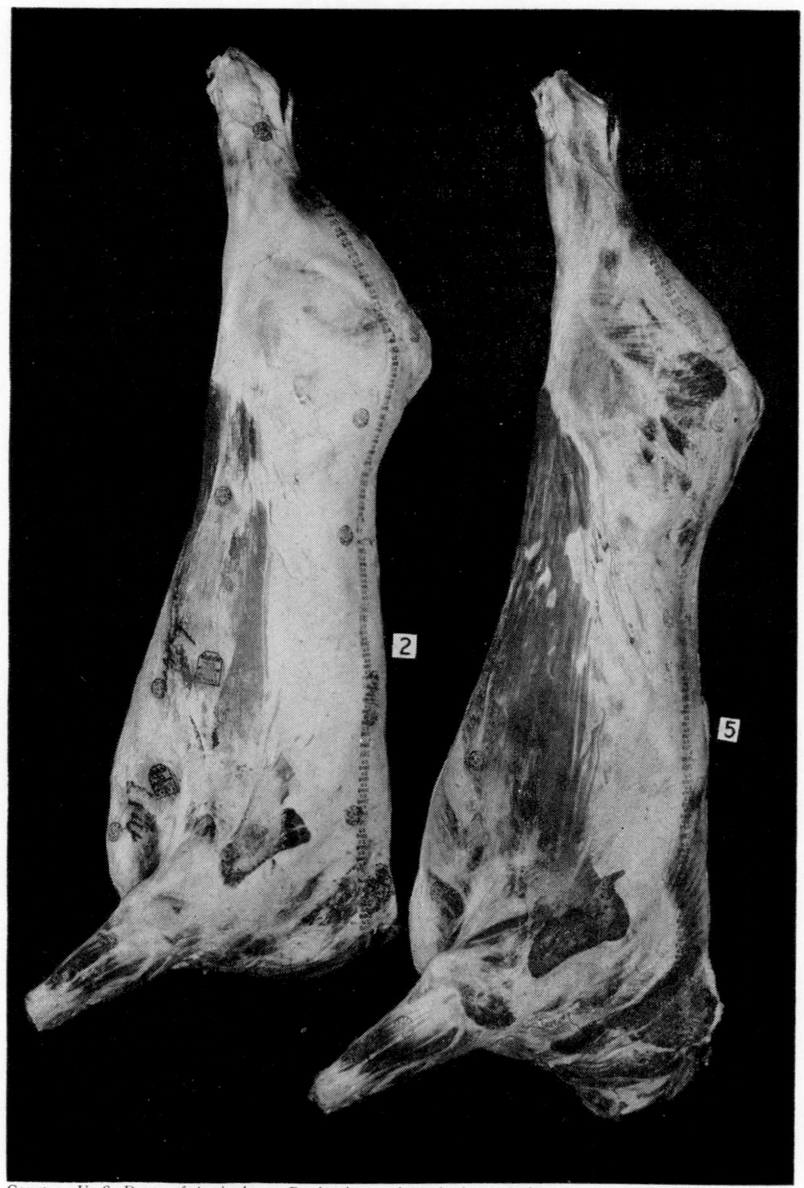

Courtesy U. S. Dept. of Agriculture, Production and Marketing Admin.

Fig. 16. Sides from Choice grade steer (2) and Utility grade steer (5).

The color of beef of high quality is rich and bright, the texture is fine and firm, and the chine (backbone) is reddish and soft. There is red color along the inside of the ribs of a young animal, and considerable cartilage along both backbone and breastbone.

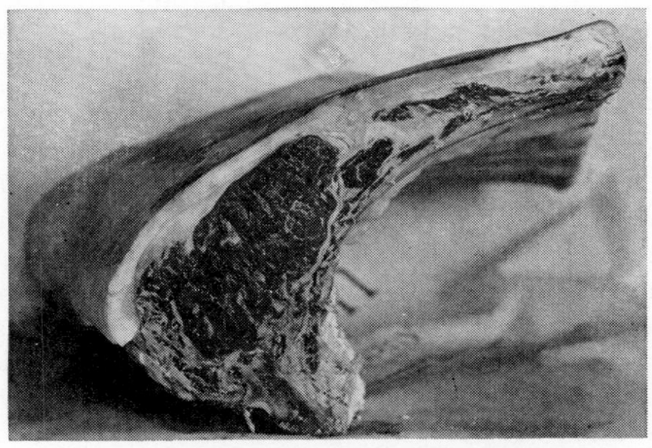

Fig. 17. Standing rib roasts: top, *from a Prime steer;* bottom, *from a Utility cow.*

Following are the grades for which standards have been promulgated.

Beef	*Veal and Calf*	*Lamb*	*Mutton*
Prime	Prime	Prime	Choice
Choice	Choice	Choice	Good
Good	Good	Good	Utility
Standard	Standard	Utility	Cull
Commerical	Utility	Cull	
Utility	Cull		
Cutter			
Canner			

TABLE 13. SOME PACKERS' DESIGNATIONS OF QUALITY OF BEEF

Packer	*1st Quality*	*2nd Quality*	*3rd Quality*
Armour	Star	Quality	Banquet
Cudahy	Puritan	Cudahy	Thrift
Swift	Premium	Select	Arrow
Wilson	Certified	Leader	Wilsco

Meat from "prime" and "choice" carcasses has considerable fat and is juicy and flavorful. Perhaps more "good" than other grades of meat is found on many markets; it is pleasing in quality and less expensive than the first two grades. "Standard" beef is from younger animals than "commercial" beef. "Utility" meat is low in fat and requires long cooking. The last two grades of beef are ordinarily not found on the retail market. In addition to the grade stamp, VEAL or CALF is stamped on meats when they apply to the meat being graded.

If a consumer were shown two similar cuts of two grades of beef, as "Prime" and "Choice," or "Good" and "Commercial," it would probably be difficult to identify them. The variation between grades that are farther apart is evident in Figures 16 and 17.

Having the grade designation stamped on the meat is a distinct help to the homemaker when she is buying meat. Considerable education and co-operation on the part of retailers are needed if homemakers are to choose wisely in markets where two or three grades are available. They need to learn what the grades are and what grades are suitable for different purposes within the range of their food budgets.

Trained graders are available in many cities throughout the country, and graded meat may be obtained on some markets.

Packers have their own quality designations which are helpful in choosing meat that is not stamped with the grade. Table 13 lists some of the packers' designations.

Buying meat. When the majority of consumer-buyers order meat, they ask for "a nice steak—enough for four," or "a tender roast." One person even telephoned for "two pounds of meat." This lack of specific knowledge places a responsibility on the retailer which he should not be expected to assume. Why should not intelligent orders, such as "a sirloin steak cut 1½ inches thick" or "an undercut roast weighing about 4 pounds" become common? In markets where more than one quality of meat is carried, and particularly when there is a definite way to know the grade, orders may be specific as "a sirloin steak cut 1½ inches thick—choice."

Homemakers may, with a little effort, learn to know not only government grades but also standard cuts. With these in mind and a few general marketing suggestions, satisfactory purchasing of meat in variety should follow. A few suggestions are:

1) Order roasts by animal source, cut, and approximate weight.

2) Order steaks and chops by animal source, cut, and thickness.

3) Choose a cut that is suitable for the purpose and cookery method, e.g., cuts from loin or rib for dry heat cookery; chuck or plate, rather than round, for ground meat.

4) In comparing costs, consider the amount of waste, including bone.

5) Use inexpensive cuts frequently. They are equal to higher priced cuts in nutritive value and may be superior in flavor. Local demand may make "inexpensive" cuts higher in price than "expensive" ones. Such fluctuations need to be noted by the family food buyer.

6) Buy roasts and stew meat for more than one meal. Roasts weighing four or five pounds cook to advantage and the meat may be used in various ways. Stew may be changed for serving a second time by adding another vegetable or by using it for meat pie.

7) A cut of beef, including two or three ribs from the rib and two or three from the chuck, may be purchased and separated into pieces for cooking in three or four ways. The "eye" of the meat may be stripped out for steaks or a roast; there will be meat for a pot roast, perhaps a stew, and certainly bones for soup stock.

8) A thick round steak may be divided into top and bottom round, the former for broiling or roasting; the latter for Swiss steak or pot roast.

9) Be sure to include one of the meat specialties, especially liver, once each week. Calf liver is no more nutritious than liver from other meat animals, but is usually more expensive.

10) Learn to distinguish meat from the various animals.

11) Learn the cuts of meat, including comparable cuts from the various animals, and order specifically.

12) Be able to identify the cuts, both cut to order and already cut. Prepared cuts are convenient for both merchant and consumer-buyer. Steaks and chops are usually thin but if thicker ones are wanted, they may be cut to order.

13) Meat may be not only precut but also prepackaged. Such packages are labeled to identify the animal source, cut, total weight, weight per pound, and price. It is well to try a few such packages to be sure, for instance, that all chops included are the same thickness and quality. If the market is reliable in this respect, this manner of handling meat makes shopping very easy.

14) Know the relative tenderness of cuts and cook them accordingly.

Because meat is one of the most expensive food items, buying in large quantities may be an economy. Buying a side or quarter of beef, a side of pork, or a lamb and storing the meat either in a frozen-food locker or a home freezer is an increasing practice. Some families prefer to purchase meat once a month, choosing the wholesale cuts from which they cut suitable portions, and those which the family uses most, and storing them in a home freezer. Table 14 shows a comparison of prices obtained during the spring of 1958, at Austin, Texas.

TABLE 14. INFLUENCE OF SOURCE ON COST OF MEAT TO CONSUMER *

Kind of Meat	*Produced, Processed, and Stored at Home*	*Purchased from Producer, Processed and Stored at a Locker Plant*	*Purchased at Retail Store*
Side of beef (175 lb.)	$139.00	$182.50	$253.51
Side of pork (90 lb.)	46.60	61.13	83.53
Lamb (50 lb.)	21.00	29.50	40.86

* Computations by students of Food Economics, The University of Texas, Spring, 1958.

Factors which are associated with tenderness of meat. The muscles that are known as lean meat are built up from many small, enlongated fibers bound together in bundles by fine strands of connective tissue. These bundles are held together by stronger connective tissue. The muscles are held together by even stronger connective tissue, and the ligaments and tendons that give support and bind muscles to the bones are also composed of connective tissue. In all instances where the function of the tissue is that of binding, white connective tissue is formed. Where elasticity is also required, the connective tissue is yellow.

The two proteins found in connective tissue are collagen and elastin. Both are found in larger quantities in meat from an old than from a young animal and exercise that develops firm muscles also increases the connective tissue and therefore the percentage of elastin. These proteins are definitely related to tenderness. Collagen is hydrolyzed by moist heat, but the moisture *in the meat itself* is enough to increase tenderness. (See Ref. 4, p. 150.) Thus if a piece of meat from the neck, which because of much exercise is tough, is cooked in moist heat, it is made more tender by the degree to which collagen is hydrolyzed during the cooking. It has been found that rations of high concentrates do not influence tenderness significantly, but heritability is a factor in tenderness.[1]

Elastin is not affected by any method of cookery. Hence meat that contains considerable elastin is never as tender as meat in which there is very little of this protein. There is a high percentage of elastin in the yellow ligament that extends along the backbone and enables the animal to raise its head. Obviously, it is impossible to make this ligament tender.

It is easy to classify cuts of meat with regard to tenderness by considering the relative exercise of muscles. Thus the neck is not as tender as the round, and the round is not as tender as the loin. The outside muscles of the round (bottom round) receive more exercise than the inside muscles (top round).

[1] Sylvia Cover, et al., *The Relationship of Ration and Inheritance to Eating Quality of Meat from Yearling Steers.* Jnl. Animal Science, 16:4, 1957.

TABLE 15. CUTS OF MEAT CLASSIFIED AS TO RELATIVE TENDERNESS

	Beef	*Veal*	*Lamb*	*Pork*
Tender.......	Rib roasts Sirloin steaks Porterhouse steaks T-bone steaks Club steaks Tenderloin steaks (fillet) Loin roasts	Rib roasts Rib chops Loin chops Loin roasts Cutlets	Rib roasts Rib chops Loin chops Loin roasts Leg	Rib roasts Rib chops Loin chops Loin roasts Fresh ham
Less tender...	Round steaks Roasts from round Rump roasts Chuck roasts Chuck steaks	Breast Shoulder	Breast Shoulder	Spareribs Shoulder Boston butt Picnic Jowl Feet
Tough........	Shanks Flank Plate Brisket Neck		Shanks Neck	

Reference has been made to the suitability of these cuts for pot roasting, roasting, or broiling.

The protoplasmic proteins are complicated in structure and "new" ones have been identified. They are coagulated by heat; hence, meat cooked at high temperature and/or to the well-done stage is less tender than similar meat cooked at a lower temperature and/or to the rare stage.

Another structural factor that affects tenderness is the grain of meat. If the fibers and the bundles of fibers are small, the grain of the meat is fine and the meat is more tender than when the grain is coarse. The meat from a well-finished animal is more tender than that from a poorly-finished one because of the greater amount and better distribution of fat.

After slaughter, most muscle tissue becomes rigid. After rigor passes, the muscle softens. If the meat is left hanging for a period of time under refrigeration, the glycogen is changed to lactic acid by enzymes, and the lactic acid in turn converts parts of the collagen to gelatin. Thus aged (or ripened) meat is more tender than meat used without ripening.

Efforts are being made to increase tenderness. Exposing meat to ultraviolet rays makes it possible to use a somewhat higher storage temperature, since the rays inhibit growth of bacteria and mold. This results in greater tenderness in a given time. In one research problem [1] it was found that with

[1] F. E. Deatherage, and W. Reiman, "Measurement of Beef Tenderness and Tenderization of Beef by the Tenderay Process," *Food Research,* 11:525–534, 1946.

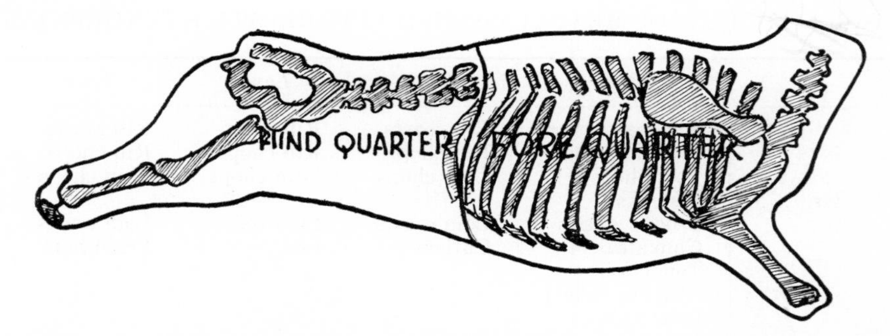

Fig. 18. Diagram of side of beef showing quartering line and skeletal structure.

the Tenderay process, beef graded "U. S. Commercial" was even more tender than that graded "U. S. Good." There are prepared proteolytic enzymes which are sometimes used on meat when it is cooked to increase tenderness. When a tenderizer is used, texture as well as tenderness should be noted.

Selected cuts of meat are classified in Table 15 as to degree of tenderness. Table 16 shows the comparable cuts from the various meat animals.

Meat cuts. Methods of cutting meat vary to some extent in different parts of the country, but standard cuts are usually known by retailers and should be recognized by homemakers. When local cuts are not standard, the homemaker should learn the cuts used but, if possible, encourage use of standard cuts.

Beef. The size of the beef creature makes it necessary to cut the carcass into two sides by splitting it lengthwise along the backbone, and then cutting each side into two pieces, called quarters. The quartering line (see Fig. 18) is between the last two ribs, one rib being left on the hind quarter to give firmness and to add to the ease with which the quarter can be handled. Figure 16, page 128, illustrates the side of beef.

As beef is transported from the central packing houses to branch houses or distributing centers, it is usually shipped in quarters. The distributors sell to local markets or to such institutions as restaurants and hotels. These merchants and institution buyers buy large pieces of meat—sometimes quarters, but more frequently smaller cuts known as wholesale or major cuts. Figure 19 shows the major cuts into which a side of beef is divided.

From the major cuts, the retailer sells the roasts, steaks, stew meat, and other portions ordered by the homemaker. Such small cuts are known as retail or minor cuts. As a rule, definite minor cuts are made from each major cut, as observation of meat charts or cutting at a market show. Figures 20–23, inclusive, show the usual cuts of beef.

Veal. Veal is the meat from calves from three to twelve weeks old. The size of the carcass immediately suggests that the major cuts, at least, differ from those of beef. The carcass may be split along the backbone, dividing it

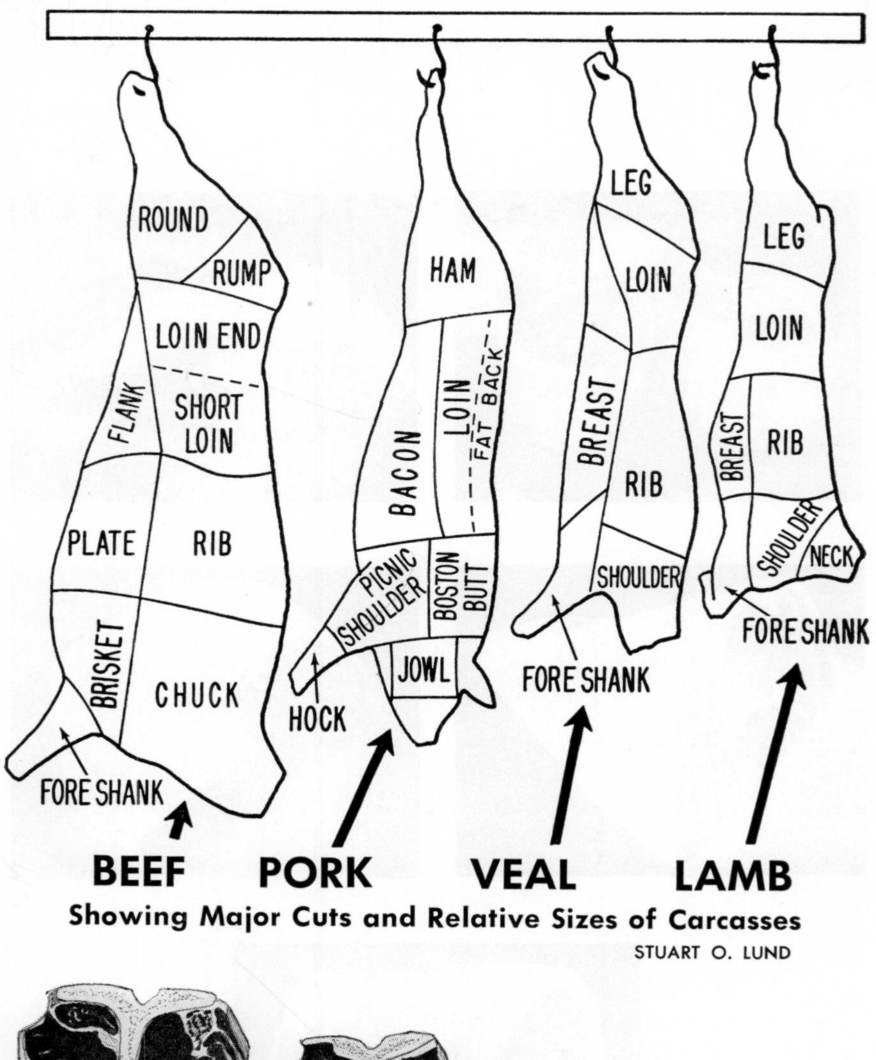

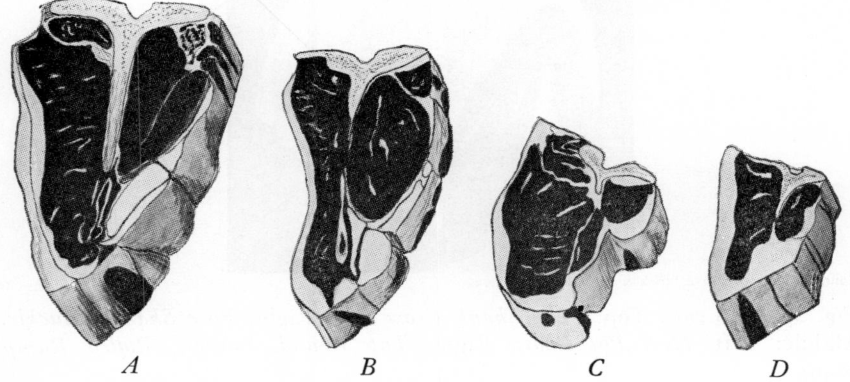

Fig. 19. (Top) *Diagram showing relative size and major cuts of beef, pork, veal, and lamb.* (Bottom) *Comparable T-bone cuts: A, beef T-bone steak; B, veal loin chop (T-bone); C, pork loin chop (T-bone); D, lamb loin chop (T-bone).*

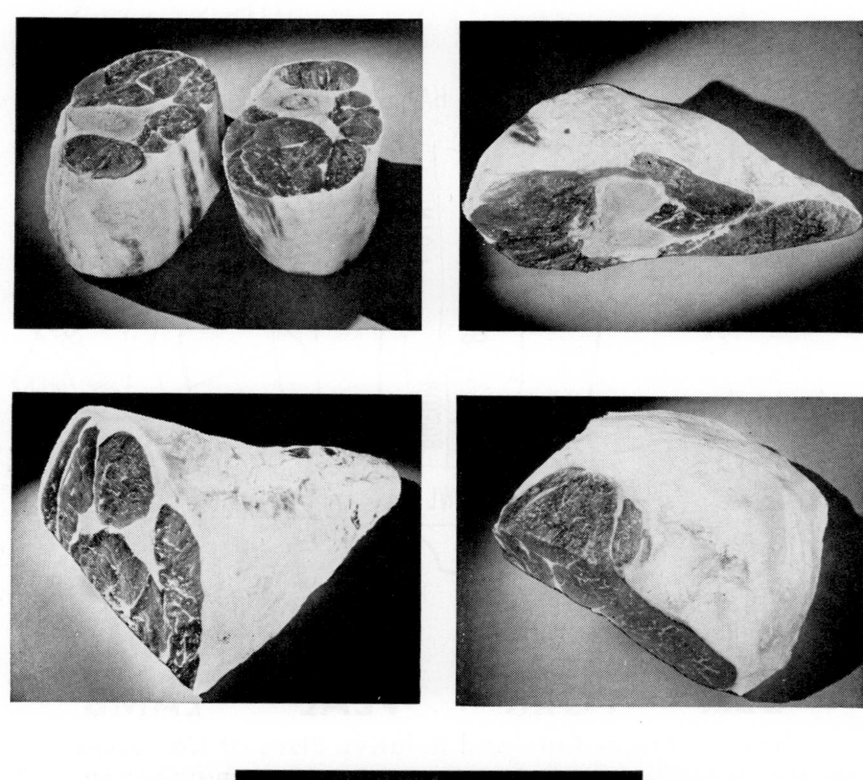

Courtesy National Live Stock & Meat Board, Chicago

Fig. 20. Beef cuts. Top: Left, *Shank Cross Cut;* Right, *Fore Shank Knuckle.* Middle: Left, *Heel Pot Roast;* Right, *Top Round.* Bottom: *Rolled Rump Roast.*

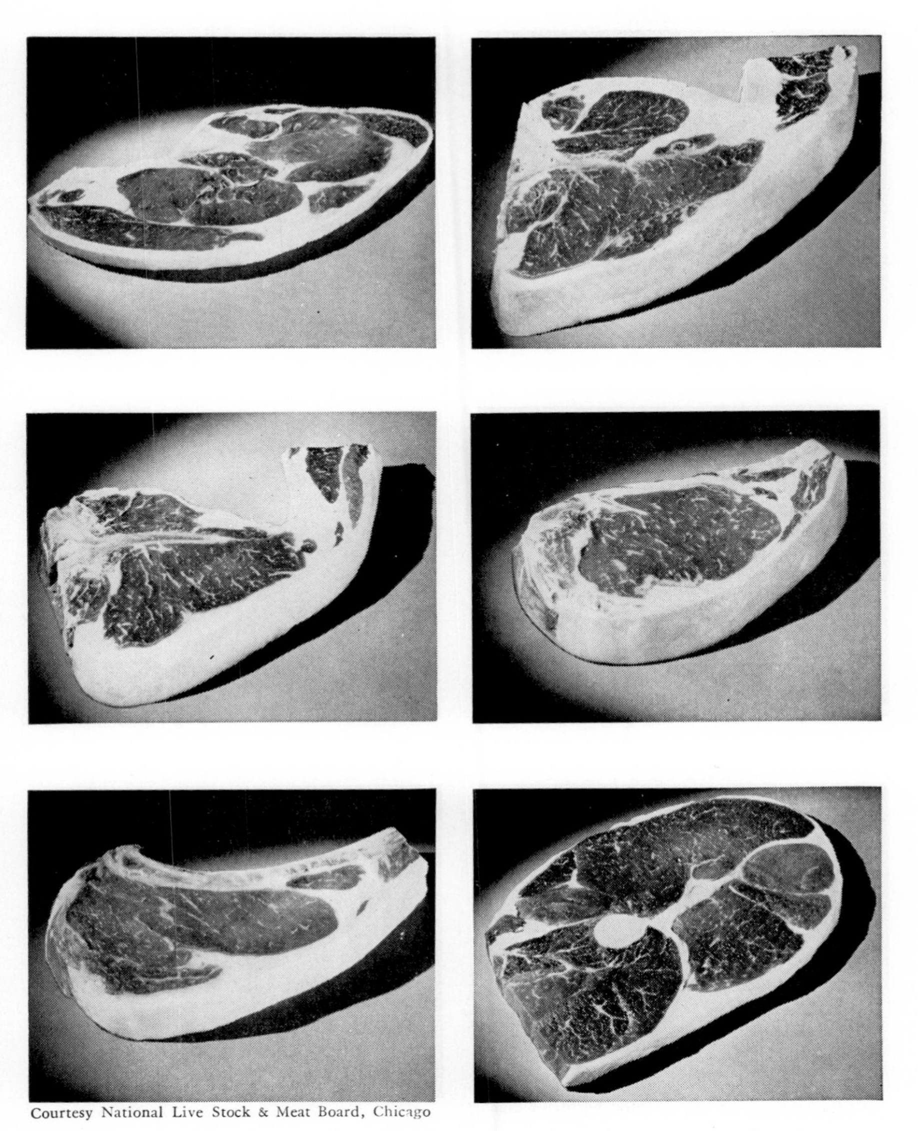

Courtesy National Live Stock & Meat Board, Chicago

Fig. 21. Beefsteak cuts. Top: Left, *Sirloin;* Right, *Porterhouse.* Middle: Left, *T-bone;* Right, *Club.* Bottom: Left, *Rib;* Right, *Round.*

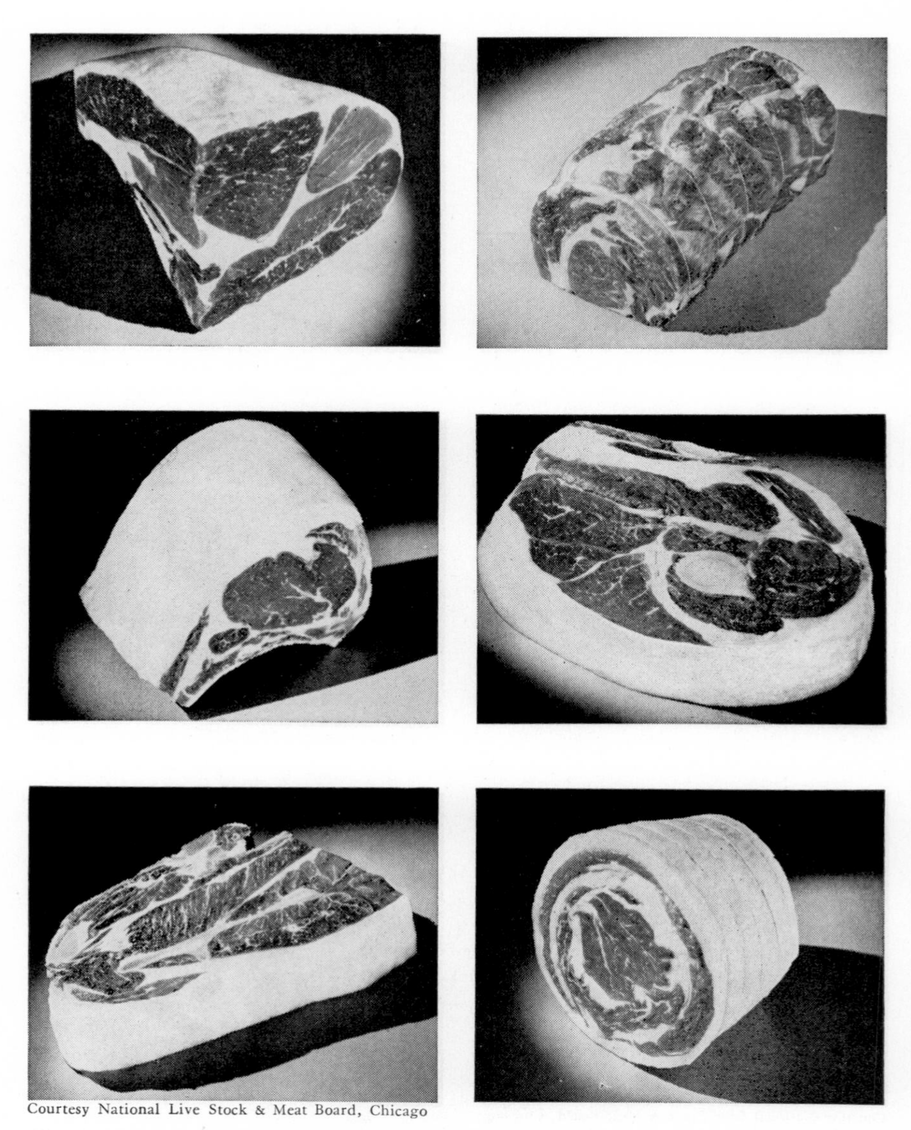

Courtesy National Live Stock & Meat Board, Chicago

Fig. 22. Beef roasts. Top: Left, *Standing rump;* Right, *Boneless Chuck.* Middle: Left, *Standing Rib;* Right, *Arm Pot.* Bottom: Left, *Blade Pot;* Right, *Rolled Rib.*

Courtesy National Live Stock & Meat Board, Chicago

Fig. 23. Beef cuts. Top: Left, *Plate;* Right, *Short Ribs.* Middle: Left, *Boneless Stew;* Right, *English or Boston.* Bottom: *Flank Steak.*

Courtesy National Live Stock & Meat Board, Chicago

Fig. 24. Pork cuts. Top: Left; *Rib Chops;* Right, *Loin Chops.* Middle: Left, *Canadian Bacon;* Right, *Boston Butt.* Bottom: *Picnic Shoulder.*

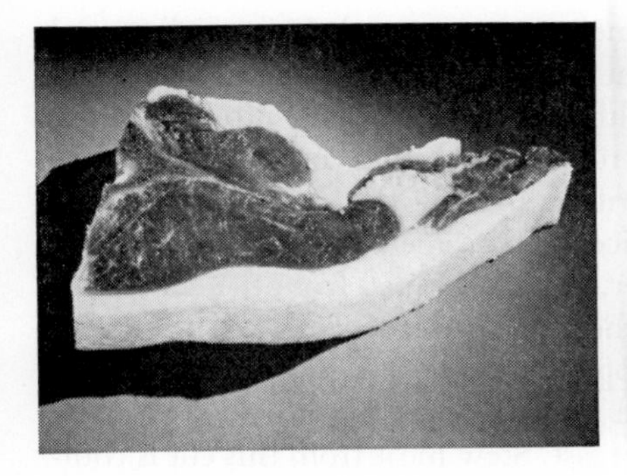

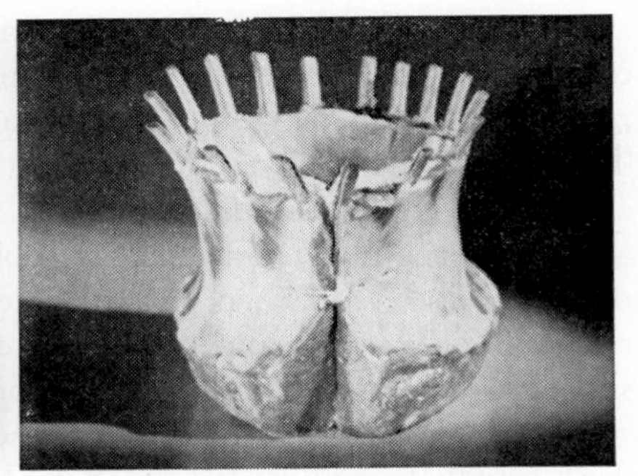

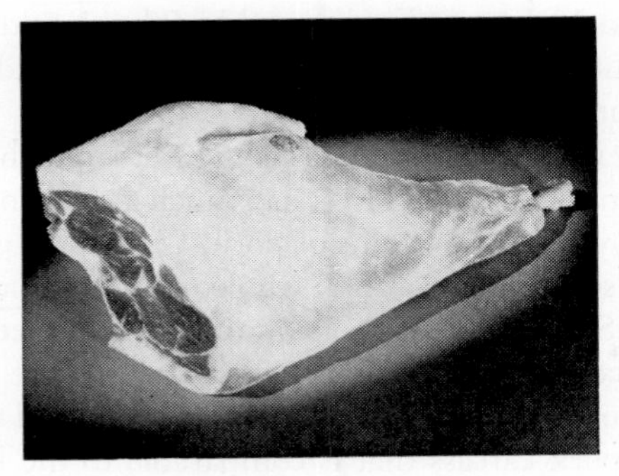

Fig. 25. Lamb cuts. Top: Left, *Loin Chops;* Right, *Roast* (*Crown*). Bottom: *Frenched Leg.*

into two sides. Sometimes it is divided into two saddles, cutting along the quartering line but not along the back. In the latter instance, the hind saddle is divided into the major cuts, leg, loin, and flank—two cuts of each. From the foresaddle, hotel rack, shoulder, and breast are cut.

The leg may be used for roasts. Cuts similar to the round steaks of beef are made; they may be used for veal cutlets. The loin is frequently sold as roasts, but it is more commonly cut into loin chops, or, more specifically, sirloin or T-bone chops. The shanks are used for soup bones. The flank may be cut from the loin, rolled, stuffed, and roasted. It is sometimes left as a part of a loin roast.

The hotel rack, split along the backbone, is frequently divided into rib roasts, although it is probably more popular cut as rib chops. The breast may be boned, rolled, and roasted, with or without a stuffing. Breast, shoulder, and flank are also used as stew meat. A number of interesting recipes using veal stew meat and cutlets may be found in cook books from other countries. Some of these, in addition to those in Section IV, might be well worth trying during the laboratory period. Figure 19 shows the major cuts of veal.

Lamb. Lamb is cut in about the same manner as veal. It is smaller, and consequently less flexible from the point of view of retail cutting. The leg is roasted, and the loin is often roasted, although it may be cut into loin chops. The rib is sometimes used as a crown roast. More often the ribs are sold as chops. The chops may be single—one rib to a chop—or double—two ribs to a chop—depending upon personal choice and the method of cooking. They may be plain or Frenched. For the latter, meat is scraped from the end of the rib bone for about an inch. After the chops are cooked, a paper frill may be slipped over this part of the bone. Chops are usually broiled or panbroiled.

The breast is often boned, rolled, and roasted, preferably with stuffing, the flank usually being cut along with the breast. Stew meat from this cut is common. Stews and roasts come from the shoulder; and inch-thick slices from the neck, properly cooked, are most acceptable. The shoulder may be roasted plain, boned and stuffed (cushion shoulder), or boned and rolled. Figure 19 shows the major cuts of lamb.

Pork. The physical characteristics of hogs are somewhat different from those of the other meat animals. Hogs are much fatter and the fat is much softer. Figure 19 shows the major cuts of pork.

The ham may be sold fresh or cured, whole or sliced. Ham is popular both boiled and roasted. Slices may be broiled, and center pieces cut at least two inches thick are excellent for roasting. Thinner ones are baked.

The strip of fat along the back is trimmed off and cured to make salt pork. The portion of the pork carcass that is comparable to the loin, rib, and part of the chuck of beef is one wholesale cut—the loin. It retails as loin and rib roasts or loin and rib chops. Boned and cured, it becomes Canadian-type bacon (see Fig. 24). Chops are sometimes smoked.

The short ribs (ribs below the loin) are trimmed and sold as spareribs. The belly, comparable with the plate and brisket of beef, is used for bacon. The part of pork which is comparable with the chuck and brisket of beef is treated in several ways. It is usually cured. The major portion of it, used as one cut, is shoulder, New York style. It may be trimmed and cut to make the picnic shoulder (see Fig. 24) and the Boston style butt. Both may be sold either fresh or cured and are usually cooked by roasting. The jowl is usually cured and sold as bacon.

Comparable cuts. The skeletal structure of the four principal meat animals is essentially the same. The cuts vary with the relative size of the animals and with custom and use. The table on page 143 lists the comparable cuts. Figure 19 shows a T-bone cut from each of the animals commonly used for meat.

Meat specialties. A number of internal organs and glands are both popular and nutritionally important. Probably tongue, heart, and liver are used most frequently. Kidney, especially lamb kidney, is a delicacy. Sweetbreads are found in young animals. They are the thymus gland which extends along the front of the base of the neck and the upper edge of the heart, and which disappears as the animal matures. Sweetbreads are very tender and have a very delicate flavor. Brains are similar in texture and are also delicate in flavor.

TABLE 16. COMPARABLE CUTS OF MEAT

	Beef	*Veal*	*Lamb*	*Pork*
Major cuts......	Round	Leg	Leg	Ham
	Rump	Rump	....	....
	Loin end	Loin	Loin	Loin
	Short loin	Loin	Loin	Loin
	Rib	Hotel rack	Hotel rack	Loin
	Chuck	Shoulder	Shoulder	Shoulder
	Flank	Flank	Breast	Belly
	Plate	Breast	Breast	Belly
	Brisket	Breast	Breast	Belly
Selected minor cuts..........	Round steak	Veal cutlets	....	Ham slices
	Sirloin steaks	Loin chops	Loin chops	Loin chops
	Porterhouse and T-bone steaks	Loin or T-bone chops	Loin or T-bone chops	Loin or T-bone chops
	Club steaks	Rib chops	Rib chops	Rib chops
	Rib roasts	Rib roasts	Rib roasts	Rib roasts

Tripe is the inner muscular lining of the stomach. It is used both fresh and pickled. The tails of beef animals—oxtails—are generally used for braising or for making soup.

Cured and prepared meats. A visit to a few grocery stores and meat markets reveals an interesting array of cured meats and of meats which are ready to eat. Boiled and baked ham, either fresh or cured, a variety of sausages, pressed meats, head cheese, dried beef, and pickled tongue are a few of the meats from which the buyer may choose. Barbecued meat is popular on many markets. Canned meats, which need very little preparation, also add their appeal to the busy consumers, and their use is increasing rapidly. There are at least three types of cured hams, and some have been treated in such a way as to require only a very short period of cooking. There are also imported canned hams which compare with the domestic product. All canned hams are more expensive than other cured hams, but are convenient for many purposes. Bacon varies in both quality and price. Canadian bacon is usually expensive but there is no waste, and a relatively large number of satisfying servings per pound are obtainable. Cured shoulder of pork is popular, especially the trimmed picnic shoulders.

Corned beef is delicious in flavor. It is sometimes available in bulk at the market but is more often sold canned. Tongue may be smoked, and those merchants who sell barbecued meat find barbecued tongue very popular. The flavor of Kosher-cured tongue is also popular. Both tongue and pigs' feet are frequently sold pickled. Canned lambs' tongues are a delicacy.

Frozen meats. Meats frozen for locker storage are usually frozen at a rate called "sharp freezing." Roasts, steaks, and chops frozen by packers are usually frozen more rapidly. The rate of freezing has been found to influence the quality of the product; the more rapid the freezing, the better the product. From this point of view, flash freezing for small cuts should have a distinct advantage. Storage temperatures have also been studied in relation to keeping time. The results show that storage should be at 0° F. or lower.

MEAT COOKERY

Reasons for cooking. The reasons for cooking meat are (1) to sterilize it, (2) to make it palatable, (3) to increase tenderness of less-tender cuts, and (4), in the case of pork, to be sure that trichinae, parasites that may be in pork, are destroyed.

The stage to which meat is cooked depends upon personal taste and the kind of meat. Pork and veal should always be cooked to the well-done stage. Lamb is usually preferred well-done, but may be medium. Beef may be rare, medium, or well-done.

Cooking methods. The cookery method should be such that the cooked meat is juicy throughout. The center should be cooked to the desired stage without hardening the surface. Tender cuts should remain tender; less-tender cuts should be more tender when cooked. A great deal of careful research has been done, the results of which should make well-cooked meat more common. Definitions of terms commonly used in connection with meat cookery may be found in the glossary.

The superiority of low temperatures for meat cookery has been well established. This method makes meat more juicy and therefore improves flavor, requires less fuel, and results in more servings from a cut that is to be sliced. Searing gives brown color, characteristic flavor, and more drippings for gravy. However, these advantages may be less important than those resulting from low temperatures.

Beef may be cooked until rare (140° F.; 60° C.), medium (160° F.; 71° C.), or well done (170° F.; 77° C.) or to some intermediate temperature. Other meats are best cooked to the well-done stage, with higher temperatures for lamb (175° F.; 79° C.), and for pork (185° F.; 85° C.).

Cooking tender meats. Standard cookery methods for tender cuts are roasting, broiling, pan-broiling, and frying, all of which involve application of dry heat to the meat. (For definitions of terms, refer to glossary.) Certain discrepancies arise because of custom. Some cuts are said to be "roasted," but ham is "baked." Both are cooked in a closed oven, with dry heat. Yet a

Photographs by Visual Instruction Bureau, University of Texas

Fig. 26. Oven temperature affects the appearance and shrinkage of roasts cooked to 160° F. internal temperature: above, *cooked at 300° F. (149° C.);* below, *cooked at 450° F. (232° C.) for 10 minutes, then at 300° F. for the remainder of the time. Note difference in amount of drippings in the graduated cylinders.*

cut may be "roasted" in a rotisserie, which is the modern version of roasting portions of meat, including a whole carcass, on spits over coals. This is an interesting return to old ways for originally a "roast" was not cooked in an oven. "Broiling" is considered to be the application of dry heat directly to the meat and is used for comparatively thin cuts—steaks and some chops. However, a center slice of ham is usually "baked," even if it is only an inch thick. Cover [1] has applied the oven method to steaks, calling them "oven-broiled," with excellent results. For present purposes, a large cut or a cut more than two inches thick is referred to as "roasted"; a thinner cut, as "baked" if both are cooked in an oven.

Roasting. Some of the recommendations for roasting are summarized as follows:

1) Meat is more juicy and tender and has finer flavor if the cooking temperatures are low; for example, a constant temperature of 300° F. (149° C.) for roasting rather than a searing temperature of 450° F. (232° C.) followed by a lower temperature. (See Fig. 26.)

2) The use of a meat thermometer is a more accurate method of judging the stage to which meat is cooked than the "time-per-pound" method. (See Fig. 27.) In Table 38a, p. 556, both internal temperature and approximate minutes per pound are listed as indications of stage of doneness for roasts from the four meat animals. The same temperatures apply to braised meats.

3) Cooking losses are less when meat is roasted in an open pan than in a covered pan.

4) Hot metal skewers inserted to the center of a roast reduce the roasting time, but usually increase the cooking losses.

5) The total cooking time for a large roast is longer than for a small roast, but the time per pound is less if the two roasts are the same in shape.

6) The total cooking time varies with the distance to the center of the meat—the greater the distance, the longer the time.

7) If two roasts weigh the same, but one has a larger surface area than the other, the one with the larger surface area will cook more quickly than the other.

8) If paired rib roasts of equal original weight are roasted at the same temperature, one with the bone in and the other boned and rolled, the former will cook more quickly than the latter.

9) Well-ripened meat cooks in less time than meat that is not well-ripened.

Broiling. It is not uncommon to hear people comment on the superiority of steak cooked over coals—out-of-doors. Several factors doubtless influence the opinion, but the fact that the broiling temperature is low is certainly important. Intense heat, even at the beginning of the cooking period, is no longer recommended, but emphasis is placed on lower temperature in order to produce a more juicy steak or chop. A temperature of 350° F. (177° C.) at the top of the meat is recommended by the National Live Stock and Meat

[1] Cover, Sylvia, Jo Ann Bannister, and Ella Kehlenbrink, "Effect of Four Conditions of Cooking on the Eating Quality of Two Cuts of Beef." *Food Research,* 22:635–647, 1957.

Fig. 27. Placing meat thermometer in a roast (left) *and in a steak* (right).

Board. The broiler should be preheated, and the meat placed so that the top is about 3 inches below the source of heat. It should be turned only once. If the meat is thick enough so that a meat thermometer can be used, it may be turned according to Table 39 on page 557. Figure 27 (*right*) shows the placing of the thermometer in such a cut.

Broiled meat is transferred to a hot platter and salted when done. While salt added to meat before cooking does not draw out the juices of the meat, as was formerly supposed, it penetrates only about ½ inch, darkens the meat to that depth, and is apt to result in gravy that is too salty for some people.

Beef steaks, lamb chops, bacon, center slices of ham, and liver are suitable for broiling. Pork and veal chops are usually dry when cooked by this method.

Pan broiling. Pan broiling is a satisfactory method of cooking the same cuts of meat as are recommended for broiling.

Pan broiling requires the use of a very small amount of fat to prevent the meat from sticking to the frying pan. The error of using a larger quantity of fat should be avoided. As the meat cooks, fat melts and some juice is drawn from the meat. When the meat has a high fat content, as is the case with some beef steaks, fat should be poured off as it accumulates in the frying pan.

Frying. In general, meat should not be fried. Veal cutlets (usually breaded), croquettes, and liver are often fried. Frying is a good dry-heat cookery method from the standpoint of the retention of the B vitamins, but frequent use of this method adds to the total fat consumption and therefore many people question its use. Pan-frying, oven-frying, or sautéing are equally as effective as deep-fat frying in so far as flavor and appearance are concerned.

Baking. A steak, chop, or slice of ham, from one to one and a half inches thick, may be baked at 350° F. (177° C.) to the desired stage. The meat is salted when done. It is juicy, tender, and nicely brown if the oven is vented. The fat does not spatter during cooking.

Cooking less tender meats. The age of the animal and the amount of exercise it has had have been mentioned as factors which influence the tenderness of meats. The higher the percentage of elastin in meat, the less tender it is.

Whether or not meat, as eaten, is tender may be a matter of the tenderness of the meat itself, the cookery method, the stage to which it is cooked, or a combination of some of these. Dividing meat into small pieces—from stew-size to ground meat—helps to increase "tenderness-as-eaten." Removal of heavy connective tissue helps in some cuts. Carving across the grain and in thin slices shortens the fibers. Combining tissue removal, broiling at low temperature to the rare stage, and clever cutting are responsible for the tenderness of the broiled flank steak described on p. 557.

Use of acid to increase tenderness is still controversial. Tomatoes are usually added to meat for Swiss steak and some of the less-tender thin cuts are often marinated in a French dressing for several hours before cooking. These seem to increase tenderness as well as give desirable flavor.

Braising. The flavor that is developed as meat is browned in fat is generally pleasing. During the long, slow cooking in moist heat that follows, other flavoring may or may not be added, depending upon whether herbs, spices, or vegetables are used.

Pot-roasting is braising. The vegetables served with the pot roast are usually cooked in the liquid in which the meat is cooked. The vegetables should be added with reference to the time needed to cook them so that all will be cooked to the right degree of doneness.

Many cuts of meat are suitably cooked by braising, including the less-tender cuts of beef and lamb, chops from pork and veal, breast and shoulder of veal, liver, heart, and kidney. Swiss steak is one very popular form of braised steak.

Cooking in water. Cuts of meat that are used for stews and soups are cooked in water. These include the tough cuts listed in Table 15 on page 133. Meat from the shank, breast, and shoulder of veal and from the shoulder of pork are also sometimes used.

Meat for stew is cut into cubes about 1½ to 2 inches on a side. The pieces may be browned in fat or not, depending upon the flavor and color desired. The meat is simmered in a larger amount of liquid than is used for braising, and vegetables are usually added when the meat is nearly done. Seasonings, both from vegetables and from herbs and spices, are frequently used and may be characteristic of certain stews. Paprika, for example, is used generously in Hungarian Goulash.

When meats are used as a basis for soup stock, as much as possible of the soluble proteins, fat, and minerals as well as the extractives which contribute flavor are transferred to the stock. The cooked meat should be used in soup or in some other way because considerable nutriment remains in it. The flavor of vegetables, herbs, and spices is usually desirable in soup stock, and suitable combinations of these are simmered with the meat.

Soup stock forms the basis for many kinds of soup. After it cools, excess fat that has risen to the top is removed. The stock may be cleared for use as consommé or bouillon, or used for vegetable soups, broths, or bisques. Often there is sufficient gelatin in the stock so that it may be chilled and served as jellied bouillon or consommé.

Other meats that are cooked in water are heart, tongue, and kidney. These also may be seasoned by adding herbs and spices to the water while they are being cooked.

Frozen meats. It is sometimes recommended that quick-frozen steaks and chops be cooked without previous thawing, and that roasts be thawed before cooking. After meat is taken from the freezer, it may be thawed either in or out of the refrigerator, as desired. The same low temperatures are used as for cooking fresh meats but the cooking time must be extended somewhat. If the meat is completely defrosted, the time per pound is less than for similar meat that has not been frozen, but the cookery method is the same. Some studies have resulted in preference for meat thawed before cooking because of less drip loss and hence greater juiciness of the meat.

SUGGESTIONS FOR LABORATORY

The students' experience with meat cookery will depend upon time allotment in the course, emphasis considered desirable by instructor and students, money available, possibilities for use of the cooked meats, and perhaps other factors.

Familiarity with cuts makes the laboratory work quickly meaningful. Different ways of acquainting students with cuts may be used—illustrations included in the text, wall charts, bulletin board exhibits, slides, a meat-cutting demonstration, a field trip to wholesale and/or retail meat establishments are some of the ways. Preceding the laboratory, knowledge of cookery terms and their application to meat cuts, together with reasons why, in general, certain methods are suitable for specific cuts, should be gained.

REFERENCES

Bull, Sleeter, *Meat for the Table*. McGraw-Hill Book Co., New York, 1951.

Cover, Sylvia, Jo Ann Bannister, and Ella Kehlenbrink, "Effect of Four Conditions of Cooking on the Eating Quality of Two Cuts of Beef." *Food Research*. 22:635–647, 1957.

Cover, Sylvia, G. T. King and O. D. Butler, *Effect of Carcass Grades and Fatness on Tenderness of Meat from Steers of Known History*. Texas Agricultural Experiment Station, College Station, Texas, Bulletin 889, 1958.

Cover, Sylvia, and R. L. Hostetler, *An Examination of Some Theories about Beef Tenderness by Using New Methods*. Texas Agricultural Experiment Station, College Station, Texas, Bulletin 947, 1960.

Cullen, M. O., *How to Carve Meat, Game, and Poultry*. McGraw-Hill Book Co., New York, 1941.

Griswold, Ruth, "The Effect of Different Methods of Cooking Beef Round of Commercial and Prime Grades. II, Collagen, Fat and Nitrogen Content." *Food Research*. 20:171–179, 1955.

Hiner, R. L. and O. G. Hankins, "Tenderness of Beef as Affected by Aging With and Without Subsequent Freezing." *Refrig. Eng*. 42:172 (1941).

Hughes, Osee, *Introductory Foods*. 3rd. Ed. The Macmillan Co., New York, 1955.

Lowe, Belle, *Experimental Cookery*. 4th Ed. John Wiley and Sons, Inc., New York, 1955.

McLean, Beth Bailey, and T. H. Campbell, *The Complete Meat Cookbook*. Chas. A. Bennett Co., Inc., Publishers, Peoria, Ill., 1953.

National Live Stock and Meat Board, Chicago:
Let's Cook Meat—Recipes You'll Like.
Meat Manual—Identifying, Buying, Cooking.

Troelstrup, Arch W., *Consumer Problems and Personal Finance*. 2nd Ed., McGraw-Hill Book Co., Inc., New York, 1957.

U.S.D.A. Agricultural Marketing Service: *Buying Beef by Grade*.

UNIT

11 Poultry and Game Birds

Wild birds were hunted for food by many ancient people and some varieties were domesticated by people in early civilizations. Some of our common breeds of poultry originated in ancient China. In the United States, the inhabitants of Mesa Verde domesticated turkeys, keeping them at the back of the cliff spaces where there was not height enough to build dwellings. Indians in the eastern part of the country introduced wild turkey as a food to the colonists, and thus gave us our traditional Thanksgiving bird.

Dietary importance. Considered chiefly as a source of protein, poultry is on a par with other meats. Chicken breasts are particularly valuable as a source of niacin; legs and thighs, of thiamin and riboflavin. Thus the person who eats "some light and some dark" chicken as a serving gets a well-balanced contribution to the day's supply of these three B vitamins. Of the minerals, phosphorus and iron are present in important amounts, and the calcium is a good addition to the basic supply provided by the milk recommended as part of the usual day's food. Meat from turkey contains larger amounts of all three of the above minerals than does that from chicken. The vitamin content of the two types of poultry is approximately the same.

Production. Wild birds are still popular and include pheasant, partridge, quail, woodcock, dove, duck, goose, and turkey. To insure the game supply, hunting seasons and game limits are specified.

Among the domesticated birds, chickens are most abundant, but many turkeys, ducks, geese, guinea fowls, pigeons, and squabs are marketed annually. Recently a new item has been added to the variety of poultry on the market—the Northwester or pheasant-chicken. Originating in Centralia, Washington, this hybrid is the result of a complex pattern of cross-breeding including two varieties of pheasants and two breeds of chickens. The Northwester has a broad breast, meaty thighs, and a high percentage of meat to bone because of the small bones inherited from the pheasant. The flavor is slightly like that of pheasant and the birds are excellent for broiling, frying, and roasting. Rock Cornish game hens are found on the market increasingly.

Poultry comes from two sources: the many farms where small flocks are kept and the surplus birds are sold, and poultry farms where large numbers are produced. Often a produce-house operator owns farms where poultry is raised, and contracts with farmers in the area for poultry raised to his specifications. The specifications include breed, type of feed, and care of the houses in which the birds are raised. It has been mentioned that the lighter weight breeds of poultry are usually chosen for egg production. Many of these birds appear on the poultry market as broilers or fryers when the young male birds are sold, and as hens and roosters when the flocks are culled. Fowls raised specifically for meat are heavier breeds, such as Plymouth Rocks, Rhode Island Reds, or crossbreeds, among which are New Hampshire Reds, Indian Rivers, and Vantress Cross. The crossbreeds are popular with poultry raisers because they grow rapidly and develop evenly. Consequently, they are ready for market in a comparatively short time. They are large, plump, and sell at a premium on some markets.

Concerted effort, on a nation-wide scale, to decrease disease and otherwise improve chickens has been in progress since 1935. Earlier, efforts were made to control pullorum disease by using only eggs from disease-free flocks in hatcheries and emphasizing sanitation. Charts showing volume of testing and disease control indicate spectacular results, but not eradication of pullorum. In 1930, 5.85 per cent of tested chickens and 3.55 per cent of turkeys were reactors. In 1956, these percentages were 0.05 and 0.06 per cent. The National Poultry Improvement Plan specifies stages of breeding to improve flocks and of pullorum control and indicates the stages by the proper labels on packages of hatching eggs and baby chicks (see Fig. 28). A similar plan is used for improvement of turkeys.

Marketing. Poultry is marketed alive, dressed (New York dressed), ready-to-cook (drawn), and frozen. The live poultry industry in some cities thrives because of the demands of people of certain nationalities and religions. The bird may be selected by the consumer-buyer and processed as the buyer chooses. Today most consumers prefer to purchase dressed poultry which has been killed, bled, and picked. In addition, ready-to-cook poultry has been eviscerated, the head and feet removed, washed, and pinfeathers have been removed. The clean edible organs are wrapped in paper and placed inside the cavity of the bird. It may also be frozen and packaged for shipment. Frozen poultry should be kept in frozen storage until purchased by institution- or consumer-buyer.

Both turkey and chicken parts are available increasingly. Turkey halves, quarters, steaks, patties, backs, wings, and giblets may be purchased. Chicken breasts for baking, legs, wings, and backs for stewing, and giblets may be bought separately.

Fig. 28. Identification of poultry under the National Poultry Improvement Plan.

Smoked turkey is popular on many markets. The smoking may be done as a preservation method, in which case the turkey may need to be soaked to remove some of the smoke flavor. Turkey, duck, or roasting chicken may be smoked lightly, simply as a means of giving flavor to the meat. This may be done at home or for a local market.

Rock Cornish game hens are usually marketed frozen, one being considered a serving. They are rather high in price, one checked comparison being ninety-eight cents per pound as against thirty-five cents per pound for a large fryer that might be roasted. They are popular for guest meals and as a "treat" for families.

Fig. 29. Grade and inspection marks for ready-to-cook poultry. Left, *official grade mark;* center, *official inspection mark;* right, *combined grade and inspection mark.*

On some markets cooked poultry is available. It is appreciated by homemakers who also work outside the home and by those whose ranges are not large enough for roasting birds which they may wish to serve on special occasions such as Thanksgiving and Christmas.

Many grocers feature barbecued chicken. A merchandising technique is the revolving rotisserie on which chickens are cooked. The appeals of tempting appearance and aroma as well as the fact that there is no home preparation are important in the sale of this product. Here again, the price includes service. For example, the thirty-five cent per pound fryer, barbecued, may become seventy-nine cents per pound.

Standards of quality and specifications for grades for both live and ready-to-cook poultry were made effective by the United States Department of Agriculture on January, 1, 1950.

For live poultry, standards are based on health and vigor, feathering, conformation, fleshing, fat covering, and degree of freedom from defects. Qualities are A or No. 1, B or No. 2, and C or No. 3. Grades are U. S. Grade A or No. 1, U. S. Grade B or No. 2, and U. S. Grade C or No. 3. Dressed and ready-to-eat poultry may be graded, considering fleshing, conformation, fat in and under the skin, absence of defects, such as bruises, tears, and pinfeathers, as well as broken bones and some other factors. Ready-to-eat poultry may also be inspected for wholesomeness (see Fig. 29). This must be done by an official inspector, who examines the birds inside and out to determine whether they, including edible organs, are fit for food. Grading and inspection services are available for poultrymen who care to use them.

Classes of poultry are based on age and sex and the designation usually suggests the cooking method that is suitable. Classes of chickens are broilers or fryers, roasters, capons, and hens (stewing chickens or fowls). Turkey classes are fryers or roasters, young hens and young toms, and mature hens and toms. The first may be broiled, fried, or roasted; the second, roasted; the third, stewed. Ducks may be broiler or fryer ducklings, roaster ducklings, or mature ducks. Geese and guineas are classed as young or mature, and pigeons as squabs if young.

TABLE 17. POULTRY CLASS, APPROXIMATE WEIGHT, AND ALLOWANCE PER PERSON

Poultry Class	*Weight (pounds)*	*Allowance per Person (pounds)*
Chickens:		
Broiler	1 to 2½	¼ to ½ (bird)
Fryer	2½ to 3½	⅔ to 1
Roaster	4 to 6	½ to ¾
Capon	4 to 8	½ to ¾
Fowl (fricassee)	4 to 6	½ to ¾
Fowl (creamed)	4 to 6	about ¼
Ducks:		
Duckling	2 to 4	1
Duck	3 to 6	1
Geese:		
Young ("green")	8 to 11	1
Older	12 or more	1
Guinea	1½ to 2½	¾ to 1
Pheasant-chicken	1½ to 2½	¾ to 1
Rock Cornish game hen	1	1 (bird)
Pigeons:		
Squabs	¾ to 1	1 (bird)
Pigeons	about 1½	1 (bird)
Turkey:		
Fryer	3 to 7	¾ to 1
Mature	8 to 30	¼ to 1

Selection. When buying poultry, the first consideration is the method to be used for cooking. It would hardly be wise to buy a broiler for roasting or a hen for broiling. Since most poultry purchased is either dressed or ready-to-cook, in any market where the grade and inspection marks are used, these should be noted. In other markets, the smooth skin, plump breast, well-developed thighs, supple wing joints, and pliable breast bone are indications of poultry of good quality. The last two points indicate that the bird is young.

The price of poultry varies with the market, the season, the available supply, the day of the week, and holiday trade. Price in comparison with that of other meats should be considered in terms of edible portions. In general, from 50 to 60 per cent of the ready-to-cook weight is edible meat. Thus if a three-pound fryer costs 45 cents per pound, and 50 per cent of it was edible, that portion would really cost 90 cents per pound. Cocks are usually cheaper than hens and may be used to advantage for fricasseeing, in a salad or creamed.

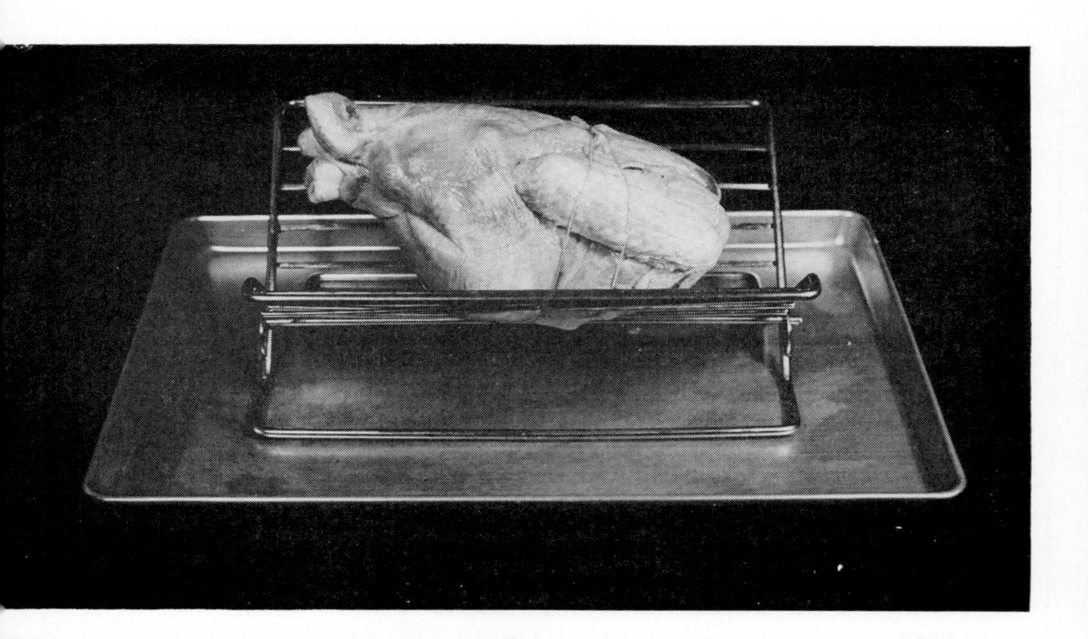

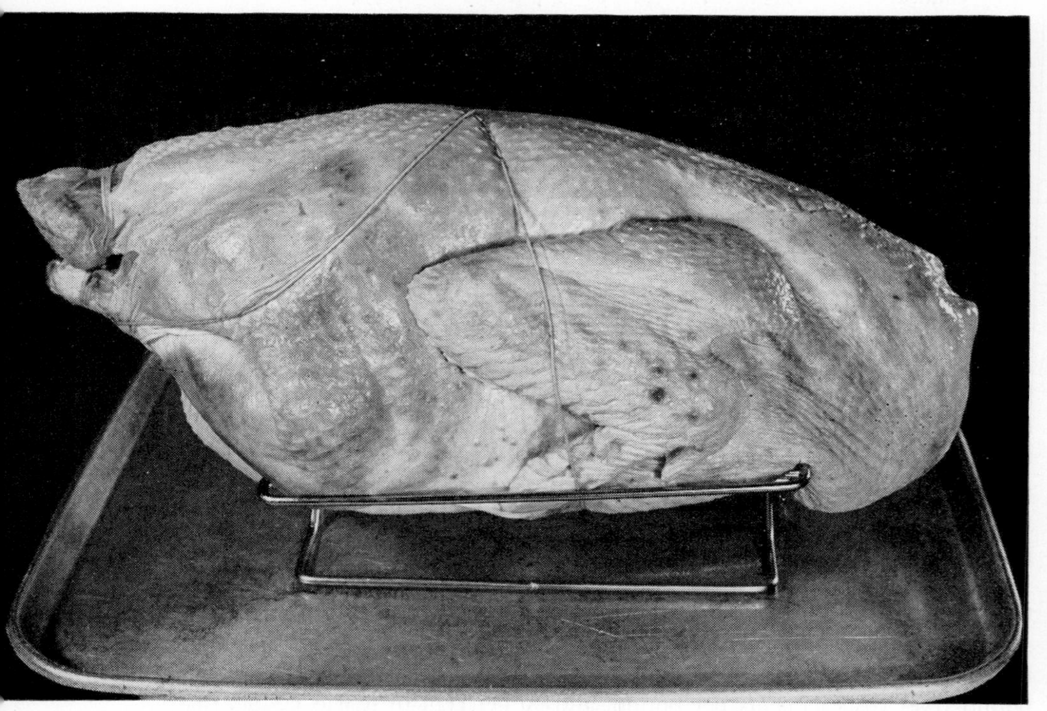

Fig. 30. Turkeys vary greatly in size: above, *a 3-pound 10-oz. turkey;* below, *a 29-pound turkey.*

Turkeys are becoming increasingly popular. They vary in size, as Fig. 30 illustrates. Young birds of the smaller breeds, such as Beltsville Whites, are often used for broiling or frying. However, even the small ones roast well. Turkeys of the Broad-breast Bronze (baby-beef) type average about 33 pounds in weight. Their breasts and thighs are very heavy and the percentage of edible portion is high.

The homemaker may choose between fresh and frozen poultry, packages of the latter being either whole birds or parts. In some markets fresh poultry is prepackaged in cellophane and ready for the purchaser to pick up quickly from the refrigerated counter where it is stored. It should be removed from the package before storing in the home refrigerator.

If a home freezer or space in a community locker plant is used, poultry raised or purchased at the peak of the season may be frozen to advantage. Packaging for later use is important. A few whole birds for roasting and broilers cut in half or left whole may be stored. Birds for frying and stewing may be packaged, or the meaty and bony pieces may be wrapped separately. Packaging of turkey breasts and thighs, and of boned turkey in the form of steaks and ground turkey,[1] has the advantages of occupying little space and having turkey in small amounts ready for various preparation methods.

Cooking poultry. Young poultry may be broiled, fried, or roasted. Older birds require moist heat, and long, slow cooking, or shorter cooking in a pressure pan. For young birds broiling is a highly desirable cooking method. (For directions, see p. 569.) Frying may be done in several ways. The pieces may be rolled in seasoned flour or meal, dipped in egg and then in crumbs after being floured, or dipped in batter. In the last case, frying is done in deep fat. The food being raw and the pieces comparatively large, the temperature of the fat is 350°–360° F. (177°–182° C.). Less fat is needed when chicken is not batter-dipped (see p. 571), and for oven-frying even less fat is used (see p. 571).

Roasting is one of the most popular cookery methods for capons, ducks, geese, and turkeys. There are a number of acceptable ways to roast poultry, one of which is described in Section 4, p. 569. It may be cooked with the breast up, cooked at a high temperature to start or finish the cooking period, be covered or foil-wrapped. The small birds may be cooked in a rotisserie where cooking is even and rather slow and the poultry is juicy and of fine flavor.

Questions sometimes asked by homemakers concerning roasting turkey are, "Is it all right to stuff the turkey one day and cook it the next?" "Can I cook the turkey until it is about half done one day and finish it the next?" There are stuffed, frozen turkeys on the market that are undoubtedly processed under conditions of sanitation that make them safe. This is not neces-

---

[1] Rose A. Erisman, "Production, Storage and Preparation of Turkey Parts, Including Steaks" (Thesis, University of Texas, 1950).

sarily true when carried out at home. A better way to save time would be to prepare the stuffing ahead except for the liquid, including egg if used. In carefully controlled work, it has been found that the divided-cooking method required nearly twice as much time as when the cooking was continuous.[1]

Stewing or braising (fricasseeing, see p. 572) are the moist-heat methods used for older birds. Use of a pressure-pan is advantageous. The meat is often used in salads, loaves, and creamed or casserole dishes. The bones, simmered with suitable seasonings, are a source of delicious soup stock.

In all cookery methods, temperature should be low, since high temperature toughens the meat and makes it less moist.

SUGGESTIONS FOR LABORATORY

There are many excellent methods for preparing poultry. Recipes from standard and special sources include such universal favorites as fried, roasted, broiled, stewed, and fricasseed chicken, with interesting variations. Based on recent research, modern recipes for these are likely to indicate lower cooking temperatures and often suggest the use of contemporary appliances. Students might find it interesting to compare the older with the modern methods.

REFERENCES

Carpenter, Rowena S. and Alfred W. Otte, *Poultry Buying Guide for Consumers*. U.S.D.A., Home and Garden Bull. No. 34, 1953.

Carpenter, Rowena S., *Poultry Grading and Inspection*. U.S.D.A., Production and Marketing Adm., Poultry Branch, PA-96, 1950.

Know the Poultry You Buy. U.S.D.A., Production and Marketing Adm., Poultry Branch, 1952.

Let's Eat Turkey. Extension Foods and Nutrition Specialists, Texas A. & M. College, College Station, Texas.

McLean, Beth Bailey and T. E. Campbell, *The Complete Meat Cookbook*. Chas. A. Bennett Co., Inc., Publishers, Peoria, Ill., 1953.

Stewart, G. F., et al. "Effects of Aging, Freezing Rate, and Storage Period on Palatability of Broilers." *Food Research,* 10:16 (1945).

Troelstrup, Arch W., *Consumer Problems and Personal Finance*. McGraw-Hill Book Co., Inc., New York, 1957.

Von Loesecke, Harry W., *Outlines of Food Technology*. 2nd. Ed. Reinhold Publishing Corp., New York, 1949.

[1] Lowe, Belle, *Experimental Cookery,* 4th Edition. John Wiley and Sons, Inc., New York, 1955.

UNIT

12

Seafood

James Truslow Adams [1] has given a clear picture of the importance of the fishing industry in early days in New England.

If no precious metals rewarded search, if the beaver retreated farther and farther into the wilderness, if the soil gave but grudging yield, here, at least, was limitless wealth. The industry . . . became the cornerstone of the prosperity of New England; and in the colonial history of that section, commerce smells as strongly of fish as theology does of brimstone.

Marblehead maintained her independence of all restraining law and precept by providing fish in plenty.[2]

Literally true was the Marblehead fisherman's reproof to an exhorting preacher: "Our ancestors came not here for religion. Their main end was to catch fish!" Equally true was Marblehead's protest against an export tax in 1669. "Fish is the only great staple which the country produceth for forraine parts and is so benefitiall for making returns for what wee need."

Fishing always furnishes a certain amount of thrill, whether the fisherman is a small boy angling for bass in an inland creek or one of a party seriously engaged in the business of deep-sea fishing. Deep-sea fishing is not only fascinating but dangerous, as the following news item testifies: [3]

Gloucester, Mass., Aug. 4—Fifteen heroes of the most dangerous calling were honored today as Gloucester observed a memorial day that is exclusively her own. On the first Sunday in August each year, when the rocky gardens of Cape Ann are in gayest bloom, the old port pays homage to the men who have given their

---

[1] James Truslow Adams, *The Founding of New England,* p. 11. By permission of Little, Brown and Co., Boston, publishers.

[2] Samuel Eliot Morison, *Maritime History of Massachusetts,* p. 13. By permission of Houghton Mifflin Co., Boston, publishers.

[3] *San Antonio* (Texas) *Express,* Aug. 5, 1936. Reprinted by permission.

lives during the preceding year while serving her chief industry, the fishery. As the name of each lost mariner was called by Rev. George E. Russell, Chaplain of the Fishermen's Institute, who has conducted the services many years, a bright-hued wreath was cast on the running tide to be borne away to an unmarked grave.

Persons who are fond of sea food find delight in the favorite fish of various places. They never fail, when their travels take them there, to enjoy a broiled brook trout at a hotel in the Rockies, where the fish are brought in fresh from the stream; to have pompano and shrimp creole in New Orleans, or a clam bake on the shore, where such an outing is possible. Neither would they miss lobster at one of New England's famous lobster pounds or their favorite brand of clam chowder wherever it is to be had. Probably a visit to San Francisco would not be complete without a meal at Fisherman's Wharf.

An inlander who is fond of trout from a local lake is due to be surprised if, at a restaurant along Atlantic City's board walk, he orders sea trout. The fat fish with which he is familiar is not the same as the lean trout caught in salt water. Similar differences may exist in other cases.

Nutritive value. Fish is an excellent source of protein. Its usual tenderness is due to the fact that the bundles of muscle fibers are held together by connective tissue that is largely made up of a protein, collagen, that is converted to gelatin when heated. Fat fish—such as salmon, butterfish, and catfish—are good sources of fat and the livers of some, chiefly cod and halibut, are rich in oil which is used to provide in concentrated form vitamins A and D. Fish furnish considerable amounts of the B vitamins and important amounts of minerals—copper, iron, and phosphorus. Salmon canned with the bone is a good source of calcium if the bone is eaten. All salt-water fish are excellent sources of iodine.

Types and sources. Sea foods are usually referred to as *fin fish* and *shellfish*. The former are classified as fresh-water and salt-water fish; the latter as mollusks and crustaceans.

Many inland lakes and streams abound in fish. Artificial lakes are frequently stocked with fish. In most states agricultural experts encourage many farmers to construct ponds for watering cattle and as a part of projects to prevent soil erosion. These ponds are frequently stocked with fish. Fish for stocking both natural and artificial inland waters are obtained from hatcheries maintained by the states. Laws regulating the season during which fish may be caught and the size of those that may be retained keep a constant supply available. Trout, bass, pike, pickerel, and whitefish are a few of the common fresh-water fish. Some varieties are found in one locality only. Lampreys, which prey upon fish in the Great Lakes, are being exterminated so that a "normal" supply of lake fish may soon be expected.

Salt-water fish are always abundant. Cod, halibut, haddock, flounder, mackerel, tuna, salmon, and herring are some of the common varieties. Some of these fish grow to be very large, cod frequently weighing 20 to 40 pounds, tuna, as much as 300 pounds, and swordfish up to 500 pounds. In contrast, smelts usually weigh less than ¼ pound.

The mollusks—shellfish that are soft and partly or wholly encased in a shell—include oysters, clams, scallops, mussels, and abalone. Oyster farming has been carried on as an important industry for centuries. Oysters thrive in shallow water, frequently near the outlet of streams. The importance of keeping this water pure cannot be overestimated, as oysters taken from polluted waters are a serious health hazard. Clams are firmer than oysters. The two main species are hard-shelled little-neck clams and soft-shelled long-neck clams.

Edible scallops are only the hard muscle that opens and closes the shell of the scallop. Mussels, while not used extensively, are considered superior to oysters by some people. In Europe they are more popular than in America. Abalone is a Pacific Coast mollusk.

The crustaceans—segmented shellfish whose protective covering is a crusty shell—include lobsters, crabs, shrimp, and crayfish. Lobsters are available in large numbers along the New England Coast; crabs and shrimp are more plentiful farther south. Lobsters are caught in traps (lobster pots). The owners go to their traps frequently, pull them into their boats, and sort the catch. Lobsters that are too small, and any other fish that are in the trap, are thrown back. Fresh lobsters are marketed alive.

Crabs are either hard-shell or soft-shell. These are the same species. During the molting season they shed their shells and until the new shells harden, they are called soft-shell crabs.

Shrimps are caught in large numbers along the South Atlantic and Gulf coasts. The heads are usually removed before they are marketed. On many markets they may be purchased either raw or cooked. They vary in size.

Crayfish (crawfish) are found in both fresh and salt water, but are not important commercially. The crayfish bisque which is popular along the Gulf Coast is available canned on some markets.

Preservation. Fish are cold-blooded; hence the enzymes that are present in their bodies are active at much lower temperatures than is true of poultry or meat. Consequently, they must be used quickly after catching, stored at a low temperature, or preserved for later use. On the boats they are stored on ice or may even be quick-frozen. Fish are placed on ice at the piers, where much of the selling to wholesalers and jobbers is done. The fish that are not taken for immediate marketing are sent at once to storehouses where they are washed and frozen. A glaze of ice over the fish prevents evaporation and makes relatively long-time storage possible. Such fish are thawed just before being sold on the retail market.

For longer preservation, fish are quick-frozen, dried, salted, smoked, pickled, canned; or a combination of some of these methods may be used. Cod is dried and salted; herring is pickled or cured with salt and smoke. Salmon, tuna fish, anchovies, herring, sardines, lobster, shrimp, crab, and abalone are the most popular canned fish. The roe of some species of fish is preserved and canned, and the resulting caviar is used as a material for hors d'oeuvres. Fresh roe from several fish, including the shad, is sometimes served broiled or baked.

Since it has been possible to quick-freeze fish and to transport them satisfactorily, the variety available to most homemakers has been enlarged greatly. For example, salmon was known only as a canned product, while now frozen steaks are available the country over. Lobster tails, imported from South Africa, are found on many markets.

Buying. It is most important that fish should be fresh. The odor, especially around the gills, should be fresh. The gills of most fish are red. The eyes are bright and shiny. Scales should cling firmly to the skin. The flesh is firm, and should not pit when pressed, especially around the backbone.

Lobsters should be purchased alive, cooked, or frozen. When alive, they are often very inactive, but if the tail snaps back quickly over the back when it is flattened out, the lobster is fresh. This test holds true, also, of cooked lobster. The tail will do the same if the lobster was alive when cooking began.

Fish should be chosen with the method of cooking in mind. A slender fish like a trout or a small redfish is excellent for broiling, while a thicker fish, such as a red snapper or a good-sized bass, is better for baking.

In general, lean fish such as cod, halibut, or red snapper, are selected for steaming or poaching, and fat fish, such as salmon or lake trout for broiling or baking. However, fat may be added to the lean varieties in the form of a strip of bacon while the cooking is being done, so that the rule does not prevent baking a red snapper or other lean fish. Either may be fried satisfactorily. Swordfish is rather dry and is a good example of a fish that may well be poached or steamed.

Because the variety of fresh fish and shellfish differs with the location, the prospective buyer should visit the markets and learn the varieties available, how to distinguish them, and the ones suitable for different cooking methods. The shellfish available and the fish that are preserved in different ways should also be known. This will make it possible to choose or order intelligently and within the money allowed for food.

Cooking. Fish are tender and require a rather short cooking time. If a fish is to be boiled, it should be wrapped in cheesecloth and perhaps placed on a plate so that it can be removed from the water easily. The temperature of the water should be simmering—about 185° F. (85° C.). Temperatures should be low, no matter what the cookery method used, because high temperature tends to toughen the meat.

Fish that are fat may be cooked with little, if any, additional fat. Lean fish should be basted with melted fat during broiling. Strips of salt pork or bacon are laid across them during baking. They may be marinated in French dressing (see p. 519) for about an hour before broiling.

Lobsters, when boiled, are plunged head-first into boiling water. This kills them instantly. The water is kept below the boiling point for the remainder of the cooking period. This also applies to crabs. If lobsters are baked or broiled, they are laid on their backs and split very quickly from head to tail, thereby being killed instantly. The dull green color of the live lobster changes to lobster-red as the shellfish is cooked.

The shells of shrimp are removed; also the intestinal vein—the dark streak along the back. They are cooked in boiling, salted water until the characteristic coral-pink color appears.

Oysters and clams are washed and cooked at a low temperature to prevent toughness. Clams are often steamed in the shells until the shells open. They are served with melted butter and perhaps lemon.

SUGGESTIONS FOR LABORATORY

The frequency with which fish is included in the American diet does not reflect, in many instances, its abundance in this country. Considering its widespread availability, especially fresh frozen, its superior food value, ease of preparation, and the relatively low cost of many varieties, it is difficult to understand why the genuine goodness of seafood is not generally appreciated. Its rejection is probably due in part to a lack of understanding of the simple fundamentals involved in its preparation. It need not be tough, tasteless, dry, coated with a soggy breaded mixture, or fat-soaked. Such abuses of fish in its preparation mask the flavor of the delicate, tender flesh and destroy its juiciness.

Because of the prevalence of distaste for fish, laboratory projects involving its preparation and use need to be carefully selected. A wise choice of recipes to illustrate the basic principles of cooking would be those that stress simplicity of preparation techniques, new interesting flavor combinations, and attractiveness. Since cooking time for fish is very short, interest might be aroused first by a short demonstration given by the instructor or a group of students who are seafood enthusiasts. The recipes on pp. 575–585 give an interesting range of both methods of cooking and types of fish dishes. The general and special references should also be consulted before making final plans for laboratory work.

REFERENCES

Brown, Cora, Rose, and Bob, *Fish and Seafood Cook Book*. J. B. Lippincott Co., Philadelphia, 1940.

De Gouy, Louis P., *Gourmet's Cook Book of Fish and Game*. Gourmet, Inc., New York, 1947.

Faust, Hilda and Vera Greaves Mrak, *What About Fish?* University of California College of Agriculture, Agricultural Extension Service Cir. 144, Revised, 1952.

Kerr, Rose G., *Basic Fish Cookery*. U.S.D.I., Fish and Wildlife Service, Test K Series, No. 2.

Todoroff, Alexander, *Food Buyer's Information Book*. The Grocery Trade Publishing House, Chicago, 1946.

Von Loesecke, Harry W., *Outlines of Food Technology*. 2nd Edition, Reinhold Publishing Corp., New York, 1949.

UNIT

13

Fats and Oils

Fats and oils from various sources are used in many cookery processes, and a study of food habits would show that people living in different parts of the United States differ in both choice of fats used and amounts commonly used. Also, people in different countries vary in their choice of fats; for example, many people from both Asia and Europe insist upon olive oil, whereas most Americans prefer oil from cotton, corn, or peanuts.

Pure fats have no odor or taste. They feel greasy. Their specific gravity is low, as evidenced by the facts that cream rises on milk, and that if most French dressing is allowed to stand, the oil separates from the acid and seasonings and rises to the top. At "ordinary" temperatures—65° to 70° F. (18° to 21° C.), fats are solid and oils are liquid.

Carbon, hydrogen, and oxygen are the elements of which fats are composed. They are defined as glyceryl esters of fatty acids, one molecule of glycerine combining with three molecules of fatty acid to form one molecule of fat. The three molecules of fatty acid are seldom the same acid; hence, the term "mixed glycerides" is often applied to fats. There are many fatty acids. Some contain all the hydrogen possible in relation to the carbon present, while others do not. The former are called saturated; the latter, unsaturated. To illustrate, oleic acid, found in practically all fats and oils, is unsaturated, as its formula ($C_{17}H_{33}COOH$), indicates:

$$\begin{array}{ccccccccccccccc} & & H & & H & & & & & & H & & & & \\ & & | & & | & & & & & & | & & & & \\ H & - & C & - & C & - & C & = & C & - & C & - & C & = & O \\ & & | & & | & & | & & | & & | & & | & & \\ & & H & & H_7 & & H & & H & & H_7 & & OH & & \end{array}$$

There are two carbons to which hydrogen might be attached. If the carbon is added, the formula ($C_{17}H_{35}COOH$) is written thus:

$$\begin{array}{ccccccc} & & H & & H & & \\ & & | & & | & & \\ H & — & C & — & C & — & C{=}O \\ & & | & & | & & | \\ & & H & & H_{16} & & OH \end{array}$$

This fatty acid, saturated with respect to hydrogen, is stearic acid. Most fats and oils contain several fatty acids. The higher the proportion of saturated acids, of which stearic and palmitic acids are examples, the harder the fat. Suet, for instance, contains a large proportion of saturated fatty acids. On the contrary, the higher the proportion of unsaturated fatty acids, the softer the fat. Lard is an example. Oils, of course, contain a very high proportion of unsaturated fatty acids.

Fats in the diet. Personal liking for foods rich in fat and the popularity of such foods as fried chicken and French fries tend to make the American diet relatively high in fat. As carriers of Vitamins A, D, and E, and of essential fatty acids, as well as sources of energy, fats are important. Continued use of milk products and decreased fried foods would give desirable "balance" in the diet. More fat may be used by persons doing hard physical work than those of sedentary habits and more may be used in cold weather than in warm.

Per unit weight, fat yields the most energy of the three foods that are chiefly energy-giving. For example, a pound of butter furnishes 3251 calories; a pound of cooking fat, 4,013; while a similar weight of pure starch yields 1644, and of sugar (granulated), 1748. These figures may be deceiving, however, from the point of view of eating habits, because of the tendency to include much more starch and sugar than fat. If the following foods were eaten within a day, the comparison is obvious.

Starch	*Cal.*	*Sugar*	*Cal.*	*Fat*	*Cal.*
2 sl. bread	126	2 tb. sugar	96	3 tb. butter	300
1 sweet roll	178	1 oz. milk chocolate	143	2 sl. bacon	97
1 Irish potato	105	3″ sec. cake—fudge icing	314		397
½ c. spaghetti	109	3½ oz. ice cream	129		
	518		682		

Sources of fats and oils. Fats of direct animal origin are suet and tallow from beef and lamb, lard from pork, and fat from poultry. Formerly, animal fats had more uses than now: candles were made from tallow, and soap from scraps of fat. Among farm families, lard rendering is common, and soap is made by some families. Fat from poultry should be rendered, strained, and may be used in soups, sauces, and many baked products. Drippings from bacon and other cuts of pork are excellent for seasoning and, in some instances, shortening. Suet may be used for both puddings and pastries.

Lard. Lard of the finest quality is made from the fat that lines the visceral cavity of hogs, rendered at low temperature. It is known as "neutral lard No. 1," and also as "leaf lard." "Kettle-rendered lard" is from the fat back of hogs. "Prime steam lard" is rendered by steam from trimmings when hog carcasses are cut, and from the fat which surrounds the intestines. Not all of these grades of lard are available on every retail market. The highest grade, leaf lard, is always more expensive than the lower grades. Because it is milder in flavor, leaf lard is often preferred as a fat for cooking purposes. Both flavor and texture of lard are improved by the addition of hydrogen, and there are several brands of such lard on the market. Also, antioxidants are added to lards to increase their keeping qualities, and most commercial lards are filtered and deodorized.

Compounds. Compounds are made by combining animal fats with vegetable oils. The mixture is bleached and deodorized and antioxidant is added. These fats are used in the same ways as lard and may be less expensive than good quality lard.

Hydrogenated fats. Many of the cooking fats that are available to the consumer are made from oils by adding sufficient hydrogen to make a fat of the desired texture. The hydrogen is added under controlled conditions in the presence of a catalyst, usually, finely divided nickel. These fats are practically flavorless and are extensively used as cooking fats. They frequently vary in price more than in quality and are usually more expensive than lard. They, too, have antioxidant added, and many are creamed before packaging, making their texture light and fluffy. These fats are superglycerated during the manufacturing process. The result is that a pound of such a fat measures 2⅓ cups rather than 2 cups, as in the case of butter, margarine, or fats in pound cartons.

Butter. Butter was made and used by many ancient peoples. "It has been known for at least two thousand years prior to the Christian Era, being used as food to some slight extent in early days, but mostly as medicine, and as an ointment after bathing, and sometimes in lamps in place of oil." [1] It gradually became a generally accepted item of food, and was made in the homes of most people who raised milk-giving animals. As trade developed, extra butter was packed in earthenware crocks and sold or exchanged for other goods. This practice is still common. Rural families who produce their own supply of butter frequently pack it in special containers and store it in a locker.

Butter is important from a nutritive point of view as a source of energy and of the fat-soluble vitamins, A and D. The quantity of vitamin A is dependent to some extent upon the feed of the cows and the season of the year.

The bulk of the butter used in the United States is made in creameries. It may be churned from either sweet or sour cream. The conditions under

[1] *The New International Encyclopedia,* IV (2nd ed. New York: Dodd Mead, 1935), p. 223.

which it is made are usually carefully standardized. Coloring may be added. The law specifies 80 per cent butterfat as a minimum and 16 per cent moisture as a maximum. As a rule, salt is added to give flavor, to act as a preservative, and to assist in removing buttermilk during the buttermaking process. "Sweet butter," popular with some people, is butter that is not salted.

Butter of good quality is firm, neither brittle nor oily. It is free from streaks due to poor working, mild in flavor, and agreeable in odor. The price fluctuates considerably with the season, the brand, the quality, and the package. The grade is sometimes included on the label or in the package if it scores 92 or more, but this is not widely customary. Desirable butter should score at least 90 points, and if the score is below 88, the butter is not considered good for table use. Sour-cream butter is cheaper than that made from sweet cream, and country butter is usually cheaper than creamery butter. Whipped butter, popular because it spreads easily, is a semi-luxury item. On the local markets choice may usually be made from several brands of butter.

Renovated butter is made from low-grade or rancid butter which has been melted, clarified, aerated, and re-churned in whole or skim milk or in fresh cream. It must be labeled to prevent its sale as fresh butter. Butter of low melting point is being produced for shipment to the armed forces overseas and to foreign countries.

Research has shown that it is highly important to use pasteurized cream for the making of butter. The bacilli that cause undulant fever in human beings, *B. abortus,* remain active fifteen times as long in butter as in the cream from which it is churned. The label on packages should state that the butter was made from pasteurized cream.

Margarine. Technically, there is a distinction between the terms "margarine" and "oleomargarine." The former is made from oils from vegetable sources; the latter, from a combination of vegetable oils and animal fats, principally oleostearin from beef and leaf lard from hogs. The term "margarine" is commonly used to apply to all these fats. In either case, the constituents are churned in whole or skimmed milk. Practically all margarines are fortified by the addition of not less than 15,000 U. S. Pharmacopoeia units of vitamin A per pound. Many brands of margarine also contain vitamin D. Because these vitamins are added in the manufacturing process, their amounts can be known exactly.

Federal legislation[1] effective since July 1, 1950, includes the following points concerning colored margarine:

1) Packages must have a net weight of one pound or less. Both the whole package and each portion if the package contains more than one unit must be clearly labeled "oleomargarine" or "margarine." The label must include a complete and accurate statement of all ingredients.

---

[1] *World Almanac,* 1953.

2) The color content is specified as a tint or shade containing more than 1.6° of yellow and red collectively, but excess of yellow over red, "measured in terms of Lovibond tintometer scale or equivalent."

3) If colored margarine is sold in a public eating place, a conspicuous notice must be displayed and each serving must be either labeled to identify it or cut in the shape of a triangle.

4) Colored oleomargarine or margarine "sold in the same State or Territory in which it is produced shall be subject in the same manner and to the same extent to provisions of this chapter as if it had been introduced in interstate commerce."

5) Nothing in the Federal law "shall be construed as authorizing the possession, sale, or serving of colored oleomargarine or colored margarine in any State or Territory in contravention of such State or Territory."

Nearly all the states have enacted legislation which conforms to the Federal legislation.

Olive oil. Olive oil has been known as long as records reveal the foods used by mankind. It is still the chief oil used in many countries. The oil of finest quality is expressed[1] from ripe olives. A second pressing, or the use of a low grade of olives, yields an inferior oil. Filtering is all that is needed to prepare the expressed oil for the market. It has a distinct flavor which many people prefer to the bland flavor of other oils. Imported olive oil is much more expensive than the domestic product.

Cottonseed oil. Oil is obtained from the seeds of cotton by pressing and refining. The dark color and disagreeable odor and flavor of the crude product are removed during the refining process, and the refined oil is desirable for use in salad dressings and for cooking purposes. A great deal of cottonseed oil is hydrogenated to provide cooking fats.

Corn oil. When cornstarch and corn sirup are manufactured, the germ of the corn kernel is ground and pressed to produce oil. This requires refining to improve the color and flavor. It is used extensively for salad dressings and as a cooking oil.

Peanut oil. Production of oil from Spanish peanuts is increasing. It is expressed, allowed to settle, filtered, and refined. It is used as both salad and cooking oil and for cooking sardines that are to be canned.

Other oils. Many other plants are sources of oil used in food preparation. Included are coconuts, pecans, sesame seed, rape seed, poppy seed, sunflower seed, and soybeans. Of these, oil from coconuts is more extensively used in the United States than that from the other sources listed. Mineral oil is not recommended for use in either salad dressings or other foods.

Oil that has been refrigerated sometimes looks cloudy. Some mayonnaise at similar temperature separates. This is because some of the fatty acids

[1] "Expressed" means that olives or other products are subjected to pressure with the result that the oil is separated from the rest of the product.

solidify at a higher temperature than others. Ideal oil for home use should not contain fatty acids that become solid at temperatures higher than about 40° F. (4° C.). In order to prevent this separation, most of the oil used in mayonnaise and sold for home use has been "wintered." This is a simple process. The oil is chilled to the temperature at which fatty acids that are not desirable have separated, and then it is pumped through filter presses which retain the solid portion and allow the liquid to run out. The solid portion is used in making compounds, candles, and soap.

USES OF FATS AND OILS

Aside from their specific inclusion in the diet from a nutritional point of view, the fats and oils are used in connection with food preparation in a number of ways:

For flavor. Fats are commonly used as a seasoning for vegetables, in sauces and gravies, and as a spread for bread.

To act as solvents for other flavors. Sandwiches made with parsley, water cress, or orange butter are popular. The aroma of onions, celery, and various herbs may be held for considerable time in fat or oil. The seasoned fat or oil is quickly available for seasoning purposes.

In emulsions. An emulsion consists of two liquids which are immiscible,[1] one of which is dispersed in tiny droplets throughout the other. The common liquids in food emulsions are oil and water. The emulsion may be temporary, as in the case of fresh milk or French salad dressing. If a third substance, such as egg, starch paste, or gelatin, is combined properly with oil and water, the droplets of oil are held suspended throughout the water and the emulsion is permanent. This substance is called an emulsifier, emulsifying agent, or stabilizer. All salad dressings are emulsions, and so are many sauces and gravies. The emulsification of fat in a cake made with fat has much to do with the quality of the finished product.

As shorteners. A mixture of flour and water, baked, would be tough. Addition of fat would result in a tender product. In some flour mixtures, for example, pastry, both tenderness and flakiness are desirable. Fat produces these qualities by surrounding both particles of starch and strands of gluten, keeping the latter short. Hence the term "shortening." The quantity of fat used and the method by which it is added influence the tenderness and flakiness of the products.

As a cooking medium. Fat is used as a cooking medium, the term applied depending upon the amount of fat used and where the cooking is done. (See Glossary.)

The temperature best suited for frying depends upon size of pieces and whether the food is raw or cooked before it is fried. Small and thin items may

[1] When two substances will not mix, they are said to be immiscible.

be fried in hotter fat than large and thick ones. Raw food requires longer cooking than cooked food; therefore the fat must be cooler, else the outside will be too brown before the inside is cooked. Cooking time of raw foods can be estimated by judging the size of the foods being cooked.

Altitude. At the temperature recommended for frying foods at sea level, foods become too brown by the time they are cooked. Hence temperature of fat must be reduced. Instructions which are suited to the altitude should be followed.

DIFFERENCES AMONG THE FATS AND OILS

The fats and oils differ materially in a number of ways:

In their melting points. The melting points of fats that contain a large percentage of saturated fatty acids are higher than those of oils or of fats that contain a small percentage of saturated fatty acids.

In their smoking temperatures. The temperature at which fats start to smoke varies considerably. Overheating should always be avoided. When fats are heated until they reach the decomposition point, the smoke given off is very irritating to the mucous membrane of the digestive tract and to the eyes. This irritation, resulting in coughing and tears as the body attempts to rid itself of the offending smoke, is due to the acrolein that is formed when the fat becomes hot enough to smoke. The approximate temperatures at which some of the commonly used fats smoke are listed in Table 18. Repeated use of fats for frying lowers smoking temperature. This decrease is caused in part by the effect of repeated heating and in part by the influence of particles of the fried food. It is important that fat be strained after each use, and sometimes it may be clarified by frying raw potato which absorbs part of the decomposition products, fatty acids and glycerol. This cannot be continued indefinitely, however. Fat in which fish has been fried may retain the flavor of fish. In that case, such fat should be stored separately from fat used for frying other foods.

A frying utensil that is relatively small in diameter is better for frying than a large one because the surface area affects the smoking temperature. Electrically heated utensils, both separate units and part of the standard equipment for a range, are advantageous because most of them have thermostats which regulate the temperature. Naturally, when food is added to the fat the temperature is decreased. The advantage of the thermostat is that as the temperature rises again it does not exceed that at which the food is to be fried.

In their shortening power. Fats vary in their effectiveness as shorteners. Shortening power is measured in the laboratory by the pressure required to break or crush a thin baked product, such as a cracker, cookie, or piece of pastry. At home, the shortening power is judged by the ease with which

TABLE 18. SMOKE POINTS AND FREE FATTY ACID AS OLEIC OF TYPES OF FATS AND OILS COMMONLY USED IN COOKERY *

Fat	*Container and Amount of Fat* †				*Free Fatty Acid*
	AOCS ‡ Cup, 70g	Skillet 100g	Enameled Kettle 2,000g	Dutch Oven 2,000g	
	° *F.*	° *F.*	° *F.*	° *F.*	*per cent*
Lards:					
1. Steam rendered	333	311	313	298	0.49
2. Steam rendered	343	316	320	311	0.23
3. Steam rendered	327	307	313	302	0.45
4. Leaf	374	345	352	342	0.20
5. Deodorized, stabilized	432	390	397	378	0.07
All-hydrogenated fats:					
1.	354	298	309	302	0.06
2.	340	306	307	304	0.09
3.	432	385	397	379	0.03
4.	356	322	311	315	0.09
Blended shortenings:					
1. Animal-vegetable	390	361	381	361	0.12
2. Vegetable-animal	441	412	410	394	0.07
3. All vegetable (major component named first)	417	414	392	387	0.08
Oils:					
1. Cottonseed	426	387	406	399	0.05
2. Peanut	378	343	349	336	0.17
3. Corn	408	374	376	365	0.17
4. Soybean	439	405	415	383	0.07

SOURCE: Ve Nono Swartz, *Smoke Points Affected by Determination Method*. Journ. of Home Economics. 40:251, 1948. By permission, Journ. of Home Economics.

* Two to four determinations on each fat.

† Diameters of containers: AOCS Cup, about 2½ in.; Skillet (cast iron), 5.8 in.; Enameled Kettle, 8 in.; Dutch Oven (cast iron), 9.2 in.

‡ American Oil Chemists' Society.

such products are broken, bitten, and chewed. Tender, flaky pastry is "short," while tough, hard pastry is not.

The degree to which fats act as shorteners depends upon a number of factors. The more highly saturated a fat, that is, the higher its proportion of saturated fatty acids, the less desirable it is for shortening. This is probably due to the ease with which the more plastic fats spread on damp surfaces as the ingredients are combined. Flakiness in pie crust is definitely increased if part of the fat is left in relatively large pieces so that as the crust is rolled it forms a layer between two layers of the mixture. Since plasticity is affected by temperature, the fat should be at a temperature suitable for the product being made. Suitable methods for combining fat with other ingredients will be discussed under the various types of flour mixtures. The shortening power of some commonly used fats is listed in Table 18.

FAT SPOILAGE: BUYING FATS AND OILS

A fat which has spoiled is said to be rancid. Rancidity may be caused by oxidation and it was formerly the custom to keep fats in a cool or cold place, free from light and air. The general use of antioxidants in the manufacture of fats makes a cold storage temperature unnecessary. They should be kept in a closed container, however. Fats may also be spoiled by hydrolysis, the process by which glycerol and fatty acids are formed from the fats. Some fats are more susceptible to this form of spoilage than others, butter being rather easily hydrolyzed because of the specific fatty acid, butyric, which is one of its components. Because they absorb odors readily, fats should be kept covered.

The quantity of fats and oils purchased should be related to the size of the group and the approximate amount that will be used in flour mixtures, salad dressings, and as a cooking medium. They are cheaper in relatively large amounts, and if the larger quantities can be used without spoiling, they should be purchased. Butter and margarine should be stored, covered, in a refrigerator. Cooking fats seldom need refrigeration, but oils do if the weather is warm.

SUGGESTIONS FOR LABORATORY

The current emphasis on lessening the amount of fat in the diet is commendable. However, in the minds of some people it has, perhaps, been carried to the point of exaggeration, making use of fat almost taboo. Plans for the laboratory may include emphasis upon decreased fat, both when it is used as a cooking medium and when it is listed in recipes. In the latter case, high-fat ingredients, such as cheese and cream, should be considered when questioning the total quantity of fat in a recipe.

REFERENCES

Arenson, S. W., "Shortenings for Frying and Baking." *Food Inds.,* 22:1015 (1950).

Cawood, J. F., "Shortening Value of Plastic Fats." *Ind. Eng. Chem.,* 26:968 (1954).

Hornstein, L. R. et al., "Comparative Shortening Value of Some Commercial Fats," *Food Research,* 8:1 (1943).

Jacobs, Morris B., *Food and Food Products,* 2nd. Ed., Vol. 2. Interscience Publishers, Inc., New York and London, 1951.

Rose, T. S. et al., "The Effect of the Method of Fat and Water Incorporation on the Average Shortness and the Uniformity of Tenderness of Pastry." *J. Home Econ.,* 44:707 (1952).

U.S.D.A., *Know Your Butter Grades.* Production and Marketing Adm., Leaflet No. 264 (1949).

UNIT

14

Sugar; Crystallization

Some native source of sugar has been found and used by people in different parts of the world from prehistoric times. Honey made by bees and stored in trees was one such source. It is still exciting to find and cut a "bee tree." Sweet sap extracted from certain grasses was concentrated to supply a product even sweeter than honey in areas where these grasses grew. In some countries sugar was made from a native palm. Early settlers on the shores of America as far south as Virginia found the Indians making sugar from the sap of the sugar maple. Governor Berkeley, in 1706, wrote: "The sugar tree yields a kind of sap or juice which by boiling is made into sugar. It is said that the Indians made one pound of sugar out of eight pounds of the Liquor." [1] In tracing the origin of the use of maple sap for sugar-making Chamberlain [2] quotes a delightful legend:

> One day Nokomis, the grandmother of Manabush, was in the forest and accidentally cut the bark of a tree. Seeing that a thick syrup exuded from the cut, she put her finger to the substance, and upon tasting it found it to be very sweet and agreeable. She then gave some of it to her grandson, Manabush, who liked it very much, but thought that if the syrup ran from the tree in such a state it would cause idleness among the women. He then told Nokomis that in order to give his aunts employment and keep them from idleness he would dilute the thick sap. Whereupon he took up a vessel of water and poured it over the tops of the trees, and thus reduced the sap to its present consistency. This is why the women have to boil down the sap to make sugar.

The word "sugar" usually brings to mind the granulated sugar from cane or beets so constantly used, together with the cubed and powdered forms.

[1] Alice Morse Earle, *Home Life in Colonial Days* (New York: Macmillan, 1913), p. 111.

[2] A. F. Chamberlain, "The Maple Amongst the Algonkian Tribes," *American Anthropologist,* Vol. 4 (1891), pp. 39–43.

The nation's total sugar supply includes brown sugar; molasses; corn sugar (cerelose) and sirup; maple, sorgo, and cane sirups; and honey.

Sweets in moderation. Refined sugar is a concentrated source of food that supplies energy. While other sweets are also principally valuable as energy foods, some make other contributions to the dietary. For example, molasses, sorgo sirup, and maple sirup all contain both calcium and iron. This fact does not imply that very dark molasses has therapeutic value. As defined by refiners, "blackstrap" molasses is not suitable for human food.

Persons interested in improved food habits, especially when considered on a nation-wide scale, are concerned about the trend in sugar consumption. In the United States, the per capita consumption of sugar has risen steadily with increased supply and lower price until the amount for 1956 was 98.4 pounds. In terms of energy food, this would provide more than ¼ pound per person per day, or more than 400 calories. For a person whose calorie requirement is 2,400, at least 16.66 per cent would be from sweets. In a recent survey it was found that 12 per cent of the calories were from sugar and sirups. Recommendations vary from 5 to 10 per cent, or 120 to 240 calories. Thus the average now consumed is distinctly above that considered desirable. The fact that sugar is not specified as a *basic* food is significant.

Regarding the habit of eating too much sweet food, Bogert says, "If such a one-sided food is allowed too prominent a place in the diet there will be a shortage of the essential proteins, mineral elements, and vitamins. It should be used chiefly as a flavoring material, in more dilute forms (fresh fruits), or at the end of meals (desserts). . . . When taken in concentrated form or in excessive amounts, especially on an empty stomach, it may irritate the lining of the stomach or cause distress by fermenting in the intestine. Much sugar in the diet has been shown to be a contributing factor in causing tooth decay, overweight, or diabetes."[1] In agreement with other authorities, Proudfit and Robinson[2] state, "It is not the presence of sugar in the diet itself which is harmful but rather the omission of essential foods which may result when sugar is used in large quantities."

Production. Refined sugar is made from sugar cane and sugar beets. Both products are very nearly 100 per cent sucrose. They are therefore chemically identical. Both are satisfactory for all the purposes for which sugar is used, including making preserves and jellies. Both may be found on the market in coarse or fine granulation, and both may lump in damp weather. They are, of course, equally sweet.

The granulated sugar used for most purposes is called "standard fine" or "extra fine." Finer sugar—"fruit," "dessert," or "superfine"—is preferred for

---

[1] Jean L. Bogert, *Nutrition and Physical Fitness* (6th ed., Philadelphia: Saunders, 1957), p. 323.

[2] Fairfax T. Proudfit and Corinne Mogden Robinson, *Nutrition and Diet Therapy* (10th ed., New York: Macmillan, 1950), p. 608.

some uses, e.g., to serve with fresh fruit, and as an ingredient in cakes and homemade cake mixes.

Considerable confusion exists about the labeling of the sugar that is made by grinding or pulverizing granulated sugar. Designations vary in different sections of the country. The product is confectioners' powdered sugar and, to prevent caking, contains 3 per cent starch. This fact appears on the label. The X's that are used in some parts of the country may or may not refer to the fineness of the product. This sugar is used for frostings, for dusting on doughnuts and other flour mixture desserts, for sweetening fresh fruits, and in a number of other ways.

Lump sugar is available in several sizes and in boxes containing different amounts. In a 1-pound box of tablet sugar, there are 100 pieces; cube sugar, 90 pieces; "cubelets," 110 pieces.

Cane sugar. Sugar cane is a subtropical plant that resembles Indian corn. It is propagated by cuttings which are planted in furrows. It is cut when mature, and the tops and leaves are removed. Trucks and special trains that run over very narrow-gauge tracks are used to haul the cane to mills where the juice is expressed by crushing the stalks between heavy rollers. The juice is tested to determine its sugar content, clarified, evaporated, and crystallized. At this stage the raw sugar is usually shipped if it is to be exported. Refining is then done in the importing country.

Refining involves washing and then melting the crystals of raw sugar, clarifying the sirup, filtering through boneblack to remove color, evaporating, and re-crystallizing. This final crystallization determines the fineness of granulation. Careful control is necessary to produce crystals of the size demanded by the market. Slow crystallization and slow agitation during the process produces coarse sugar; rapid crystallization with constant, rapid agitation produces fine sugar. When the crystals have formed, they are separated from the liquid (molasses) by centrifuging.

Beet sugar. Beets of high sugar content have been developed and are raised in many countries. In the United States, over three billion pounds of beet sugar were made in 1940. The beets are washed, sliced, and the sugar is removed by placing them in warm water into which the sugar is diffused as the water passes through a series of tanks. These contain sliced beets from which different amounts of sugar have been extracted. The sirup is strained, clarified, treated to improve color, filtered, concentrated, and crystallized.

Brown sugar. In the process of making granulated sugar, the sirup from the first centrifuging of raw sugar is called affination sirup. From this the brown or soft sugars are made. The process is much slower than that of making granulated sugar. To produce a strike of light brown sugar, the sirup is boiled in a vacuum pan for eight or nine hours, as contrasted to comparable time for granulated sugar of 95 minutes. The resulting mass is put into a mixer and centrifuged and the sugar is then separated from the sirup. The crystals are soft and combine with the molasses, some of which is retained by them after the centrifuging. Soft sugars vary in color from almost white to very dark.

Because of their moisture content—two to five per cent—soft sugars become hard if stored in a place that is too dry, too hot, or too cold. Ideal humidity is 60 to 70 per cent; temperature, below 75° F., but not much below the usual temperature of a room. Freezing temperature hardens the sugar by solidifying the molasses retained by the crystals.

Maple sugar. As the sap rises in the sugar maple trees in the spring, they are tapped by boring a hole just through the sapwood. A metal spout may be driven into the hole and a covered bucket—metal or plastic—hung on it. Sap is poured into a gathering tub drawn on a sled over woods "roads" and transferred to a large sap holder at the sugar house. Increasingly, plastic lines that have special spouts attached to the trees are used. Given convenient land slope, sap runs directly into the sap holder. From this it flows through a small pipe into the front pan of an evaporator. As the sap is concentrated, it is siphoned to pans farther back, and any impurities that rise to the top are removed. In the last pan, the sirup is concentrated until the temperature is about 220° F (104° C.), the concentration at which sirup weighs eleven pounds per gallon. Thinner sirup is apt to ferment, and thicker sirup crystallizes as it stands.

Sirup of top quality is very light in color and the flavor is mild. Dark sirup is stronger in flavor and may be preferred for use in cookery processes. Most of the maple product is now sold as sirup, but further concentration and stirring result in crystalline sugar usually sold in cakes. The most common are the very small "cakes" sold as candy.

Sorgo sirup. Sugar sorghum is a cane that grows abundantly in some sections of the country. Juice is pressed from the cane, clarified, and evaporated until the sirup is nearly as thick as molasses. It has a distinct flavor which is pleasing when the sirup is used on griddle cakes or waffles or in such flour mixtures as gingerbread, molasses cookies, and brown bread.

Ribbon cane sirup. Another cane yields ribbon cane sirup, milder in flavor than sorgo sirup, and delightful in cake and cookies. It is also excellent as a table sirup.

Honey. Honey is the "nectar and saccharine exudations" of plants that are gathered and modified by bees and stored in honeycombs. It varies in color and flavor with the flowers which are its source. The color may be nearly white, and it ranges through shades of lime, lemon, orange and amber to a deep, reddish mahogany. The flavor of the lighter honeys is usually milder than that of the darker. Popular mild, light-colored honeys are made from many flowers, including clover, basswood, citrus, apple, locust, mesquite, and guajilla (wä·hēl′yá) blossoms. Dark honeys with a stronger flavor include buckwheat, horsemint, broomweed, and sage. Cotton honey is light in color but somewhat stronger in flavor than the light honeys mentioned above. Many interesting varieties of honey are imported; for example, hymettus honey from Greece, linden honey from England, and coffee honey from Guatemala.

Honey may be purchased strained, extracted, or in the comb. In producing strained honey, the comb is crushed. Extracted honey is separated from the comb by centrifugal force and the comb is not crushed. Such combs can be returned to the beehive and repaired by the bees in much less time than is required to build a new comb. The secretion of wax for a pound of honeycomb requires the consumption of about ten pounds of honey by the bees. This high cost of comb production is the reason why extracted honey can be sold at a lower price than comb honey.

Sometimes a stick of honey in the comb is put into a container of extracted honey. This is called "chunk" honey. Honey spread is another form in which much honey is used.

Honey is popular as an accompaniment for biscuits, griddle cakes, and waffles. It gives a delicious flavor to many baked products and to preserves. The stronger honeys may be used to advantage in such products as dark breads, spice and chocolate cakes and cookies, or pumpkin pie; while the milder ones are more likely to be appreciated to sweeten apple pies or apple sauce, plain cakes, ice cream, candies, or light-colored breads.

Kinds of sugar. Sugars are built up from the elements carbon, hydrogen, and oxygen, but these combine in different ways to give several sugars which vary considerably in their chemical structure and characteristics. Some sugars are composed of but one saccharide (sugar) group, and are known as simple sugars or monosacchrides. They cannot be split to simpler forms by any simple chemical means. The two simple sugars which occur most frequently in foods are glucose (dextrose) and levulose (fructose). A third sugar of this class, galactose, is found in the digestive process as a hydrolytic product of lactose. Glucose is found in many plants and is an important constituent of sirup or sugar made from corn. Levulose is present in many fruits, the term "fruit sugar" frequently being applied to it. Honey contains much levulose.

Sugars which are composed of two saccharide groups are sucrose, lactose, and maltose. A molecule of one of these disaccharides, upon hydrolysis, yields two molecules of simple sugar, thus:

sucrose → glucose and levulose
lactose → glucose and galactose
maltose → glucose and glucose

Cane and beet sugar are practically all sucrose, while maple and palm sugar contain considerable amounts. Brown sugar and molasses contain some sucrose, the percentage depending upon the degree to which it has been separated during the refining process. Lactose is the sugar in milk. Maltose is found in germinating grains, and is made commercially by hydrolyzing starch. Bakers frequently use maltose to hasten yeast activity in bread making. In the digestive process, it is an intermediary product as starch is broken down to the simple sugar, glucose.

Corn sugar is a hydrolytic product of starch. It may be used in canned fruits and other products without being designated on the label. It is approximately three-fifths as sweet as sucrose.

Sugars have certain characteristics in common, all those mentioned being sweet, soluble, and crystallizable. In addition, monosaccharides are all reducing sugars,[1] and are fermentable and diffusible. The sugars differ from one another in degree of sweetness. There have been a number of attempts made to determine this difference and to assign numbers which would indicate the relative sweetness of the various sugars, using sucrose as 100. The results vary too greatly to be of definite value, but levulose is sweeter than sucrose, and the others are less sweet. Some sugars are more readily soluble than others; some, once dissolved, re-crystallize more easily than others. Levulose absorbs moisture from the air more freely than any of the other sugars.

Buying and storing sugar. Most of the sugar used in the home is granulated sugar. It may be purchased in packages or sacks ranging in weight from 1 to 100 pounds. Sugar does not deteriorate when stored, and the larger quantities are usually cheaper in terms of price per pound, even when prices of a ten-pound and a two-pound package are compared. Consequently, it is economical to buy sugar in as large amounts as seem wise considering reasonable estimated use and storage space, and this economy should be kept in mind. Brown sugar, molasses, and sirups deteriorate, especially in warm weather, and should be purchased in relatively small amounts. Brown sugar for use in the home should be stored in a tightly covered glass or tin container. Occasionally something must be added to increase humidity within the storage container, for example, half an apple placed skin side down. Honey keeps for a long time. It may crystallize on standing but becomes liquid again when the container is set into warm water for a short time. It needs no refrigeration.

Maple sirup is usually retailed in small containers. If it is purchased by the gallon for use over a considerable period of time, it may be heated to the boiling point, poured into sterilized fruit jars, and sealed.

Effects of sugar in cookery processes. Sugar is an important ingredient in many flour mixtures, in desserts, including frozen desserts, and in food preservation. It has a definite effect upon fruit cooked in sirup.

---

[1] A simple test for the presence of sugars in foods is made with Fehling's solution. The blue cupric hydroxide, which is one component of the solution, changes to cuprous oxide which is brick red, the chemical change being a reduction process.

In flour mixtures. In varying amounts sugar is used in most flour mixtures. In each case it affects the flavor. Other specific effects are these:

1) Sugar helps to prevent tunnels in flour mixtures by retarding the formation of gluten (see p. 227).
2) Sugar accelerates yeast activity and helps to produce a desirable brown crust on yeast bread.
3) Sugar in appropriate amounts helps to make good texture in cakes and cookies. In excess, it makes the texture of cakes heavy and they fall at the center.
4) Sugar in doughnuts contributes to the flavor. In excess, it causes too much fat absorption when the doughnuts are fried.

In frozen desserts. Sugar as an ingredient in a frozen dessert mix lowers the temperature at which the mix will freeze. Any substantial increase over the probable quantity specified in a frozen dessert recipe will prevent freezing unless a higher ratio of salt to ice is used in the freezing mixture.

In food preservation. Sugar acts as a preservative and is therefore used in connection with a number of food preservation methods. It is generally used when fruits are canned, is sometimes used in connection with the quick-freezing of foods, particularly fruits, and is an ingredient in the pickle used in the preservation of various fruits, vegetables, and meats.

Sugar is used in large amounts in making jams, conserves, marmalades, and fruit butters. Sugar is essential in making jellies. The interrelation of pectin, acid, and sugar results in jelly of excellent quality. Too much sugar produces a thin, sirupy jelly; too little produces a tough, rubbery jelly.

In sirup in which fruit is cooked. This use of sugar has been discussed in Unit 3 (see p. 49).

Sugar cookery. The term "sugar cookery" suggests that sugar is the chief ingredient of the food being prepared. This is true of candies and frostings. The same precautions are needed in the preparation of both to be sure that the final products will be excellent in quality. Frosting may really be "candy" cooked to a lower temperature, e.g., fudge and fudge frosting.

There are many kinds of candy, but they may be classified as belonging to one of two types—crystalline and noncrystalline (amorphous). In making crystalline candies, the object is to dissolve the original sugar crystals completely and recrystallize the candy mixture so that the finished product is smooth in texture and free from large crystals. Examples of this kind of candy are fudge, fondant, panocha, and divinity.

In making noncrystalline candies, the procedure is such that crystal formation is prevented. Brittles, lollypops, taffies, caramels, and nougats are examples of this type of candy.

Crystalline candies. In making crystalline candies, each step in the process contributes to the uniform smoothness throughout the mass that is characteristic of good candies of this type. This involves use of utensils, regulation of heat, and the techniques involved in cooking, cooling, and beating the mixture.

The following paragraphs pertain to use of utensils and regulation of heat:

1) The size of the utensil should be suitable for the quantity of ingredients used. A two-quart saucepan is desirable for recipes in which two cups of sugar are used. A larger one increases the evaporation surface and may hasten the cooking process so that the sugar will not dissolve completely before the mixture has cooked sufficiently. If a smaller pan is used, the sirup is likely to boil over.

2) The shape and material of the utensil have an influence on the success of candy-making. Crystals form at the edge of the sirup as it cooks, and in a steel or heavy aluminum pan these caramelize easily. Lighter aluminum or enamel pans are preferable. A convex saucepan is less desirable than one whose sides slope outward.

3) Accuracy in measuring all ingredients is of major importance. Consequently, standard measuring cups and spoons should be used.

4) When a thermometer is used, it is important that it be checked by taking the boiling point of water before beginning to make candy. If the boiling point does not register 212° F. (100° C.) on the thermometer, a correction should be made in the temperature at which the candy is removed from the fire. For instance, if the boiling point is 210° F. (99° C.), and the recipe designates 236° F. (113° C.) as the temperature at which the candy is done, remove it at 234° F. (112° C.). The temperatures stated in most recipes are correct at sea level. The thermometer check is necessary to make any needed correction for difference in altitude (see Appendix F, p. 675) or inaccuracy of the thermometer used.

5) When reading a thermometer, the eye must be on a level with the mercury, and the bulb of the thermometer must be immersed in the sirup but not touching the metal of the pan. What would happen if:—

a) the reading were taken from above the mercury level?
b) the reading were taken from below the mercury level?
c) the saucepan were raised while the reading is taken?
d) the thermometer were removed from the sirup during the reading?
e) the bulb of the thermometer rested on the metal container?

6) A fire that keeps the sirup boiling rapidly is desirable. Long, slow cooking makes the product too soft because too much invert sugar is formed.

Some suggestions regarding the technique involved in cooking, cooling, and beating the mixture follow:

1) The sugar must dissolve completely. Sometimes, in an effort to hurry, the amount of water designated in the recipe is reduced and the speed of cooking is not lessened. The sirup reaches the designated temperature quickly, but the candy is coarse because not all of the original sugar was dissolved. Undissolved or incompletely dissolved crystals act as nuclei [1] around which large crystals form as more sirup adheres to them.

---

[1] A nucleus is a central mass around which matter is gathered.

2) Agitation while the sirup is cooking and cooling should be avoided. The ingredients should be stirred until all the sugar is dissolved to avoid scorching. After that, the sirup for many crystalline candies should be cooked without stirring. As sirup boils some of it adheres to the side of the utensil and crystals form. This occurs more readily if the sirup is stirred. These crystals may be removed by washing occasionally with a bit of thin cloth wrapped around a fork and dipped into water. They may be melted if the pan is covered for a few minutes. This, however, delays evaporation and lengthens cooking time. In candies containing milk or chocolate, occasional stirring is necessary because these ingredients scorch easily.

While candy is cooling, a very little agitation may start the formation of crystals. A thermometer is placed so that it can be read without moving it.

3) "Seeding" must be avoided. If crystals of sugar drop into the sirup during the cooking process or while the candy is cooling, these act as nuclei and large crystals result. Particles of dust from the air occasionally have the same effect. More frequently, the crystals which form on the sides of the pan at the edge of the sirup are responsible for "seeding" the whole mass. After the sugar is completely dissolved, the saucepan may be covered for 2 or 3 min., allowing the steam to dissolve crystals around the edge. The cover may be replaced once or twice during the cooking. After covering once, perhaps it is better, however, to remove crystals with a fork wrapped with a strip of cheesecloth and dipped into cold water. This should be done only when needed. Too frequent removal of these crystals has the same effect as stirring.

4) Ingredients other than sugar and water are important in controlling crystallization. These "foreign substances" include such ingredients as milk, cream, butter, and chocolate, which act as barriers to crystal formation. Other ingredients, such as simple sugars found in corn sirup, brown sugar, maple sirup, or caramel sirup, and acid materials—lemon juice, vinegar, or the acid salt, cream of tartar—are used to keep the crystals small. The same results are obtained by the use of either simple sugar or an acid, but by different processes.

a) Corn sirup is used in the ratio of one tablespoon per cup of sugar. The glucose which it contains does not crystallize easily and, as the crystals form when the candy is beaten, it keeps them apart so that many small crystals are retained throughout the mass. Candy in which corn sirup is used is very smooth. It does not absorb moisture easily and so may become dry if it is stored very long.

b) The presence of one of the acid ingredients hastens the hydrolysis of sucrose, producing glucose and levulose. These, in equal amounts, are called invert sugar. Invert sugar interferes with crystal growth, being adsorbed [1] by the nuclei as they form. In some ways acid ingredients are less reliable than corn sirup, since the formation of invert sugar depends upon the amount of available acid and the time through which it acts. The ratio of 1/16 teaspoon of cream of tartar, or 1/4 teaspoon of vinegar or lemon juice for 1 cup of sugar is generally reliable. The alkalinity of the water exerts an

---

[1] The term "adsorb" should not be confused with "absorb." A substance is adsorbed when it adheres to the surface of another substance. It is absorbed when it is taken up by the other substance.

influence. Halliday and Noble [1] found that twice as much cream of tartar was needed when slightly alkaline water (pH 8.4 to 8.6) was used as when candy was made with distilled water. The suggested amounts of acid ingredients included in standard recipes are satisfactory unless water is excessively hard or unless the rate of cooking is hastened or retarded unduly.

Because levulose absorbs moisture from the air more freely than other sugars do, candies in which an acid ingredient is used remain moist for a considerable length of time. If the atmosphere is very damp, this may not be desirable, and it is wise to use corn sirup on a rainy day. Commercially, invert sugar is often added to candy, particularly fondant, to keep it moist. "The amount of invert sugar required should be accurately determined and once known should be strictly adhered to. If too much is used or made during process, the finished fondant will not set up properly, and finished centers will be thin." [2]

If candies made with corn sirup and with cream of tartar are compared, some difference in both flavor and texture will be noticed. The very slight acid flavor when cream of tartar is used is disagreeable to some persons. The texture of this candy lacks the extreme smoothness of that made with corn sirup. Individual preference will be the principal influence in choosing between the two ingredients.

c) When recipes include sufficient honey, brown sugar, caramel, molasses, or maple sirup, the use of corn sirup or an acid ingredient is unnecessary, since the simple sugars present have the same effect upon the size of crystals.

5) The temperature at which candy is removed from the fire is important. While candy cooks, the water evaporates and the sirup becomes increasingly concentrated. This concentration is registered by the increase in boiling temperature because as the number of dissolved particles increases in a solution, the boiling point rises. The thermometer reading is the most accurate record of concentration, although testing with cold water is a reliable gauge after considerable experience with this test. Study of Table 19 will indicate the greater reliability of the thermometer.

6) Candy must be cooled before it is beaten. When sirup is ready to be removed from the fire, it is a rather highly concentrated solution and is very hot. If such a solution is stirred, the nuclei formed are large and the candy will be grainy. Cooled to 110° F. (43° C.) or a little lower, the solution is highly supersaturated [3] and is more viscous than the hot solution. Stirring the cooled solution produces a large number of very small nuclei and results in a smooth candy. The increased viscosity of the cooler sirup acts as a further hindrance to the formation of large crystals.

---

[1] Evelyn G. Halliday and Isabel T. Noble, *Hows and Whys of Cooking* (Chicago: The University of Chicago Press, 1946), p. 207.

[2] Jordan Stroud, *Confectionery Problems* (Chicago: The National Confectioners' Assn., 1930).

[3] As long as more solute can be dissolved in a solvent at a given temperature, the solution is said to be *unsaturated*. At the point when no more solute will dissolve, the solution is *saturated*. Raising the temperature enables more solute to dissolve. In some solutions, including sucrose dissolved in water, when the solution is cooled the solute remains dissolved instead of being precipitated as the temperature declines. Such a solution is *supersaturated*.

7) Beating must continue until crystallization is complete. If candy is beaten until only part of the sugar is crystallized, the crystals formed will grow and the candy will be coarse. Fondant is beaten as long as possible and the lumpy mass is then kneaded with buttered hands until smooth. If it is set aside in a closely covered jar for two or three days to ripen, it will be very smooth and creamy.

Fudge is beaten until the gloss disappears. Just before the sugar is completely crystallized, the candy seems softer and is warmer, and the inexperienced candy maker frequently becomes discouraged. Then suddenly the candy stiffens. This

TABLE 19.* TEMPERATURE AND COLD WATER TESTS FOR VARIOUS TYPES OF CANDY

Type of Candy	*Temperature*	*Soft Ball, Firm Ball, etc.*
Fudge, penuchi, operas, maple creams, etc....	234° or 236° F.	Soft ball
Fondant................................	238° or 240° F.	Soft ball
Caramels...............................	246° or 248° F.	Firm ball
Taffies................................	265°–270° F.	Hard ball
Butterscotch, toffee, etc..................	290°–300° F.	Crack
Brittles................................	300°–310° F.	Hard crack
Clear hard candies......................	310° F.	Hard crack

* From May B. Van Arsdale and Ruth Parrish Casa Emellos, *Our Candy Recipes and Other Confections*, p. 6. M. Barrows and Co., New York, 1941.

increased warmth is called heat of crystallization. It is possible to use a heavy electric beater for beating candy until it is nearly ready to be turned out. Quick action in removing the beater and continuing beating with a spoon is important.

Noncrystalline candies. Crystallization is partially prevented in noncrystalline (amorphous) candies by the use of large amounts of foreign materials. Caramel recipes include milk, cream, butter, a high percentage of corn sirup, and, frequently, condensed milk and chocolate. All these tend to prevent crystal formation. The lactose of the milk caramelizes and adds flavor as well as color to the candy. The milk is apt to curdle, especially if chocolate is used. Lowe [1] suggests reserving most of the milk and adding it slowly to the other ingredients after the mixture becomes thick, as a means of preventing curdling. Caramels must be stirred almost constantly while cooking, since a number of the ingredients scorch easily. The use of an asbestos mat under the utensil during the latter part of the cooking period is helpful in preventing scorching.

Some taffies contain molasses, brown sugar, butter, and perhaps vinegar, all of which tend to delay or prevent crystal formation. They are pulled, and the air which is incorporated during the pulling makes them comparatively light in color.

[1] Belle Lowe, *Experimental Cookery* (New York: John Wiley and Sons, 1943), p. 66.

Brittles and hard, clear candies contain large amounts of corn sirup and other ingredients that hinder crystal formation. They are not stirred during cooking. They are poured onto a cold surface in a thin layer and the sirup sets before it can crystallize.

The other factor which is important in making noncrystalline candies is temperature. All are cooked to a higher temperature than crystalline candies, making the sirup in such candies as brittles very viscous. The temperature for caramels is not so high, but the ingredients account for the viscosity of the mixture. These candies become stiff before crystals have time to form.

Altitude. From the Table listing boiling points of water at various altitudes (see Appendix F, p. 675) it is possible to figure the temperature to which sirups for candies and frostings should be cooked. The boiling point is lowered about one degree F. (four tenths degree C.) for a rise of 500 feet in altitude. Thus sirup to be cooked to 236° F. (113° C.) would reach the proper concentration at 235° F. (112.6° C.). It must be remembered that atmospheric conditions affect the exact boiling point and that thermometers may not be accurate. This approximation is not sufficiently accurate for precise work with sugar cookery and in sugar cookery in a food preparation laboratory or at home it is important to check the boiling point of water before making the product. Thiessen has suggested a formula for calculating the temperature to which sirup should be cooked so that the product will be comparable to that cooked at sea level.[1] Using 5,000 feet altitude:

1) Temperature at sea level minus boiling point at sea level:

$$234° \text{ F.} - 212° \text{ F.} = 22° \text{ F.}$$

2) Boiling point at location plus the above figure:

$$203° \text{ F.} + 22° \text{ F.} = 225° \text{ F.}$$

Sugar in jelly. Correct relation among pectin, acid, and sugar is responsible for formation of jelly that has desirable characteristics. Many fruit juices supply pectin and acid. The ratio of sugar to juice may be varied considerably, but if the mixtures are cooked to the same temperature the concentration of sugar will be equal. Jelly with too little sugar will be too firm while that with too much will be too soft or runny; but no crystals will form in any of them. If sugar concentration is too high, however, crystals will form and, after storage, the glass of jelly may be almost entirely crystallized. (Further information concerning jelly will be found in Unit 21).

Crystals in frozen desserts. In ice creams and other frozen desserts that are stirred during freezing, desirable texture is a matter of control of crystal size. Some of the same processes apply to both candy and ice cream-making if a smooth product is to result. Crystalline candy mix must be cooled before

[1] Thiessen, Emma J., "High Altitude Cooking" *Kitchen Reporter,* Kelvinator Kitchen, Detroit, Feb. 1951.

stirring; ice cream mix, cooled before freezing. When making candy, once stirring is begun, it must be continuous; in ice cream, slow, even turning exposes the mix to the cold wall of the freezer-can evenly, and faster, even turning when the mix has begun to freeze incorporates air. Certain ingredients are added to candy to interfere with formation of large crystals; such ingredients as cream, evaporated milk, eggs, starch, and gelatin add to the viscosity of ice cream mix and, with the air, interfere with crystal growth.

Another factor that is important in making smooth ice cream is the temperature of the freezing mixture, controlled mainly by the ratio of salt to ice used. In brief, ice cream is smooth if (1) ingredients are conducive to a smooth product, (2) the mix is cooled to about 50° F. (10° C.) before freezing, (3) salt to ice for the freezing mix is in the ratio of 1:8, and (4) stirring is slow and even at first, then faster and even.

When freezing these desserts in a refrigerator or freezer, a larger proportion of foreign ingredients is used, sugar is usually decreased, and a special method of combining ingredients is helpful. The mixture is beaten two or three times during the freezing period.

Ices and frappés are coarser in texture than ice cream. A salt to ice ratio of 1:3 makes a good freezing mix and frappé is frozen only to a mush.

Further information is included in Unit 19.

SUGGESTIONS FOR LABORATORY

The term "sugar cookery" is generally considered to apply to candies and cake frostings. Both may be purchased ready to eat or partially prepared, and both are frequently made at home. With the current emphasis on less sugar in the diet, especially in concentrated form, sugar cookery as such is frowned upon by many people. Approached from the point of view of *crystallization,* an interesting and informative group of laboratory projects may be planned.

Relation between sugar and fruit juice is chiefly responsible for jellies that range in consistency from runny to almost entirely crystallized.

Texture of frozen desserts is also a matter of control of crystal formation—"ice" rather than sugar.

REFERENCES

Fitch, Natalie K., and C. A. Francis, *Foods and Principles of Cookery.* Prentice-Hall, Inc., 1948.

Honey and some ways to use it. Human Nutrition Research Branch, U.S.D.A. Research Service, Home and Garden Bulletin No. 37.

Lowe, Belle, *Experimental Cookery.* 4th Edition. John Wiley & Sons, Inc., New York, 1955.

Todoroff, Alexander, *Food Buyer's Information Book*. The Grocery Trade Publishing House, Chicago, 1946.

Van Arsdale, May B., and Ruth P. Casa Emells, *Our Candy Recipes and Other Confections*. M. Barrows & Company, New York, 1941.

Von Loesecke, Harry W., *Outlines of Food Technology*. 2nd Edition. Reinhold Publishing Corporation, New York, 1949.

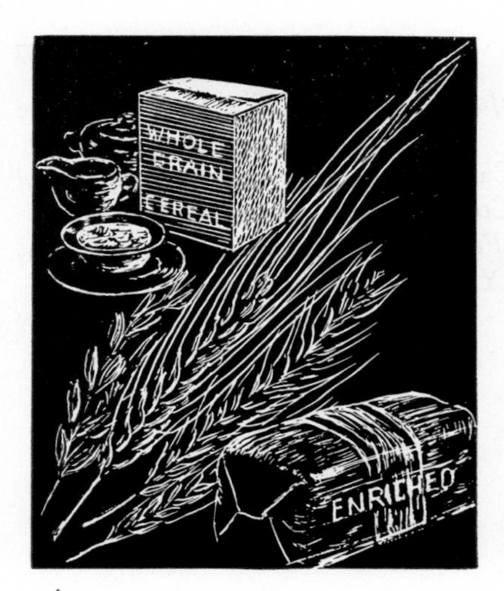

UNIT 15

Cereals and Their Products

Among the foods easily accessible to primitive man were the seeds of native grasses. Removing the seeds from the stalks and discarding the outer husks were the only preparations necessary. As time went on, men learned to crush the grain, using a push mill or a mortar and pestle—both implements made from stone. Still later, the grain was ground to meal. The cliff dwellings at Mesa Verde show the use of stone mills. At one end of the cave in which a tribe built its home a series of three push mills was arranged. The first was of coarse stone, and the grain was merely crushed in it. The second was of a finer-grained stone, and the third was the finest. As the grain was passed on from one mill to the next, it was reduced to meal. The work of grinding was done by the women. This was also true among the primitive Hebrews, whose mills consisted of two stones. The lower one was permanently set. A long wooden handle was attached to the upper stone, extending beyond the edge at opposite sides. Grain placed between the stones was ground as two women pulled the upper stone back and forth across the lower one.

In some places, including Rome and ancient Britain, two millstones were used together. The lower stone was stationary, with radiating lines cut from the center to the outer edge. The upper stone was turned on the lower one. Grain reached the lower stone through a hole in the upper, and was ground to meal as it was forced outward along the grooves. Primitive milling devices may still be found in some sections of both Europe and Asia. The metate and mano, used by the Mexicans in making tortillas, is a stone push mill. (See Fig. 31.)

In early history the meal from these simple mills was eaten raw, or parched before an open fire. Later it was mixed with water or oil and cooked. At least three methods of cooking are recorded. Pits, heated by throwing hot stones into them, were used for baking the mixture; meal was boiled in water in

Fig. 31. Metate and mano, used by Mexicans in making tortillas.

pottery bowls, heat being supplied by hot stones; thin cakes were baked on a flat, hot surface or in an oven. The ancient method has been changed but slightly by the Pueblo Indians, who bake their cakes on the heated floors of their adobe ovens.

The native cereal was a staple food of the early inhabitants of nearly all parts of the world. Among other things in its favor, it was easily stored and could be ground as needed. All through the ages, the abundance and cheapness of grain have made its products the staff of life, particularly among low-income groups.

Through trade or colonization, cereals were taken from one region to another, and now several cereals rather than one are used as food in most countries. Thus a great deal of wheat is used in the Orient, where rice or sorghum, depending upon whether the region is well watered or arid, is the native grain. The oats used so commonly in Scotland have become the source of one of America's most popular breakfast foods, and American maize or corn has found favor in many European countries.

Nutritive value. In general, cereal products are considered sources of energy. They contribute importantly to the protein requirement and are good sources of phosphorus. Their value depends upon their preparation.

The milling process removes much of the mineral and vitamin content of the grains, thus extending their storage time without excessive loss from weevil infestation. From the point of view of good nutrition, this is serious, especially for families who depend largely upon cereals for food. To improve this condition, the cereal enrichment program is now well established for wheat, and most of the corn meal from large mills is enriched. Many of the smaller mills are also enriching meal. Rice, too, may have food value in addi-

TABLE 20. VITAMIN AND IRON CONTENT OF WHEAT FLOUR, CORN MEAL, AND RICE—(MG. PER LB.)

Cereal Product	*Thiamin*	*Riboflavin*	*Niacin*	*Iron*
Wheat flour:				
Unenriched *	0.28	0.21	4.1	3.6
Enriched *	2.00	1.20	16.0	13.0
Whole wheat	2.49	0.54	19.7	15.0
Corn meal:				
Unenriched †	0.61	0.21	4.7	5.0
Enriched †	2.00	1.20	16.0	13.0
Whole ground (bolted)	1.36	0.35	8.6	8.2
Rice:				
Milled	0.30	0.12	7.4	3.6
Enriched	2.00	0.14	16.0	13.0
Converted	0.92	0.15	17.4	3.6
Brown	1.43	0.23	21.0	9.1

* All-purpose flour
† Degermed corn

tion to that of polished rice, brought about by enriching or by converting.

Minimum and maximum standards are stated in milligrams per pound of wheat flour. Required for enrichment are thiamin, 2.0–2.5; riboflavin, 1.2–1.5; niacin, 16–20; and iron, 13–16.5. Optional are calcium, 500–625, and Vitamin D (U.S.P. units), 250–1000.

Converted rice is whole-grain rice which has been parboiled before milling. It is based on the method used in preparing rice by some of the women in a part of India where beri-beri is not prevalent. It is creamy rather than white in color.

Minerals and vitamins in outside layers are thus dispersed throughout the grain. Some white rice is enriched, some has thiamin only added, and some is not enriched. If it is not enriched, that fact is printed on the label of the package.

Whole-wheat products, whole ground corn, and brown rice are available and are preferred by many to either milled or enriched products. Table 20 shows the differences in food value of wheat, corn, and rice that are unenriched, enriched, and whole-grain.

"The outer layers and the germ of grain with (in the case of wheat, at least) the adjacent part of the endosperm, contain most of the mineral and vitamin values. They also furnish proteins which have a special value both directly and as a supplement to the otherwise inferior protein of the inner part of the grain used in making patent flour. 'Enriched' flour and bread, or 'restored' breakfast cereals have received back through the enrichment program a significant part but not all of the mineral and vitamin values lost in the milling process; but the supplementary protein value is not restored." [1]

[1] Henry C. Sherman, *Nutritional Improvement of Life* (New York: Columbia University Press, 1950), p. 132.

TABLE 21. PER CAPITA CONSUMPTION OF GRAIN PRODUCTS IN THE UNITED STATES IN 1955 *

Grain	*Pounds*
Wheat	
Flour	123.0
Cereals	2.9
Corn	
Meal	8.8
Cereals	1.7
Rice	5.4
Oats	3.2
Rye	1.4
Barley	1.1
Total	147.5

* Agricultural Statistics, U.S.D.A., 1957

The enrichment of corn makes it more nutritious than whole ground corn and this is highly important in parts of the country where a great deal of corn is used. Yellow meal contains more vitamin A than white.

Wheat. Wherever wheat has been used, it has become popular, largely because the light loaf of bread which can be made from it is well liked. Some varieties of wheat are found in many countries. Its widespread use and the extensive areas where it is produced give it a place of importance on the whole market.

In the United States wheat is the principal cereal grain used as human food. The central plains are well adapted to wheat-raising—Minnesota, Wisconsin, the Dakotas, Kansas, and Nebraska being the great wheat-producing states. Indiana, Illinois, Ohio, Missouri, and Texas add a large quantity to the total amount of wheat produced, and in smaller quantities this grain is grown in many other states.

Varieties of wheat may be classed as either spring or winter wheat, depending upon the season when the grain is planted. Some wheat contains a high percentage of two proteins, gliadin and glutenin, which, when combined with water and stirred or kneaded, form gluten.[1] Such wheat is called hard, as opposed to soft wheat, in which these proteins are not found in large quantity or in which the gluten formed is not of as good quality for bread-making.

The amount of gluten, together with its tenacity and elasticity, determine the strength of flour. Strong, hard-wheat flour has several characteristics which weak, soft-wheat flour does not possess.

Because of the characteristics of hard-wheat flour, it is well adapted for bread-making. Soft-wheat flour, on the other hand, is better suited for cakes and pastries. By combining the streams of flour obtained in the milling proc-

[1] Gluten is a tenacious and elastic substance formed when flour is stirred or kneaded with liquid. It is formed by the hydration of wheat proteins.

TABLE 22. CHARACTERISTICS OF FLOUR

Hard Wheat	*Soft Wheat*
1. Creamy white in color unless bleached.*	1. White in color.
2. Gritty in texture.	2. Soft and velvety in texture.
3. When pressed in the hand, the imprint of the fingers is slight.	3. When pressed in the hand, the imprint of the fingers is marked.
4. When used for flour mixtures, it absorbs a large amount of water.	4. When used for flour mixtures, it absorbs a relatively small amount of water.
5. The percentage of gluten-forming proteins of good quality is high.	5. The percentage of gluten-forming proteins of good quality is low.

* The popular demand for a very white loaf of bread has led to bleaching flour, so that color cannot be relied upon as an indication of the type of flour. The bleaches most frequently used are nitrogen peroxide and chlorine.

ess, it is possible to make flour that meets definite specifications. Bakers' orders for flour are very specific. Flour for use in the home may be bread, pastry, general-utility, or cake flour. Bread flour is especially adapted for breadmaking; cake flour is for cakes and cookies. In general-utility flour, sometimes called "all-purpose" or "family" flour, the characteristics of hard- and soft-wheat flours are present and the flour may be used for all flour mixtures. Cakes made with it will not have as high quality as when cake flour is used. On many markets bread flour is not available. A "hard" general-utility flour is chosen for making yeast breads.

Production on a large scale in relatively few mills, and the consequent shipping for long distances, has increased the time element from producer to consumer appreciably. While it was possible to use the small quantities of whole wheat flour which was milled at local mills from wheat grown on the near-by farms without its becoming infested with weevils, that became impossible when there was a long storage time for the milled flour. As a result, much more refined than whole-wheat flour has been used by most families and most bakers. This may be largely responsible for the strongly-entrenched food habits of many people who prefer white bread and who refuse to use whole wheat bread, even when its superior food value has been demonstrated. For these people, the enrichment program has done much to improve nutritional adequacy.

One variety of wheat which is produced in large quantities in the United States is durum wheat. Its protein content is high, but it does not produce gluten of good quality. It is used in making alimentary pastes. Paul de Kruif has written interestingly of the search for a wheat which could be grown successfully in certain parts of the Wheat Belt of the United States, and the subsequent effort to make Americans macaroni-conscious, because the flour from the wheat was suitable for macaroni but not for bread.[1] This illustrates

[1] See Paul de Kruif, *Hunger Fighters* (New York: Harcourt, Brace, 1928).

Courtesy Quaker Oats Company

Fig. 32a. Farm scene showing a grain field harvested, with shocks drying and ripening in the sun.

Courtesy American Can Company

Fig. 32b. From field to table, grains make their appearance in many favorite dishes. French toast, shown here, is a popular breakfast and luncheon bread.

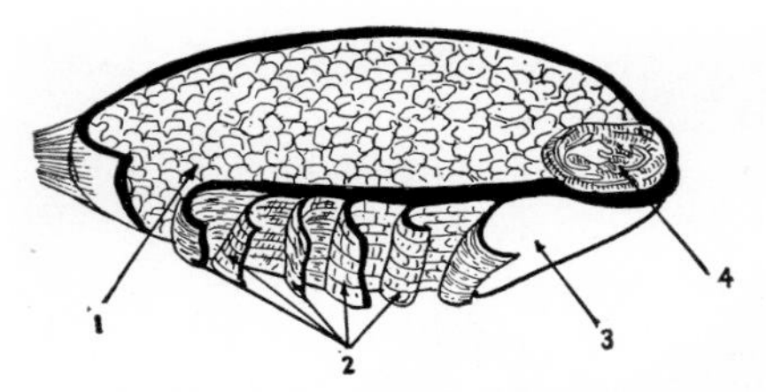

Fig. 33. A grain of wheat. 1, *endosperm;* 2, *bran;* 3, *husk;* 4, *germ or embryo.*

a change in the food pattern of a nation through the efforts of an industry.

A grain of wheat is made up of several parts, each of which has certain food value, as shown in the table below and in Figure 33.

Corn. In terms of quantity production, corn leads all other cereal grains in the United States. Much is used as animal feed. As human food it is used as fresh, canned, frozen, and dried corn, cornstarch, corn meal, breakfast cereals, hominy, corn oil, corn sirup, and corn sugar. The embryo and hull are removed in the milling process. The embryo is the source of corn oil. The endosperm is the source of most of the starch used for both cooking and laundry purposes.

Rock-ground meal is obtainable on some markets, and some corn is ground at home. Most meal comes from large mills, although in many localities there is a small mill which furnishes most of the meal for the community.

TABLE 23. COMPOSITION OF PARTS OF WHEAT KERNEL

Bran	Cellulose, minerals
Aleurone layer	Protein, minerals
Endosperm	Starch, protein, minerals, fat
Embryo	Fat, ash, vitamin A, thiamin, ascorbic acid

Rice. Rice is the principal cereal food of millions of people who live in parts of the world where there is a sufficient natural water supply, or where the cultivation of rice is made possible by irrigation. Rice was first successfully raised in the American colonies in 1694 by Thomas Smith of South Carolina. After the War Between the States, rice culture in Louisiana grew rapidly, and Louisiana, Texas, Arkansas, and California now produce more than is used by the whole United States.

Rice is used as a cereal, in place of a starchy vegetable, and as a dessert. Rice starch is used for very fine laundry work or combined with cornstarch for laundry purposes. Rice flour is important in the diet of persons who are allergic to wheat.

When polished rice is used as one of the main items of food in a restricted diet, beri-beri, a thiamin-deficiency disease, often results. The use of brown rice or of enriched or converted rice is increasing and is being emphasized in countries where the chief or only cereal used is rice.

In shallow waters of the Great Lakes and the Mississippi River, a grass known as wild rice or Indian rice is found. The Indians used this cereal as food and introduced its use to the settlers in those regions. It is available on many markets and is popular in place of a vegetable or as stuffing for game birds.

Rye. Rye resembles wheat more closely than does any other grain. It contains gliadin, but its glutenin content is low, so that a light loaf of bread cannot be made from rye flour alone. Combined with wheat, it makes excellent bread. Rye grows in a cooler climate than the other grains and is used extensively in Russia, Scandinavia, and northern Germany.

Oats. Oats are used principally as feed for animals. Oatmeal and rolled oats are important breakfast cereals and are used to some extent in flour mixtures and meat loaves. Oats contain more protein and fat than any other cereal. The outer layers adhere closely to the endosperm and are not easily removed during milling. Hence oat cereals are always whole-grain products.

Buckwheat. Buckwheat is not a true grain, but the pyramid-shaped seeds are ground to give a rather dark flour. It is used, alone or mixed with wheat, for making the griddle cakes which are frequently a part of the breakfast menu in some sections of the country. Buckwheat is used in some of the commercial griddle-cake flours.

Sorghum grains. Grain sorghums, including millet, milo maize, and kafir, are raised in regions that have comparatively little rainfall. They are used chiefly as stock feed, but very delicious quick breads and cookies are made by combining the meal from these grains with wheat flour.

Cottonseed meal. For a long time cottonseed meal has been used throughout the Cotton Belt as feed for livestock. At one time there was some use of the refined product, from which a harmful product (gossypol) had been removed, in flour mixtures. The possibility of its increased use as human food at some future time is being kept in mind by research workers interested in sources of protein other than those now most commonly used.

Flour mixes. Some of the flour mixes on the market contain only salt and leavening material in addition to flour, while others contain a number of other ingredients, including dried milk, dried egg, sugar, and fat. There are the popular mixes, such as biscuit, pastry, and cake mixes, and others which are doubtless used occasionally only, such as hush puppy, popover, and macaroon mixes. Mixes are distinctly time savers. Packages containing fat that are not used at once should be stored in a cool place or refrigerator. There is increasing use of home-made mixes, some of which will be discussed later in this unit.

Breakfast cereals. Within recent years the use of cereals in the form of breakfast foods has increased rapidly. Some are not cooked at all during the process of manufacture, some are partially cooked, and others are ready to be served. Cereals that require cooking are of four types: entire grain, such as rice; flaked, such as rolled oats; coarsely ground, such as hominy grits; and finely ground, such as cream of wheat. Cereals that are ready to eat are also sold in many forms; flaked cereals from corn, wheat, and rice, puffed rice and wheat, and wheat in shredded form are all popular. Cereals may be made from more than one grain, e.g., corn-soya.

Cooking breakfast cereals. The length of time required for cooking breakfast cereals depends upon how finely divided the cereal is and whether it has been partially cooked before being marketed. The long cooking time that used to be recommended for the purpose of breaking the starch granules has been found unnecessary, because raw starch is completely digested, although not so quickly as cooked starch. The palatability of cereals is increased by a reasonably long cooking time, the very short time recommended on some of the packages being insufficient to give a good flavor. More time is required to cook raw cereals than partially cooked ones, and coarsely divided cereals cook more slowly than finely divided ones.

The amount of water which cereals of different types will absorb while they are cooking varies with the time required for cooking, the fineness of division, and the absorptive power of the starch. Finely ground cereals require more water than the coarser cereals, and flaked cereals require less than coarsely ground ones.

The water in which cereals are to be cooked should be boiling rapidly when the cereal is added. Salt should be added to the water, and the cereal should be shaken into the water slowly enough so that the boiling does not cease. No stirring is necessary, and it should be avoided because it gives the cereal a pasty consistency. After the cereal has been added, the heat is lowered, the saucepan covered, and cooking is done slowly for the time needed. During this time the water is absorbed. As a precaution, an asbestos mat may be put under the saucepan. Shaking the pan at the end of the cooking time will help to insure fluffiness.

The methods used in processing rice result in products that need certain differences in cookery methods. The chief difference is in the time needed to cook it thoroughly. In decreasing order of time required, the types are brown, converted, white, and instant. In the first three, the appropriate amount of salted water is brought to a boil, rice added slowly, the saucepan covered, heat lowered; and cooking proceeds until the water has been absorbed and the kernels are tender. For instant rice, the heat is turned off entirely after the pan is covered. Accurate directions are printed on the packages.

Cereals may be cooked to advantage in pressure pans. The time saved by this method may be important enough to mean the difference between including cooked cereals on the breakfast menu frequently, and not doing so. It is also possible to effect the modern equivalent of the custom of leaving cereal in a double boiler at the back of a coal range all night after starting the cooking process. If one of the units of a range is a deep well, rice or rolled oats or wheat may be partially cooked late in the evening and left in the well until morning. Specific directions are included in the booklet accompanying the range.

Buying cereal products. Cereal products are needed daily as most homemakers prepare their own meals. It is well to keep a supply of white flour for different purposes, as well as whole-wheat flour; corn meal; brown, converted or enriched, and white rice; and breakfast cereals. Rye flour, alimentary pastes, and wild rice may be added.

Flour and meal. The nutritional superiority of enriched flour and meal over refined products indicates the importance of using them in preference to those that have not been enriched.

The type of flour purchased should depend upon the use that is to be made of it. If use and storage space are not sufficient to justify buying special flour for bread and/or cakes, general-utility flour may be all that is needed. Otherwise, the flours adapted for special uses are recommended. The ease with which amounts may be adjusted to family size makes this a simple matter. Sacks or boxes of flour weighing two or three pounds are available for the small family in which little cooking is done; 48-pound sacks, or even barrels, may be purchased by those who can use flour in such quantities; and there are sacks and boxes of various weights for groups between the two extremes. It is usually economical to buy fairly large amounts, but the size of the group, the amount of cooking requiring flour, storage space, and climate need to be considered in choosing suitable amounts.

Whole-grain flour and meal spoil more quickly than the refined products, because of the fat present and the speed with which they become infested with weevils. They should therefore be purchased in relatively small quantities.

There are various brands from which to choose. Because flour varies in hardness from year to year and different brands of the same type vary in hardness, it is well to find brands that give satisfactory results and to continue their use. Price is not a guide to quality. If satisfactory flour at a relatively low price is available, it is better to buy that than a higher priced flour.

Rice. Rice of all varieties may be purchased in packages. White rice is often available in bulk and is usually cheaper than the packaged product. The price of white rice usually varies with the grade, the larger perfect, polished, coated grains being more expensive than the smaller grains or broken rice. Wild rice is usually sold in packages. In most places there is not much demand for this product, and the price is correspondingly high.

Breakfast cereals. Cereals that are ready to serve are higher in price than those that require cooking. If a cereal comes in packages of more than one size, the large package is cheaper in terms of cost per serving. In figuring cost, the nutritive value as well as cost per serving should be considered. Sugar-coated cereals, which are such a present fad, may or may not be an advantage. Children are likely to use entirely too much sugar on cereals. In many instances, the sugar-coating satisfies them and they really get less sugar than formerly. If, however, they insist on adding sugar to the coated cereals, or if they make a meal of the sugar-coated cereal instead of eating it along with other desirable foods, the coating is distinctly detrimental.

Storage of cereal products. A closely covered tin can is an excellent storage utensil for flour. Cans of various sizes may be purchased to suit the need of any group. Cake flour and cereals are nearly always used quickly enough so that the cardboard packages in which they are purchased are satisfactory for storage purposes when the weather is cool. If it is hot, however, these also should be stored in closely covered metal or glass utensils to lessen the possibility of their becoming weevily. In damp weather, the ready-to-eat cereals may be made crisp by heating them in the oven.

SUGGESTIONS FOR LABORATORY

The term "cereals" is often interpreted "breakfast cereals," and their use is sometimes confined to just that. An hour or so spent looking into cookbooks may result in finding many ways to use them, several of which might add pleasant surprises to the family's meals. A brief study of ways in which one cereal grain is used by people in other sections of the country as well as in other countries would be an interesting project for the students. Preparation for this laboratory would be rewarding if done well in advance.

REFERENCES

Justin, Margaret M., L. O. Rust, and G. E. Vail, *Foods,* 5th Ed. Houghton Mifflin Co., Boston, 1960.

Todoroff, Alexander, *Food Buyer's Information Book*. The Grocery Trade Publishing House, Chicago, 1946.

Tracy, Marian, *The East-West Book of Rice Cookery*. The Viking Press, New York, 1952.

Von Loesecke, Harry W., *Outlines of Food Technology*. Reinhold Publishing Corp., New York, 1949.

UNIT 16

Flour Mixtures

The term "flour mixtures" applies to all batters and doughs because in all of them except sponge-type cakes, flour is the basic ingredient. In making flour mixtures, the choice and use of suitable utensils and the care with which ingredients are measured are important. The effect of the various ingredients upon the finished products should be known in order to understand methods used in combining the ingredients, to judge the probable reliability of recipes, and to account for inferior products.

BASIC CONSIDERATIONS

Utensils. When making flour mixtures, utensils are needed for measuring, for combining ingredients, and for cooking. Thermometers for measuring temperature are sometimes needed.

Measuring utensils include cups and spoons. Cups of glass, metal, or plastic, marked to indicate fractional parts of a cup, are useful for measuring liquids. Preferably, those that hold more than a cup are used for liquids, since it is easier to fill them to the appropriate line than to fill a cup exactly full. For dry ingredients, sets of cups, including one-fourth, one-third, one-half, and one-cup measures are more satisfactory, because they can be leveled accurately by filling them and scraping across the top with the edge of a knife blade or spatula. Spoons should include those that measure one tablespoon, one teaspoon, one-half teaspoon, and one-fourth teaspoon.

Measuring instruments for temperature should include an oven thermometer, even when the oven is equipped with a regulator. The accuracy of all regulators needs to be checked from time to time, and the use of an oven thermometer makes adjustment of temperature easy, if the regulator is not accurate, until the latter can be adjusted. Special thermometers may be used for frostings and for frying flour mixtures in deep fat. One thermometer which registers a temperature of 400° F. (204° C.) is, however, sufficient for the measurement of temperatures.

A dial thermometer is easy to read, since the dial is parallel to the cooking surface and is equipped with an indicator for quick recognition of the end-point temperature.

Utensils for combining ingredients and preparing them for cooking include mixing bowls, beaters, spoons, spatulas, knives, forks, cutters, dough boards, rolling pins, and mixers.

1) Mixing bowls should be relatively deep, with sloping sides, and the bottom should be rounded to facilitate quick and efficient combining of ingredients. Bowls made from a good quality of glass or earthenware are better than metal or enamel bowls because the metal ones discolor some mixtures and the enamel ones chip fairly easily. Some plastic bowls are very practical. Bowls of several sizes are needed.

2) Beaters are of two types. Rotary beaters are needed for various purposes and should be sturdily built and easy to hold. Both a double blade and a single blade beater are advantageous. Wire whips may be desirable for beating egg whites because more air is incorporated than when a rotary beater is used. They should never be used for such heavy service as beating frostings after the sirup has been added. Where they are available, piano-wire whips are excellent in place of the more common flat ones, and may be used for more purposes.

3) Spoons, spatulas, knives, and forks are all of use in making flour mixtures. Wooden spoons are more desirable than metal ones because they blend the ingredients more thoroughly and more easily. In a laboratory where many students are working at once, wooden spoons make less noise. Some metal spoons discolor such a mixture as fat and sugar that is being creamed when a cake is made.

A spatula is used for leveling ingredients and for scraping batter from bowls. A rubber spatula is an effective implement for the latter purpose. Flexible spatulas are also useful for removing some baked products from the pans in which they were cooked, and wide, rather inflexible spatulas are convenient for many purposes.

Flour and fat may be combined for such flour mixtures as biscuits and pastry by two knives, a dough blender, a fork, or the fingers. The dough blender is superior to the knives because there are six wires rather than two blades. Strokes must be light to blend fat and flour, but avoid mashing fat and flour together. Mashing is likely to result if fork or fingers are used by an inexperienced worker.

4) Cutters of various shapes and sizes are desirable for shaping biscuits and cookies. They can be made from the tops of cans if the edges of these tops are sufficiently sharp. For special occasions such as Christmas, unusual sets of cutters are available which make interesting additions to the basic sets.

5) When rolling dough for some rolls, biscuits, cookies, and pastry, a dough board or pastry cloth, or both, and a rolling pin are needed. The rolling pin may be of wood, glass, or metal, and may be ball-bearing. The pastry cloth, marked with circles indicating size of crust for pans of two sizes may be purchased. One may be made from a piece of canvas. Such circles may be stitched with colored thread that will not run on the canvas if the pastry cloth is made at home.

If the dough board and rolling pin are of wood, they should be of good quality hard wood that does not splinter. Dough which sticks to them should be scraped off and then the wood should be wiped with a damp cloth—not put into water. They should be dry when stored.

Mixers are effective and save both time and energy. A blender is useful for several purposes, including making some frostings, chopping nuts, and combining some ingredients.

Utensils for cooking include some that have various uses and others that are limited to a specific use. Among the former are baking sheets, muffin, cake, pie, and bread pans. A frying pan is sometimes used for baking an upside-down cake or griddle cakes, and puddings may be baked in molds or in ovenware mixing bowls. However, a griddle is a better utensil for the griddle cakes, and a waffle iron is necessary for waffles. Cornstick pans also have a specific purpose, but there are several shapes and materials.

For cooling cakes, cookies, and bread, wire cake racks are almost indispensable. These products should be cooled where air circulates all around them.

Measuring ingredients. There are many stories of experienced cooks who scorn special measuring utensils because they never measure ingredients when preparing baked products. The result, however, when the cup or mixing bowl that has been used for years is broken, is sufficient to convince them that in reality, they *have* been measuring. Wilder, in *Jack-Knife Cookery,*[1] emphasizes a fair degree of accuracy in measuring when he refers to a "heaping fistfull" of flour, a "fistfull" of water, and 2, 3, 4, or 5 finger pinches of salt, baking powder, etc. Experience would doubtless make these measures reliable, and for outdoor cookery they would at least be fun to try. However, inexperienced persons should learn how to measure accurately and should always rely upon such measurements (see Fig. 34). Following are some directions for measuring ingredients:

1) Measures of all ingredients should be level. "Heaping" and "scant" are not definite amounts.

2) Flour is always sifted before measuring. It is then heaped into a cup, using a large spoon, and leveled with the edge of a spatula or knife. (See Fig. 34, top). Soft wheat flour is apt to stick to the sides of the cup and should be removed by tapping the cup. Other dry ingredients—sugar, salt, baking powder, and some others, should be measured also by heaping the cup or spoon and leveling with spatula or knife.

3) Lumpy sugar should be sifted before it is measured. Confectioners' sugar and brown sugar frequently need to be sifted or rolled to remove lumps. Brown sugar should be packed into the measuring cup.

4) Fats that are measured in cups or spoons should be packed well and leveled with a spatula or knife. Measuring spoons are not very substantial; consequently,

[1] James Austin Wilder, *Jack-Knife Cookery* (New York: E. P. Dutton, 1937).

if one is used for measuring fat, one finger of the hand that holds the spoon should be held firmly under the bowl to prevent bending or breaking the handle. (See Fig. 35.)

5) Eggs are measured in cups when large quantities are used, as in angel cakes. Otherwise, medium-sized eggs—those weighing about 50 grams each, or about 20 oz. per dozen—are best for flour mixtures. (See p. 120.)

6) Measurement of liquids is, perhaps, more likely to be inaccurate than measurement of other ingredients. If a cup that is marked to designate fractional parts is used, the liquid should come to the correct mark. If the whole measure is to be filled, the liquid should come to the top. Some cup measures hold more than a cup. In measuring one cup, the liquid should, of course, come to the 1-cup mark—not to the top of the cup. (See Fig. 34, bottom.)

Measures for oils should be full but even. Oil adheres to the measuring utensil and must be scraped from it to be sure that the full amount is used.

7) Sirups, such as corn sirup used in frostings, are viscous, and the full measure is likely to be heaped. The measure should be leveled with a spatula or knife.

8) If a recipe specifies 3 t., time is saved by measuring 1tb.; if 4 t. is specified, 1 tb. and 1t. may be measured. If 4 tb. are specified, ¼ c. is measured more easily. Fat that is packed in a carton may be measured accurately by using a portion of a pound or quarter pound, and cutting the amount needed. (See Fig. 35, top.) Some butter and margarine is packaged in paper that is marked to indicate tablespoons. These "short-cuts" should be kept in mind from the points of view of timesaving and accuracy.

Ingredients. *Flour*. Flour is probably the most important ingredient in flour mixtures from the point of view of the structure of batters and doughs. It has already been pointed out that flour with a high percentage of gluten-forming proteins of good quality is best for making yeast bread, that finely ground soft-wheat flour is most desirable for cakes, and that a general-utility flour that combines the characteristics of both is chosen for other flour mixtures and may be used for both bread and cakes (see pp. 191–192).

The term "general-utility flour" is far from specific. Flours from different mills, from wheat raised in different parts of the country, or from the same kind of wheat one year as compared with another year differ materially. Bakers buy flour by specification but subject it to a baking test before using it in a large amount of dough. The extensibility of the gluten may vary enough from one year to another to necessitate changing the formula, increasing the height of the troughs in which the dough rises, or both. In the home, this same variation in flour is frequently responsible for variation in a dependable recipe. It may also be responsible for failure when an unfamiliar recipe is used. A slight change in quantity of flour is all that is needed, in either case, to produce excellent baked products. Continued use of brands of flour that have been found satisfactory is wise.

Sugar. Sugar is used primarily for sweet flavor. It makes the crust of a flour mixture brown readily, hinders gluten formation, and raises the coagulation point of the protein in eggs. In mixtures leavened by means of yeast, it speeds yeast activity. It also affects the texture. Finely granulated sugar combines with fat in a cake or cookie mixture more satisfactorily than does coarsely granulated sugar.

It is possible to substitute sirups of various kinds or honey for part or all of the sugar in a flour mixture. (See *Substitutions,* Appendix E, p. 674.) The flavor of honey in cakes and cookies, of ribbon cane or maple sirup in sponge cake, or of molasses in whole-wheat quick breads, is delicious and an interesting change from the use of granulated sugar.

Salt. Salt adds flavor to flour mixtures, preventing a "flat" taste. It retards yeast activity and retards the development of microorganisms that would not be desirable from the point of view of bread-making.

Baking powder and soda. Baking powder is used in many flour mixtures as a source of leavening. When sour milk is the liquid, soda is used. Their use will be discussed in detail later in this unit. They should be measured accurately. If they are lumpy, they should be sifted before measuring. Recipes should be checked in accordance with recent recommendations with regard to quantities needed, because older recipes specified larger amounts than are now considered desirable and too much of either ingredient imparts a disagreeable flavor.

Liquid. Liquid helps to combine all ingredients, gelatinizes some of the starch, and is necessary for the development of gluten. Milk is the liquid used most frequently in flour mixtures. Water, or water in which potatoes have been cooked, is sometimes used in yeast bread; and fruit juices are frequently used in cakes and cookies and sometimes in muffins, biscuits, and pastry.

The importance of accuracy in measuring liquids has been mentioned (see p. 202). The effect of inaccuracy is nearly always apparent when a class makes muffins. From the same recipe, batters often range in consistency from thin to thick, usually because the liquid was not measured accurately. Sometimes it is due to packing the flour into the cup.

Fat. The chief reason for using fat in flour mixtures is to increase tenderness. As gluten is developed by stirring flour with liquid, it tends to form long strands. Fat in the mixture shortens these strands by being adsorbed by them as they form, thus causing the formation of a relatively large number of short gluten strands. Fat is also distributed in flour mixtures by being emulsified by egg and by being adsorbed by starch granules and sugar.

Some fats, such as bacon fat, add to the flavor of baked products. Because they are good solvents of flavors, fats help to blend the flavors of the other ingredients and to prevent evaporation of flavoring extracts.

In recipes for batters that designate "melted fat," the use of oils is a distinct advantage. The fat is usually mixed with liquid, and the liquid is frequently cold. Melted fat added to cold liquid congeals immediately, whereas oil does not. Some time and the use of an extra utensil are saved by using oil.

Courtesy Wheat Flour Institute, Chicago

Photos by Betty Wallace

Fig. 34. Measurements for flour mixtures must be accurate. Top, *flour is measured and leveled.* Bottom, *a measuring cup for liquid is filled to the rim* (left) OR *to the measure indicated* (right).

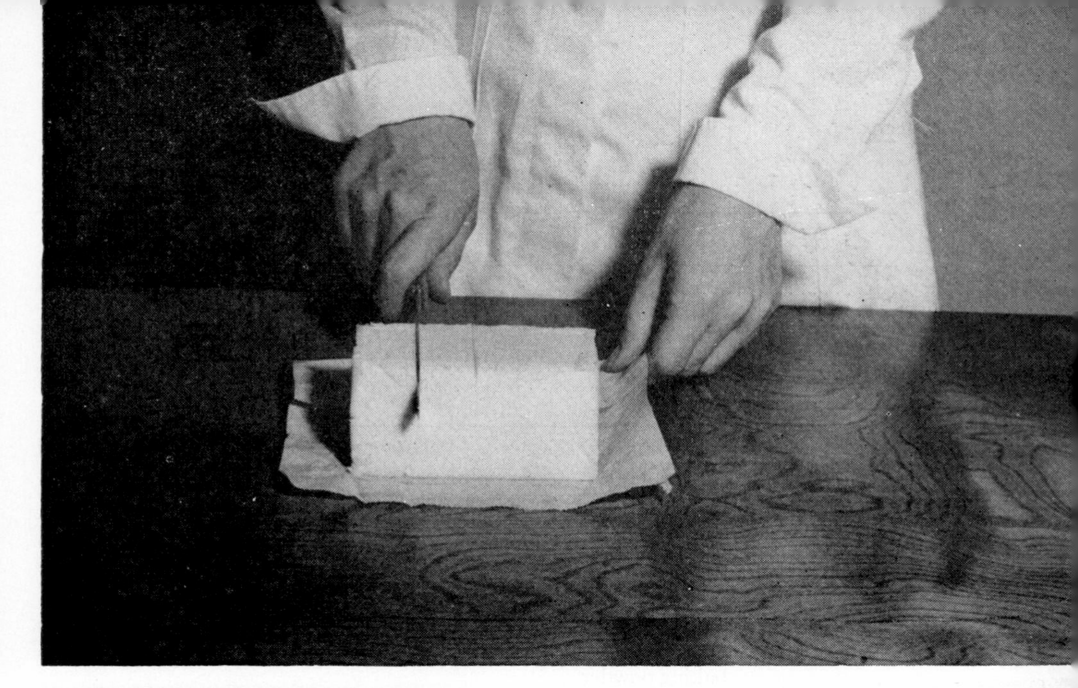

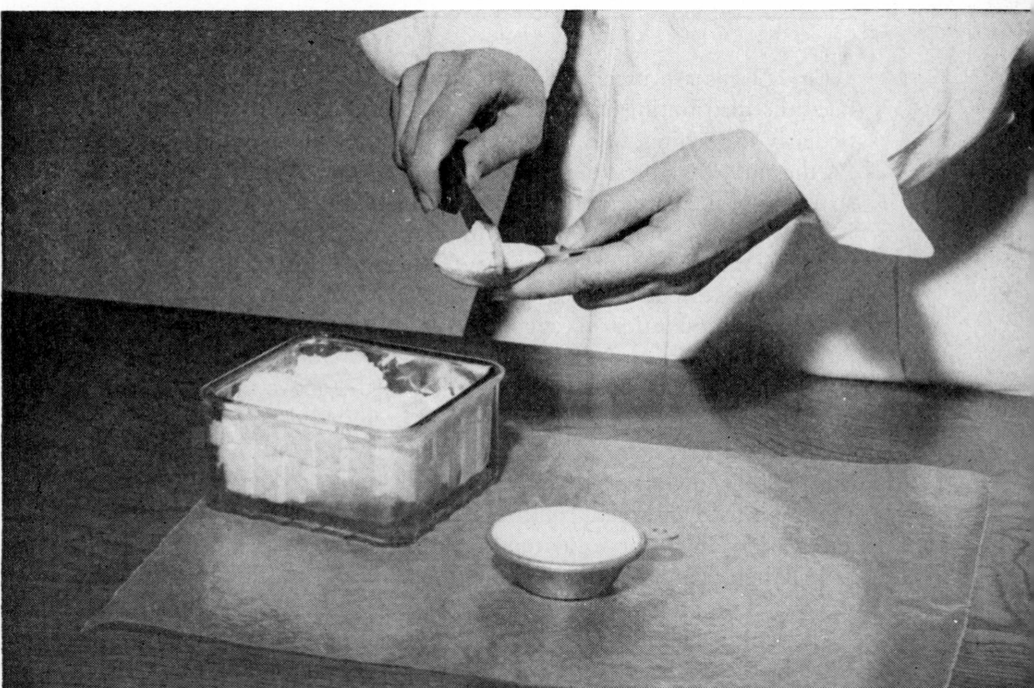

Photos by Betty Wallace

Fig. 35. Top, *fat from a 1-lb. package is being measured by cutting—¼ lb., or ½ c.;* bottom, *fat is packed into the measuring utensil and leveled.* (*Note finger under the spoon.*)

TABLE 24. LEAVENING AGENTS

Agent	*Source*	*Flour Mixture*
Air	Beating egg white	Sponge cakes; cakes containing fat; spoon bread; some macaroons
	Beating mixtures	Popovers; beaten biscuit
	Rolling dough, enclosing fat	Puff pastry
	Creaming fat	Cakes containing fat; cookies
	Sifting flour	Sponge cakes; all flour mixtures
Steam	Heating liquid as flour mixture cooks	Popovers; cream puffs; puff pastry; all batters and soft doughs
CO_2 gas	Fermentation due to yeast activity	Yeast bread; rolls; raised doughnuts; muffins and other flour mixtures in which yeast is used
	Fermentation due to bacterial action	Salt-rising bread
	Chemical reaction from soda and sour milk etc., or from baking powder	Griddle cakes; waffles; muffins; cakes containing fat; biscuits; other quick breads

Eggs. Eggs are used in flour mixtures for several reasons. They emulsify fat, thus distributing it evenly through the mixture. If they are beaten, particularly the whites, they incorporate air. They make gluten more extensible. As the mixture bakes, the coagulation of protein from eggs is a factor in the structure of the batter or dough and in the texture of the product.

With the exception of recipes for most sponge-type cakes, eggs are designated by number. The inaccuracy resulting from such designation has already been discussed (see pp. 117–119). The best results, when a relatively small quantity of egg is used, will be obtained by using eggs of medium size; when a large quantity is used, by measuring.

Flavoring and seasoning. In addition to the above ingredients, others that give characteristic flavor are often used in flour mixtures. Flavoring extracts, spices, chocolate, honey, fruits or fruit juices, and nuts are frequently used in cakes. Seeds, including those from poppy, anise, sesame, caraway, and cardamom are used in bread, cookies, and cakes. Spice, fruit, nuts, and preserves add variety in flavor to a number of quick breads. Flavor should be mild rather than pronounced, and should be studied carefully as flour mixtures of various kinds are made.

Leavening. The leavening agents are carbon dioxide gas, air, and steam. Various materials and processes are responsible for their effectiveness in flour mixtures. These are summarized in Table 24.

Leavening by means of carbon dioxide gas. In many parts of the world the staple bread is a flat, unleavened cake. Nearly all the bread and other flour mixtures used in the United States are leavened, and an understanding of leavening is essential to the study of these products, particularly in the case of yeast where lack of understanding can result in total failure.

Early methods of leavening required longer time and were far less certain than methods with which we are familiar. "A little leaven leaveneth the whole lump" probably refers to the custom of saving a little dough from one baking, putting it into the dough prepared for the next baking, and leaving the whole to become light. Corn meal, salt, sugar, and milk are the basic ingredients for salt-rising bread. It used to be thought that the bread was leavened by "wild yeast" from the air. Actually, bacterial action results in development of carbon dioxide gas and hydrogen, and these gases are the leavening agents in genuine salt-rising bread.[1]

Yeast. When it was found that yeast could be kept in liquid form and used over a period of several weeks, an important progressive step had been taken in advance of the use of a lump of leavened dough as a "starter." Liquid yeast was stored in a cool, dark place and, as it was used, part of it was left in the container; more ingredients were added; and the container was replaced. Yeast plants developed rapidly in this new material, and a supply of yeast for the next baking was soon ready. Some liquid yeast is still used by those who prefer it in this form.

For most people, compressed and dry yeast have entirely replaced the use of liquid yeast. Compressed yeast is quick to act and is always available in most communities. Compressed yeast should be moist, the odor should be fresh and clean, and it should not be discolored. The dry yeast now on the market is granular. Unlike the older dry yeast, it acts quickly, being made from an active strain of yeast. Its keeping quality is good, owing to air-tight packaging. Packages are stamped with the date beyond which it is not satisfactory.

Yeast produces the leavening agent, carbon dioxide gas, by a fermentation process. Starch in the flour is broken down as a result of enzyme activity in the following way:

Starch + diastase (from flour) + water → maltose
Maltose + maltase (from yeast) + water → glucose
Glucose + zymase (from yeast) → CO_2 gas + alcohol

For development, yeast needs moisture, food, and warmth. It grows well at temperatures ranging from 80° to 85° F. (27° to 29° C.), with 82° F. (28° C.) as the optimum. The plants are destroyed by a high temperature and rendered inactive by a low one. Glucose is the ideal food, but other sugars also serve to hasten yeast activity. A thin batter is more conducive to rapid growth than is a dough; consequently, the sponge method frequently

[1] H. A. Kohman, "Salt-Rising Bread and Some Comparisons with Bread Made from Yeast," *Industrial and Engineering Chemistry*, Vol. 4, No. 20, pp. 100–106.

used in bread-making is considered for this reason an advantage (see p. 235).

Sodium bicarbonate and an acid. Sodium bicarbonate is an acid salt which, when heated, breaks down to sodium carbonate, carbon dioxide gas, and water:

$$2NaHCO_3 + \text{heat} \rightarrow Na_2CO_3 + CO_2 + H_2O$$

Used by itself, sodium bicarbonate is not a practical leavening material because the residue, sodium carbonate, is distinctly disagreeable in flavor and, in excess or if not well distributed throughout the flour mixture, it is responsible for brown or yellow spots scattered through the product. Moistened, this salt becomes alkaline in reaction, so that when it is used in combination with certain acids, the two substances neutralize each other, the leavening agent—CO_2 gas—is formed, and the residues have no undesirable flavor. If soda is not used in too large a quantity and the techniques for mixing ingredients are correct, there will be no discolored spots.

Sour milk, which contains lactic acid, was probably the first ingredient thus combined with soda. Many early recipes called for sour milk and soda instead of sweet milk and baking powder, because of milk sanitation and the lack of refrigeration. Since sour milk was more readily available than sweet, it was convenient to use it for baking. Some people still prefer to use the combination of sour milk and soda for all types of flour mixtures. Cultured buttermilk is the most reliable type of "sour" milk to use in recipes calling for sour milk, since the degree of acidity is scientifically controlled in the manufacturing process.

Other ingredients included in flour mixtures that are acid are molasses, honey, chocolate, brown sugar (especially dark), maple sirup, and corn sirup. Of these, dark molasses is sufficiently acid so that soda is used with it. The usual amount of soda per cup of sour milk or dark molasses is one-half teaspoon. The leavening power of these is equivalent to that of two teaspoons of quick-acting or one and a third teaspoons of slow-acting baking powder. For some kinds of honey (usually dark in color) about one-fourth teaspoon of soda is used. Chocolate cake recipes in which the amount of chocolate is rather large include soda. The acidity of the others is low enough to be negligible from the point of view of cookery.

There are always the questions, when sour milk or molasses is used, "How sour is it?" If only slightly sour, how much soda should be used? And how much additional baking powder will be needed to give the right leavening to the product? Thus this source of carbon dioxide gas is rather undependable, and the convenience as well as greater dependability of a dry source of acid is obvious. Such a substance is cream of tartar and many people use it with soda, in the ratio of two to one, despite even more convenient leavening materials.

Baking powder. Baking powder is a mixture of sodium bicarbonate, an-

Courtesy National Dairy Council

Fig. 36. Assorted tarts for a family dinner or a dessert party.

other acid salt, and starch. The starch acts as a drier. There are three classes of baking powder, depending on the second acid salt used. Tartrate powder contains cream of tartar, tartaric acid, or both; calcium phosphate powder, monocalcium phosphate; S.A.S.-phosphate powder, both monocalcium phosphate and sodium aluminum sulphate. Tartrate powder may be made by sifting two parts of cream of tartar, one part of soda, and one part of starch together. Cream of tartar and soda may be substituted for baking powder. Remembering that there are four "parts," one of which is starch, the amount of cream of tartar and soda together would be three-fourths that of the tartrate or calcium phosphate baking powder in the recipe. Two-thirds of this would be cream of tartar; one-third, soda. Thus, if a recipe lists 4 teaspoons of baking powder, 3 teaspoons of cream of tartar plus soda would be needed—2 teaspoons of cream of tartar and 1 teaspoon of soda. Typical reactions of the three types of powder are shown by the equations on the following page.

It might be interesting for a group of students to choose a simple recipe, for example, biscuits, and use as leavening materials two or three types of baking powder, the home-made baking powder described above, cream of tartar and soda, and soda and sour milk. Both time spent in preparation and quality of product might be compared.

TARTRATE

$$KHC_4H_4O_6 + NaHCO_3 \rightarrow KNaC_4H_4O_6 + H_2CO_3 \nearrow H_2O + CO_2$$

Cream of tartar + soda → Rochelle salt + carbonic acid ↗ Water + carbon dioxide

CALCIUM PHOSPHATE

$$3CaH_4(PO_4)_2 + 8NaHCO_3 \rightarrow Ca_3(PO_4)_2 + 4Na_2HPO_4 + 8H_2CO_3 \nearrow 8H_2O + 8CO_2$$

Monocalcium phosphate + soda → dicalcium phosphate + sodium acid phosphate + carbonic acid ↗ Water + carbon dioxide

S.A.S.-PHOSPHATE

The second reaction above and the following:

(1)

$$Na_2SO_4AL_2(SO_4)_3 + 6H_2O \rightarrow Na_2SO_4 + 2AL(OH)_3 + 3H_2SO_4$$

Sodium aluminum sulphate + water → sodium sulphate + aluminum hydroxide + sulphuric acid

(2)

$$3H_2SO_4 + 6NaHCO_3 \rightarrow 3Na_2SO_4 + 6H_2O + 6CO_2$$

Sulphuric acid + sodium bicarbonate → sodium sulphate + water + carbon dioxide

Brands of baking powder are easily classified by finding the name of the distinguishing acid salt on the package. Thus if a powder contains cream of tartar and/or tartaric acid, it is tartrate; if it contains sodium aluminum sulphate, it is S.A.S.-phosphate powder. The type should be ascertained before a baking powder is used.

Residues from the three types of baking powder differ but all are harmless. All the types of powder may be used satisfactorily. The principal difference is in the speed with which they react in cold liquid. In order of their speed of reaction, they are tartrate, calcium phosphate, and S.A.S.-phosphate. Obviously, a smaller quantity of a slow-acting powder will be required for leavening than of a quick-acting powder. The difference between the tartrate and calcium phosphate powders is not sufficient to warrant listing different amounts in recipes. As a general rule, 1½ teaspoons of the two quick-acting powders are needed for each cup of flour, and 1 teaspoon of slow-acting powder.

All baking powders must, according to federal law, contain at least 12 per cent of available carbon dioxide gas. Practically all exceed this requirement. For effectiveness, the quantity purchased should be small enough to admit of being used within a reasonable time, and the can should always be closed except while the powder is being measured. This prevents moisture from the air from being absorbed by the powder and thus helps in the retention of available carbon dioxide gas.

Habit usually accounts for preference for one brand of baking powder. It should be expected that the powder will provide a large volume of gas in ratio to the amount used, that most of that gas will be available during the actual cooking process, and that the residue will not be tasted in the finished product. It may be well to try several brands and to continue the use of one that gives excellent results for a reasonable price.

It is simple to use baking powder with sweet milk and soda with sour milk interchangeably if equivalents in leavening power are kept in mind. The list of substitutions (see Appendix E) includes these equivalents. The following recipes for muffins show how such a substitution is made.

Sweet Milk		Sour Milk	
Flour	3 c.	Flour	3 c.
Salt	½ t.	Salt	½ t.
Baking Powder	3 t.	Baking Powder	⅓ t.
Eggs	2	Soda	1 t.
Oil	2 tb.	Eggs	2
Sweet Milk	2 c.	Oil	2 tb.
		Sour Milk	2 c.

Because of the seeming increased use of the slow-acting type of baking powder, recipes included in this book are based on that type. For one of the quick-acting powders, the quantity should be increased by half.

Leavening by means of air and steam. Air may be incorporated in flour mixtures by beating egg whites. They foam readily, and the air enclosed is the principal leavening agent in sponge cakes, spoon bread, and many macaroons. Air is also added by sifting flour, three times being sufficient. Thin batters may be beaten to add air. When fat is creamed and when sugar is added to it, air is incorporated. In beaten biscuit air is added by folding the dough and beating it, and in puff pastry, by folding the dough and rolling it.

Steam is formed as the liquid in batters and doughs is heated, and is an effective leavening agent. In thin batters it is, of course, more effective than in thicker batters and doughs.

One leavening agent is seldom entirely responsible for the lightness of flour mixtures. Some air is present in most of them, and steam is effective in all except the mixtures that are so thick that little water is available to form steam. Most, however, depend primarily upon carbon dioxide for their lightness.

TABLE 25. TYPES OF FLOUR MIXTURES

Type	*Ratio of Liquid to Flour*	*Product*
BATTERS		
Thin	1 c. liquid—1 c. flour	popovers; cream puffs.
	1 c. liquid—1¼ c. flour	timbale cases; thin pancakes.
Medium	1 c. liquid—1½ c. flour	griddle cakes; waffles.
	1 c. liquid—1¾ c. flour	thick cover batters.
	1 c. liquid—X c. flour *	cakes.
Thick	1 c. liquid—2 c. flour	muffins; fritters.
	1 c. liquid—2½ c. flour	drop biscuits; drop cookies.
DOUGHS		
Soft	1 c. liquid—3 c. flour	biscuits; bread †; doughnuts.
Stiff	1 c. liquid—4 c. flour	pastry; rolled and refrigerator cookies.

* The amount of liquid remaining constant, the amount of flour varies with the quantity of the other ingredients.
† The quantity of flour required for one cup of liquid varies from three to four cups, depending upon the absorptive quality of the flour. This ratio is for a good quality of bread flour.

Types of flour mixtures. Flour mixtures are classified as batters and doughs, the former being thinner than the latter. The stiffness of the mixture before cooking varies with the ratio of liquid to flour and with the kind and quantity of such other ingredients as fat, sugar, and eggs. The finished products also vary in texture largely because of these differences. The above table lists flour mixtures of several types and ratio of liquid to flour for each.

Mixes for flour mixtures. Commercial mixes of many varieties and brands are available. Directions for their use accompany them and trial will show which are satisfactory to a homemaker who wishes to use them for at least a part of the flour mixtures needed. There are also a number of sources for home-made mixes, including a bulletin for use at high altitudes.

Altitude. Baking at high altitudes is different from baking at sea level or up to about 3,000 feet. In general, more liquid, less sugar, and less leavening material are needed. At very high altitudes, eggs may be increased. A general guide for adjusting cake recipes is presented in Table 27, p. 219.

BATTERS

Thin Batters

The proportions of ingredients and cooking methods used for thin batters are tabulated in Table 26. While the liquid remains constant in the five mixtures, the other ingredients vary.

As the ingredients for thin batters are combined, there is little opportunity for the formation of long gluten strands because the ratio of liquid to flour is high and the hydrated gluten particles are floated by the liquid and do not

TABLE 26. PROPORTIONS OF INGREDIENTS AND METHODS OF COOKING THIN BATTERS

Flour Mixtures	*Liquid*	*Fat*	*Eggs*	*Flour*	*Salt*	*Method of Cooking*
Popovers...	1 c. milk	1 tb.	2	1 c.	1/8 t.	Bake at 450° F. (232° C.) 20 min.; continue at 350° F. (177° C.) until thoroughly dry (about 20 min.)
Cream puffs.....	1 c. water	1/2 c. butter	4	1 c.	...	Bake at 425° F. (218° C.) 10 min.; continue at 375° F. (191° C.) about 20 min. (longer for large cream puffs).
Timbale cases.....	1 c. milk	1 tb.	1	1 1/4 c.	1/8 t.	Cook on heated iron in deep fat at 370°–375° F. (188°–191° C.) until brown. Drain on unglazed paper.
Cover batter or Rosettes..	1 c. milk	1 tb.	1	1 1/4 c.	1/8 t.	Cover pieces of fruit, vegetable, meat, etc., with batter and fry in deep fat at 370°–385° F. (188°–196° C.) until brown. Drain on unglazed paper.
Thin pancakes.	1 c. milk	1 tb.	2	1 c.	1/8 t.	Cook on hot griddle to brown; turn; brown other side.

form a continuous network throughout the batter. Eggs are needed in thin batters because the protein they provide is extensible and tenacious.

Popovers. Good popovers are (1) thin—in fact, mere shells; (2) crisp; (3) shiny; (4) evenly browned.

Popovers are leavened principally by steam. The large amount of liquid is quickly turned to steam as the batter bakes, and the batter is sufficiently tenacious to retain its shape as the steam stretches it, so that the finished product is a thin, crisp shell. Muffin pans of cast iron or heavy tin or ramekins of ovenized glass or earthenware are recommended. The pans may be heated before the batter is poured into them, but this is not necessary. A high oven temperature, 450° F. (232° C.) is usually recommended for the beginning of the baking period, but a constant temperature of 375° F. (191° C.) may be used, or the batter may even be placed in a cold oven and allowed to heat gradually as the oven temperature rises. If the temperature is maintained or increased while steam is forming the "shell" of the finished popovers, they will be as large and thin as they should be. The shell should be dry and crisp when the popovers are removed from the oven. Otherwise, they will collapse. Frequently, if the oven is well insulated, the heat is turned off when the popovers have popped, are well browned, and feel firm; and they are left in the oven to dry. They slip from the pans easily and are very shiny on the bottom when done.

Cream puffs. Good cream puffs are (1) shells, but not as thin shells as popovers; (2) tender, but not as crisp as popovers; (3) moist, but not gummy inside; (4) irregular in shape; (5) evenly browned.

The same ratio of flour to liquid is used for cream puffs as for popovers. They contain four times as much fat, however, and twice as many eggs are generally used. The water and fat are heated to boiling and the flour is added all at once. The mixture is stirred vigorously to combine the ingredients thoroughly. It is then removed from the fire and the unbeaten eggs are added immediately, one at a time, stirring each in thoroughly before adding the next. As the first one or two eggs are added, the batter is slippery and heavy in appearance and, to the beginner, may appear to be a failure. As the other eggs are added, the batter becomes creamy and light in appearance. The resulting batter is thick and may not seem to belong to this group of flour mixtures. The thickness is of course due to the swelling of the starch granules as the flour is heated in the hot liquid. The flour does not lump because of the large amount of fat present in the liquid and the rapid stirring.

The batter is dropped by spoonfuls on a slightly oiled baking sheet. It expands as it is baked in the same way that popover batter does and for the same reason. Undercooked cream puffs collapse. To be sure they are done, one may be removed at the end of the stated time and allowed to stand 2 or 3 minutes. Insufficient cooking is perhaps the most common reason for failure, another being cooling the mixture before adding the eggs. As has been noted, cream-puff batter may be fried in deep fat.

Timbale cases and rosettes. Good timbale cases and rosettes are (1) crisp and thin; (2) evenly and delicately browned; (3) firm enough to hold their shape when as heavy a mixture as creamed chicken is served in them.

The liquid and dry ingredients are mixed separately, and then combined. Stirring produces a smoother batter than beating, and one that is more nearly free from bubbles. Bubbles in the batter result in a rough surface on the timbale case.

Both timbale cases and rosettes are cooked on the outside of special irons in deep fat. The irons are placed in the fat as soon as it is nearly melted and are allowed to heat as the fat heats. When the fat has reached the temperature stated in the recipe, the iron is usually ready to use. If the iron is too cool, the batter will not cling to it; if it is too hot, the batter spreads as it cooks and drops from the iron while it is frying. The temperature of the fat should be 375° F. (191° C.). The iron is lifted from the fat, touched to absorbent paper to remove excess fat, and dipped into the batter to about three-fourths its depth. The batter should be in a utensil that is not much larger in diameter than the iron. The reason for not dipping the iron into the batter to its full depth is that the batter expands as it heats and cooks around the upper edge of the iron, making removal difficult. Drain the brown cases on absorbent paper.

Other thin batters. Yorkshire pudding (see p. 555) is a thin batter. Decreasing flour and omitting baking powder, griddle cakes (see p. 604) become thin pancakes. In French and Swedish pancakes no fat is used; in the latter, sugar is added. Thin pancakes may be served in many ways; e.g., for breakfast, with butter and crushed, sweetened berries or a table syrup; for lunch, rolled around ham or chicken strips; as a dessert for dinner, rolled with jelly or jam and sprinkled with powdered sugar.

Medium Batters

Medium batters are used for griddle cakes, waffles, thick cover batters, and cakes. In this unit, cakes made both with and without fat (sponge cakes) are discussed. Because eggs are the basic ingredient, the making and baking of sponge cakes are much more closely related to problems of egg cookery than of flour mixtures. They are included here because it is frequently convenient to consider the two types of cake together in order to contrast them.

Griddle cakes. In form, griddle cakes resemble some of the unleavened breads. However, because they are leavened, they are light and tender rather than compact and crisp. Good griddle cakes are (1) light; (2) tender; (3) free from tunnels; (4) evenly browned on both sides; (5) free from a crisp, greasy crust around the edge.

Ingredients. The flour used for griddle cakes may be wheat flour alone or wheat flour combined with whole-wheat, rye, buckwheat, corn meal, or flour or meal from other sources. Salt is always needed for flavor. Baking powder is the leavening material used with sweet milk, and soda and baking powder with sour milk. The ratio of leavening material may be slightly higher in batter for griddle cakes than the theoretical quantity because some carbon dioxide gas escapes while the batter stands during the cooking process, and some escapes while the griddle cake is cooking before it is turned.

Eggs improve the texture and flavor of griddle cakes. Fat or oil makes them tender. Bacon fat is sometimes used in whole wheat or corn meal griddle cakes to add flavor. Milk is usually the liquid used. The ratio is 1½ cups of flour per cup of liquid when sweet milk is used. When sour milk is used, about 1⅓ cups of flour are usually satisfactory. This depends upon the thickness of the sour milk, less flour being needed for very thick milk. The amount of flour also depends, of course, upon its hardness (see p. 202) and adjustments may need to be made.

Manipulation. The "muffin" method is used in combining ingredients for griddle cakes. This means that all dry ingredients are sifted together, all liquid ingredients—usually eggs, fat or oil, and liquid—are combined, and then the two combinations are mixed. The liquid ingredients should be well combined. The eggs are beaten thoroughly, the melted fat or oil is added—preferably not more than 1 tablespoon at a time—and beaten well; then the liquid is added and the mixture is again beaten well. If fat is melted, the eggs and liquid should be at room temperature to prevent solidifying of the fat as the liquids are combined. The liquid ingredients are added all at once to the dry ingredients and the two are combined by stirring just enough to dampen the dry ingredients thoroughly. The mixture should not be beaten, and the batter should be lumpy. The reason why care must be taken not to overstir is that the ratio of flour to liquid is higher than in thin batters, and the gluten particles are not floated but form in long strands. Griddle cakes made from batter that is stirred too long are heavy, tough, and full of tunnels.

Cooking. The griddle used for cooking the cakes should be hot. Iron griddles are usually oiled slightly, and are considered hot enough if the oil smokes very slightly. If there is much smoke, or if the smoke is irritating to the nose and throat, the griddle is too hot. If sufficient fat is used in the batter—usually 1 tablespoon more than is specified in the recipe—oiling may not be necessary. Aluminum griddles should not be oiled. If a little water, dropped on an aluminum griddle, scatters and rolls around like mercury, the griddle is sufficiently hot. Special griddle thermometers are available.

Sufficient batter is poured on the griddle from the tip of the mixing spoon or from a pitcher to make a round cake of the size desired. When the top is bubbly and the edges are beginning to dry, the cake should be turned. If it is allowed to cook until the whole surface looks dry, the cake will not brown when turned. As soon as it is turned, a griddle cake rises perceptibly, particularly in the center. As cooking continues, it settles, being nearly level when the cake is done. Griddle cakes should never be turned more than once, as repeated turning makes them heavy.

Griddle cakes should be served immediately. If they are stacked and left to stand, they steam and become soggy in a very short time.

Waffles. Good waffles are (1) crisp, (2) tender, (3) evenly brown in color, (4) the perfect shape of the baker.

Ingredients. The ingredients for waffles are the same as those used for griddle cakes, but the amounts of fat and eggs are increased. The whites of the eggs are usually beaten and folded in after the other ingredients are combined. The quantity of baking powder may be less than in griddle cakes because of the air incorporated in the beaten egg white and because there is no appreciable loss of carbon dioxide gas during the cooking process.

Manipulation. With the exception of the fact that the egg whites are beaten separately and folded in at the last, waffle batter is made in the same way as griddle-cake batter.

Cooking. Specific directions for the use of electric waffle bakers are included with them. These should be followed implicitly. Some are equipped with indicators showing when the iron is at the right temperature. Waffle bakers not heated by electricity are usually made from cast iron and need to be oiled slightly before the batter is poured into them. While they are heating, they should be turned as needed to insure even heating of both sides. As soon as batter has been poured into the iron, and the top has been lowered, the iron should be turned to keep the heat as even as possible. The iron is turned several times during the cooking process so that the waffle will brown evenly.

Batter is poured quickly into the baker at the center and should spread to within an inch of the edges. As the top is lowered, the batter is pushed to the edges. Batter that is too thin does not fill the depth of the baker, and the waffles from such batter are crisp and brown on one side, but soggy and pale on the other. Batter that is too thick never produces a crisp waffle.

"Cover" batters or fritters. The griddle-cake batter (see p. 604) may be used for dipping pieces of some vegetables, fish, chicken, or meat before frying. Spoonfuls of batter fried in deep fat are interesting fritters, served with a fruit sauce or, sprinkled with powdered sugar, as an accompaniment for fruit. Pieces of fruit may be dipped into the batter and fried. The Orientals serve various foods which have been coated in batter and fried.

Cakes. Two or three generations ago, cakes made by increasing the fat and sugar in bread dough and adding chopped dried fruit and probably eggs, were used a great deal. Such cakes are seldom made now, but sweet rolls, used as bread rather than as cake, are similar.

Cakes belong to one of two classes: those made without fat and those made with fat. The former are called sponge cakes, and include the various kinds of sponge and angel cakes. Cakes made with fat include plain, white, chocolate, spice, apple sauce, and pound cake, and gingerbread. Chiffon cakes have many characteristics of sponge cakes, but salad oil is an ingredient. There are many recipes, differing slightly or considerably for each of these varieties. The form in which they are baked and the fillings and frostings that may be used make many more variations possible.

Cakes containing fat. Good cakes are (1) even and delicate in color; (2) even in shape; (3) thin and tender as to crust; (4) possessed of the following qualities as to crumb: (a) moist, (b) elastic, (c) tender, (d) easily broken without crumbling, (e) "velvety," that is, soft and smooth to the touch, (f) even in texture, and with no large holes or tunnels.

Ingredients and their proportions. The fat chosen for cakes should be one that can be creamed well and that is not unpleasant in flavor. Butter or margarine is usually chosen, but lard, hydrogenated fats, or chicken fat may be used. The amount may vary considerably but should be used in ratio to the liquid and the eggs. Too little fat results in a dry cake that is not tender; too much makes the cake heavy and crumbly and may make it fall in the center.

If flavoring extracts are used, they should be added to the fat because fat absorbs flavor readily. Other flavoring materials, such as chocolate, dried fruits, nuts, spices, or the grated rind from citrus fruits, are added later in the cake-making process.

Finely granulated sugar is an advantage in cake-making. The quantity may vary from one to two cups in a cake containing three cups of flour. The proportion of sugar affects both texture and volume as well as flavor. Cake batter that contains a relatively high proportion of sugar should be stirred longer than cake batter with less sugar, in order to blend the sugar thoroughly with the other ingredients. If too little sugar is used, the product is more like muffins than cake, and the crumb is apt to be tough. If too much sugar is used, the crust is sugary and sticky, the crumb is heavy and crumbly, and the cake falls at the center.

Eggs are used to incorporate air, to give the properties of an emulsion to the batter, and to increase the elasticity of gluten. They also influence the temperature at which the batter sets during the baking process. Eggs increase the volume and lightness of the cake unless too many are used, in which case the cell walls are thick and the cake is tough. The number of eggs used should be related to the amount of fat. Eggs of medium size should be chosen. Too little egg makes a cake of small volume that seems to contain too much fat. Too much egg results in a spongy cake of greater volume than is desired (see p. 120).

Although good cakes can be made from general-utility flour, appreciably better cakes result when cake flour is used because the crumb is more velvety. Too little flour, of course, makes the batter too thin, and the cake will be heavy and will fall at the center. Too much makes a compact, dry cake that usually forms a peak as it bakes. The crust usually cracks and, even though the cake is palatable, the appearance is unattractive.

If the fat is unsalted, salt should be added to the recipe, ⅓ to ½ teaspoon being sufficient.

Baking powder is the usual source of carbon dioxide gas—the principal leavening agent in cakes of this type. The general ratio of 1½ teaspoons of tartrate or calcium-phosphate, or 1 teaspoon of S.A.S.-phosphate baking powder per cup of flour is correct for a cake in which one egg is used. As the number of eggs is increased, especially if the whites are beaten and folded in, the quantity of baking powder is decreased correspondingly.

The air incorporated when fat is creamed and when sugar is creamed with it may be sufficient to influence the quantity of baking powder needed. Evidence of this air when fat is thoroughly creamed is the fluffy texture. Continued creaming as sugar is added gradually and as eggs are added retains the air so that less baking powder is needed. It would be difficult to state this influence quantitatively because of individual differences in the interpretation of "cream well." Experimentation might be interesting in either laboratory or home.

TABLE 27. CAKE RECIPE ADJUSTMENT FOR HIGH ALTITUDES *

Adjustment	*3,000 feet*	*5,000 feet*	*7,000 feet*
Reduce baking powder For each teaspoon, decrease........	1/8 t.	1/8 to 1/4 t.	1/4 to 1/2 t.
Reduce sugar For each cup, decrease........	No change	Usually no change	1 to 2 tb.
Increase liquid For each cup, add..	1 to 2 tb.	2 to 3 tb.	3 to 4 tb.
Shortening........	In very rich cakes, it is sometimes necessary to reduce shortening by 1 to 2 tb.		

* *Handbook of Food Preparation*, American Home Economics Association, 1954.

Milk is the liquid commonly used in cakes. It may be sweet, sour, or evaporated. Powdered milk may be used, with water as the liquid. Fresh, unsweetened fruit juice gives a pleasing flavor and is frequently used. Too little liquid has the same effect as too much flour; too much has the same effect as too little flour.

Possible variations in proportions of ingredients may be illustrated by a series of "patterns." (See pp. 607–608.) In these, the amounts of flour and sugar remain the same. The cakes made by these "patterns" vary in texture and in richness but each possesses the qualities of a good cake. The following relationships appear in the "patterns":

1) The amount of sugar is half that of the flour.
2) The combined quantities of milk and fat equal the quantity of sugar.
3) One egg is used for each 1/4 c. of fat.
4) As the fat is increased, the milk is decreased by an equal amount.
5) As the number of eggs is increased, the quantity of baking powder is decreased for each added egg, in the amount of 1/2 t. of tartrate or phosphate, and 1/3 t. of S.A.S.-phosphate powder.
6) As the fat is increased, the final stirring time is increased, but not in definite ratio.

Altitude. Certain general changes are needed when cakes are baked at high altitudes. These are listed in Table 27. If a person has occasion to bake a cake at a distinct change in altitude, it is best to rely upon recipes prepared for that altitude.

Manipulation. It is possible to make cakes by any one of several methods, including the cake method, the muffin method, the conventional sponge

Courtesy Mary Anna Olson

Fig. 37. A Swedish student shows pride in her provincial Swedish cake— spettkaka. *This cake is baked on a spit.*

Courtesy Margaret Ryser

Fig. 38. Braided bread is traditionally made in many countries.

method, various cake-mixer methods, and the method of putting all ingredients into a bowl and stirring. The object of manipulation is to combine all ingredients thoroughly to produce the qualities listed on page 217. Four methods will be described: cake method, muffin method, short method, and cake-mixer method.

1) The *cake method* is often called the conventional method. The fat is creamed until it is light and fluffy. This incorporates air and makes it easy to combine with other ingredients. Flavoring extract is added while the fat is being creamed, because fat retains the flavor well.

Sugar is added and the creaming continued. Sugar crystals adsorb fat, distributing it evenly as the mixing proceeds. Usually the egg yolks are beaten and added, blending the three ingredients well. Whole eggs rather than the yolks are often added, either with or without prior beating.

The sifted flour is measured and sifted again with leavening material and salt. Half of it is added to the first mixture, stirring enough to combine well. The liquid is added and stirred in. The remaining dry ingredients are added and the batter is stirred to combine all ingredients thoroughly. When quick-acting baking powder is used, less stirring time is considered optimal than when slow-acting powder is used.

When egg whites are added separately, they are beaten and folded into the batter.

2) If the quantity of fat is small, the *muffin method* may be used. (See pp. 215–216.) The fat is melted and added with eggs and milk, being sure that they are warm enough not to solidify the fat. If this happens, the cake will not be very tender, nor will the crumb be velvety. When the fat does not solidify, an oil-in-water emulsion is formed. The product is good but does not stay fresh long. This method requires less time than the cake method.

3) Time is shortened still more if the *short method* is used. The dry ingredients, including sugar, are sifted into a mixing bowl. If cocoa is used, dry ingredients should be sifted three times to mix them evenly. The fat, warm enough to mix easily, if butter or margarine, is added in small pieces. Hydrogenated fats may be used. The flavoring and half to two-thirds of the liquid are added and these ingredients are stirred, carefully at first, to combine them well. Then the eggs, unbeaten, and remaining liquid are added and the mixture is stirred to combine the ingredients thoroughly. Some recipes using this method produce batter that is considerably thinner than the usual cake batter.

4) Directions for making cakes by the *cake-mixer method* are included in recipes that accompany electric mixers. It is essential to use fat at room temperature. The fat and sugar are combined, the egg added, and they are stirred until the mixture is fluffy and thoroughly blended. The flour and milk are alternated, starting with part of the flour. This helps to avoid separation that is evidenced by flecks appearing in the batter. If ingredients are inclined to stick to the bowl, the motor should be stopped occasionally and the mixture scraped from the side of the bowl with a limber spatula or a rubber spatula.

Baking. The bottom of the pan in which a cake is baked should be oiled and lightly floured or covered with heavy waxed or oiled paper. The sides of

TABLE 28. TIME AND TEMPERATURE FOR BAKING CAKES CONTAINING FAT

Kind of Cake	*Type of Pan*	*Temperature (Degrees)* F.	C.	*Time (Minutes)*
Plain	Cup	360	182	20
	Layer	360	182	35
	9-in. square	350	177	40–45
White	Cup	360	182	20–25
	Layer	360	182	35
	9-in. square	350	177	35–40
Chocolate	Cup	350	177	25
	Layer	350	177	30–35
	9-in. square	340	171	35–40
Spice	Cup	360	182	25
	Layer	360	182	30
	9-in. square	350	177	35–40

the pan should not be oiled because the rising batter will cling better to an unoiled surface.

Except in case of the thin cake batters, the batter should be spread so that it is somewhat thicker around the edges than in the center because the batter around the edges sets more quickly than in the center. Consequently, if the batter is even when the cake is put into the oven, the center of the baked product will be higher than the edges.

The oven temperature depends upon the size, thickness, and variety of cake. Small cakes and thin ones should be baked at a higher temperature than large and thick ones. Chocolate cakes require a somewhat lower temperature than plain cakes for equal quality in flavor, volume, and texture. Table 28 lists satisfactory time and temperature for baking some of the common cakes of this type.

The following tests are used to tell when a cake is done:

1) It is evenly brown and the crust looks firm.
2) It draws away from the sides of the pan.
3) When the top is pressed gently with the finger, it springs back.
4) No sound of cooking batter is heard in small or thin cakes held about 4 or 5 in. away from the ear, or, in loaf cakes, very little sound is heard.
5) A clean toothpick inserted at the center of the cake comes out clean.
6) If the bottom of the pan is touched by a finger dipped into water, there is a hissing sound.

Cakes should remain in the pan two or three minutes after they are taken from the oven, and then should be removed to a wire cake cooler. Cooling them in the pan causes them to steam and become soggy. Cakes should be stored in a closely covered tin cake box.

Chiffon cakes. Chiffon cakes are made with oil rather than fat and the large quantity of egg used gives them the lightness that is characteristic of cakes without fat. The dry ingredients are sifted into a mixing bowl and a "well" is made in the center. Oil, egg yolks, liquid, and flavoring are added and combined with the dry ingredients. Egg whites and cream of tartar are beaten until the whites are stiff and the first mixture is folded in carefully. The cakes are usually baked in tube pans but square or rectangular pans may be used.

Cakes without fat. Good cakes without fat are (1) very light; (2) tender, with thin cell walls; (3) even and fine in texture; (4) free from a sugary crust; (5) no heavy layer at the bottom.

Ingredients. Eggs are the foundation ingredient in cakes of the sponge type. Both yolks and whites are used for sponge cakes, and a given number of medium eggs generally result in a good cake. For angel cakes, only the white is used. Measuring results in accuracy because the quantity needed is large, and the amount obtained from separating a given number of eggs is not definite.

Flavoring in sponge cakes is usually added in the form of lemon juice and rind. The juice also furnishes liquid and, because it is acid, peptizes the protein of both eggs and flour, thus increasing the tenderness of the cake. Salt is also added for flavor.

In angel cakes, cream of tartar is used instead of lemon juice. It makes the cake very white because it bleaches the pigment of the flour. Like lemon juice, it increases the tenderness of the cake. It also increases the tenacity of the protein of the egg white and reduces the coagulation temperature.

Sugar should be finely granulated because it combines with the other ingredients more readily than sugar that is coarse. If it is lumpy, sugar should be sifted before it is measured. Sometimes powdered sugar is substituted for part of the granulated sugar, but the finished cake is drier than one in which granulated sugar only is used.

Cake flour is usually preferred for these cakes, but some persons use general utility or even bread flour successfully.

Proportions of ingredients that are satisfactory for some of the sponge-type cakes are tabulated on page 224.

Manipulation. The method of combining ingredients for the different kinds of sponge cake varies considerably. The skill with which they are combined is an important factor in determining the quality of the finished product. In all, the ingredients must be combined thoroughly. A heavy, gummy layer at the bottom of a cake results from under-mixing.

1) In true sponge cake the egg yolks are beaten until they are thick and fluffy. The sugar is added about 2 tb. at a time and beaten into the yolks. During this process air is incorporated and the mixture is stabilized. The lemon juice and rind are added and beaten in. Then the flour—sifted, meas-

TABLE 29. INGREDIENT PROPORTION FOR KINDS OF SPONGE CAKE

Kind of Cake	*Cake Flour*	*Sugar*	*Water*	*Salt*	*Acid*	*Flavoring*	*Egg*
True sponge....	1 c.	1 c.	2 tb.	½ t.	1 tb. lemon juice	2 t. lemon rind	⅔ c. white ⅓ c. yolk
"Boiled" sponge....	1 c.	1 c.	½ c.	½ t.	1 tb. lemon juice	2 t. lemon rind	5 med. or ⅔ c. white ⅓ c. yolk
"Sirup"..... sponge....	1 c.	1¼ c.	¾ c.	¼ t.	¾ t. cream of tartar	2 t. lemon rind	6 med.
Angel cake......	1 c.	1¼ c.		¼ t.	1 t. cream of tartar	1 t. flavoring extract	1 c. white
Sirup angel cake......	1 c.	1¼ c.	¾ c.	¼ t.	¾ t. cream of tartar	1 t. flavoring extract	1 c. white
Chocolate angel cake.	¾ c. plus ¼ c. cocoa	1¼ c.		¼ t.	1 t. cream of tartar	1 t. vanilla	1¼ c. white

ured, and sifted twice with the salt—is folded in, about 2 tb. at a time. The flour must be well combined with the other ingredients, but the folding must be done gently. The egg whites, beaten stiff enough to stand in a peak when the beater is lifted, but not dry, may be folded in after all the flour is added. Some persons prefer to add half of the flour, then all of the beaten egg white, and lastly, the other half of the flour. The egg white, like the flour, should be folded in thoroughly but carefully to insure an even texture without undue loss of air.

2) In "boiled" sponge cake the sugar and water are cooked to 238° F. (114° C.) and poured slowly over the beaten egg yolks, beating constantly during the addition. The mixture is set into a bowl of cold water and beaten until cool. During this time the lemon juice and rind are added. When the mixture is cool, the flour and beaten egg whites are folded in, alternating half the flour with half the egg white.

3) In "sirup" sponge cake the sugar and water are cooked to 236° F. (113° C.) and poured slowly over the egg whites that have been beaten until they form a peak when the beater is withdrawn. Beating is continued both during the addition and until the mixture is cool. Then the beaten egg yolks, combined with salt and lemon juice and rind, are folded in, and finally, the flour—which has been sifted, measured, and sifted twice more—is folded in.

4) In angel cakes, egg white is the basic ingredient. The whites are beaten until foamy; then the salt and cream of tartar are added and the beating continued until the peak formed as the beater is lifted bends over slightly. This leaves a little more moisture in the whites than beating until the peaks stand erect, as in the case of sponge cakes. Another way to test the stiffness of the egg whites is by tipping the bowl. When the whites flow very slowly as the bowl is tipped, they are sufficiently stiff. During this beating the flavoring may be added.

The sugar is folded in carefully, two or three tablespoons at a time. Then the flour—sifted, measured, and sifted twice more—is added in the same way. Much of the success in making angel cake is due to thorough mixing of the sugar and flour with the beaten egg white.

5) In "sirup" angel cake the sugar and water are cooked to 236° F. (113° C.) The egg whites are beaten and salt and cream of tartar added, as in plain angel cake. Flavoring is usually added toward the end of the beating. The sirup is added to the egg whites, and the flour is folded in, as in sirup sponge cake.

6) Chocolate angel cake is made like plain angel cake except that the added cocoa is sifted with the flour.

Baking. All types of sponge cake are baked in unoiled pans because, as the cake rises, it must cling to the sides of the pan. They may be baked in shallow pans or in square muffin pans, but a tube pan is used more frequently. The tube provides for circulation of heat as the cake bakes.

As the batter is poured into a tube pan, the pan is turned to spread the mixture evenly. Large air spaces are left between the layers of batter so formed, especially at the edge of the pan. These should be removed by lifting the pan about six inches above the work surface and dropping it three or four times, or, especially if the bottom and tube of the pan are loose, by cutting through the batter several times with a spatula.

Various temperatures for baking have been used satisfactorily. A constant temperature of 350° F. (177° C.) for angel cakes and 325° F. (163° C.) for sponge cakes results in cakes of excellent texture, volume, and tenderness.

When cakes without fat are done, they break away from the side of the pan, and the surface rebounds when pressed gently. The pan should be inverted over a cake cooler and left until the cake is cold. If it is removed while warm, it is likely to collapse. Sometimes these cakes fall from the pan when they are cool, but it is often necessary to loosen them with a spatula.

Frostings. The simplest frostings are made from confectioners' sugar. The sugar may be added to beaten egg white, or stirred into water, milk, coffee, thin cream, or fruit juice. Unless the liquid serves to flavor the frosting, a flavoring extract is added. Butter, sometimes used in this type of frosting, adds richness and increases the smoothness. The ingredients are combined by stirring enough sugar into the liquid to produce a frosting that will hold its shape and spread easily. Filling between cake layers may be the same as the frosting.

Cooked frostings are made like certain kinds of candy, and their quality is influenced by the factors discussed on pages 183–184. In many frostings, hot sirup, cooked to the correct temperature, is added to beaten egg whites. It should be added slowly, beating constantly, preferably with a rotary egg beater. If the sirup is added rapidly, the egg white coagulates and the frosting will not have a smooth, creamy texture. When the frosting becomes thick so that beating is difficult, a wooden spoon should be used in place of the rotary beater; and beating should continue until the frosting holds its shape when the spoon is lifted. If beating is stopped before this time, the frosting will be grainy (see pp. 183–184).

For a given quantity of sugar, the number of egg whites may vary. Frostings are more fluffy when a relatively large amount of egg white is used. The temperature to which the sirup is cooked is increased as the number of egg whites increases. For 2½ cups of sugar and 5 tablespoons of corn sirup, from 2 to 4 egg whites may be used. The temperatures are:

No. of Egg Whites	*Temperature*
2	240° F. (116° C.)
3	246° F. (119° C.)
4	252° F. (122° C.)

Frosting is put on a cake by pouring a considerable amount on the cake and spreading it, using either a large spoon or a spatula, covering both top and sides. In case of a layer cake, the top of each layer is frosted, and then the side of the whole cake. Rough or swirled frostings are especially attractive.

Boiled frosting is very much like divinity candy. Fudge frosting is fudge cooked to 232° F. (111° C.) instead of 234° F. (112° C.). It is spread quickly just as it crystallizes.

Thick Batters

Thick batters are used for muffins and other quick breads of similar texture. Good muffins are (1) evenly brown in color, (2) not shiny, (3) slightly rough but free from peaks, (4) fine and even in texture and free from tunnels, (5) tender, (6) surprisingly light for their size.

The ingredients used and the baking affect the quality of the finished product, but the way in which the ingredients are combined is the chief factor in making muffins that meet the above standards.

Ingredients. General utility flour is usually chosen for muffins, although it is possible to make good muffins with either bread or pastry flour. Muffins in which a part of the flour is coarse are likely to be of good texture. Whole wheat, soybean flour, cooked rice, rolled oats, bran, corn meal, or meal from some of the sorghum grains may be substituted for part of the flour in a recipe. Whole-wheat flour may be used entirely or combined with white flour or white flour and bran.

The type of baking powder used influences the optimal time for mixing, less mixing being desirable when a quick-acting powder is used. This difference in time is slight—a matter, perhaps, of three or four seconds, or long enough to stir the batter three or four strokes. Salt is used to give a desirable flavor. If bacon fat is used, salt may not be needed.

Sugar is not an essential ingredient in muffins, but is frequently used for flavor and to improve texture and color. Sugar inhibits gluten formation, so that sweet muffins are apt to be fine in grain and free from tunnels. To many people, larger amounts of sugar are pleasing in muffins used for luncheon or dinner than in those used for breakfast.

Eggs are not used in all muffins, but are usually considered desirable because they contribute to nutritional value as well as to flavor and color. Eggless muffins are more apt to be free from tunnels than those made with eggs. If the egg is not beaten thoroughly and not mixed well with the fat and liquid, the cell walls of the muffins are apt to be thick and heavy.

Fat helps to make muffins tender and shortens the strands of gluten. Any flavorless fat of low melting point may be used, or oil may be substituted. Since the fat is melted before it is added, the use of oil seems sensible. The flavor of bacon fat or drippings from other cooked pork may be pleasing in whole-wheat or corn-meal muffins. Chicken fat may be used to advantage.

Milk is almost always the liquid used in muffins, although water or fruit juice may be substituted. The milk is usually sweet, but sour milk may be used.

Numerous ingredients may be added to the mixture for the sake of variety. Fresh berries—particularly blueberries, cranberries, and blackberries—dried fruits, and nuts are all popular. Jelly, jam, or marmalade may also be used, being placed on the batter after it has been put into the muffin pans. Honey or sirup may take the place of sugar. When this is done, it is added to the liquid ingredients.

Manipulation. The muffin method of combining ingredients for flour mixtures has been described. (See page 215–216.) The secret of making muffins that "melt in your mouth" lies principally in combining the dry with the liquid ingredients correctly. The dry ingredients must be just dampened, but the combination of dry and liquid ingredients must be even. The batter is lumpy rather than smooth. This skill can be acquired by practice only. The extent of mixing is sometimes described in terms of time or of a definite number of strokes, but both are inadequate. The number of strokes taken in a given time varies with the worker, and the effectiveness of each stroke varies also. Each person should watch her own manipulation carefully and learn to tell accurately when the batter has been mixed sufficiently. The tendency of many inexperienced persons is to overstir because lumpy batter does not look right. Others beat the batter vigorously, thus eliminating any possibility of making good muffins. The effect of stirring is shown in Figure 39. The peak and tunnels in Figure 39–B, and the shrinkage in size, the increase in the size of tunnels as stirring proceeds, and the evident increasing heaviness which results from too much stirring are all apparent. The color of the over-stirred muffins was pale. This is due to the fact that the fat and sugar which help to produce good color have been adsorbed by the gluten and starch as stirring is prolonged.

All the muffins pictured were made from the same batter, and were baked at the same time in pans of equal size.[1]

Baking. While oven temperature may vary, 400° F. (204° C.) to 425° F. (218° C.) is satisfactory for most muffins, coffee cakes, and drop biscuits that are made from thick batters. If very small muffins are made, as for a special meal or to use as one of a variety of breads, the higher temperature would certainly be used. Yeast mixtures of similar thickness, such as Sally Lunns, bake better at a lower temperature—375° F. (191° C.) is recommended.

The bottoms of the pans in which muffins are baked are usually oiled. The sides are left unoiled. This gives opportunity for the batter to cling to the side of the pan as it rises. The pans are filled about two-thirds full with batter. Care must be taken to transfer the batter from the bowl to the pans with as little stirring as possible. The mixing spoon should be held close to the muffin pan and a spatula used to push the batter off the spoon. If the batter is dropped from a height, tunnels will form, and if the spoon pulls the batter toward one side of the pan, muffins shaped like the one in Figure 39–A usually result.

DOUGHS

Soft doughs. A soft dough contains enough flour in ratio to the liquid so that the mixture can be kneaded and rolled. Flour mixtures that belong in this group are biscuits, shortcakes, doughnuts, and yeast breads .

Biscuits. Good biscuits are (1) evenly brown; (2) evenly shaped, with straight sides; (3) about twice the thickness of the rolled dough; (4) flaky as to crumb; that is, the crumb can be pulled off in thin sheets; (5) free from yellow or brown spots throughout; (6) tender.

Ingredients. General-utility flour is usually chosen for biscuits, although good biscuits can be made from either pastry or bread flour. Part whole-wheat or rye flour, meal from a sorghum grain, or soybean flour may be used. Salt is used for flavor. Baking powder is the source of carbon dioxide gas when sweet milk is used, soda and baking powder with sour milk.

[1] Muffins made by Jane Wofford.

Fig. 39–A. A, *the batter for this muffin was stirred until the dry ingredients were just dampened.* B, *the batter for this muffin was stirred until rather smooth and was dropped into the pan from a height.*

Fat is used to make the biscuits tender. A soft fat, such as lard, a compound, or a hydrogenated fat is usually chosen.

Milk is the usual liquid. Dried milk may be used, with water as the liquid, or evaporated milk and water in equal amounts. Fruit juice is sometimes used.

Occasionally, such ingredients as celery salt, curry powder, grated cheese, or finely chopped parsley may be added to vary the flavor of biscuits.

Biscuit dough may be the basis for quick cinnamon "rolls" or the dough may be rolled very thin and a filling—cheese, ground ham, or a sweet dried fruit mixture—placed in the center and covered with a second biscuit. The edges of the two biscuits are pressed together firmly.

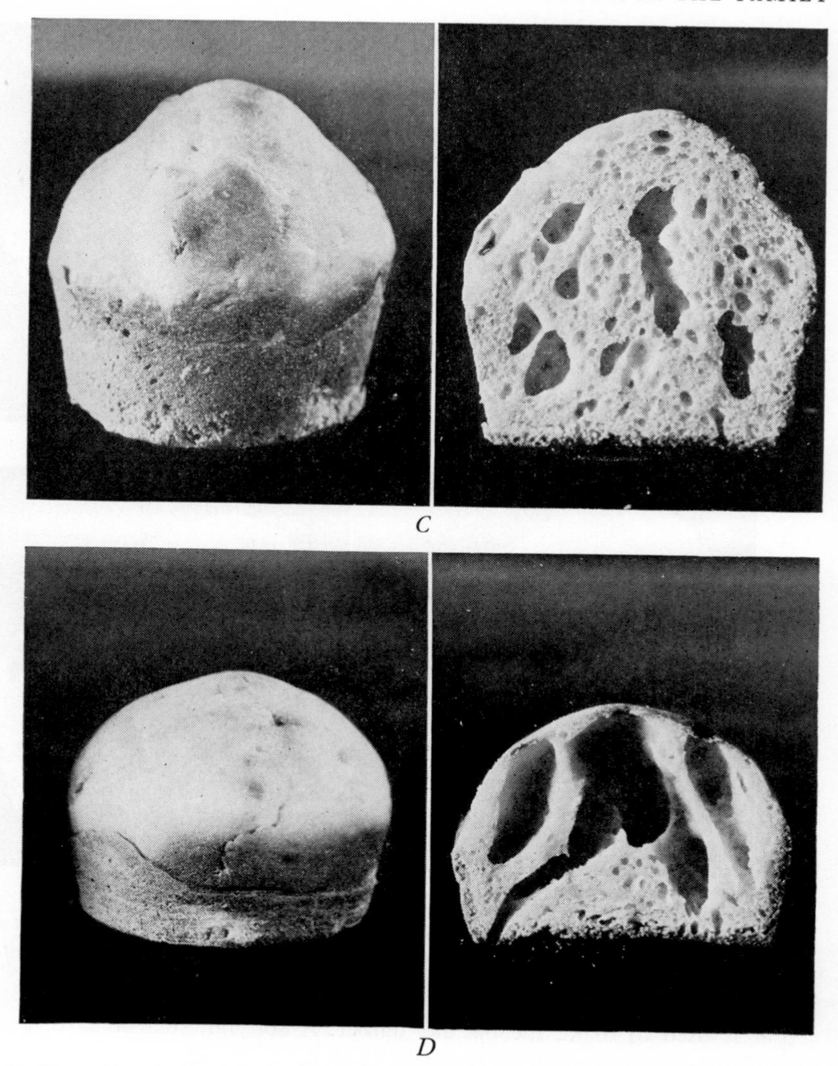

Fig. 39–B. The batter for this muffin was stirred until smooth. D, *the batter for this muffin was stirred twice as long as that for the muffin in* C.

Manipulation. The dough is made by the biscuit method. This means that the dry ingredients are sifted together. Better distribution of the baking powder results if they are sifted two or three times. The fat is added and combined with the dry ingredients by chopping it in with two knives, a dough blender, or a fork, or by rubbing it in with the fingers. Knives or a dough blender should perhaps be recommended for inexperienced persons because there is a tendency to use too much pressure with the fork or fingers, packing the flour and fat together and making the biscuits hard. When the mixture of fat and flour is about the consistency of coarse meal, the milk is added. (A fork is preferable to a spoon for adding the milk.)

The dough is placed on a slightly floured board and kneaded. "Slightly" means that only enough flour is rubbed well over the board to keep the dough from sticking. The biscuits should not be coated with flour. Light, swift strokes are used for kneading, and usually twenty or thirty strokes are sufficient to insure a flaky texture. Kneading develops gluten and distributes fat in such a way that the crumb of the finished biscuit can be peeled off in thin sheets.

The dough is rolled to half the thickness desired for the finished biscuits. Strokes should be light, from center to edge, lifting the rolling pin at the edge to maintain even thickness. The dough may be rolled between two sheets of waxed paper. The biscuit cutter should be dipped into flour, and excess flour tapped off before cutting each biscuit. This helps to give even sides. Good biscuits may be made from commercial mixes by adding liquid as directed on the packages. Both packaged and frozen biscuits, ready for baking, are also available. These are interesting from the time-saving point of view. So also is a homemade mix.

Baking. Biscuits are placed on an oiled baking sheet and baked at a high temperature—425° to 450° F. (218° to 232° C.)—depending upon the thickness of the biscuits.

Biscuits may be made in advance of mealtime. They can be rolled out, cut, placed on a baking sheet, covered and stored in the refrigerator for several hours.

Variety. Poppy seed, finely cut parsley, curry powder, and grated cheese are examples of ingredients that may be added to biscuit dough. Plain dough, rolled to a thin rectangle, may be spread with butter or margarine and sprinkled with parsley, cheese, or a mixture of sugar and spice or nuts. Parsley biscuits make a good crust for meat pie. Leftover biscuits, split and toasted, are excellent as a breakfast or luncheon bread.

Out of doors, stick biscuits may be baked by wrapping strips of dough around slightly oiled sticks and rotating them slowly over coals. The proportion of ingredients is slightly different from that used for biscuits. Results are better if a "hard" general utility flour is used and the dough stands for two or three hours before it is baked. (See pp. 620–621.)

Shortcakes. Good shortcakes are (1) evenly brown; (2) free from yellow or brown spots throughout; (3) very tender but not crumbly.

Biscuit dough in which the quantity of fat is increased is used for shortcakes. The dough is not kneaded. The rolled dough may be cut with a large biscuit cutter if individual shortcakes are desired. The dough may also be baked as one cake in a layer-cake pan or other shallow baking pan.

When the shortcake is baked, it is split, buttered, and sweetened fruit is placed between the layers and on the top.

Doughnuts. Good doughnuts are (1) an even, rich brown in color; (2) tender and light; (3) free from excess fat both inside and outside; (4) thoroughly cooked.

It is difficult to know how to define a "doughnut." In some sections of the country, yeast is the leavening material, and a similar product in which baking powder is used is called a cruller or a fried cake. In other sections, a "doughnut" is made from a twisted strip of dough or a ball of dough, while the "cruller" or "fried cake" is cut with a doughnut cutter. The term "doughnut" is applied to all these products in many instances.

Ingredients. The ingredients are usually the same as those common to cakes. Less fat and sugar are used, the ratio of flour to liquid is higher, and spices are frequently the seasoning.

Mixing. The cake method is used to combine the ingredients. (See p. 221.) If the dough is chilled before rolling it, less flour is needed and the product is better. This is because the fat hardens and the liquid is more thoroughly absorbed by the flour as the dough stands.

Frying. Doughnuts are fried in deep fat at a temperature of about 365° F. (185° C.). The problem of frying so that a minimum of fat is absorbed is one that is related to the proportion of ingredients as well as the actual cooking process. Too much fat or sugar in the recipe increases the fat absorption. If the dough is stretched as it is put into the fat, or if it cracks while frying, more fat is absorbed. Fat that is too cool leads to considerable absorption of fat by the doughnuts because of the time required for cooking.

When the doughnuts are put into the fat, they first sink but soon rise to the surface. They should be turned at once with a fork; cooked until desirably brown on the bottom, turned, and cooked until brown on the other side. When they are removed from the fat, they should be placed on absorbent paper to cool.

Doughnuts are sometimes rolled in either powdered or granulated sugar when they are partly cooled. Other variations include icing the doughnuts and using jelly as a filling.

Miscellaneous quick breads. Numerous quick breads that do not necessarily belong among the soft doughs are discussed briefly here because of the desirability of studying them together.

By varying ingredients and methods of combining ingredients it is possible to make a large number of delicious quick breads. One cereal product may be the foundation for breads which are very different in texture; for instance, corn meal is used in making muffins, corn bread, griddle cakes, waffles, corn pone, corn sticks, and spoon bread. These vary in texture from the soufflé consistency of spoon bread to the crisp, crusty texture of corn pones or corn sticks. Thick batter in which the ratio of liquid to flour is 1 to 2½ is used for drop biscuits and some coffee cakes. The substitution of one flour for another changes the texture and flavor of such quick breads as biscuits and muffins. The flavor of spices, dried or fresh fruits, nuts, or a combination of these helps to make many quick breads delicious. Loaf breads that are baked are very different from the same or similar breads steamed.

Yeast bread. In many parts of the world the term "bread" means a light loaf which is leavened by means of yeast. In other places, "bread" is a flat, unleavened cake. The tortillas of Mexico, the cassava cakes of many parts of South America, and the oat cakes of Norway are examples. Breads of many shapes which seem strange to us are a part of the everyday food of other peoples.

Even though bread-making has been taken from the home to a great extent, the pride of the homemaker and of the student of foods in an excellent loaf of bread continues.

A good loaf of bread is (1) symmetrical in shape; (2) evenly brown in color; (3) light; (4) tender; (5) fine, even, elastic, and moist as to crumb.

Where the top crust meets the sides and ends of the loaf there is sometimes a break, and sometimes the top crust seems to be a smooth continuation of the sides. In the first case, the break should be well filled in, and the fill-in should have a finely shredded appearance. This break and shred is considered by some people to be one of the characteristics of a good loaf of bread; others prefer a loaf in which there is no break and shred.

The preparation of bread of good quality requires careful manipulation, with special attention to the temperature while the dough is being made, and during the rising and baking.

Ingredients. The essential ingredients for making yeast bread are flour, liquid, and yeast. Salt, sugar, and fat are usually added.

1) Flour. Bread of very good quality may be made from soft-wheat flour. However, if it can be obtained, hard-wheat flour is usually chosen. Gluten, the gummy, elastic substance formed when flour is stirred with water (see p. 191), is generally considered to be made during the stirring process from two insoluble proteins —gliadin, which is responsible for the adhesiveness of gluten, and glutenin, which gives tenacity. Some investigators believe that gluten is a distinct protein. Whichever is true, the gluten development which is so carefully avoided in most flour mixtures is essential in making yeast bread. Elasticity is necessary so that as carbon dioxide gas is formed, the dough will stretch. Tenacity is essential to prevent collapse of the cell walls as the dough rises.

Wheats of different varieties, wheat of the same variety raised under different soil and climatic conditions, and wheat of one variety, grown in the same soil year after year may vary greatly in the quality of gluten furnished. Millers blend the streams of flour obtained during the milling process differently so that flour from the same wheat coming from different mills also varies.

2) Liquid. Fresh water, water in which potatoes have been cooked, or milk may be the liquid used in bread. Milk is best from a nutritive point of view. Many

bakers use powdered milk and water as the liquid. From the points of view of convenience and sanitation, this is a good practice. In the home, when fluid milk is high in price and a cheaper form of milk is available, it is wise to use the cheaper form for bread-making.

3) Yeast. Yeast is the leavening material used in bread. The leavening agent, carbon dioxide gas, is formed as a result of fermentation (see p. 207). The yeast must be fresh, if compressed yeast is used; and dry yeast is effective unless older than the date stamped on the package.

4) Salt. Salt improves the flavor and texture of bread. It controls the fermentation process and strengthens gluten. If omitted, fermentation is too rapid and the bread is porous. If too much salt is used, the loaf is heavy.

5) Sugar. Sugar accelerates yeast activity. It also improves the flavor, and because heat caramelizes it, helps to produce a brown crust.

6) Fat. Fat increases the tenderness of both crust and crumb, makes the crust smoother and the crumb more velvety. Bread made with fat has better keeping qualities than bread made without it. It also increases the energy value of bread.

Proportions of ingredients. The ratio of flour to liquid varies from three to four cups of flour for each cup of liquid, depending upon the hardness of the flour. If three cups are not sufficient to make a dough that is not sticky, more should be added gradually until the dough is stiff enough to knead.

Yeast may be used in varying amounts, depending upon the fermentation time. For laboratory use, formulas have been worked out by which fairly satisfactory bread can be made and baked in an hour. Such bread has a yeasty flavor. If the laboratory period is two or three hours, better results may be expected. At home, even though the fermentation time may not be limited, bread-making habits vary from the use of quick to overnight methods. For two loaves of bread, in which one cup of liquid is used, the following amounts of yeast are satisfactory for the rising times listed.

Cakes of Yeast	*Rising Time*
One-half	Overnight (about 12 hrs.); 1 hr., second rising; 1 hr. in the pans
Two-thirds	2 hrs., first rising; 1 hr., second rising; 1 hr. in pans
One	1½ hrs., first rising; ¾ hr., second rising; ¾ hr. in pans

The quantities of salt, sugar, and fat may vary somewhat. Amounts that give consistently good results when one cup of liquid is used are one and one-half teaspoons of salt and two tablespoons each of sugar and fat.

Manipulation. The milk is scalded to destroy any bacteria that might interfere with yeast activity or develop an unpleasant flavor in the bread. The salt, sugar, and fat are usually added to the scalded milk and the mixture is cooled to lukewarm temperature, about 85° F. (29° C.). The yeast, which has been softened in lukewarm water, is added and stirred into the mixture.

1) When the sponge method is used, enough sifted flour is added to make a batter—1½ to 2 c. per cup of liquid. The batter is allowed to stand, covered, in a warm place until it has become light. Then flour is added to make a dough that can be handled, and the dough is kneaded on a slightly floured board until the gluten is developed sufficiently. A little experience enables a person to know, by the way it feels, when dough is kneaded enough. It becomes smooth and elastic. If a depression about ½ in. deep is made in the dough with the finger, it does not close immediately if the gluten has developed as it should. Care must be taken not to add too much flour during either mixing or kneading, because the dough will be so stiff that it will not rise well. After kneading, the dough should be placed in a bowl, oiled, covered, and left to double in bulk. A temperature of about 82° F. (28° C.) should be maintained.

2) The straight-dough method differs from the sponge method in that all the flour is added to the other ingredients at one time. The dough is left to double in bulk; then it is punched down to remove excess gas, to introduce air which stimulates renewed yeast activity, to blend the ingredients more thoroughly, and to help keep the temperature throughout the dough as even as possible. The dough is left to rise about half the first rising time. In the interest of time, the second rising is sometimes omitted, but the final product is not of as high quality.

Usually more than one loaf of bread is made at a time. When the dough has risen sufficiently, it is divided into loaf-size pieces. Each piece is kneaded lightly, shaped into a ball, and allowed to stand, covered, about 15 min. The dough is flattened, folded, and the edges are pressed together. It is stretched to about three times the length of the pan, folded in thirds, and flattened and stretched to about three times the width of the pan. It is then folded and rolled with the hands to complete the shaping. The edges are sealed and the loaf is placed, seam side down, in the center of a pan that has been oiled on the bottom. Results are better if the sides are not oiled. Some of the bread dough may be reserved for making rolls.

The tops of the loaves may be brushed with oil or melted fat. They are covered and left to rise about half the first rising time, again keeping the temperature as nearly 82° F. (28° C.) as possible.

Bread pans differ in relative depth. Use of rather shallow pans results in loaves of better volume than use of deep pans. Loaves placed in the center of the pan have better shape and volume and are less likely to crack than loaves placed toward one side. Round loaves may be made by using casseroles or other round utensils.

Baking. During baking, protein is coagulated, and some of the starch is gelatinized. As the crust browns, the starch dextrinizes and the sugar caramelizes. Fermentation ceases as the heat destroys both yeast and enzyme activity. Oven temperature depends upon the size of the loaves. For relatively small loaves, a constant temperature of 400° to 425° F. (204° to 218° C.) may be used. For larger loaves 400° F. (204° C.) for about 15 minutes, followed by 350° F. (177° C.), is satisfactory.

When the loaves are placed in the oven, care should be taken to insure free circulation of air around each loaf. If loaves are placed too close together, the temperature along the outer sides is higher than that between the loaves. The bread stops rising on the sides where the temperature is higher, and the loaves are uneven in shape, being higher on the sides where the temperature is low. When it is not possible to place the loaves far enough apart to give good air circulation, they should be turned after about five minutes, and again if necessary, to insure well-shaped loaves. Figure 40, p. 237, shows how pans should be placed.

When bread is done, the crust is an even, golden brown. The sides and bottom of the loaf are lighter in color than the top, but are evenly colored. The loaves slip from the pans easily. When they are tapped gently, they sound hollow. Bread should be cooled on a wire cake rack before it is stored, and should be stored in a covered, ventilated, metal breadbox.

Bread should never be wrapped while warm because wrapping while steam is evaporating develops a moist, soft crust which favors mold growth and sometimes, especially if the weather is hot and damp, the development of the bacillus that causes ropy bread. The latter condition is particularly to be avoided because of the very bad odor and taste of bread spoiled by this bacillus.

Variations. A number of varieties of bread may be made at home.

1) When soft-wheat flour is used for bread-making, it is necessary to make some changes in the proportion of ingredients used and in the manipulation. The proportion of yeast and of sugar is increased to about double that which give good results with hard flour, and the ratio of liquid to flour is approximately 1:4. The dough is allowed to rise to double in bulk once, and the loaves should double in bulk before they are baked.

2) Excellent bread may be made when about 50 per cent of the whole wheat or rye flour is used and the nutritive value may be increased by the use of wheat germ and/or soy flour.

Raisins, currants, nuts, or a combination of these are frequently added to bread. Caraway seeds are often used in rye bread.

Texture and flavor may be varied by increasing the amounts of fat and sugar, adding eggs, or both.

3) Salt-rising bread may be made by using dried cultures of the bacteria that develop as a mixture of corn meal, salt, sugar, and water stands several hours at a temperature of about 100° F. (38° C.). This bread is more compact than yeast bread and has a characteristic flavor and odor.

Rolls. Good rolls are (1) very light; (2) an even golden brown in color; (3) even and fine in texture; (4) moist; (5) elastic; (6) tender.

Rolls are made from a yeast bread mixture, usually modified by an increase

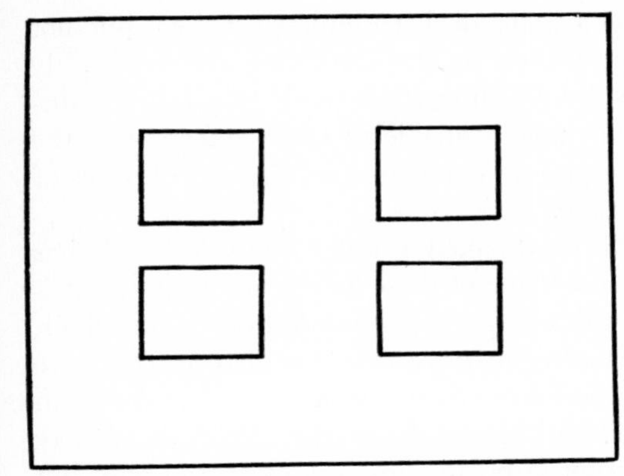

Fig. 40. Correct method of placing bread in an oven when several loaves are baked at a time.

in the proportion of fat and sugar. Eggs are frequently added. Chopped dried fruits, nuts, and spices may be added to the dough or added as the rolls are shaped. The flavor of cardamom seed is pleasing in rolls. Poppy seed or sesame seed may be sprinkled on the tops of rolls. Butter and brown sugar, with or without chopped nuts, may be put into the bottom of the pan in which rolls are baked. The dough may be used for tea rings. Rolls are made interesting by varying their shape. Among the popular shapes are Parker House, clover leaf, crescent, butterhorn, rosette, fan-tan, and butterfly. Rolls may be baked until nearly done and then frozen to be used at a later time.

Storing. Staling is retarded if bread is stored at about 50° F. (10° C.), or refrigerator temperature. Wrapping and storing in a metal container also retards staling. Reheating reverses the moisture distribution in stale bread and this may be repeated several times if staling is a problem.

Selecting Bread

The majority of American homemakers buy at least a part of the bread used in their homes. Bread from any one bakery is of uniform quality, and the fact that it is fresh daily makes it popular. There are many varieties, and usually most of them may be bought sliced or unsliced. Pullman loaves are specially made for sandwiches. They are baked in covered pans, so that they are square in shape, and the crumb is much closer-grained than that of other bread. Formulas and manipulation used by bakers vary; hence a difference between loaves from their bakeries. Sometimes day-old bread is sold at bakeries or stores. It is cheaper than fresh bread, and so is of special interest to families concerned with economical buying.

Foreign breads may be purchased on many markets. French bread, German and Swedish rye bread, Mexican tortillas, Armenian sesame-seed bread, and Bohemian kolaches are a few of the interesting ones. Many kinds of rolls are also available—plain, whole-wheat, sweet rolls of many kinds and for special occasions, and coffee cakes. Frozen rolls are increasing in popularity and

"Brown 'n' Serve" rolls are used a great deal. Completely baked, but not browned, these rolls are desirably brown by the time they are thoroughly heated ready to serve. The process by which this was made practical was discovered by accident and has been made available to many bakers over the country. The rolls keep well, especially if stored in a refrigerator. Loaves of bread baked similarly are also made.

In a number of instances special bread baked at home and sold locally has developed into an extensive business. Some of these breads are high in nutritive value because of the flour used and perhaps the addition of soy flour, wheat germ, or both. These are higher in price than bread from the large bakeries, but their flavor, texture, and sometimes nutritive value make them important additions to the breads available on the market. With the variety on the present market, no monotony in bread chosen is likely to occur, but emphasis should be placed on whole-grain and enriched breads.

Stiff Doughs

Cookies. The variety of cookies seems to be almost endless. Some are used by certain groups of people in connection with specific festivals. A Swedish man remarked as he entered his home one day, "I smell molasses cookies. That means Christmas is almost here!" A generous supply of cookies is part of the preparation for Christmas in many lands. Cookies are used as a dessert and as a part of the refreshments for teas, coffees, and other occasions when light refreshments are served. The cookie jar has long been popular as a source of between-meal snacks.

Most cookies may be classed as rolled, refrigerator, or dropped cookies, or as macaroons. Many, however, do not belong in any of these classifications and are usually listed as "miscellaneous." The cookie mixtures that are classified as stiff doughs are those used for rolled and refrigerator cookies. Other cookies are included here for the sake of convenience of discussion and laboratory study.

Rolled cookies. The dough for rolled cookies is a stiff dough. The general ratio of liquid to flour is one to four, but this ratio varies somewhat with the absorptive quality of the flour, and the "liquid" is not entirely accounted for by the milk or corresponding liquid listed in the recipe. The temperature of the dough when rolled also affects the amount of flour needed.

The ingredients are combined by the cake method. (See p. 221.) Only enough flour to make a dough which can be handled should be used. If the dough is chilled before it is rolled, less flour will be needed. Chilling is usually done by placing the dough in the refrigerator for several hours. If there is no refrigerator, but there is a cellar, the covered bowl of dough may be cooled by leaving it in the cellar for several hours. The custom of making the dough in the evening and baking the cookies the following morning is commendable. If too much flour is used, either when the dough is made or when it is rolled, the cookies are hard and the flavor is impaired. The board or pastry cloth on which the dough is rolled should be clean, dry, and lightly floured. After one portion of dough has been rolled, particles which might cause the next portion of dough to stick to the surface should be removed with a spatula or knife, and the surface should be floured lightly again.

As the cookies are cut, there are usually scraps of dough left. These should be saved and rolled a second time after all the dough has been rolled once. Cookies made from dough that has been rolled more than once are less excellent than those made from the first rolling because the flour that is added each time the dough is rolled increases the hardness of the cookies.

Interest is added by varying the shapes of rolled cookies, by decorating them with nuts, dried fruits, tiny candies, or thin slices of gum drops, or by icing them. Before baking an entire pan of cookies, it is a good idea to bake samples to test the stiffness of the dough and the stability of color of such decorations as candies and gumdrops. If the dough is rolled very thin, filling may be placed on one cookie, a second cookie put on top, and the edges pressed together.

Rolled cookies are baked on an oiled baking sheet, leaving a little space between them to allow for spreading as they bake. Most rolled cookies bake best at temperatures ranging from 375° to 400° F. (191° to 204° C.), but some require as low a temperature as 350° F. (177° C.). When done, cookies should be removed to a wire cake rack to cool. A covered earthenware crock is a good storage utensil.

Refrigerator cookies. The dough for refrigerator cookies is also stiff. The ratio of liquid to dry ingredients is the same as that used for rolled cookies, although there is frequently no liquid, as such, specified in the recipe. The reason for this is that as the amount of fat in a flour mixture increases, the amount of liquid decreases. (See "Cake patterns," diagrammed on p. 607 for proportions.)

After the dough for refrigerator cookies is made, it is shaped into rolls or packed into cookie molds and chilled. The molded dough is cut in slices about one-eighth inch thick, using a sharp knife. A sawing motion is better than straight downward pressure. If the edges of the dough crumble as it is sliced, the knife blade may be warmed slightly. The cookies are baked on unoiled baking sheets, usually at 375° F. (191° C.). Cookies of this type are convenient. The dough can be kept for some time in the refrigerator and the cookies baked as needed. Also, frozen dough may be purchased.

Dropped cookies. There are many recipes for dropped cookies. The essential difference, however, between these and rolled cookies lies in the ratio of liquid to flour. Decreasing the flour in any rolled cookie mixture is all that is necessary for making a stiff batter of the right consistency for dropped cookies. The batter is dropped by spoonfuls on an oiled baking sheet and baked at about 375° F. (191° C.). A few test cookies may be baked to check on the thickness of the batter. The temperature is, in general, lower, and the time required for baking is longer than for rolled cookies because of their thickness and sometimes their ingredients.

Ingredients frequently used in dropped-cookie mixtures include dried fruits, nuts, and rolled oats. Home-ground wheat and meal from sorghum grains make cookies of interesting flavor and texture.

Macaroons. Macaroons, while usually considered as cookies, are more like confections, since they contain no flour. Many have a "chewy" texture. The basic ingredient in macaroons is either egg white or condensed milk. When egg whites are used, they are beaten stiff enough so that the peak formed as the egg beater is lifted bends over slightly. The sugar may be either white or brown and is usually beaten gradually into the beaten egg whites. Such ingredients as chopped nuts, coconut, or one of the ready-to-eat cereals may be folded into the mixture. The macaroons are dropped by spoonfuls on an oiled baking sheet and baked at a low temperature, usually 250° to 300° F. (121° to 149° C.). As soon as they are done, they should be removed from the baking sheet to a wire cake rack to cool.

To condensed milk, various ingredients—including melted chocolate, chopped nuts, dried fruits, coconut, or a mixture of these—may be added to make macaroons. These cookies are relatively expensive, but they are easily and quickly made and are delicious to serve as a dessert or as an accompaniment to ices. Like macaroons made with egg white, they are baked at a low temperature—250° to 300° F. (121° to 149° C.)—and should be removed from the baking sheet and cooled in the same way as the other macaroons.

Miscellaneous cookies. Among the many cookies and small cakes that belong in the "miscellaneous" class are sand tarts, shortbreads, and mixtures that are baked in a shallow pan and cut into squares or "sticks" when done. The latter include brownies, date sticks, the various cookies referred to as "bars," and the apple-sauce-cake cookies mentioned on pages 610–611. Many of the Christmas cookies of Europe, such as honey cakes, pfefferneusse, springerle, and lebkücken, may well be used more commonly in our homes.

Pastry. Pastry is a stiff dough used for the crusts of fruit or meat pies, for tarts, and for pastry shells in which such mixtures as creamed chicken are served.

Pastry is often distinguished as plain, flaky, and crumbly, depending upon the amount of fat used in relation to the flour and the method of combining fat with the flour. Puff pastry is a much richer and more flaky product than any of the others and is used frequently for some varieties of French pastry and for pastry shells, and sometimes for the top crust of both fruit and meat pies. Good plain pastry is (1) tender, but not crumbly; (2) flaky; (3) crisp; (4) evenly and delicately browned.

Mixing. There is more than one "pastry method" for mixing ingredients.

The one described is a combination of two techniques, one for combining fat and flour; the other for adding water. The ingredients for plain pastry are pastry or general utility flour, salt, fat, and water. The salt is sifted with the flour. It may be desirable to remove about one third of a cup of the flour and salt to mix with the water. This is not absolutely necessary, however, the fat may be cut into the entire amount. About half the fat is cut into the flour until the texture is about like a coarse meal, then the rest is cut in until it is about the size of small beans or peas. As the fat and flour are mixed, the particles of fat adsorb flour.

A light mixing stroke is necessary, otherwise, the fat and flour will be pressed together too firmly and the pastry will be tough. Two knives or a pastry blender should be used lightly by beginners. A fork or the fingers may also be used.

Not all the flour is adsorbed by the fat. As water is added, the remaining flour absorbs it and the ingredients are held together. The quantity of flour needed varies inversely with the fat used. If none of the flour has been removed from the mixture, as suggested above, the water is added gradually, mixing with a blender or fork after each addition. If flour has been removed, a definite quantity of water is mixed with it to form a paste. This is added to the dry ingredients and fat, and mixed until the dry ingredients can be gathered into a ball.

Oil may be used as shortening in place of fat. It may be mixed with either hot water or cold milk and stirred into the flour and salt. This pastry is less firm than that made with fat and, especially in warm weather, needs to be chilled before it is rolled. It is handled more easily if rolled between pieces of waxed paper rather than on a board or pastry cloth.

Shaping. Sufficient dough for one crust is pressed into a ball and rolled. The rolling may be done on a lightly floured board, between two pieces of waxed paper on a board or cabinet surface, or on a pastry cloth. (See p. 200). Light strokes must be used as the dough is rolled from the center toward the edges. It is important to lift the rolling pin at the edge of the dough, because it is easy to roll the dough thinner at the edge than at the center. It should be rolled so that it is as nearly round and as nearly the right size for the pan as possible. If the dough sticks to the board, it may be lifted and a little more flour may be rubbed over the board.

The pie pan should not be oiled because there is enough fat in the pastry to keep it from sticking to the pan. The dough may be folded, lifted, and placed in the pan, or it may be folded over the rolling pin and placed in the pan. In either case, it is important that it be fitted to the pan, because air is enclosed between the pan and the dough, and as this is heated and expands, it may make the crust uneven.

For a one-crust pie, the crust is cut about one-half inch beyond the edge of the pan. Shears are handy for this cutting. The edge of the crust is then placed along the edge of the pan, allowing the fold of crust thus made to stand up all around the edge of the pan. By using the forefinger of one hand and the thumb and forefinger of the other, this fold of crust is fluted, making an attractive edge, as well as "extending the depth of the pan" so that a larger amount of filling may be used and still leave room for meringue. Even when the crust has been well fitted to the pan, some air is enclosed between the pan and the crust. If the crust is baked with no filling, holes are punched with the tines of a fork over the bottom and around the sides so that as the crust bakes, steam may escape.

For a two-crust pie, the lower crust is fitted into the pan and trimmed half an inch beyond the edge of the pan. The top crust is rolled and a few slits are cut near the center for escape of steam. The filling is put into the pan and the top crust placed already trimmed, if a pastry cloth with the proper size shown on it has been used. If it has not been trimmed, scissors are used to trim it to the size of the pan after it is placed over the filling. The wider, lower crust is folded over the top crust and the two are pressed together with the tines of a fork or the handle of a knife. This seals the edge and helps to prevent leakage of juice.

Fillings for two-crust pies may be fresh, canned, or frozen fruit or mincemeat. Fresh apples are sometimes steamed to shrink them. If not, they should be heaped into the pan. Juicy fruit is not heaped. It may be pushed away from the center so that juice will concentrate there and be less likely to run out around the edges. Juice may be thickened with cornstarch or flour before the pie is cooked, or one of these or tapioca may be mixed with the juice and the thickening will occur as the pie bakes.

Baking. Temperatures used for baking pies vary with the type of pie. The following have been found satisfactory:

Pie crust	450° F. (232° C.).
Fruit pie	450° F. (232° C.) for 10 min., then 425° F. (218° C.) for about 30 min.
Custard pie	425° F. (218° C.) for 10 min., then 325° F. (163° C.) until a thin knife inserted at the center comes out clean.
Pumpkin pie	450° F. (232° C.) for 10 min., then 325° F. (163° C.) until a thin knife inserted at the center comes out clean.

The upper crust of a two-crust pie should be an even, golden brown in color. The under crust should not be soaked. The above temperatures are such that the under crust is fairly well cooked when the temperature is lowered, and the crust is not likely to be soaked. Custard pie probably gives more trouble along this line than do fruit pies. If the milk is scalded, thus decreasing the time required for the custard to coagulate; if one-and-one-half eggs are used for each cup of milk, so that the coagulation temperature will be lowered; and if the above baking temperatures are used there should be no difficulty.

Altitude. Directions for baking pies at altitudes over 3,000 feet include warning to have the oven hot enough to bake the crust before the filling boils. Temperatures suggested on p. 242 are the same as those suggested for those altitudes.

SUGGESTIONS FOR LABORATORY

Prior to laboratory work the student needs specific knowledge of the ingredients, manipulation, and baking procedures that are appropriate for the type of flour mixture to be made. Familiarity with suitable equipment and how and why it is used will help to make the work easy. A demonstration by the instructor is recommended for introducing students to laboratory work dealing with flour mixtures. Choice of recipes to show a fairly wide variety of products made from each type of mixture adds interest and perhaps new ideas of ways to "enliven" family meals by new uses for familiar foods.

While an excellent product is of primary importance, it may be that in several instances experiments to "test the validity" of statements in the text might be carried out. For instance, after making griddle cakes according to directions, the batter might be stirred until smooth and the cakes compared with those made first in appearance, texture, and tenderness. Griddle cakes of one variation or another are universal favorites. An interesting laboratory project may result from making pancakes characteristic of countries such as Germany, France, Russia, Poland, and Switzerland. Other ideas will occur to students as they prepare for or work in the laboratory.

REFERENCES

BOOKS

Fitch, Natalie K. and C. A. Francis, *Foods and Principles of Cookery*. Prentice-Hall, Inc., New York, 1948.

Griffin, Marjorie, *How to Cook*. Garden City Books, Garden City, New York, 1945.

Halliday, Evelyn G. and Isabel T. Noble, *Hows and Whys of Cooking*. The University of Chicago Press, Chicago, 1946.

Lowe, Belle, *Experimental Cookery*. 4th Ed. John Wiley and Sons, Inc., New York, 1955.

Sweetman, Marion D. and I. MacKellar, *Food Selection and Preparation*. 4th Ed. John Wiley and Sons, Inc., New York, 1954.

Various Cook Books, both American and Foreign.

BULLETINS

Colorado Agricultural Experiment Station, Fort Collins:

1) Bowman, Frene, and E. Dyar, *Quick Mixes for High Altitude Cookery.* Bul. 415-A, 1953.
2) *Mile High Cakes.* Bul. 404-A, 1954.
3) Pyke, W. E. and M. Brown, *Cakes and Cookies—Recipes for Different Altitudes.* Bul. No. 489, 1946.

Thiessen, Emma J., *Baking in Mile High Kitchens.* Bul. 328, Agricultural Experiment Station, University of Wyo., Laramie, 1953.

UNIT

17

Appetizers

The first course served at a luncheon or dinner may be said to "introduce" the meal. The food should be attractive without being ostentatious; the portions served should be rather small; the flavor should be tempting. Among foods used as first courses are soups, fruit or fish cocktails, salads, and a great variety of appetizing tidbits called hors d'oeuvres. Each of these offers an opportunity for combining attractive appearance with delightful flavor, thus sharpening both interest and appetite at the beginning of the meal.

It is unfortunate that a first course, with the exception of soup, is so often considered to belong only to dinners at which guests are present. Family meals are certainly worthy of being made more interesting by the occasional serving of an appetizer. First courses provide an excellent means of utilizing small amounts of certain left-over foods and so may be a thrift measure rather than an expensive luxury. By using the tidbits which normally accumulate in the refrigerator, it is a simple matter to prepare a tray of varied hors d'oeuvres. This will permit a choice of generally welcome appetizers.

The first course for either family or guest meals may be served in the living room. Not all appetizers lend themselves to such service, but many do. (See p. 367.)

Soups. Of the origin of soups we have no certain knowledge, but their widespread use is evident as we read of soups which are characteristic foods in many countries. The Crécy soup of England, the cucumber soup of Greece, the borsch of Russia, and the pot-au-feu of France are a few of the nationally popular soups. A large variety of soups may originate from the stock pot on the back of the range in a French kitchen into which go odds and ends of meats and vegetables. Cleared, this stock may become bouillon or consommé; substituted for a part of the milk in white sauce, it may give unexpected flavor to a cream soup. It may also be the basis for a delicious vegetable soup.

Cream soup, fish chowder, clam broth, bouillon, consommé, and fruit soup are the varieties commonly served as a first course. Relatively small servings of cream soup are used at dinner because such a soup tends to satisfy, rather than stimulate, the appetite. Larger servings are appropriate at luncheon if a main course is to follow.

Bouillon is a clear soup made from beef. Veal, chicken, or both, as well as beef, are used in making the stock for consommé. Both bouillon and consommé may be served either hot or jellied. The seasonings should be well blended, especially in consommé, no one flavor being predominant. Varied by the addition of bits of meat or vegetables, the kind of consommé is recognized by the characteristic food served in it. For example, *consommé princess* is served with green peas and chicken meat; *consommé aux pates,* with some form of Italian paste.

Fruit soups are more popular in Europe than in America. They are made from tart fruit juices, usually thickened with arrowroot. Juice from cherries, oranges, currants, or raspberries is suitable for these soups. They may be served hot, but are usually chilled.

Accompaniments suitable for soups may be any of the large variety of commercial crackers, tiny biscuits, muffins, rolls, cheese sticks, salt sticks, beaten biscuit, or toast strips. Croutons (toasted cubes of bread) may be served in the soup; otherwise, the breadstuff should never be broken into the soup.

Cocktails. Originally, the term "cocktail" was applied only to a mixture of alcoholic drinks. Common usage has applied the term to mixtures of fruit juices; tomato juice, either plain or spiced; sauerkraut juice; shellfish served with a highly flavored sauce; and small pieces of tart, fresh fruit with juice. People sometimes serve sweet canned fruits as a cocktail. These lack the crisp or tart quality that is desirable for an appetizer. "Fruit cocktail" as served in some public eating places is the same as the "fruit cup" which is served as dessert.

Most cocktails are accompanied by a breadstuff. With the exception of croutons, any of those served with soups may be used. The "cereal snacks" (p. 598) are popular accompaniments for cocktails. A garnish, such as a sprig of mint for a fruit cocktail or a bit of water cress for a fish cocktail, may be added. Fresh strawberries or cherries are pleasing with a fruit juice cocktail.

Hors d'oeuvres. This is a French phrase and its literal translation means "outside of work." In other words, tasty, appetite-whetting food is eaten before the "work" or "labor" of the main courses begin. When we consider that, traditionally, French dinners include four or more courses and dining is more leisurely than in America, this phrase is understandable. It is impossible to stipulate foods that are appropriate for serving as hors d'oeuvres since there is considerable controversy on the subject. One English writer says

Arranged by the authors

Fig. 41. An assortment of appetizers. Spiced cucumbers, anchovy eggs, and pickled eggs and beets.

they must always be *cold* in order to stimulate the appetite. However, most authors writing on the subject define them as both *hot* and *cold* foods. There is general agreement that hors d'oeuvres must be *tempting* and *unusual* if they are to fulfill their function of whetting the appetite. Opinions differ as to whether the hors d'oeuvres should be a single dish or a variety of dishes. When the choice is so variable, the best guide for selecting food to serve as a first course (whether it is called an hors d'oeuvre or something else) is the meal that is to follow. An interesting attitude when planning hors d'oeuvres or other appetizers is to consider them as a promise of what is to come. A single thick slice of a luscious tomato delicately seasoned with salt, pepper, and a fresh herb, and dressed with oil and vinegar, is a suitable hors d'oeuvre for a three-course dinner to follow. Also appropriate would be the tomato served with one or two anchovies, a crisp cluster of water-cress, and a few slices of cocktail mushrooms. The skillful combination of foods for *any* course requires thought and experience but the hors d'oeuvres course is a special challenge. It can also be a test of the homemaker's resourcefulness and creativity. In so far as possible using foods in their natural form—clams in the shell, whole sardines, peeling left on the cucumber, etc.—will simplify the preparation and serving of the hors d'oeuvre course and it will generally be more appealing. Fig. 41 shows a simple assortment of appropriate appetizers.

Canapés. This is a loosely-used word to denote many kinds of tidbits. Canapés are generally defined as small pieces of toasted bread or crackers carrying a savory morsel or spread. However, a more practical description is that they are designed to be eaten with the fingers. Hence the necessity of a "support" or a "base" on which to place the savory food so that it may be eaten gracefully as finger food. The canapé need not be open faced. It may be a finger sandwich, toasted or untoasted, also the base may be a tiny tart shell or a slice of raw vegetable. Because in general canapés are tedious to prepare and are likely to become soggy and dry on standing (even for a short while), they are not the most practical thing to serve. In many social situations, service of canapés is simplified if family and guests prepare their own. This is accomplished by arranging a tray with the canapé ingredients—crusty bread, crackers, smoked fish, cheese, meat or fish spreads, spiced ham, pickles, etc.—and inviting people to help themselves. Such service is also friendly and relaxing and less time-consuming in contrast to an elaborate array of ready-prepared canapés representing many hours of labor.

Antipasto. This is the Italian first course and the word has the direct meaning of "before the meal." The antipasto, like the hors d'oeuvre, has many interpretations. In Italy its components vary with the season, the region, individual taste, etc. The antipasto, too, may be simple or elaborate as ingredients and taste dictate. Suggestions for a simple antipasto will be found in the food preparation section on pp. 642–643.

In many Italian homes and restaurants the antipasto is often dispensed with in favor of starting the meal with soup or a pasta such as ravioli or macaroni. Risotto (rice with sauce) sometimes is served instead of a pasta. If an Italian meal is opened with either a pasta or risotto, it is followed by the meat or fish accompanied by vegetables and/or a green salad. Cheese and fruit top off the typical meal. However, sometimes an additional dessert is served.

SUGGESTIONS FOR LABORATORY

Attention can be given to the preparation of a limited number of appetizers in most of the laboratories dealing with familiar family foods in this section. If the instructor and students wish to plan a separate laboratory on the subject, left-overs form a good basis for such a project. Since only small quantities of any one food are used and so many different foods are suitable for the purpose, it is both an economical and an interesting way to dispose of left-overs. If such a project is preceded by exploratory reading, students will find that it is simple to create appetizers of varied types that are representative of different countries.

UNIT

18

Beverages

Fundamentally, we use beverages because our bodies require liquid. In various lists which are guides for daily food, 1½ to 2 quarts of water or other liquid are included. Some liquid is included with the food eaten, but most of the needed amount is in the beverages which accompany meals or are drunk between meals.

These beverages include fruit juices, carbonated beverages, milk, water, and alcoholic drinks, as well as infusions from the leaves, roots, or berries of widely different plants. Tea, coffee, cocoa, and chocolate are the most common beverages of the latter variety. The leaves of two other plants, cassina and maté, both members of the ilex family, are used rather extensively for beverages.

TEA

"When I think of tea," said a Chinese poet, "I am conscious of peace. The cool breath of Heaven rises in my sleeves, and blows my cares away." [1] Many years before the Christian Era, tea was used as a beverage in the Orient. Tradition tells of a scholar who lived about 2800 B.C., who valued tea highly, saying of it, "Tea is better than wine, for it leadeth not to intoxication, neither does it cause a man to say foolish things, and repent thereof in his sober moments. It is better than water for it does not carry disease, neither does it act as a poison, as does water when the wells contain foul and rotten matter." [2] The Chinese classics attribute to tea such virtues as "relieving fatigue, delighting the soul, strengthening the will, and repairing the eyesight." [3] In both China and Japan, tea drinking has become a ceremonial, a room being

[1] Agnes Repplier, *To Think of Tea* (Boston: Houghton Mifflin, 1932), p. 149.
[2] *Ibid.*, p. 137.
[3] Okakura Kakuzo, *The Book of Tea* (New York: Dodd, Mead; 1926).

set apart for the purpose. In Japan, a path winds through a garden to the tea-house—*Sukiya,* the abode of Fancy. The entrance is by way of a door so low that all who enter must bow as a symbol of humility. The plain room with its simple decoration, the arrangement of the articles used in making and serving the beverage, the traditional forms used in the ceremony, and the attentive silence of all present create almost a religious sense of rest and aesthetic stimulus. "The world drinks tea, but its history and traditions are indisputably Chinese. Japan has the ritual, England the pure comfort and delight, Tartary and Thibet the needed stimulant in a land of snows. But the 'China drink' is China's child, and China's inspiration." [1]

Customs concerning the use of tea have differed widely. There were famous tea or amusement gardens in England: among them, Vauxhall where the refreshments served included both tea and coffee. "For the custom of afternoon tea as a distinct and definite function . . . the world is indebted to Anna, wife of the seventh Duke of Bedford (1788–1861). In her day, people ate prodigious breakfasts. Luncheon was a sort of picnic, with no servants in attendance. There was no other meal until eight o'clock dinner, after which tea was served in the drawing room. The Duchess of Bedford struck out on a new line; she had tea and cakes served at five o'clock, because, to quote herself, she had 'a sinking feeling.' " [2]

Production of tea. While the time of the first use of tea is unknown, a horticultural book on tea production was written in 780 A.D.[3] The first tax on tea was imposed in the same year.[4] It is probable that the Dutch introduced tea in New Amsterdam before it was used by English colonists.[5] Tea is produced extensively in China, Japan, Ceylon, Java, Sumatra, and Formosa. The principal countries that import tea are Great Britain, the United States, Australia, Russia, Canada, and the Netherlands. Tea bushes are cultivated carefully and are pruned to increase branching and so increase the production of leaves. Leaves are gathered several times during a year and sorted as to size. The leaf buds at the ends of the branches are the source of highest quality tea.

Teas are classed as green, black, and oolong. After sorting, leaves for green tea are steamed slightly, rolled, dried, and fired. For black tea, the rolled leaves are fermented, thus changing their color and the flavor of the beverage. In firing, the temperature is slightly higher than that used for green tea. Oolong teas are semi-fermented. For special flavor, dried petals of flowers—jasmine, orange, or rose—are sometimes added. Commercial teas are blends of leaves from different countries or gardens in one country, or even from the same garden if the leaves are gathered at different seasons.

---

[1] *Ibid.,* pp. 148–149.

[2] William H. Ukers, *All About Tea,* Vol. II (New York: The Tea and Coffee Trade Journal Co., 1935), p. 405.

[3] *Ibid.,* Vol. I, p. 4.

[4] *Ibid.,* p. 5.

[5] *Ibid.,* p. 49.

Composition. In itself, tea has no food value, although the sugar, and lemon or cream often added to the beverage furnish some nutriment. Tea is enjoyed because of its flavor, which is due to the presence of volatile oils, and to the methods used in the process of preparing the leaves for market. It is mildly stimulating because it contains caffeine identical with that of coffee. Bitterness is due to tannin, and is not noticeable in tea which is made properly.

Purchase and storage. Tea may be purchased in small metal or paper containers, in cardboard boxes, or in bulk. It is best packed in metal containers, carefully sealed. Tea is also packaged in small bags for individual service, commonly used in public eating places, but also convenient for the home. Packages vary from one-fourth to one pound in weight. At home tea should be stored in a metal container with closely fitting cover, and should be kept cool and dry. Instant tea is also available.

For the hot beverage, the choice of black, green, or oolong tea is a matter of personal preference. Black tea is usually considered superior for the preparation of iced tea, and green tea is frequently one of the ingredients in fruit punch. The terminology designating grades of tea from various sources differs, as do the flavor and color of the infusion from these teas. The consumer will find it interesting to try different kinds of tea, comparing their flavor, and considering the use of some of the less common teas for special occasions.

Importation laws. In 1883 the first law in the United States which forbade the importation of adulterated tea was passed. The strict enforcement of the Tea Inspection Act of 1897 has made adulteration and mislabeling of teas very uncommon. Carefully trained inspectors at the port of entry examine the tea for broken leaves and stems, added coloring, and the presence of leaves from other plants.

Preparation of the beverage. Whenever tea has been introduced to a new group of people, it has been necessary to teach them the method of preparing it. Tales of tea cooked in a frying pan or boiled at least an hour are amusing; yet it is not strange that these methods should have been tried by people who had no idea how to prepare this new beverage.

An earthenware or other nonmetal teapot is best for making tea, because metal alters the flavor of the beverage. Freshly drawn water that is heated just to the boiling point should be used. If water is allowed to boil, it tastes flat because of loss of air and other dissolved gases. Tea in which boiled water is used is inferior in flavor. The teapot should be heated by allowing boiling water to stand in it a few moments. Connoisseurs of tea would never omit this step. When this is poured out, fresh boiling water may be poured into the teapot and a teabag allowed to stand in the water until the tea is of the desired strength, as indicated by color. This requires from one to three minutes. By another method, the leaves are put into a fine strainer and freshly boiled water is poured over them slowly, either directly into the heated teapot, or into a nonmetal saucepan from which the infusion is poured into the teapot. In any case, leaves should not be allowed to remain in the tea, because tannin is extracted, making the beverage bitter and entirely masking the finest tea flavor.

When a large quantity of hot tea is needed, a strong infusion is often made by increasing the quantity of tea leaves in ratio to the water. A small quantity is poured into the cups as the serving is done, and the cups are filled with hot water. Thus tea varying in strength to please the guests may be provided easily. That strong tea can be made by allowing the water to stand on the leaves for a long time is a mistaken idea. This process merely extracts larger quantities of tannin, and makes the infusion bitter. Doubling the quantity of tea leaves gives a strong infusion of good flavor. If it is to be iced, the beverage is made strong and poured over ice while hot. Occasionally, especially when a large quantity of iced tea is made, tannin precipitates, making the beverage cloudy. This is due to the readiness with which tannin dissolves in hot water, and to the fact that it precipitates when the beverage is cooled quickly. The addition of a little boiling water will redissolve the tannin and will usually prevent further cloudiness. When lemon is added to tea, the color becomes lighter, due to the action of the acid upon tannin. If ice is not available, cold tea may be made by allowing tea leaves to stand in cold water for approximately two hours. Of course less tannin is extracted by this method than if hot water is allowed to stand on the leaves. The same ratio of leaves to water is used as for making iced tea.

COFFEE

Numerous legends tell of the first use of coffee. One relates the story of a dervish, Hadji Omar, who in 1275 was banished from Mocha, to die in the desert. As time went on and the banished man still lived, his enemies asked how he obtained food. Claiming to be Allah's messenger bringing a wonderful new plant to the attention of his countrymen, Omar was allowed to return to Mocha, where he showed the scholars berries which, when roasted and boiled in water, made a most refreshing drink. He was not only exonerated, but was also made a saint.

About the middle of the sixteenth century, a coffee house was established in Constantinople.[1] Wherever coffee was introduced, coffee houses became popular as the gathering places of wits, scholars, and businessmen. According to one writer, "These houses, which are very numerous in London, are extremely convenient. You have all manner of News there; you have a good Fire, which you may sit by as long as you please; you have a dish of Coffee, you meet your friends for the Transaction of Business, and all for a Penny,

[1] William H. Ukers, *All About Coffee* (New York: The Tea and Coffee Trade Journal Co., 1935), p. 17.

if you don't care to spend more."[1] As Boswell relates of Samuel Johnson and his companions, "merry groups of men gathered at the coffee houses." At the Cheshire Cheese in London Johnson's seat is still pointed out. While the leisure suggested by accounts of the coffee houses is rare nowadays, the habit of leaving the office for a cup of coffee with friends prevails in many places and affords relaxation that is important.

Composition and production of coffee. Before coffee was known as a beverage, it was used as a food and as a medicine. Coffee, like tea, has no food value in itself. Native to Abyssinia and Arabia, its cultivation in both East and West Indies, Brazil, Mexico, and other parts of tropical America has become important. Brazil produces about one-half of the world's coffee supply.

The coffee tree is kept pruned to a height of from 8 to 12 feet, to facilitate picking. Coffee berries are a deep red when ripe, and contain one or two coffee beans each. After the berries are gathered, the pulp which covers the beans and the parchment and silvery skins which are inside the pulp are removed. The beans are then cleaned, dried, graded, and packed for shipment. Coffee may be named for the place where it grows—Java or Mocha—or from the port from which it is shipped—Rio or Santos. To those acquainted with the various kinds of coffee, the name indicates definite characteristics of flavor.

As the green coffee arrives at ports in the United States, it is inspected. Distributors—wholesalers, jobbers, or retailers—roast it and blend berries from different sources to procure flavors which are popular with their buyers. The degree of roasting may be light, medium, dark, or very dark (Italian or French), depending upon the demand of consumers. Roasting gives flavor to coffee by developing an aromatic, water-soluble complex, caffeol. Caffeol is sometimes confused with the oils of coffee, which, in themselves, give some aroma and flavor to the beverage. Caffeol is held in the coffee oils much as the perfume of flowers or spices is held in such products as oil of cloves. Thus the aroma and flavor of the caffeol is retained in the coffee bean. In coffee which is roasted to the dark and very dark stages, some of the true oils are decomposed, and the flavor of coffee made from such beans is partly due to these decomposition products. Carbon dioxide, also developed during the roasting process, improves the keeping quality and the retention of aroma and flavor.

Some coffee is bitter. This may be due to a high percentage of very strongly flavored coffee in the blend, to heavy roasting, or to a coffee pot which has not been kept clean, but it is most frequently due to the extraction of too much tannin when the beverage is made. Coffee owes its stimulating property to caffeine. This alkaloid is found in larger amounts in tea, but since the quantity of coffee needed to make a cup of the beverage is much larger than

[1] Edward R. Emerson, *Beverages, Past and Present,* Vol. II (New York: Putnam, 1908), p. 224.

the quantity of leaves used to make a similar amount of tea, more caffeine is found in a cup of coffee than in a cup of tea.

Buying and storing. Coffee is marketed in containers of tin, glass, cardboard, or paper. It may be purchased unground, or ground to varying degrees of fineness. In many instances, it is ground to suit the purchaser at the grocery. The price varies greatly, some widely advertised brands being at least twice as expensive as others less advertised. Such attractions as containers which may be used for another purpose, coffee pots, and premiums catch the attention of consumers, but they obviously have no bearing on the quality of the coffee itself. Price and type of container are not indications of either freshness or good flavor. In one "blindfold test" two coffees of equal price were rated 80 and 50 on the basis of 100 as a perfect score for flavor. Incidentally, the one receiving the lower rating was in reality more expensive, because a larger quantity of coffee was required to make a beverage of equal strength. A few suggestions may be helpful in choosing coffee:

1) The best coffee is that which has been freshly roasted.

2) Unground coffee retains its flavor and aroma longer than ground coffee. The best results may be expected if the coffee is purchased unground and ground as needed. In one test the beverage made from a certain blend of coffee, when freshly roasted and ground, was rated 90 in flavor. When this same blend of coffee had been standing on the shelf of a grocery store for several days, the beverage made from it was rated 60 in flavor, even though the coffee was in a sealed tin container, and the container was opened just before the beverage was made.

3) If it is impractical to grind coffee as needed, it is advantageous to buy it in a small quantity, grind it at the time of purchase, and store it in a closely covered metal container.

4) The grind should be suited to the method of preparation used. For boiled coffee, a coarse grind is desirable; for percolated coffee, a medium grind; for coffee made in a dripolator, a fine grind; and for coffee made with a glass coffee-maker, the grind should be very fine.

5) After trying several brands of coffee, the one which gives satisfaction for the least money is the one to be chosen.

Preparing the beverage. Coffee should be clear and sparkling, the color depending upon the strength desired. It should possess a fresh aroma and flavor and should not be bitter. Several methods of preparation and many types of containers are used. In general, no matter what the utensil, good coffee can be made if the right procedure is used. Ideally, the coffee grounds should remain in contact with water as short a time as possible, and a metal utensil alters the flavor of the beverage.

All caffeol and caffeine are extracted quickly at a temperature below that of boiling water. A range of from 185° to 195° F. (85° to 91° C.) is considered best. When the grounds remain in the water longer than necessary, tannin is extracted, giving a bitter flavor. Coffee grounds should not be used a second time, since the desirable flavor has been extracted.

The utensil must be clean. An oily film which affects the flavor of coffee forms on the inner surface of any coffee pot. This can be removed by means of hot soapy water, supplemented by the occasional use of scouring powder.

Filtered coffee. The coffee used is finely ground or pulverized. The utensil may be some form of glass coffee-maker, or a dripolator of glass, earthenware, enameled metal, or metal. The first may have two compartments, water being placed in the lower and coffee in the upper. The funnel-like tube is closed by a filter or rod. As the water heats, steam forces it into the upper compartment, through the coffee. The mixture is stirred slightly, allowed to bubble two or three minutes, and the utensil is removed from the heat. The beverage filters to the lower compartment. The principle on which the "expresso" type of coffee maker operates is similar. Steam from one compartment passes through coffee grounds and a very fine strainer into another compartment. There are several designs for this type. With them explicit directions for their operation are included. The coffee is clear and strong, intended for demitasse rather than regular "breakfast" coffee. Another utensil for filtered coffee is of glass, molded in one piece. A filter paper is fitted into the upper portion, coffee is placed on it, and water below boiling—about 185° F.—is poured over the coffee slowly. The beverage filters downward.

A dripolator consists of three compartments. The middle compartment, in the bottom of which there are many small holes, is placed over the lower compartment. A filter paper is put in the bottom of the middle compartment, and the coffee is added. The upper compartment is set over this, and boiling water is poured into it. The water drips slowly over the coffee through a few tiny holes in the bottom of the upper compartment, and the beverage drips into the lower compartment. The scale on the upper compartment of some dripolators, indicating the amount of water and a similar scale on the middle compartment, showing the quantity of coffee, make the use of separate measuring utensils unnecessary. The filter paper is not necessary, but clearer coffee is made when it is used.

Coffee made by filtering is free from even the finest grounds and its aroma and flavor are excellent, since the maximum caffeol is retained and the amount of tannin extracted is very small.

Percolated coffee. The advantage of a percolator, as compared with the older type of coffee pot, is that the grounds are held in a strainer above the water. As the water boils, the steam forces it up through a tube and sprays it over the grounds. However, if the percolation is violent, percolated coffee differs only slightly from boiled coffee in flavor. When the water starts to spray over the coffee grounds, the heat should be lowered so that the action is steady but gentle. The coffee used should be of a medium to rather fine grind.

Cold water is used in an automatic percolator, with the same proportion of coffee to water as is used in the other percolators. The very small quantity of water which goes into the well of the percolator is heated very rapidly so that percolation starts almost immediately. The thermostat controls the action and after the proper time, the percolation stops but enough heat remains to keep the beverage hot.

Boiled and steeped coffee. About two tablespoonfuls of coarsely ground coffee are used per cup of water. It may be put directly into the coffee pot or tied loosely in a thin cloth bag. In both cases, freshly boiled water is poured over the grounds. For boiled coffee, the water is brought to a boil and allowed to boil gently for about five minutes. For steeped coffee, the water is kept simmering for from two to seven minutes.

Boiled or steeped coffee is cloudy, due to suspension of fine particles of grounds through the water. This may be lessened by adding a little cold water to the beverage and letting it stand for about five minutes. A better method is to stir egg white and clean, crushed egg shell into the dry grounds. The particles adhere to the viscous white and the beverage is clear.

Decaffeinated and instant coffee. Because coffee is, or seems to be, too stimulating to some individuals, the market carries a product from which part of the caffeine has been removed. Such coffee preparations are sold under trade names. They may be used like standard coffee in the preparation of the beverage.

Coffee extract is sometimes reduced to a very fine powder which dissolves completely in hot water. It is available under several trade names. This product is high in caffeine and is, consequently, more stimulating than standard coffee. It is quickly and easily made, and therefore very popular. Decaffeinated coffee is also on the market in soluble form.

Liquid coffee. For making liquid coffee, roasted coffee is extracted in tanks heated by steam. The ground coffee may be agitated with water and then filtered or a percolator may be used in which the coffee is placed on a filter and hot water is allowed to trickle through it. The product contains from 2 to 6 per cent of dissolved solids. "Since there may be a loss of volatile aromatic flavoring material during concentration, liquid coffees do not at present have the full aroma and flavor of the best coffee, freshly brewed from high-quality beans."[1]

Frozen coffee. Coffee concentrate is frozen and may be used for making either hot or iced coffee. A suitable quantity of the concentrate is placed in cup or glass, hot or cold water is added, and the mixture is stirred. Thus it is as simply made as is the powdered instant coffee.

[1] Harry W. von Loesecke, *Outlines of Food Technology* (New York: Reinhold Publishing Corp., 1949), p. 402.

CEREAL PREPARATIONS

Various cereals have been roasted and prepared as beverages. Perhaps the psychological effect of these preparations is their greatest contribution. The roots of the chicory plant are sometimes roasted and ground, a beverage being made by using the ground product in the same way that coffee is used. Chicory was formerly used extensively as an adulterant in coffee. Coffee to which chicory is added is still considered superior by many people. It may be purchased and added to coffee, or coffee which contains chicory may be sold if the chicory content is printed on the label. In some markets there is a great demand for this combination.

COCOA AND CHOCOLATE

Sources and production. Cocoa and chocolate, native to Mexico, Central America, and parts of South America, are among the contributions of the New World to the foods of many nations. The fruit of the cocoa tree contains many seeds or "beans," which are removed and fermented. The pulp is removed and the beans are dried and sent to factories. Here they are sorted and roasted to improve the color and flavor and to remove the outer shell from the inside portion. The "beans" at this stage are called cocoa nibs. Cocoas from different places are blended before grinding to improve the flavor. If the cocoa nibs are held at a high temperature during the grinding process, they melt, and, as the mixture cools, it is molded, and is sold as bitter chocolate. To this chocolate, sugar and cocoa butter are added to produce sweet chocolate.

Composition. Cocoa differs from chocolate chiefly in fat content. About 50 per cent of the fat present in bitter chocolate is removed, the product is ground, and the resulting cocoa is ready for packing.

Cocoa and chocolate contain fat, protein, carbohydrate, and minerals, and are therefore nutritious in themselves. Milk is usually used in preparing these beverages, thus increasing their food value. Theobromine, an alkaloid similar to caffeine, is present in small amounts, making the beverages somewhat stimulating. The tannin content is very slight.

Buying and storing. Several brands of cocoa are available on most markets, because nearly everyone who uses it has a favorite brand. The brands vary considerably in color, flavor, and thickening power. Trying some of them will show the variations and lead to the homemaker's preference. It is packaged for the convenience of households of various sizes, the larger packages being somewhat cheaper per unit of weight than the small ones. Cocoa does not lose flavor on standing as coffee does, and so may be purchased in relatively large quantities. There are several brands of prepared cocoa. These are sweetened, and some of them contain dried milk. They need only the addition of hot liquid, either milk or water. While popular with some people, others consider the quality inferior.

Chocolate is usually purchased in half-pound cakes that are divided into squares, each square weighing one ounce. Both cocoa and chocolate should be stored in a cool place because of the fat content. The fat melts during very warm weather and appears, in the case of chocolate, as light-colored spots. The texture and flavor are made undesirable by such a change. Consequently, in very warm weather chocolate should be stored in the refrigerator.

Preparing the beverage. The fact that the carbohydrate of cocoa and chocolate is chiefly starch suggests a cooking period which is long enough to insure a smooth product free from the flavor and consistency characteristic of raw starch. Sugar, cocoa or chocolate, and water are combined and cooked until they form a rather thick paste; then milk is added. The beverage may be spiced, and many consider it improved when a little vanilla is added. "When, to sugar, to cinnamon, and to cocoa, the delicious aroma of vanilla is added, we obtain the highest state of perfection of this preparation."[1] In those sections of the country where dietary habits have been influenced by the foods of Mexico, Mexican chocolate is popular. The cakes as purchased contain both sugar and spice. The chocolate is melted in hot liquid and is delicious when used as a beverage or in the preparation of ice cream and other desserts in which chocolate is used. Instant cocoa which is dissolved in hot water or milk is used by many families to avoid the time required to cook regular cocoa.

MATÉ AND CASSINA

The leaves of maté and cassina, plants that belong to the ilex family, are used in preparing beverages. Maté is often called Paraguay tea. The plant is native to South America, and the beverage is used extensively in Brazil and Argentina. Maté is being served in many public eating places in the United States. It is also used in the preparation of maté bottled drinks. The color of the beverage resembles that of weak black tea. The flavor is mild and pleasing. The beverage is prepared like tea, and it is served in the same ways.

Cassina grows natively in the southern part of the United States. In southeast Texas the plant is called Evergreen Yaupon. The Indians used the leaves in the preparation of a beverage used as a stimulating drink and in connection with religious ceremonies. During the War Between the States cassina was used in the Confederacy by both army and families at home.

As analyzed by the Bureau of Chemistry, cassina contains about 1 per cent caffeine, as compared with 1.2 per cent in coffee and 2.7 per cent in tea. Experimental work has shown that a pleasing beverage can be produced with it more cheaply than with tea, since "(1) unlike tea, all the leaves on the

[1] Jean Anthelme Brillat-Savarin, *The Physiology of Taste* (New York: Liveright, 1926), p. 82.

plant contain the active principle, caffeine, (2) unlike tea, all the leaves can be removed from the pruned branches with live steam, (3) the number of steps in the process of production can be substantially reduced, and (4) in the preparation of cassina very little hand labor is necessary."[1]

The leaves of the plant may be picked when they are tender and dried in an oven at 150° to 180° F. (66° to 105° C.). The beverage is made by simmering the dried leaves in water for about three minutes. It is delicious by itself or with lemon or lime; with or without sugar.

REFERENCES

BOOKS

Emerson, Edward R., *Beverages, Past and Present*. G. P. Putnam's Sons, New York, 1908.

Kakuzo, Okakura, *The Book of Tea*. Dodd, Mead and Co., New York, 1926.

Repplier, Agnes, *To Think of Tea*. Houghton Mifflin Co., Boston, 1932.

Todoroff, Alexander, *Food Buyer's Information Book*. The Grocery Trade Publishing House, Chicago, 1946.

Ukers, Wm. H., *All about Coffee*. The Tea and Coffee Trade Journal Co., New York, 1935.

———, *All about Tea*. The Tea and Coffee Trade Journal Co., New York, 1935.

Von Loesecke, Harry W., *Outlines of Food Technology*. Reinhold Publishing Corp., New York, 1949.

Ward, Artemas, *Encyclopedia of Food*. Baker and Taylor Co., New York, 1929.

[1] G. F. Mitchell, J. W. Sale, and J. B. Wilson, *Beverages Produced from Cassina*. Bureau of Chemistry, U.S.D.A.

UNIT 19

Desserts

While it is customary to bring a meal to a satisfactory close by serving a dessert, too often desserts are considered as something "extra" in the meal and are not planned to take their part in the over-all meal pattern. This is not only unwise from the nutritional standpoint, but is likely to be a very costly practice. Eating such substantial desserts as pie, steamed pudding, and rich cake at the close of an otherwise heavy meal may be largely responsible for the overweight problem of many people and the digestive disturbances of others. However, such desserts can make an appropriate contribution to a meal of low calorie value.

A single piece of candy, a few nuts, a sweet cracker, or a small serving of fresh fruit may be just the right finish for a thoroughly satisfying meal. The dessert may furnish a generous portion of the day's milk or fruit. As a rule, desserts that are appropriate for children are equally good for people of all ages because they are usually both nutritious and easily digested. In some families the most popular desserts are the simplest ones to prepare and at the same time rank high in furnishing protective food values. Included in these are baked and soft custard, brown betty, baked apples, gingerbread, and rice pudding. One homemaker with a large family and limited time for meal preparation trained her family to enjoy, as a favorite dessert, graham cracker "shortcake," which was simply spiced apple sauce placed between two graham crackers with more apple sauce and a little whipped cream on top. Another family's favorite dessert is fresh grapefruit sections sprinkled with crushed peppermint stick candy. In addition to its contribution of ascorbic acid such a dessert is interesting and palatable from the standpoints of texture, flavor, and color combination.

Cheese is never too elegant or too simple as the finish for a meal; in fact, it seems to have universal appeal, whether it be individual portions of one type served with toasted water crackers or a variety offered from a cheese tray in combination with fancy crackers, fruits, and jelly.

Group or national custom is often responsible for the type of dessert usually chosen, as is evidenced by the pie or cake of some sections of our own country, the fruit and cheese of France, and the ostkaka (cheese pudding) of Sweden. The term "dessert" is often synonymous with "sweet." The Mexicans serve *dulce* and the Japanese *okashi,* both terms meaning "a sweet," but not referring to a specific dessert. Festivals often bring to mind desserts seldom served on other occasions, or which are considered a part of the designated feast, even though they are used frequently at other times. Special cookies are made only at Christmas time in many countries (see p. 238). In England, plum pudding is the traditional Christmas dessert. In the United States, pumpkin pie is quite as characteristic of the Thanksgiving dinner as is turkey. Mince pie is the Christmas dessert habitually used by some families; others would not think of Christmas dinner without plum pudding; while ambrosia, a combination of orange sections and coconut, is always served in many homes.

Many desserts are discussed in other units of this book and need only to be mentioned here. Pastries and cakes, cookies and custards, and cornstarch puddings, are all popular.

It is easy to vary many basic desserts and so add interest and variety. Chilled soft custard may be used by itself in individual servings, or it may be served in an attractive bowl with spoonfuls of light, fluffy meringue scattered over it. In this form, it is known as "floating island." Bits of bright, tart jelly make it even more pleasing in both appearance and flavor. Soft custard is often used as a sauce for puddings which have a distinct flavor, such as orange cream, raspberry whip, or chocolate cornstarch pudding. Congealed with gelatin, soft custard takes on a festive air when served with fresh fruit and whipped cream. Baked custards are easily varied by the addition of a sauce, such as caramel, fruit, or ginger sauce, or by jelly, fresh or canned fruit, maple sirup, or honey.

MISCELLANEOUS DESSERTS

Gelatin desserts. As already mentioned, when collagen, a protein found in meat, is subjected to moist heat, it is changed to gelatin (see p. 132). This possibility of hydrolyzing collagen is the basis for an industry of some importance. Bones and the inner layer of the skin of calves and hogs yield a considerable amount of gelatin. The product is made under very careful supervision, and the strictest sanitary conditions are maintained. Gelatin may be purchased in four forms—granulated, which is the common form used in the home; pulverized, which is used in making jelly powder; and sheet and shredded gelatin, both of which are suitable for use in large quantity food units. Directions are included with all packages. Gelatin is easily digested and is frequently used in the dietaries of infants and persons who are ill.

Gelatin is the basis for many simple, attractive desserts, including sponges, soufflés, and Bavarian creams. It is commonly used as a stabilizer in commercial ice cream mixes and is frequently so used in homemade ice creams. The jelly powders, as purchased, are already flavored, sweetened, and colored. They may be used plain, and served either with or without whipped cream. They are usually considered more attractive when used as a means of molding fruits. A light texture is obtained by whipping the jelly just as it begins to congeal. Most gelatin desserts are relatively low in calories.

Meringues. Meringue, a delicious combination of beaten egg white and sugar, to which flavoring is usually added, is frequently baked in special forms or in shallow pans, and is the basis for numerous desserts. It is not difficult to make if directions for adding sugar to the egg whites are followed carefully, and if the baking temperature is correct.

Meringue cases may be filled with ice cream or fruits. Meringue baked in shallow pans may be served with fresh or quick-frozen fruits, such as strawberries, raspberries, or peaches, and garnished with whipped cream. It may also be spread in a pie pan to leave room for a filling, baked, and a filling of either fresh fruit, the "cream" type of pie filling, or a combination put into it shortly before serving. Meringue is one of the three ingredients for Baked Alaska—so festive in appearance and so delightful in flavor. In place of meringue cases, circles or ovals of meringue may be shaped with a pastry tube. These are interesting when ice cream is served in them, with, perhaps, a sauce or a sprinkling of chopped nuts.

Rice. Rice, so often used as a cereal or in place of a starchy vegetable, is excellent as a dessert. Boiled rice, cooked so that the kernels are distinct, served with sugar and cream, brown sugar and butter, or maple sirup, is easily prepared and delicious. Rice puddings are popular and may be either hot or cold. Rice may be molded and served with fruit, used as an ingredient in Bavarian cream, or in some frozen desserts.

Tapioca. Tapioca is a starchy food made from the tuberous roots of the cassava plant, native to South America. It is usually available in two forms—pearl tapioca, which is in balls of three sizes, large, medium, and small; and granulated tapioca, which is in much smaller, less regular shapes, known as "minute" tapioca. The large pearl tapioca needs to be soaked before it is used and requires a longer cooking period than the small pearl or granular tapiocas. Granular tapioca is cooked without soaking. Tapioca is cooked in a double boiler in water, milk, or fruit juice until the particles are clear.

Because of its bland flavor, tapioca is often combined with some ingredient which provides a distinct flavor. Fruits may be cooked with tapioca, and the

Courtesy National Dairy Council

Fig. 42. A delicious drink also serves as dessert.

use of chocolate, caramel, butterscotch, or ginger makes interesting flavor for this dessert.

Bread puddings. Bread pudding is another example of a simple and inexpensive dessert which may be varied interestingly by the use of fruits, either canned or dried, preserves, chocolate, or butterscotch. Left-over cake is sometimes used in place of bread, omitting sugar from the recipe.

Beverage desserts. Any milk, ice cream, or fruit beverage served with or without cookies or sweet crackers makes an acceptable finish to a meal. Fig. 42 shows a milk and berry juice beverage attractively served as dessert.

Cheese and fruit desserts. As stated above, whether these foods are used alone, together, or with simple cookies or crackers they are highly popular as dessert foods. Many individuals consistently shun pastries, cakes, and puddings in favor of a fruit and cheese dessert.

Desserts stored in the home freezer. For those families who have home freezers, desserts for the future may be made at the same time that they are made for immediate use. Considerable time is saved and the desserts are ready for quick use when needed. Cakes, pies, and steamed puddings are among those that may be frozen, to be thawed or heated at will. It is not always necessary to make a large recipe for this purpose. If a cake that will serve sixteen is made for a family of four, it may become tiresome. If three parts of it are wrapped and stored separately, the variation in frosting used as these portions are taken from the freezer makes the one cake the basis for four. Square pies pack to better advantage than round ones.

FROZEN DESSERTS

In some form, frozen desserts have been known since the days of ancient Rome and the Chinese of Kubla Khan's day.

Ice cream is said to have been known in the United States since 1786. Its commercial manufacture was begun in 1851 and through the years it has maintained the position of America's favorite dessert. It is considered as a great morale builder in time of war, as was demonstrated by the "ice cream" ships used in the Pacific in World War II.

Because of the varying opinions on the value of ice cream as a food, the National Dairy Council has been working for over a decade in co-operation with the U. S. Department of Agriculture and the ice cream industry to supply accurate and current information on this subject. A study sponsored by the National Dairy Council shows that commercial vanilla ice cream of high quality can make a significant contribution to the daily intake of riboflavin and vitamin A.[1]

Types of frozen desserts. Frozen desserts are usually divided into two groups: those that are stirred during the freezing process and those that are frozen without stirring. To the first group belong ice cream, ice, frappé, punch, sherbet, and sorbet. Included in the second are mousse, parfait, biscuit, and bombe. To this latter group, some ice cream mixtures that are frozen in a mechanical refrigerator should be added. The various frozen desserts are described briefly as follows:

1) Ices:
   A *water ice* is made from fruit juice and a sirup made from sugar and water.
   A *frappé* is a water ice frozen to a mush.
   Punch is a frappé with alcoholic liquor, spice, or both added.
   Sherbet may be water ice with either egg white or gelatin added; or it may be water ice in which milk or cream is used as part of the liquid.
   Sorbet is water ice made with the juice of several fruits, to which the pulp of one of the fruits is added.
2) Ice creams:
   Philadelphia ice cream is an uncooked mixture of thin cream, sugar, and flavoring.
   French ice cream is a cooked mixture of milk, sugar, and a bit of salt, thickened with eggs. Cream and flavoring are added after the mixture cools somewhat.
   American (plain) ice cream uses cornstarch or flour in place of some of the eggs used in French ice cream for thickening. Gelatin may also be included as a stabilizer.

---

[1] A. C. Dahlberg, and J. K. Lossi, "The Food Value of Commercial Vanilla Ice Cream," *Journ. Am. Diet. Assn.*, Jan. 1948.

3) Desserts frozen without stirring:
   Mousse consists of whipped cream flavored and sweetened.
   Parfait is made by beating hot sirup into beaten egg whites, adding flavoring, and folding in whipped cream.
   Biscuit is parfait packed when partially frozen into individual paper containers and re-packed to complete freezing.
   Bombe is a combination of frozen desserts packed into a round or melon-shaped mold and re-packed long enough to set the shape.
   Some ice creams are frozen in a mechanical refrigerator. These use heavy rather than light cream and the mixes are made more viscous by the use of eggs, starch, gelatin, or a combination of these and by the substitution of corn sirup, maple sirup, or honey for part of the sugar.

Standards for frozen desserts. Forty-eight states have minimum standards for composition and sanitary manufacturing conditions for ice cream. These vary greatly. Proposals for a Federal Standard are for: milk fat, 10 per cent; total milk solids, 20 per cent; total solids per gallon, one and six-tenths pounds; weight per gallon, four and five-tenths pounds; and stabilizer, 0.5 per cent. Such regulation would do much to remove striking differences in quality of ice cream of different brands sampled in various places.

Factors which influence the quality of ice cream. Ice cream should be smooth but not sticky, firm but not rubbery, and should melt slowly to a creamy rather than a watery liquid. These qualities are obtained by the use of satisfactory ingredients and by proper manipulation. Frozen mixtures resemble some candies, in that they are crystalline. A velvety texture is due to the formation of a large number of tiny crystals during the freezing and packing of the cream. As has been stated, the use of ingredients which interfere with the formation of large crystals and proper beating help to keep the crystals in candy small. (See p. 183.) In frozen mixtures, these factors help to keep the ice crystals small. Other factors are the temperature of the mix when freezing begins, rate of freezing, temperature of the freezing mixture, and packing.

The ingredients. The ingredients used in ice cream are largely responsible for the texture and consistency of the finished product. A high percentage of milk results in a thin, icy product of inferior flavor. A desirable amount of cream produces a flavor which no other ingredient imparts. Too much cream makes the ice cream hard, and the fat often clumps (agglutinizes) so that it sticks to the roof of the mouth when the ice cream is eaten. Such ice cream is referred to as "buttery." Homogenization (see p. 90) increases the viscosity of milk and is often recommended for milk used in commercial ice cream. In homemade frozen desserts, evaporated milk, which is homogenized, is frequently one of the ingredients. Viscosity of the mix is increased by starch, egg yolk, and gelatin, any or a combination of which may be used in ice cream. During the process of making ice cream, some of the milk proteins absorb water, thus removing part of the crystallizable water and tending to increase the smoothness of the product. Lactose crystallizes as the ice cream hardens after freezing; consequently, if a relatively high percentage of lactose is present, as it may be if a large amount of evaporated milk is used, the product is apt to be sandy.

Sugar, in the amount of 14 to 16 per cent by weight, is desirable from the point of view of sweetness. The sugar content may consist entirely of granulated sugar, or a part of it may be corn sirup, maple sirup, or honey. The sirups and honey, being viscous, tend to add to the smoothness of the product. Because sugar dissolves in the liquids used, it lowers the freezing point of the mix.

Flavor is added to the ice-cream mix in the form of extracts, fruits, nuts, spices, candy, chocolate, coffee, tea, and other ingredients. The flavor should be pleasantly mild. It is always improved by the addition of a small amount of salt.

Freezing. In order to understand the influence of possible variations in freezing methods, a few facts concerning freezing and the construction of ice cream freezers should be kept in mind.

When a sufficient amount of heat has been withdrawn from a liquid, it becomes solid; in other words, the liquid has been frozen. The freezing point of any liquid is that temperature at which the vapor pressure of the liquid is in equilibrium with that of the solid, and this temperature is definite for all pure liquids, other conditions being the same. Thus pure water freezes at 32° F. (0° C.). If a substance (a solute) is dissolved in the water (a solvent), the vapor pressure of the resulting solution is lower than that of the water; consequently, the freezing point of the solution is lower than that of water. Thus, since an ice-cream mix contains numerous ingredients, some of which are dissolved in the liquid, the freezing temperature is lower than that of water. The average freezing temperature for ice cream is about 29° F. (−2° C.).

Since the temperature required to freeze ice cream is lower than the melting point of ice, surrounding the mix with ice would cool but not freeze it. It is therefore necessary to lower the point at which ice melts, and this may be done by adding salt. Rather fine rock salt is preferred. The salt dissolves in the film of water that covers the ice, causing the ice to melt. In the process of melting, or of the change from solid to liquid, heat is absorbed. In order that most of this heat may be derived from the mix that is being frozen, the outside tub of an ice cream freezer should be made from a material that is a poor conductor of heat. Wood is the material most frequently used. On the other hand, the can which contains the mix should be made from metal, which conducts heat readily. The speed at which ice melts depends partly upon the size of the pieces, finely chipped ice melting more rapidly than larger pieces because the surface area exposed to heat is greater.

The freezer should be filled about one-third full of ice before salt is added; then a mixture of ice and salt should be used. This insures a more even freezing mixture after the ice has been melting a few minutes. As the ice melts, more ice and salt are added.

As the handle of the freezer is turned, wooden paddles scrape the cooled or frozen part of the mix away from the cold sides of the can, allowing more of the unfrozen mix to reach the cold can, thus freezing the mix evenly. Another part of the dasher whips the mix, incorporating air.

Temperature of mix before freezing. It will be recalled that in candy-making, when the sugar solution is cooled before stirring, the crystals in the resulting candy are small. The same is true of ice creams. The sugar solution is cooled to 110° F. (43° C.) before beating, but a mix at that temperature, frozen, would become a very coarse ice cream. The difference in texture when portions of the same ice-cream mix are frozen at 100°, 80°, and 50° F. (38°, 27°, and 10° C.) is easily shown by means of a laboratory problem. (See p. 593.)

Rate of freezing. During the first part of the freezing period, the handle of the freezer should be turned slowly, because rapid turning makes the fat globules clump, giving the ice cream a buttery consistency. When the mix has cooled to about 34° F. (1° C.), or when turning the handle of the freezer begins to require some force, turning should be rapid. At this temperature, crystals begin to form, and rapid turning will produce small crystals. Also, air will be held by the cream when it has cooled to about 34° F. (1° C.). This results in the velvety texture which is desirable. Too much air makes the texture disagreeably fluffy. This sometimes occurs when crystals are formed too slowly. From three to five minutes are usually sufficient for the slow turning period—three minutes for a one-quart freezer, five minutes for a two-quart freezer. The rapid turning should proceed as evenly as possible until the mix is frozen. As freezing continues, the speed will necessarily be somewhat slower because of the difficulty of turning the handle. When a mechanical freezer is used, directions usually state that freezing should be done for five minutes at low speed, then at second speed until the mixture is frozen —about ten minutes for a two-quart freezer.

Continuous, even turning results in a smoother ice cream than turning that is interrupted or not even. This may be demonstrated by freezing part of a mix in a mechanical freezer, and part in a hand-turned freezer. In one class in which this comparison was being made, the creams from the two types of freezer were equally smooth. The instructor could not understand why there was no difference until the student who had used the hand-turned freezer explained that the speed had been guided exactly by that of the mechanical freezer. Such precision is seldom maintained by a person operating a hand-turned freezer.

Temperature of freezing mixture. As the ratio of salt to ice is increased,

Courtesy American Can Company

Fig. 43. Baked Alaska is a popular and somewhat "dramatic" dessert. There are many different ways to execute this "insulated" ice cream favorite. In this illustration, a loaf cake is used and the accompanying fruit is canned peach slices. An angel or sponge cake, baked in a tube pan, is frequently used for baked Alaska. Cup cakes or thick slices of loaf cake are desirable for individual servings.

the temperature of the freezing mixture is lowered, and the time required for freezing is lessened. When a relatively large amount of salt is used, the resulting ice cream is compact and somewhat crystalline, because there has not been sufficient time for beating air into the mixture, and the crystals have formed too rapidly. Various recommendations may be found, but the consensus seems to favor the use of one part of salt to eight parts of ice. This gives an overrun [1] of about 30 per cent, and a delightfully velvety ice cream. (See p. 528.)

Packing. After ice cream is frozen, the brine that has accumulated in the tub should be poured off so that the ice and salt can be pushed down below the level of the cover of the can. All traces of ice and salt should be removed from the top of the can so that no salt will fall into the cream when the cover is lifted. The dasher should be taken out and the mixture packed down, the cover replaced, and the opening of the cover closed. The space

[1] "Overrun" is a term used to indicate increase in the quantity of a frozen dessert over that of the unfrozen mix.

between can and tub should be filled with an ice-and-salt mixture in the ratio of four to one. The ice cream should then stand from one to two hours to ripen. This ripening improves the texture of the ice cream. If freezing has been insufficient, ripening serves to make the crystals larger. This result is similar to that found when crystalline candy is beaten—when beating is discontinued before crystallization is complete, the mixture which has not crystallized will adhere to crystals already formed, thus making the candy granular.

Other desserts frozen with stirring. The comparatively coarse texture of water ice, frappé, and punch suggests that they should be frozen more rapidly than ice cream; consequently, a lower ratio of ice to salt is used in the freezing mixture, usually from three to six parts of ice to one part of salt. Sherbet and sorbet, on the other hand, should be smooth; hence, the same ratio of ice to salt is used as is recommended for freezing ice creams.

Mixtures frozen without stirring. Commercially, it is possible to freeze ice cream very rapidly, by the use of a temperature much lower than can be obtained at home. This quick-freezing method results in a smooth ice cream because many very tiny crystals are produced.

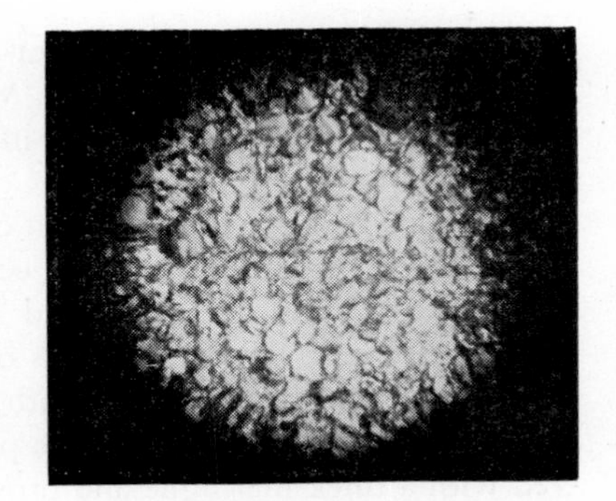

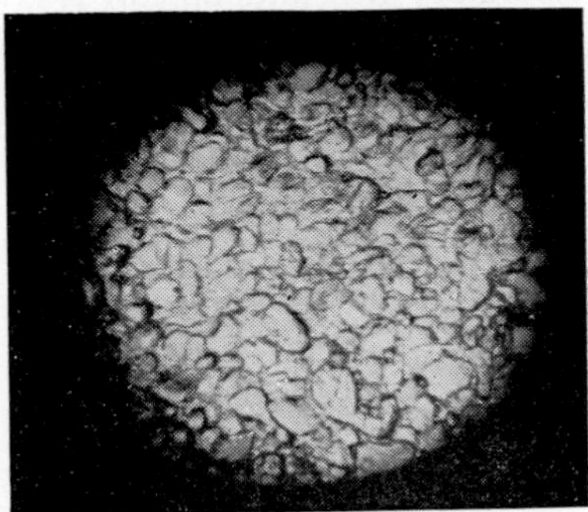

From *Photomicrographic Study of Physical Structure of Ice Cream* by Isora Locke Cooke. Unpublished thesis, University of Texas, 1940.

Fig. 44. Top, *ice-cream mix cooled to 90° F.—turning, even;* center, *mix cooled to 50° F.—turning, even;* bottom, *mix cooled to 50° F. —turning, uneven.*

There are numerous recipes for ice creams that may be made satisfactorily by freezing them in mechanical refrigerators, the only stirring being one or two thorough beatings with a rotary egg beater before the mixes have become too hard. The coldest possible temperature in the freezing unit is necessary. Use of a high proportion of cream—possibly heavy cream—and such ingredients as egg white, gelatin, or fruit purée, help to make desserts frozen in a refrigerator desirably smooth. Mousse, parfait, biscuit, or bombe may be frozen in a refrigerator or packed in a mixture of salt and ice with a ratio of one to two.

Frozen desserts are often used in combination with other food items in the preparation of desserts for special occasions. For example, sponge-type cakes may be stuffed with ice cream and "frosted" with whipped cream or a jelly frosting. Perhaps Baked Alaska is one of the most popular desserts of this type. Cake is placed on a board with a piece of heavy paper or aluminum foil under the cake. Brick ice cream is placed on the cake and the whole is covered with a thick meringue and browned in the oven. It is usually served in this form, may be further decorated, as the one in Fig. 43 illustrates.

SUGGESTIONS FOR LABORATORY

With the exception of the meat, poultry, and seafood units in Section II—Familiar Family Foods—all other units include some suggestions for using the specific foods as desserts. This means that they can be incorporated into any number of laboratory situations and related to the basic principles of cookery of the different food groups. Because of the popularity of desserts, using them in this way may stimulate greater interest in other uses for the foods being studied. A Swiss carrot torte made during a vegetable cookery laboratory will undoubtedly spark interest in carrots. There are many additional examples to be found in other units.

UNIT 20

Seasonings

A Hungarian shopkeeper described American food as unskillfully seasoned due to lack of "culinary courage" on the part of our cooks. The same thought was expressed by a man with a Swiss-French background, who considered himself somewhat of a gourmet. He was heard to remark, "The trouble with American food is that there are too many salt, pepper, and vanilla cooks." While it is undoubtedly true that these three, plus vinegar, constitute the traditional quartet of condiments and flavoring for American cookery, we are mustering increasing "culinary courage," and more and more homemakers are learning the fascinating art of herb cookery. During the last quarter century in this country the Old World skill of growing and using herbs has had a great revival and nowadays, even in the smallest garden, at least a few culinary, aromatic herbs are likely to be seen. (See Fig. 45.) However, Europe still remains the principal source of supply, where for generations herb growers have mastered the arts of selecting, harvesting, and curing herbs.

Some individuals take food purely for sustenance, but certainly they are in the minority, most people considering eating as a cultural, healthful, enjoyable experience. To make it such, artistry in seasoning every dish, for every meal, is essential. The absence of appropriate seasonings, especially for bland foods, is probably responsible for the habit some people have of automatically salting and peppering food before tasting. While such a practice is not complimentary to the hostess, it is often an indication of complete lack of imagination in seasoning. Even a beginning cook can turn out dishes that are culinary "masterpieces" by following a few simple suggestions for using herbs, spices, and flavoring extracts. She will soon learn which flavors are most popular with her family. Naturally, there are many dishes which require only the simplest seasoning to bring out the desired flavor.

Courtesy House of Herbs, Inc.

Fig. 45. A formal herb garden.

Salt. Salt (sodium chloride) was perhaps the first commercial food product. It is added to the majority of foods during their preparation, and no matter how distinct or subtle the flavor of a food may be, salt seems to "bring out" additional flavor. It is obtained by evaporating salt water from the ocean or salt lakes, by mining, or by pumping water into salt beds, forming brine, which is pumped out and evaporated. The salt so obtained may be almost pure sodium chloride, or it may be combined with other mineral substances which must be removed by refining.

As a safeguard against iodine deficiency, a small quantity of potassium iodide is added to some salt, together with sufficient sodium carbonate to stabilize the iodine. Salt is hygroscopic and therefore, to prevent caking or even melting as it stands in the air, calcium phosphate is an ingredient added to some brands of table salt.

Salt is extensively used as the medium for carrying other flavors. Celery, garlic, and onion salt are popular, as are hickory-smoked salt and others which combine a blend of spices.

Pepper. The dried berries of *Piper Nigrum,* a vine indigenous to India, some of the East Indies, and the Malay Peninsula, are dried to produce the pepper of commerce. Immature berries, dried, are called peppercorns and are used as seasoning in soups, stews and some sauces. These berries, ground, produce the black pepper so commonly used. Pepper may be freshly ground at the table by using a small pepper mill. If the berries are allowed to mature and to ferment slightly after gathering, the outside portion is easily rubbed off and the remainder is ground. This is the less pungent white pepper used when the color of black pepper is considered undesirable and when a milder pepper flavor is preferred.

The fruit of a number of varieties of capsicum is used as seasoning. Red pepper is made from the milder capsicums, and cayenne and chili pepper from the hotter varieties. Paprika, used for its color as well as its flavor, is made from ripe, sweet red peppers. These peppers are the pimientos which are so popular as a garnish or as an ingredient in vegetable salads and meat loaves.

Several varieties of chili peppers are available on many markets. They are pickled, used to season other vegetables that are pickled, served with salads, and used in connection with many Mexican foods. It is important to select the right ones because some are milder than others. These may be appreciated by persons who do not like the hotter varieties. They may be more suitable than the hot varieties for certain uses.

Vinegar. The unmodified term "vinegar" is understood to mean a product made by the fermentation of apple juice. The first fermentation is alcoholic in nature, producing cider. Acetic fermentation converts cider into vinegar. Several other kinds of vinegar are used—wine vinegar from the juice of grapes, corn vinegar from corn sirup, malt vinegar from the malt of cereals, and white vinegar made by fermenting dilute, distilled alcohol. Vinegars vary in strength and may be purchased by the percentage of acetic acid.

Herb-flavored vinegars, which may be made at home or purchased ready for use, open up new avenues in cooking adventures for those not familiar with their many possibilities. The herb flavors most often introduced into vinegar are tarragon, garlic, and basil. Dill, marjoram, rosemary, and thyme, while less common, also make interesting flavors for vinegar. In addition, there are mixed herb vinegars which are appropriate for various purposes. These vinegars as prepared for retail sale include, among others, one suitable for soups, sauces, and meats, and another for salads, chicken, and fish. In addition to the use of herb vinegars in salads, a few interesting possibilities are basil vinegar for mashed potatoes, added during the last whipping; tarragon vinegar for such sauces as Béchamel and Béarnaise; basil or any other herb vinegar for marinating steaks or chops before broiling; tarragon or basil vinegar added to melted butter for broccoli and spinach; and garlic and basil vinegar in spaghetti sauce and hamburgers. The vinegars should be used cautiously as to amount, since it is the subtle flavor of the herb in combination with acid that is desired rather than a strong vinegar taste.

Homemade herb vinegar costs only a fraction of that purchased in epicure shops and is prepared simply by placing either one-half teaspoon of crushed dried herb or a clove of garlic in a pint of good quality cider vinegar which has been heated to the boiling point. The mixture should stand in a tightly covered jar at room temperature for ten days, during which time it should be shaken once a day, and then strained through a muslin cloth.

Herbs and spices. Herbs and spices are obtained from different parts of plants (See Table 30). Ginger comes from the root; basil, sage, and bay are leaves; pepper is a fruit; capers and cloves are buds; dill, mace, and mustard are seeds; and cinnamon is bark.

Wherever herbs are grown in the home garden, they are used fresh. However, they are most widely available and used in dried form. Recently herbs and spices in liquid form have appeared on some markets. These are prepared on the same principle as vanilla and other extracts; in other words, the essential oils of the herbs or spices are combined with alcohol and water to give a concentrated essence. Some of the spices available in this form are cinnamon, allspice, ginger, anise, and nutmeg. The liquid herbs that have been noted are marjoram, rosemary, tarragon, thyme, garlic, and mint. Celery in this form is also available. There are some advantages in the liquid flavorings, since they impart their flavors immediately to a dish. The beginner sometimes uses excessive amounts of dried herbs, not realizing that flavor is brought out in cooking. While oils in the alcohol solution cannot escape, they do evaporate in time and for this reason they are usually obtainable only in very small bottles or jars.

TABLE 30. SOURCES OF COMMON HERBS AND SPICES

Roots	*Leaves*	*Buds and Flowers*	*Fruits*	*Seeds*	*Barks*
Ginger	Angelica	Capers	Allspice	Anise	Cassia
Horse-radish	Basil	Cloves	Paprika	Bitter almond	Cinnamon
Sassafras	Bay leaf (laurel)	Saffron	Pepper	Caraway	
Turmeric	Borage		black	Cardamom	
	Burnet		cayenne	Celery	
	Chervil		chili	Coriander	
	Chives		red	Cumin	
	Lemon balm		white	Dill	
	Lemon verbena			Fennell	
	Mint			Mace	
	Parsley			Mustard	
	Rosemary			Nutmeg	
	Rose geranium			Poppy	
	Sorrel (French)			Sesame	
	Sage				
	Savory				
	Sweet marjoram				
	Tarragon				
	Thyme				

Dried herbs and spices are available in small packages of different types. Some may be purchased in both whole and ground form. The size of the package selected should be in relation to the popularity of the seasoning with the family. Spices do not keep well in warm weather and are usually bought only in small containers. They should be kept closely covered in order not to lose their flavor.

Some people are reluctant to use herbs and spices because they are fearful of not choosing the right one for a given dish. There really are no fixed rules for seasonings. There are a few customs but even they do not have to be followed. Customs for using herbs and spices are based on accepted affinities—mint for lamb, cinnamon for apple pie, sage for stuffing and sausage, basil for tomato dishes, oregano for Italian dishes, rosemary for meats, tarragon for fish, savory as the "bean herb," etc. This does not mean that these are the only correct flavors for the foods mentioned. It is advisable for the beginner to learn the use of herbs and spices by starting with such suggestions and then expand and develop an individual culinary "philosophy." The most interesting flavor combinations are often those which are not presented in any book of cookery. The authors know a New England family where for four generations apple pie has always been prepared with a liberal sprinkling of caraway seed over the apples, just before the top crust is put on. To those accustomed to caraway only in rye bread and in cheese, such a flavor combination may not sound appealing, and only experimentation would determine its acceptability. Since cheese is a traditional accompaniment to apple pie, and caraway seed an herb frequently used in certain cheeses, it seems only logical that caraway would be a "natural" for use in apple pie.

Sometimes just the right combination of flavors is discovered purely by accident. One homemaker in preparing hard sauce for Christmas pudding added a liberal sprinkling of curry powder, mistaking it for ginger. The hard sauce took on new goodness that escaped none of the guests, thereby establishing curry powder as a regular seasoning for hard sauce made in this particular household.

Regardless of what seasonings are selected, there are a few points which it is well to keep in mind as a guide.

1) A good rule of thumb on amounts of dried herbs to use is ¼ t. to a recipe for 4.

2) When using green or fresh herbs, about 4 times as much is needed as when dry herbs are used.

3) If the cooking time of a dish is very short (e.g., scrambled eggs), dried herbs will give a more delicious flavor if they have been moistened with a little warm water or salad oil and allowed to stand for about 30 minutes. Another method of releasing flavor of dried herbs is a hot and cold "bath." The herb is put in a tea strainer, dipped into hot water for 10 seconds, then plunged immediately into cold water for 10 seconds, and then drained.

4) Stews and soups which require long cooking should have the herb added during the last hour of cooking for the best flavor.

5) When seasoning uncooked foods such as tomato juice cocktail, the dried herbs should be added well in advance of serving in order to release their full flavor.

6) To avoid specks in a finished dish, dried herbs may be tied in a cheesecloth bag and removed before serving.

7) Green condiments, such as sorrel, parsley, mint, and chives, can best be chopped by cutting with scissors.

Flavoring extracts. Flavoring extracts are made by extracting essential aromatic oils and combining them with alcohol to give a concentrated essence. The flavoring extracts most widely used include vanilla, lemon, orange, and black walnut. Synthetic flavorings in increasing variety are found in retail stores, their appearance often resulting from some emergency. Imitation black walnut was first manufactured during World War I when walnut trees were in demand for making gun stocks. Synthetic sage was developed during World War II for meat packers, in the absence of the genuine herb.

Many fruit extracts are a combination of the actual oil of the fruit and syn thetic flavoring. "Pure" strawberry, raspberry, and banana flavorings are poor flavorings unless they have infinitesimal amounts (approximately 2 per cent) of the esters added to restore the right flavor. Some of the exotic and elusive fragrance of certain fruits is lost during their processing and hence the necessity for adding the synthetic flavor. By law, labels must supply information as to the purity of the extract. Some will be labeled "imitation," others "pure," giving exact alcohol content, etc.

Extracts vary in price and in quality, the better qualities usually selling at higher prices. To give the same strength of flavor, more mild extract than strong must be used, so that it may be less expensive to buy more highly priced extracts. By trying extracts of different brands and comparing them as to real cost and flavor, the consumer will learn which are most satisfactory.

Another precaution when buying extracts is to notice the quantity mentioned on the label as well as the size and shape of the bottle. Bottles are sometimes so shaped as to seem to contain more than they do.

Flavoring extracts may be used singly or in combination. Two parts of vanilla and one of almond give an excellent pistachio flavoring; vanilla and lemon, in equal parts, are used for the flavor known as nectar; rose flavoring may be too pronounced when used by itself, but when combined with almond, it imparts a delicate flavor which is pleasing.

Flavorings are available in bottles of several sizes and should be purchased in quantities suitable for the size of the group. They should be kept corked to prevent evaporation and stored for convenient use.

Miscellaneous flavoring agents. One of the most common in this group is the onion and its related family of shallots, scallions and chives. Garlic is also widely used for flavoring meats, soups, salads, and other dishes. Mushrooms impart a delicate flavor and because they are not inexpensive, are often used to season foods instead of being served as a separate dish. Truffles belong to the fungus family. They are considered by some as having a luxurious aroma and are traditionally associated with distinctive cookery. Cepes are members of the mushroom family and are native to France. They have an unusual flavor and texture and since they are expensive they may be used sparingly as hors d'oeuvres. Monosodium glutamate is not actually a seasoning but is a powder used to emphasize flavor. The Chinese have reportedly used it for many years. Chutney, which is a relish, is of many types. Mango chutney is perhaps the most common, but since its cost is high some people make green tomato and apple chutney to serve with certain meat and curry dishes. Bottled sauces are widely used to flavor meats, salads, and other foods. These include sauces with a mustard base and such favorites as Worcestershire and soy sauce and tabasco. Lemon and orange rind are popular as flavoring agents for certain meats, sauces, and desserts. Olive oil is considered by certain groups as indispensable for flavoring a variety of foods.

Courtesy Saroj Kahnna

Fig. 46. An exhibit of herbs featuring curry (a favorite of India), fresh potted chives and rose geranium.

SUGGESTIONS FOR LABORATORY

Student experiences in the art of seasoning should be a part of all food preparation laboratories. It is not enough to salt and pepper the vegetables or spread mustard and catsup over the meats. Seasoning goes beyond this. A student-arranged exhibit to "sniff and taste" some unusual herbs, spices, and other seasonings is an effective way of getting acquainted with unfamiliar aromas and flavors. Fig. 46 shows a portion of such an exhibit with a student from New Delhi, India, presiding. In an exhibit of this sort the seasonings may be presented in butter spreads, milk, fruit or chocolate beverages, simple soups, sauces, cookies, etc.

UNIT 21

Food Preservation

Of the foods originally available to man, few could be stored for use at any appreciable later time. The native grains were easy to store. Joseph's idea of holding grain in large storehouses for use when the crop failed was indeed wise, and few persons of his time had such forethought. The cliff dwellers of Mesa Verde stored corn in stone bins, thus providing for bread for the tribe until the next harvest. Grain is still one of the simplest foods to store.

The constant demand for food in the face of seasonal supply and the popularity of meat despite dependence for its supply on the luck of hunter or fisher led the folk of ages past to seek ways to make the supply more certain. Domestication of animals and birds was a marked advantage. Meat, milk, and egg supplies were made available throughout most of the year. In warm climates, meat was cooked as soon as an animal could be killed and dressed. In dry to arid regions meat was preserved by drying. In Arctic regions, fish was preserved by freezing. Milk was preserved in the form of cheese at an early date. Fermentation was a means of preserving fruit in the form of wine, and fruits were also dried.

Until fairly recently, the winter's food was a matter for the homemaker to consider seriously during summer and autumn. The drying of beans, peas, corn, and apples; the making of cider and wine; the curing of meat; and the storage of eggs were seasonal tasks of importance. Storage of hardy apples and winter pears and of many vegetables, including potatoes, root vegetables, celery, and late cabbage, was part of the family's preparation for winter. In the kitchens of two or three generations ago, during the autumn large trays were suspended from pulleys in the ceiling, so that they could be raised or lowered over the kitchen range. On these, apples were spread in thin slices. Sufficiently dried, they were stored in jars or paper sacks for use in pies, puddings, and sauces.

The preservative qualities of vinegar, salt, and spices made picking a popular method of extending the season of several foods. Use of sugar made the preservation of fruits by several methods possible.

In rural homes, preservation of food continues to be important. Formerly, families preserved the fruits and vegetables that were abundant or in excess of the amount needed to eat fresh. Wild berries added materially to the variety. Now, the influence of the agricultural agencies has resulted, in many instances, in carefully planned gardens and fruit plots based on knowledge of the family's need for vegetables and fruit. Planned preservation of the right proportions of green and yellow vegetables, tomatoes, and other items are undertaken. The meat, poultry, and egg supplies are also planned, and the popular slogan in one state, "canned chickens don't eat," has saved money and provided poultry at any time for many a farm family.

Since freezing has become a practical method of food preservation in the home, much of the labor involved in canning has been unnecessary. Both methods have advantages. A well-filled, well-organized food pantry and home freezer, with the possible addition of food stored in a community locker plant, are reasons for pride and a sense of security on the part of the homemaker.

A cool store room for canned foods, hardy fruits and vegetables, and eggs that are being collected for marketing is important. It may be a basement, a specially constructed cellar, or—on a smaller scale—a ventilated pantry. In the latter the temperature is about ten degrees lower than that in the surrounding rooms. It is located in a one-story part of the house, and ventilation from under the floor and in the space above the ceiling must be adequate. Air circulates by coming in through a wire grill in the floor at the back of the pantry and going out through a similar grill in the top at the front. Shelves are wire or slatted.

In some sections of the country, hardy fruits and vegetables are stored satisfactorily in pits. Usually several pits are provided and a variety of the foods are stored in each.

Drying as a preservation method is common for legumes, corn, apples, peaches, pears, apricots, and prunes. This method is more practical in relatively dry climates than where the humidity is high much of the time.

Suggestions for planning the food supply, from planting through storage and other preservation methods, may be obtained from Extension Service agents or teachers of Home Economics and Agriculture. These agents and teachers can also be helpful with plans for construction of suitable storage places.

Research workers are constantly adding to our knowledge of both canning and freezing, with advantages in superior food and time planning. Reliable directions are available in bulletin and pamphlet form from the above sources and from the Superintendent of Documents of the United States Department of Agriculture. When research shows that changes in directions should be made, publications from the U. S. Department of Agriculture and the state agricultural colleges and experiment stations incorporate them quickly. Therefore, it is wise to use methods so recommended. In addition, there are some attempts to have the methods used by all agencies within a given area as consistent as possible. For example, the Food Preservation Committee of the Texas State Nutrition Council recommends procedures for canning and freezing and keeps these up to date by noting changes in an annual report. This material is available to agencies throughout the state concerned with these types of food preservation.

WHY FOODS SPOIL

The fact of food spoilage has always been obvious; the reasons have not. Spallanzani, an Italian scientist of the eighteenth century, disagreed with the learned men of his time and proved that the tiny "animalcules" made visible by a microscope did not arise spontaneously from decaying matter. Pasteur, about the middle of the nineteenth century, demonstrated that both fermentation and putrefaction are due to living organisms.

The problem of keeping food is felt keenly when it is necessary to transport food to feed an army. This problem led Napoleon I to offer a prize to the man who could find a way to preserve food so that the French army and navy would have a constant and varied supply. In 1809, Appert announced his success and published methods by which food could be canned.

The four agents that are responsible for food spoilage are yeasts, molds, bacteria, and enzymes. Strict adherence to reliable directions for food preservation prevent their development.

Yeasts. Yeasts are microscopic plants present in the air. The value of certain strains of yeast as the source of CO_2 gas for leavening certain flour mixtures has been discussed. The same fermentation process is also responsible for spoilage of some foods, usually those containing considerable sugar. Yeast spoilage occurs with or without oxygen, but the typical yeast fermentation occurs with oxygen. Moisture must be present. Thus food spoilage due to yeasts is likely to occur in canned fruits and fruit juices if the air has not been excluded during the canning process. Because of their low water content, dried fruits do not ferment easily.

Yeasts are destroyed easily, both at boiling temperature—212° F. (100° C.)—and at pasteurizing temperature—160° to 180° F. (71° to 82° C.)—if the latter is maintained for twenty to sixty minutes. The time varies with the product and the size of the container.

Molds. Molds in spore form are present in the air. Many are fuzzy in appearance and while most are gray to black in color, others are blue-green, orange, or red. Like yeasts, molds are sometimes useful. Certain cheeses are purposely cured with added molds.

Molds develop rapidly in a warm, dark, damp place. When found in cured ham, mold is scraped off. On bread unless it is extensive, it is cut off and the bread, dampened slightly, heated. A small amount on canned fruit, tomatoes, or preserves may, with the food to which it adheres, be removed. However, if the mold is extensive, the food should be discarded. Molds grow aerobically and do not require as much moisture as either yeasts or bacteria. Because of their tolerance for acid, molds on low-acid foods are likely to destroy the acid present and other forms of spoilage may develop. Such food should be destroyed in a way that will prevent either people or animals from getting it.

Molds are destroyed by boiling temperature. Acid foods, canned by processing in a water bath, and low-acid foods processed under pressure, will not mold if there is a secure seal.

Bacteria. Bacteria, present in the air, on plants, and in the soil, cause food spoilage if not inactivated or destroyed in the food preservation process. They may be thermophilic, which grow best at temperatures from 100° to 130° F. (38° to 55° C.), or mesophilic, which develop easily at room temperature, or psychrophilic, which grow best at refrigerator temperatures. They may be aerobic, that is, require oxygen for development, or anaerobic, that is, develop with very little or no oxygen. Spoilage due to thermophilic anaerobes is of three types:

1. Flat-sour spoilage is characterized by acid formation without gas. Most of the organisms responsible for flat-sour spoilage are thermophilic; others develop over a rather wide temperature range. It occurs most frequently in low-acid vegetables, especially corn and peas. While food so spoiled is not poisonous, it is not considered edible. Handling food and equipment in a sanitary manner, avoiding overfilling the containers, processing adequately, cooling rapidly, and keeping the storage temperature below 100° F. (38° C.) are safeguards against this type of spoilage.
2. "Swell" spoilage is obvious in cans. In jars, broken seal and frothy appearance indicate this type of spoilage. Both gas and acid are formed. The hydrogen-containing gas may be identified by the fact that if a lighted match is held near when the can is opened, the gas ignites. The precautions mentioned under "flat-sour spoilage" guard against "swells." Canned food should be checked about a month after canning, since "swells" usually develop within this time. The food is inedible.
3. Sulphide spoilage is not common, and the two foods in which it is most often found are corn and peas. There is no question as to the presence of this spoilage, since the odor is that of rotten eggs. There is also a gray to black color. The precautions mentioned under "flat-sour spoilage" prevent this type and the inedibility of the product is obvious.

Mesophilic bacteria are responsible for other types of spoilage:

1. Putrefactive anaerobes cause spoilage of low-acid foods. They are soil organisms that grow in the absence of oxygen. Spoilage may be evident because of the

soft, slimy texture of the product, together with presence of gas. "If the acidity of the product is near the acid limit of growth of the organism, as in string beans, . . . the food may show only a cloudy brine, and have a faintly disagreeable odor which will become more pronounced upon heating."[1]

2. The most dreaded putrefactive anaerobe, *Clostridium botulinum,* is found in the soil and it is most likely to cause trouble in low-acid foods. Spores are not killed by a boiling temperature; hence the importance of adequate processing of all vegetables and meat products in a pressure cooker. Poisoning due to *Cl. botulinum* is not due to the bacteria themselves but to the production of a neurotoxin which is the most poisonous substance known. In case there is any doubt about the adequacy of processing of these foods, they should be heated in an open utensil for 15 to 20 minutes. Fortunately, the toxin is destroyed by this means. If, however, food is being heated to make sure there is no toxin present, and a bad odor develops, the food should be buried, with lye added, or burned.

3. In the presence of iron, mesophilic aerobic bacteria may cause beets to become black. The beets are not poisonous but are not considered edible. Avoidance of iron and correct processing are precautionary measures.

4. Spoilage of tomatoes and tomato juice has been rather common. An acid-tolerant spoilage organism that survives the process is the cause. In tomato juice, the organism has been found to be *B. thermoacidurans* (Berry). Sanitary handling, a good seal, and adequate processing are preventive measures.

Spoilage is not confined to those foods preserved for future use.[2] The "lost" left-overs (in a refrigerator) that become sour, moldy, slimy, or even putrid are obviously spoiled and promptly discarded. But some spoilage due to bacteria is not obvious. *Staphylococcus Aureus* produces a poison—an enterotoxin. The organism grows most rapidly at 70°–97° F. (21°–36° C.), hence is more likely to develop in hot weather than in cold. The chief offenders are custards and cream fillings (e.g., cream puffs), cream sauce, salad dressings, salads (especially potato), ham, tongue, and poultry. Care in preparation of such items, avoidance of preparation of potato salad too far in advance of use, and of trying to keep any of these foods for several days—even refrigerated—are precautions needed to guard against this type of food spoilage—and poisoning.

Another offender is *Salmonella.* These bacteria grow best in nonacid foods, such as meat and meat products, and the sort of cream fillings mentioned above. Similar precautions are necessary.

A recent study of bacteria found in potato, meat, and poultry salads and in egg and ham sandwiches was carried out at Cornell University and resulted in several recommendations. When cooked foods such as potatoes, meat, or poultry are being prepared for salad, marinate them in tart salad dressing and refrigerate until it is time to complete the salad. In both salads

[1] Winifred J. Leverenz and O. B. Williams, *Some Important Factors Causing Spoilage and Poor Quality in Home Canned Foods.* Mrs. Winifred Leverenz, Wallowa, Ore.

[2] Food and Home Notes. U.S.D.A., Office of Information, Washington, Aug., 1959.

and sandwich fillings, use a liberal amount of pickle, tart relish, or lemon juice. In the presence of acid, far fewer bacteria were found than in mixtures combined without "extra" acid.

Enzymes. Enzymes, the catalysts present in all food, are responsible for the ripening of fruits and vegetables, and for making meats tender as they "ripen." This process, extended, causes foods to spoil. In the preservation of food, therefore, the enzymes must be destroyed or inactivated. Heat destroys, refrigeration retards, and freezing inactivates them. Enzyme activity is beneficial until a fruit or vegetable has reached its most desirable stage of ripeness or maturity. It is then at its peak of flavor and texture. After that, softening, browning, and development of off-flavor are progressive. Hence, these products should be preserved when they are properly matured. Speed is imperative. Ideally, home-preserved fruits and vegetables should be processed or in the freezer within two hours after they are harvested. This means that relatively small quantities should be handled at a time.

PRESERVATION METHODS

The marketing system throughout the country provides storage facilities that are suitable for the various kinds of food. Common storage is used for the semi-perishable foods, such as onions and both sweet and Irish potatoes. Cool temperatures with sufficient humidity to prevent shriveling are provided for others, including apples, citrus fruits, winter cabbage, and root vegetables. Cold storage in transit as well as in warehouses assures freshness and fine quality for perishables—for example, berries, salad plants, eggs, milk, and meats. Frozen storage makes the shipping of frozen foods for long distances possible.

In many homes, some forms of storage are used. Cellars and pits are suitable for the less perishable fruits and vegetables (see p. 59). If they are stored in bins in a cellar, they should be inspected frequently, and any that show signs of spoilage should be removed. This type of storage is used extensively on farms and by homemakers in villages where part of the supply of fruit and vegetables is produced in the garden and fruit plot or purchased in rather large quantities. In most homes, a refrigerator enables the homemaker to maintain temperatures that keep perishable food fresh for a sufficient time. The home freezer also permits purchase of food in sufficient quantities to preserve by freezing and to plan for the freezing of flour mixtures, casserole dishes, and other favorite foods. In some instances, the homemaker sets aside a day now and then for preparing food for freezing and thus saves considerable time at a later date when very little time for preparing meals is available.

In many homes, foods are preserved by canning, freezing, drying, pickling, brining, and making preserves or jellies of several types. In each case, selection of the food, choice and care of equipment, preparation of food, suitable application of heat, packaging, labeling, and storing are necessary if products of excellent quality are to reward the efforts of the homemaker.

Canning. Practical application of the work of Appert was slow in becoming general. In the United States, the first records of canning were concerned with the work of Ezra Daggett and Thomas Kinsett who, in 1819 canned seafoods in New York City. Their method of processing—in boiling water—would not be considered safe today. The War Between the States spurred the efforts of people to can more foods and to improve methods. Crises still lead to increased volume of preserved foods. The bulk of food canned commercially is seasonal. Managers of plants have found that the work season can be extended by canning such foods as breads, macaroni and cheese, and baked apples after the rush season. Canning involves the exclusion of air and the application of a suitable degree of heat for a period of time that will insure a good product. Fruit juices may be pasteurized at about 180° F. (82° C.). Acid fruits and tomatoes may be processed in boiling water—212° F. (100° C.). Low-acid vegetables and all meat products require a temperature of about 240° F. (116° C.): in other words, they must be processed in a pressure cooker to insure their safety.

Selection and grading of food. Fruit and vegetables should be sorted and graded carefully as to size. Small peaches or tomatoes should be used for some containers, and larger ones for others. Grading products insures uniform cooking as well as excellent appearance. Such tender fruits as peaches bruise easily. Discolored spots must be removed. The perfect halves may be used for canning, and the others trimmed and made into jam or marmalade. Peas may be sorted by running them over wire sieves, 1/4-inch and 3/8-inch sieves being fairly satisfactory. If they are not graded, the smaller peas are thoroughly cooked before the larger ones are done, and frequently become soft, burst, and make the liquid turbid.

The light and dark meat of poultry may be canned separately if desired. Bony pieces may be canned by themselves or the meat may be removed from the bones and canned for such uses as creamed chicken. Meat for each container should be chosen with reference to tenderness and use.

Utensils. Utensils used for canning may be few or many, and of varying size, depending upon the amount of canning done and available money. Some are necessary; others are desirable. A brief list of equipment is included in Appendix H, pp. 686–687.

Preparation of containers. Glass jars must be examined to be sure they do not leak. If the edges of both jar and cover are free from chips or cracks, and if the cover fits the sealing shoulder of the jar closely, the seal will doubtless be perfect. Jars are tested for leaks by putting water into them, placing the rubber, securing the cover, and inverting. If no water leaks out, the jars are suitable containers for canned food.

Jars and glass covers must be carefully washed with soap or a detergent and rinsed. Then they may be sterilized by boiling them several minutes in a sufficient quantity of water to cover them, if the open-kettle method of canning is used. If the processing is done in a water bath or a pressure cooker, they are scalded. Rubber rings are scalded. Directions on the package of self-seal lids should be followed because not all need the same treatment.

Tin cans are scalded. The tops have a special sealing compound around the edge. They may be dipped into boiling water just before they are put onto the can. Plain cans are used for most foods but C enamel cans are best for a few foods, including corn and lima beans, and R enamel for foods with color from anthocyanins, such as beets and prunes, and for squash and pumpkin.

Preparing food for canning. Preparation includes thorough cleaning, removing skins of most fruits and vegetables, possibly removing bones from poultry, and trimming meat. Darkening of some fruits, including apples and peaches, is prevented during preparation, and scalding is necessary for certain fruits and vegetables.

All fruits and vegetables should be washed carefully before they are canned. Berries require careful handling and should be washed just before they are placed in containers. Hardier fruits, such as pears, may be washed with a brush. All root vegetables should be scrubbed thoroughly to remove soil and soil bacteria. Leafy vegetables require special attention to be sure all dirt and sand are removed.

Poultry should be washed carefully. Meat should be wiped with a clean, damp cloth.

Some foods need to be scalded by dipping them into boiling water for a few minutes. This loosens the skins of peaches, apricots, and tomatoes so that they can be peeled easily. A wire basket, colander, or cheesecloth may be used to hold the fruit. The product is cooled by dipping into cold water immediately. Greens are scalded to wilt them, thus facilitating packing. Skins of most other fruits and vegetables are removed by paring thinly.

Development of a brownish color on apples, apricots, peaches, pears, and pineapple may be prevented by handling them quickly and dropping them into water containing two tablespoonfuls each of salt and vinegar per gallon, a solution of citric acid in the ratio of 1 t. per gallon of water, or special commercial preparations of ascorbic acid. The fruit should not remain in the solution for more than 25 minutes. Ascorbic acid may be dissolved in the sirup used for canning. It may be purchased in tablet or powder form. Tablets of 25, 50, and 100 mg. are available and should be used in the ratio of 125 mg. per pint of fruit or ½ cup of sirup. The powder is used in the ratio of ¼ teaspoon per pint of sirup.

Methods used for canning. Food to be canned may be cooked in an open kettle, then packed and sealed in jars. It may be heated before it is packed into jars and cans and then processed. It may be packed into cans or jars cold, suitable liquid added, and steamed (exhausted) before processing. Since this method is most commonly used, it is described in the following paragraphs.

Packing. Careful packing is necessary if economical use of containers and attractive products are to be expected. This means using as much of the food as can be packed conveniently into the container. A jar which is being filled with berries may be shaken gently, but the berries must not be crushed. Peaches and pears which are canned as halves should be packed with the cups down. Green beans may be cut or left whole. Fancy packs require much time and are related to neither usefulness nor nutritive value of the food. A fairly close pack is nearly always desirable, but very closely packed corn, peas, or lima beans require longer processing than most directions for canning stipulate, and such packing should be avoided, because the food is likely to spoil.

Most fruits are canned in a sirup, the density of which varies with the fruit and the purpose for which it is intended. The packed containers are filled with sirup, allowing headspace in accord with directions for the food that is being canned. If the fruits that darken easily are packed as they are prepared, and the sirup is kept at simmering temperature, each container may be filled with sirup as soon as it is packed. It may be desirable to pack some fruit without sirup, to be sweetened to taste when used.

After containers have been filled with vegetables, a designated amount of salt is placed on the vegetable, and water is added to within ½ inch of the top. In canning tomatoes, tomato juice should be used instead of water. The idea that uniodized salt should be used has been discounted by recent research.[1]

Meat and poultry are packed to within ⅜ inch of the top of the container. The containers are filled to within ½ inch of the top with broth obtained as the meat is precooked. Very little fat should be included.

Steaming. The packed foods, with liquid to within about an inch of the top of the can or jar, are put into a hot water bath, with water coming to about two inches from the tops. The water bath is covered and the water is brought to a boil. Steaming time is counted from the time the water boils.

When the containers are removed, the food is pressed down to remove air and insure a good pack, and the containers are refilled if necessary. The edges of the containers are wiped, and cans are sealed. Jars are sealed or semi-sealed, according to directions that accompany the lids used.

Processing. Fruits and tomatoes may be processed in either a boiling water bath or a steam bath. The water bath is like the one described above, except that the water level is about two inches above the top of the containers. For the steam bath, only a small amount of water is used in the canner. The time is increased by one-fourth because the temperature is somewhat lower than

---

[1] Nakaji Kojima and H. D. Brown, "The Effects of Iodized Salt in Processed Fruits and Vegetables," *Food Technology,* February, 1955.

that attained in the boiling water bath. A water bath canner or any container deep enough to hold the cans or jars and that has a snugly fitting cover, may be used as a steam bath. A pressure cooker with the pet cock left open is a good steam bath.

Low-acid vegetables and meat products should be processed in a pressure cooker. In the pressure cooker, jars or cans are set on a rack. A small amount of water is added to furnish steam. The cooker is closed and heated with the pet cock open until steam has come from it for about 10 minutes. The pet cock is then closed, and the pressure rises. When it has risen sufficiently, the heat is regulated to keep the pressure as constant as possible, and the time is counted from the time the pressure indicated in the directions is reached. The time varies with the product and with the altitude. Timing must be accurate.

Altitude[1] influences the time needed for canning foods. For processing in a water bath, time should be increased one minute for each 1,000 feet above sea level if the time is twenty minutes or less, and two minutes if the time is more than twenty minutes. For processing in a pressure cooker, changes in gauge pressure need to be made, in accord with the following table.

TABLE 31. GAUGE PRESSURES FOR PROCESSING FOOD IN A PRESSURE COOKER AT DIFFERENT ALTITUDES

Temperature		*Steam pressure (pounds) at altitudes of:*			
Degrees F.	*Degrees C.*	*Sea level*	*4,000 feet*	*6,000 feet*	*7,500 feet*
228	109	5	7	8	9
240	115	10	12	13	14
250	121	15	17	18	19
259	126	20	22	23	24

At the end of the processing time, the cooker is removed from the heat and, if jars or No. 3 cans have been used, the pressure is allowed to go to zero before the canner is opened. If cans smaller than No. 3 are used, the pet cock may be opened slowly so that the pressure goes down more quickly. In either case, before the cooker is opened, the pet cock must be opened to be sure that all steam is out. The cooker is opened and the containers are removed. Cans are cooled rapidly in cold water which should be changed as it becomes warm. Jars that were semisealed are completely sealed and all jars are set aside to cool away from a draft. They should be arranged so that air circulates around them freely.

In case of disaster, a supply of drinking water is imperative. It can be purchased, but it is easily canned at home at far less cost. Glass jars are sterilized, filled level full with boiling water, and sealed with two-piece closures. Both

[1] *Handbook of Food Preparation,* American Home Economics Association, Washington.

pints and quarts are processed for 15 minutes at 15 pounds pressure and the gauge is allowed to return to zero before the cooker is opened.[1]

Methods to be avoided. Methods sometimes used, or concerning which questions are asked, which cannot be recommended are:

1. Processing in the oven. The convenience of the oven for processing foods has led to its use. If several accurate thermometers are used to check temperature in different parts of the oven, it will usually be found that they vary considerably. Hence jars of food would not heat at the same rate. Pressure is not even, and this often causes loss of liquid. Oven temperatures are not high enough to insure safety of nonacid vegetables or meats. Explosion of jars has not only ruined the food but also damaged the oven beyond repair.

2. Intermittent sterilization. Heating and cooling a product on two or three successive days subjects it several times to the range in temperature at which bacteria develop most rapidly. This increases the possibility of spoilage.

3. Use of special canning powders and antibiotics. Until (or unless) research results in conclusive evidence that antibiotics or any special canning powders are not only effective but also harmless, they should not be used in connection with food preservation. Jacobs,[2] quoting Basnard, has suggested certain criteria for a "completely adequate chemical preservative":

1) It must not under any reasonable conditions injure the health of the consumer.
2) It must not allow the utilization of unfit raw material.
3) Its use must not make possible the employment of careless and imperfect methods of manufacture.
4) It must be nonirritant.
5) It must be efficient in its action.
6) It must not retard the action of digestive enzymes.
7) It must have no tendency to decompose within the body into substances which have a greater toxicity than that of the preservative itself.
8) It should lend itself to simple methods of determination and thus simplify the control problem.

For commercial purposes, in 1955, the Food and Drug Administration permitted the use of chlortetracycline in the amount of 5 ppm. in ice in which poultry is chilled. This permission has now (1959) been extended to fresh fish, shucked scallops, and unpeeled shrimp.

Labeling. If tin cans containing more than one product are being processed at one time, an identifying mark should be placed on the cans with a wax pencil.

When cans or jars are cool, they should be wiped clean, and each should be

---

[1] *Recommendations Concerning Home Food Preservation,* Committee on Food Preservation, Texas State Nutrition Council, 1953 Supplement.

[2] Morris B. Jacobs, *The Chemistry and Technology of Food and Food Products,* 2nd Edition. Interscience Publishers, Inc., New York, 1951.

labeled. A label that will stick to the container should be used. Rubber cement is recommended for tin cans unless a large label that extends all around the can is used.

The name of the product is always on the label. Other information, such as date, variety of product, name of owner, etc., may be added.

Storing. A cool, dry place is needed for storing canned products. For glass jars a dark place is preferable. A special closet or ventilated pantry, a space in the cellar specially suited to this type of storage, or a special cellar or pantry may be used. It is a good idea to label the shelves, because these labels can usually be read more quickly than those on the containers. A record of the canned food may be tacked on the door or near the storage space and a record of items withdrawn kept. (See Appendix, p. 687.)

Freezing. Modern adaptations of the old arctic method of preserving fish and game by freezing have changed the food preservation picture materially. Use of both commercially frozen foods and foods frozen at home is increasing steadily. The advantages of freezing over canning include fresher flavor, better color of some products, and less time spent in a hot kitchen during the season when fruits and vegetables are plentiful.

Choice of food. If a frozen product is to be of excellent quality, the fresh product must also be of that quality. Fruits and vegetables should be at the peak of their maturity and meat products of Choice grade are best for freezing, although meat of Good grade is satisfactory. Information concerning varieties of fruits and vegetables that freeze well may be obtained from the County Home Demonstration Agent or Home Economics teacher. Suggestions concerning sorting fruits and vegetables for size and separating light from dark poultry meat in some cases, as were mentioned in the discussion of canning, apply here also.

Containers and wrapping materials. Containers that are satisfactory for freezing foods should be as moisture-vapor-proof as possible, provided with a closely fitting cover, or sufficiently pliable so that they can be closed securely, sturdy enough to withstand knocks as food is moved about in the freezer, and shaped to pack to advantage.

The cans used for canning may also be used for freezing, choosing them as suggested above. The newer glass jars are so shaped that they are equally satisfactory for canning and freezing. Jars made especially for freezing are very satisfactory. All these have one disadvantage—they are round and space in the freezer is wasted.

Heavy plastic containers with close-fitting lids are available in different sizes and shapes. Waxed cardboard cartons or cardboard with a plastic bag interlining are satisfactory. Both carton and bag can be reused.

There are a number of bags and sheets made from such films as pliafilm, polyethylene, and rubber latex. Heavy aluminum foil and laminated and plastic-coated papers are used extensively. All these are moisture-vapor-resistant. They lend themselves well to packaging of dry-packed vegetables and foods that may be "oddly" shaped, e.g., poultry and meats which do not fit into the rigid containers. The food wrapped in sheet material must be sealed with freezer tape.

For homemade flour mixtures and other foods, many of which are at least partially cooked before freezing, there are other possibilities. Pies and cakes baked in square pans, wrapped with foil or saran and sealed, may need further protection which cardboard cartons afford from knocks, as food is put into or removed from the freezer. For a short time, such a partially-prepared food as squash in casserole (see pp. 511–12) may be put into an ovenware dish, covered closely, and when used, partially thawed, then heated and served in the same dish.

Preparing food. Strict sanitary conditions are imperative. If fruit is to be frozen in sirup, the sirup should be made ahead so that it will be cold when poured over the fruit. Ascorbic acid may be added to it (see p. 286) for such fruits as peaches to retain color. Other preparation of fruits and vegetables is much the same as for canning.

Containers are filled with fruit to within about ½ inch from the top, and the sirup is added. Crumpled waxed paper or cellophane may be placed on top before the cover is put in place to keep the fruit under the sirup, thus helping to keep both color and texture even throughout the package.

Vegetables should be scalded in accordance with time stated in reliable tables and cooled immediately. Enzyme action is retarded by freezing but not sufficiently to prevent off-flavors and poor color after storage. This necessity for scalding was shown clearly in a study by Noble and Winter in which the storage period was only four weeks. They found that "All of the unscalded vegetable samples showed marked deterioration according to all the criteria used. . . . The scalded samples, on the other hand, showed little change in quality from the beginning to the end of the storage period."[1]

Poultry should be prepared with cookery method in mind, probably some whole birds and some cut for broiling, frying, or fricasseeing. The whole birds should not be stuffed. Boned, ground turkey has been found to be a handy product and one which is economical of freezer space.[2]

Meat which has been aged for from a few days to as much as three or four weeks has been made more tender by the process and is thus superior to meat that is not aged. Both at locker plants and at home, meat is cut as the homemaker wants it. Boning some of the more bony cuts conserves space in the freezer.

Eggs have been frozen commercially for years. For home use, they may be

---

[1] Isabel Noble and J. D. Winter, *Is Blanching Necessary When Vegetables Are to Be Kept in Frozen Storage a Month or Less?* Journ. of Home Economics, 44:1, 1952.

[2] Rose Erisman, "Production, Storage, and Preparation of Turkey Parts, Including Steaks" (Thesis, University of Texas, 1950).

frozen to advantage. Packaging is perhaps the chief problem because the package should contain the amount of egg to be used at one time. The whites need no treatment and, since one use for them might be for an angel cake, the quantity needed may be put into a suitable sterilized and cooled container such as a half-pint-jar if one cup of egg white is the amount needed. Yolks must be beaten gently to mix but not to incorporate air. Depending upon the use for which the yolk is intended, it is mixed with salt, sugar, or corn sirup in the ratio of one teaspoon of salt or one tablespoon of sugar or sirup per cup of egg. Otherwise, the yolks are gummy and do not mix well with other ingredients. Whole eggs must also be mixed with one of these but somewhat less may be used. Packaging whole eggs and yolks is a problem. One method is to put the desired amount of egg into small waxed cups until frozen; then remove them, wrap in a film-saran or some other pliable film, and pack in a cardboard container.

Packaging and labeling. Caution with regard to the fill of cartons and other containers has been mentioned. If more than one half of a broiler or one steak or chop is put into a package, a piece of cellophane or heavy waxed paper should be placed between each two to facilitate separating them while they are thawing.

Any food that might be crushed while handling other foods in the freezer should be put into a container that is substantial. Some foods may be frozen before they are packaged. For instance, creamed chicken to serve two to six people may be chilled in the double boiler in which it is made, covered, and frozen. Then, when it is removed, it is wrapped with foil or freezer paper and when it is to be used, it is placed in the same double boiler for thawing and heating. Such foods thaw more quickly if two pieces of cellophane are placed at frequent intervals between layers of the food.[1]

Each package of food should be labeled carefully. Some suggestions for satisfactory labeling are:

1. If such fruits as peaches have been frozen, using sirup of two densities, the type sirup should be included on the label.
2. The contents of a package of chicken should be on the label—two broiler halves, three chicken breasts, etc.
3. The cut of meat, with number of such cuts as steaks and chops, should be noted on the package.
4. Kind and number in a package of cookies, muffins, etc., needs to be included as well as variety of pie, cake, etc.
5. The date of freezing should be on each package. This helps to prevent too long holding. Bulletins that give directions for freezing usually include a list of optimal time for storage of various foods.

Freezing and storing. Freezing temperatures differ considerably, but the consensus is that foods that are frozen quickly are of higher quality than

[1] Faith Fenton, *Foods from the Freezer,* Cornell Extension Bulletin 692 (Ithaca, N. Y., 1951).

those frozen more slowly. The rate of freezing in most home freezers and locker plants is such that this quality may be expected. Temperatures for freezing are —10 to —20° F. (22 to 29° C.) and holding temperatures are usually well below zero. A thermometer that can be read from outside the freezer is an advantage.

The arrangement of food in the home freezer is important. A list of the foods, together with number of packages of each and location in the freezer should be handy. As a package is removed, a record should be kept. This not only enables the homemaker to know what supply she has, but also gives an idea of suitable replacements. See Appendix, p. 687. If replacements, either with similar food or with some other food which would be an advantageous item to fill space, are made frequently, satisfactory and profitable use of the freezer will result.[1]

There is considerable discussion concerning refreezing food that has been thawed. Winter *et al.*[2] warn against refreezing shellfish and vegetables because both spoil rapidly after thawing and the spoilage may be difficult to detect. Fruits and fruit juices may be refrozen, but the former are less desirable in texture. In case of power failure, the length of time that food in a freezer will remain in good condition depends partly on the quantity in the freezer. "In large-size freezers fairly full of food it usually takes several days" for the temperature to reach 50° F. (10° C.). In case of continued power failure, if foods have thawed they may spoil before they can be refrozen; hence the temperature should be watched. Concerning meats, they state, "If the product temperature has remained below 45° F., the food is probably still in good condition. Incipient spoilage can be detected by color and odor."[3]

Meals from the freezer. There are several reasons why inclusion of planned meals in the freezer is a good idea, apart from the possibility of choosing most of the food needed from a well-stocked freezer. Considerable time and effort are saved if, occasionally, twice the amount of food needed for a meal is prepared and half of it frozen. This requires a little planning. For example, if peas are one of the vegetables, those to be frozen are removed from the saucepan when scalded, cooled, packed, and put into the freezer. If the dessert is a cake, the portion not used at the meal is wrapped and frozen.

Such foods come in handy when time for meal preparation is limited or for supplementary picnic dishes. Foods which have been cooked and frozen are especially convenient in case of emergencies which cut off the regular fuel supply. Frozen meals for at least a day would postpone dependence upon canned food in case of fuel failure of a few days' duration or of an emergency which might require dependence upon stored food for two weeks or more.

[1] Smith, Marialyce, *Efficient Use of Home Freezers in Rural Homes in Belle County,* Texas. (Unpublished Thesis, University of Texas, 1954.)

[2] J. D. Winter *et al., Freezing Foods for Home Use,* Ext. Bul. 244 (University of Minnesota, 1951), p. 47.

[3] *Ibid.*

Drying, dehydrating, and evaporating. All spoilage agents require moisture for their development. Consequently, if a large portion of the water content is removed, foods do not spoil easily. This method of preserving foods is used extensively.

Water is evaporated from milk in the production of evaporated, condensed, and nonfat dry milk solids. Egg solids are possible because of evaporation of moisture. Fruits, vegetables, meats, and fish have been dried for centuries in warm, arid regions, by simply hanging suitable portions in the sun. In homes, some food is still dried, the main items being fruits, corn, legumes, and sometimes, beef. Bulletins from the agents connected with the Extension Service give directions for home-drying of foods. Herbs are sometimes dried at home. One method consists of stripping the leaves from the stems, laying them on screens covered with cheese cloth, and leaving them in the shade during dry weather where there is a gentle breeze. They must be taken in at night to avoid dampness from dew. Herbs may be stored as whole leaves or rubbed through a sieve.

Perhaps the main reason for this method of preservation is the small space into which food can be packed. Taking food to distant places, providing certain perishable foods for defense groups, or even for extended hikes, are some of the special reasons why "dried" foods are advantageous. Commercially, sun-drying is still done extensively, particularly in the western part of the country, where large quantities of fruits are dried. Both scalding and sulphuring have been found to be good techniques before drying or dehydrating fruits and vegetables. The former destroys enzymes; the latter improves color. Drying in rooms in which temperature and humidity are controlled is used more extensively than sun-drying.

Dehydrating is a method by which moisture is removed in rooms where temperature, humidity, and air flow are controlled. Food is cut into small pieces so that time for both dehydrating and reconstituting are minimized. Dehydrated vegetables, such as okra, spinach, and onions, are on the market as well as mixtures of vegetables for soups and powdered pumpkin and squash for pie fillings. Commercially, a combination of drying and freezing —"dehydro-freezing" or "freeze-drying"—has proved effective, particularly from the point of view of room needed for storage. Also, the products rehydrate rapidly.

Brining and pickling. Some vegetables are preserved by brining. For vegetables of high water content, such as cabbage, the brine is made by the action of dry salt on the shredded cabbage. Two ounces of salt (not treated to prevent caking) are sufficient for five pounds of cabbage. Other vegetables preserved by this fermentation process are turnips, lettuce, and green beans. Brining is often the first step in making cucumber pickles. The process requires several weeks, with gradual increase in brine concentration, the vegetables being held under brine by a weight. Scum must be removed at least every two days because it decreases acidity and the cucumbers are likely to soften and spoil due to development of bacteria. A variation of brining is the making of dill pickles. To a 20-degree brine, dill, spices, and sugar are added. Whether fruit, fresh vegetables, or brined vegetables are used for pickling, vinegar of about 5 per cent acetic acid concentration is used. Cider vinegar is recommended for fruits; white, for vegetables. In suitable proportions, spices are added to the vinegar for sour pickles and sugar as well as spices for sweet pickles. Crispness is desirable for some pickles. Soaking for about six hours in calcium chloride solution is the usual method. To a lesser degree, thin slices of cucumber may be sprinkled with salt, covered with ice, and allowed to stand about twelve hours, adding ice from time to time.

Pickling and brining are satisfactory preserving methods because of the effect of the materials used upon the activity of spoilage organisms. Salt and sugar both increase the density of the solution in which water or vinegar is the solvent and so make it difficult for the organism to reach the food. Vinegar prevents bacterial action. A few spices that are often used in pickles have a preservative effect—cloves, cinnamon, and allspice. Other than these, spices are valuable for flavor only.

Two characteristics of cucumber pickles of poor quality are wrinkled appearance and soft or slippery texture. The former is due to overcooking or too concentrated brine. The latter is caused by brine of too low concentration or the cucumbers not being kept under the brine. Sometimes pickles are hollow. The cucumbers may have been too mature or they may have been held in storage too long before the pickles were made.

Making preserves. Either whole or sliced fruits cooked with a rather large amount of sugar are often called "preserves" to distinguish them from jams, marmalades, and conserves. All these may be called "preserves" because all have the characteristic of high sugar content.

For the first type, the density of the sirup must be increased gradually, else the fruit will be hard and shriveled. Prepared fruit is simmered in light sirup for two or three minutes and set aside for a day or two. The sirup is then drained from the fruit, its density increased by the addition of sugar, or by the concentration of the sirup, and poured over the fruit. After a second period of standing, the density of the sirup is again increased and the sirup is poured over the fruit. As the fruit stands in the sirup, the process of osmosis causes a transfer of liquid from the fruit to the sirup, and vice versa, until equilibrium is established. Fruit that is plump and juicy results. There are other quicker methods for making preserves, but the addition of the sugar in such a way that the fruit neither collapses nor hardens is the important technique.

Jams are made from many fruits, either singly or in combination. Raspberries and currants, strawberries and pineapple, raspberries and peaches, and figs and apricots make pleasing combinations for jams. Tutti-frutti jam is made by using a small quantity of each of several varieties of fruit as they become available. A cup of the first fruit used is cooked with an equal quantity of sugar until thick, and the jam is poured into a clean jar or crock and covered. Jam made similarly from other fruits is added. When all the fruits desired have been used, the jam is poured into a large utensil and heated to boiling, stirring meanwhile to mix the entire mass thoroughly. It is then poured into sterilized jars and the jars are sealed.

A large utensil is necessary because the mixture tends to boil over easily. A bit of butter or margarine rubbed around the edge of the utensil or dropped into the mixture lessens this tendency by lowering the surface tension.

The fruit for making jam may be crushed, chopped, sliced, or, if small, used whole. During the cooking process, however, it is crushed thoroughly. Sugar is added in stated ratio, and the mixture is cooked until thick. The quantity of sugar varies with the acidity and the pectin content. Half a pound of sugar per quart of fruit may be sufficient for very ripe blackberries, but a pound would not be too much per quart of currants. The ingredients should be cooked rapidly until the mixture has thickened somewhat, stirring occasionally. Constant stirring toward the end of the cooking period is necessary to prevent scorching. Jams are thick enough when the juice almost jells. Steam decreases and the fruit piles up on the spoon when a spoonful is removed. They may be stored in sterilized jars or in jelly glasses. The former are sealed and are sometimes heated in water at 180° F. (85° C.) for two or three minutes. The latter are sealed with paraffin.

Conserve often contains more than one fruit, nuts, and usually raisins. The fruit is cut into small pieces, and the fruit mixture is cooked with sugar until it is thick but not hard. As it cools, nut meats, whole or coarsely chopped, are added. Sterilized jars, filled with the mixture and partially sealed, are processed in a boiling water bath for two or three minutes.

In marmalades, the pulp of the fruit and the rind of citrus fruits appear in very thin slices or small pieces. Marmalades are jellylike in consistency but should not hold their shape when removed from the container.

In sections of the country where currants are available, an uncooked jam is made by crushing the fruit (every currant must be crushed), adding an equal quantity of sugar by measure, and setting the mixture aside until the sugar is completely dissolved and the mixture is thick. It should be stirred frequently. It is poured into sterilized jars and may be pasteurized for two or three minutes.

Making jelly. Ideal jelly is clear and translucent. Its flavor is distinctly that of the fruit from which it is made. It holds its shape, but does not appear stiff when it is removed from the jelly glasses. It quivers when shaken and shows clear angles when cut. It is tender. These characteristics of texture depend upon the presence of pectin, acid, and sugar in correct proportions, and careful manipulation.

Pectin substances occur in the cell walls of plants. In underripe fruits protopectin is most abundant. As the fruit ripens, it is changed to pectin by the enzyme protopectinase. In later changes that lead from full ripeness to decay, pectin becomes pectic acid by the action of the enzyme pectase. These changes are not as precise as the above statements suggest, but the gradual change from immaturity to decay is accompanied by change from protopectin through a series of pectins to pectic acid.

In general, the pectin of ripe but not overripe fruit is best for jelly-making. As slightly acid, unripe fruit is heated, the acid converts protopectin to pectin so that fruit for jelly may be slightly underripe. The flavor of the juice from ripe fruit is, however, better.

Succesful jelly depends upon the correct interrelation of pectin, acid, and sugar. An experienced person who understands this relationship fully could make jelly from any fruit juice by adjusting the amount of sugar, acid, or pectin, or perhaps combining it with a second juice having desirable characteristics.

Juice may sometimes be extracted from ripe berries by crushing the berries and heating them slowly, stirring to prevent scorching. Usually, however, water is necessary for extracting juice. If berries, including currants, are crushed, the extracting time is decreased considerably. Soft fruits require only about one-fourth cup of water for each pound of fruit and an extraction time of from three to eight minutes. Firmer fruits are cut. Apples should be cut crosswise in thin slices. Pectin is more concentrated in the peel and core than in the pulp. Water varying from one to three cups per pound of fruit is used, and from ten to twenty minutes are needed for cooking the fruit.

Juice is strained through a jelly bag or two thicknesses of cheesecloth. For many fruits two or more extractions are desirable, the pulp from the first extraction being returned to the cooking utensil and water in the same ratio as for the first extraction added. This juice is thinner than the first extraction and its flavor is milder. It may be well to concentrate extractions other than the first before proceeding with the jelly-making. The first extraction from some fruits may be so concentrated in flavor that if the milder second extraction is mixed with it the flavor of the jelly will be better than if the first extraction is used by itself.

Unless the jelly maker is very sure of the juice being used, both acid and pectin tests are wise. A decided acid flavor is a simple test that is usually reliable for acid. The alcohol test for pectin is simple. Two or three tablespoons of alcohol are poured into a small glass or cup, and one tablespoon of juice is added. The container is rotated gently, and the pectin is precipitated. A solid mass of pectin indicates that the juice will make satisfactory jelly. If the precipitate is flocculent, additional pectin is needed, or the juice needs to be concentrated or combined with a juice of high pectin content.

An acid fruit juice is desirable for making jelly. However, acid in the form of lemon juice may be added to mildly acid juice. Other factors being equal, acidity increases the firmness of jellies and lessens the proportion of sugar to juice needed for the formation of jelly. This is because jelly is formed by the interaction of sugar and acid upon the pectin. The amount of sugar that is needed to form jelly of desirable texture is also satisfactory from the point of view of flavor.

The ratio of sugar to juice may be varied considerably with consequent effect upon quantity and texture of the finished jelly. If the concentration of sugar is too high, as occurs if the jelly is cooked beyond the jelly test (sheet test or temperature) crystals may form. They may also be caused by leaving the jelly unsealed too long, or if sugar is cooked too short a time with the juice so that insufficient invert sugar is formed. Potassium and tartrate crystals may be prevented in grape jelly if the extracted juice is allowed to stand at refrigerator temperature about twenty-four hours. At the end of that time, the precipitate is separated from the juice by straining the mixture through a heavy cloth. Too much sugar in the recipe gives a jelly of sirupy consistency, while too little sugar results in a tough jelly. A ratio of ¾ cups of sugar per cup of juice is satisfactory for most fruit juices. Tables and specific directions suggest the correct amount. However, juice varies with the variety of the fruit and the section of the country in which it is produced; consequently, modification may be desirable.

A large utensil is needed for cooking the juice and sugar because the sirup is likely to boil over. Butter or margarine may be added to lessen this tendency. A ten-quart kettle is not too large for three quarts of juice. This provides relatively large evaporation surface and shortens cooking time. This amount of juice is recommended as the largest quantity that should be cooked at one time when making jelly at home. Larger amounts require long cooking and the jelly is apt to be inferior.

The juice is measured and poured into the kettle, and sugar is added. A jel-meter is a handy instrument for judging the ratio of sugar to juice. Juice that is extracted so that it is desirably thick can be tested with this instrument because high-pectin juice is more viscous than low-pectin juice and runs through the jel-meter more slowly. The marks on the jel-meter indicate the amount of sugar to use for one cup of juice. Recipes and the experience of the jelly-maker are usually reliable guides to the amount of sugar.

Cooking should be as rapid as possible. When the bubbles in the boiling mixture begin to be large, and the surface is rolling, the sirup is nearly at the jelling point. The sheet test is the final reliable indication of the point at which the jelly is done. The test is made by lifting a spoonful of sirup about a foot above the surface of the boiling mass and pouring it into the kettle. At first, the last of the sirup falls from the spoon in a single drop. Later, two drops appear on the edge of the spoon. When these two drops run together and the mixture flakes off the spoon, the jelly is done. The test should be repeated two or three times with a thin-edged spoon. A thermometer may be used to indicate when the jelly point is reached. As in any cookery involving as large an amount of sugar as jelly requires, the boiling point of water should be read on the thermometer to be used before work is started. The mixture is cooked "to a temperature 8° F. higher than the boiling point of water. At that point the concentration of sugar will be such that the mixture should form a satisfactory gel."[1] This means that the technique may be used at any altitude.

Jelly should be strained quickly through one thickness of cheesecloth wrung from hot water and poured immediately into scalded, dry, glasses. After scalding, the glasses are turned upside down on a clean cloth or board and reversed just before the jelly is poured into them. They are *never* dried with a towel. The utensil containing the jelly should be held close to the glass, and the glass should be filled quickly to within one-fourth inch of the top. Bubbles may rise to the surface. These are removed with a small spoon before the jelly sets. Often spots of jelly at the edge of the glass interfere with sealing. They should be removed with a knife or spoon and the rim of the glass wiped carefully with a clean cloth dipped in either very hot water or alcohol.

Paraffin may be poured over the jelly as soon as the film of bubbles has been removed from the top of the jelly. Care must be taken to seal the jelly with paraffin completely. A cover furnishes added protection from dust and possible vermin during storage.

Jelly should be labeled. Many varieties look very much alike, and a label enables the homemaker to choose with certainty the one she wants.

Commercial pectin may be used for making jelly. It is particularly useful for making jelly from fruit juice of low pectin content, such as cherries, strawberries, and peaches. It is available in both powdered and liquid form. A higher proportion of sugar is required when these pectins are used; consequently, more jelly is made from a given quantity of juice. Neither temperature nor sheet test is used to indicate the end point, but time is included with the directions on packages of pectin. Pectin may be made at home (see Appendix pp. 687–688).

BUYING CANNED AND DRIED FOODS

The many sizes, brands, and grades; the frequent addition of new canned products or of new brands; and the lack of specific information on most la-

[1] *How to make Jellies, Jams, and Preserves at Home,* Home and Garden Bulletin, No. 56, Human Nutrition Research Division, Institute of Home Economics, Agricultural Research Service, U.S.D.A., 1957.

bels combine to make the choice of canned products difficult. Cans are standardized as to size. The principal sizes are shown in Fig. 47. On the market, a preference is being shown for No. 303 rather than No. 2 cans of fruits and vegetables, but juices are still packed extensively in the No. 2's.

There are many more cans specially shaped for various products. Those in the illustration indicate one difficulty. Some are so nearly the same size that unless a homemaker who is trying to compare prices is careful, she may not be comparing cans of equal size. The weight declared on the label should be the basis for comparison. As a rule, the larger containers are relatively cheaper than the small ones, but the size which is a wise choice depends upon the size of the family and the popularity of the food.

The homemaker will find selection of canned foods more satisfactory if a few guides are kept in mind.

1) Buy the grade or quality that is suitable for the use. Government standards have been set for canned fruits and vegetables, under the following grades:

U. S. Grade A or Fancy
U. S. Grade B; Choice or Extra-Standard
U. S. Grade C or Standard
Substandard.

For some purposes the higher qualities should be purchased; for others, the lower qualities are suitable. For example, the highest quality peaches might be purchased for a special dessert or salad; substandard peaches for a pie or to use in a sorbet. Grade A peas might be purchased to use as a buttered vegetable; Grade B for use in a casserole; Grade C for cream of pea soup. Far too few graded canned products are available, and too few are designated as Fancy, Choice or Standard. Many canning companies designate quality by brand but this is very confusing for homemakers, especially as one quality of a product from the same company may be sold under several brand labels. One person has said, "The cans do not know when they leave the canner what sort of dress they are going to wear."

The Agricultural Marketing Administration of the United States Department of Agriculture has a service whereby expert inspectors may be employed by canning companies to inspect the plant methods and pass on the grading of all canned products of that company. The label on such products includes a shield stating the U. S. Grade and "Packed under continuous inspection of the Agricultural Marketing Service of the U. S. Dept. of Agriculture." (See Fig. 48.) This sort of effort should be encouraged in every way possible.

2) Read the label to know the amount of food in the can and to obtain other helpful information.

Most dried fruits are graded, grades being based upon flavor, maturity, uniformity, size, and freedom from blemishes. The size of prunes is often on the package—20–30's, 90–100's, etc., indicating the number in a pound. The larger ones are higher in price than the smaller, but not necessarily better in flavor. For most purposes, medium size prunes are satisfactory, but for stuffing or in some salads, large ones are usually purchased.

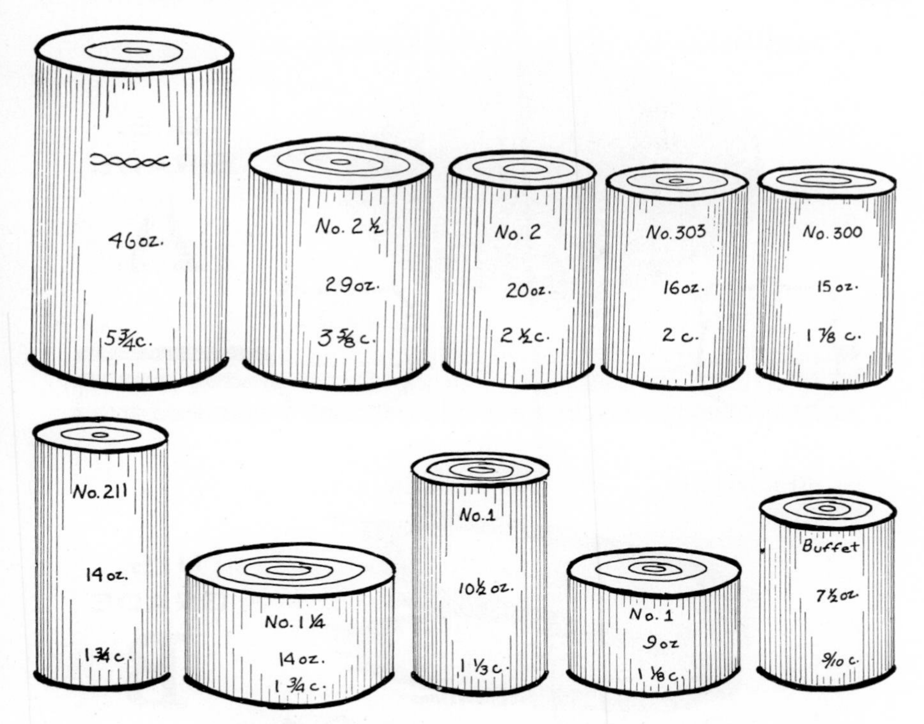

Fig. 47. Some of the most popular can sizes.

Prunes are sometimes packaged by processors in cardboard boxes or in cellophane and the size is indicated on the label. These may be disappointing to the buyer because the interpretation of such a term as "large" by various processors is not the same and may not coincide with that of the consumer buyer. Some of these have been processed so that no cooking—only soaking—is needed.

The use of a mixture of dried fruits adds interest. Packages of mixed fruits are available and may be used in various ways. Prunes and apricots served together are sometimes liked better than either by itself and prune and apricot upside-down cake is very attractive as well as delicious.

Pitted and unpitted dates serve the same purposes, the former being higher in price. For such products as date puddings, blended dates are satisfactory, and are considerably cheaper than the others. Most raisins are either seedless—Sultana—or seeded—Muscat or Malaga. They are packed in 15-ounce cardboard packages. Chiefly at Christmas time, white raisins and cluster raisins are popular. Currants are much smaller than raisins, and more tart.

Dried apples, pears, and peaches, are probably used less than the other dried fruits. The apples are satisfactory for pies, apple betty, and some other pud-

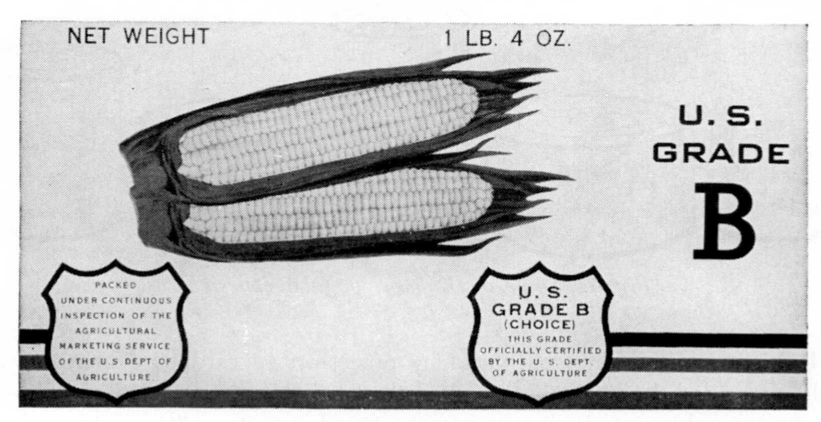

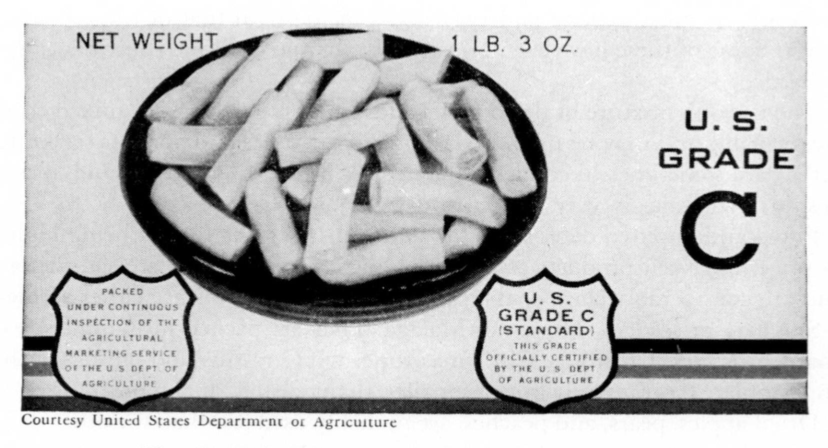

Courtesy United States Department of Agriculture

Fig. 48. United States grade labels on canned goods.

dings. The pears and peaches may be used by themselves or combined with others as fruit for breakfast or as a compote in other meals.

Legumes are the principal vegetables that are sold dried. There are interesting varieties and they vary considerably in price. Large lima beans are less expensive than small ones; beans are less expensive than lentils. Certain varieties of beans are used more than others for specified purposes, for example, navy beans for Boston baked beans, kidney or pinto beans for chili.

Other dried items include soup mixtures, herbs, onion flakes, and garlic. The soup mixtures are time savers. The others add zest to many foods that would be bland without additional flavor.

BUYING FROZEN FOODS

The display of frozen foods in most grocery stores is proof of the rapid growth of the industry. The consumer-buyer may choose among several brands of fruit, vegetables, juices, poultry, fish, meat pies, and whole main courses, as well as pies, cakes, both plain and fancy rolls, and sundry other items. The packaging is adequate, although it is well to check for possible broken seals and leakage. Directions for use, including cooking, are simple and specific. As to quality designation, of course meat pies have the official federal inspection stamp on the label. Some poultry and fish, but by no means all, is packed under continuous inspection by a federal inspector. Grades for some frozen foods have been promulgated. The fact that there are four grades —U. S. Grades A, B, C, and D—indicates that not all frozen food is of equal quality. Up to the present, few items are labeled with the government grade. An occasional package labeled "Our Grade—" will be found but its meaning is far from definite. To the extent to which these designations of quality are used, they are important when frozen foods are being purchased.

Preference among the brands of frozen foods is a matter of trial to judge quality as it is related to price. The purchaser may prefer some items of one brand, some of another.

In addition, frozen foods give the family an opportunity to become acquainted with such foods as lobster and scallops when it would never be possible to have them fresh. Also fruits and many vegetables are more nearly like fresh ones than those that are either canned or dried, and this is a definite reason for the increasing use of frozen products.

The extent to which frozen foods become a part of the food pattern of a family depends upon a number of things; they save preparation time, but not as much as the same foods canned. Like canned foods, there is little or no waste, a fact to be considered in regard to price. While preferring home-prepared foods, frozen ones may be welcome as convenience items, and it may be that some will be preferred to any other form.

Commercial frozen foods may be stored in the freezing compartment of the refrigerator for about two weeks without deterioration. In a home freezer this time would be longer.

SUGGESTIONS FOR LABORATORY

The time allotment for laboratory work in connection with food preservation may be very limited in a food preparation course. Within the food courses at specific colleges, this time may range from a few hours to a whole course. In either case, instructor and students may plan for meaningful activities (using various reliable sources). The limited number of recipes included in Section IV are chosen from the point of view of availability of ingredients at any time of the year.

REFERENCES

Jacobs, Morris B., *The Chemistry and Technology of Food and Food Products,* 2nd Edition, Vol. III. Interscience Publishers, Inc., New York, 1951.

Sweetman, Marion D. and I. MacKellar, *Food Selection and Preparation.* John Wiley and Sons, Inc. New York, 1954.

Tressler, Donald K., C. E. Evers, and B. H. Evers, *Into the Freezer—and Out.* The Avi Publishing Co., New York, 1953.

Troelstrup, Arch W., *Consumer Problems and Family Finance,* 2nd Edition. McGraw-Hill Book Company, Inc., New York, 1959.

U.S.D.A., Human Nutrition Research Branch, Agricultural Research Service, Washington 25, D. C.

(1) *Home Canning of Fruits and Vegetables.* AWI-93, 1944.

(2) *Home Canning of Meat.* Home and Garden Bulletin No. 6, 1958.

(3) *Home Freezing of Fruits and Vegetables.* Home and Garden Bulletin No. 10, Revised, 1957.

(4) *Home Storage of Fruits and Vegetables.* Farmers' Bulletin No. 1939, 1943.

(5) *Preservation of Vegetables by Salting or Brining.* Farmers' Bulletin No. 1932, 1934.

(6) *How to Make Jellies, Jams, and Preserves at Home.* Home and Garden Bulletin No. 56, 1957.

(7) Bulletins concerning food preservation from State Extension Service Offices.

SECTION 3

The Family's Meals

UNIT

22

Three Meals A Day

PLANNING THE MEALS

Food continues to hold an increasingly significant place in the economic and political affairs of the world. It is the most important single factor in keeping people and countries strong. In our own United States we are blessed with an abundance of food. This is in contrast to the hunger experienced daily by large numbers of people in underdeveloped countries.

In spite of the ample amounts and wide variety of foods available to the average American family, numerous homemakers do not appreciate their privileged position when it comes to planning their family meals. Lack of interest, like lack of money and information, is a cause for meals of low nutritional standards served in some families.

It will usually be found that the homemakers who consider family meals a challenge, and who enjoy the responsibility of three meals a day for their families are those who do it well. These are the women with alert minds who keep abreast of basic nutritional information and who accept and make use of new facts brought out through scientific research. These same women are also ready and eager to incorporate improvements based on new trends in kitchen equipment and arrangement, and aspects of food management.

In most families, great stress is placed on the proper feeding of infants and young children. However, there is not always a carry-over of this practice to meals for adolescent children and adults. As our knowledge of foods and the body's need for them has increased, more people are realizing that good nutrition is indispensable to good health for *all* age groups.

Fortunately, in the United States there is a wealth of nutritional information available to homemakers. Much of this is in a popular, simplified form rather than in the laboratory terms of the dietary expert, and technical training in nutrition is not essential in order to make use of the material.

For the homemaker who does not have an opportunity to receive formal training in nutrition, an elementary knowledge of the subject can be obtained in a number of ways. Widespread information can be secured through government agencies, public schools, universities and colleges, public health agencies, business concerns, and numerous books and magazines. Adult courses in family life education are being extensively attended in all sections of the country. Many of these courses are concerned with nutrition as it relates to family meals as well as other aspects of our food problem.

An increasing number of radio and television programs are being designed to give women assistance in planning, buying, and preparing the family's food. While much of the information on these programs is reliable, the homemaker must be on the alert for the propaganda of food faddists (see pp. 31–32), and unethical advertisers. A great deal of misleading information is publicized through these and other sources, and the person doing the planning and buying must be able to sort the good from the bad. As an example of misleading advertising, certain dessert products are frequently advertised as having "as much energy as fresh milk" and macaroni made with high protein flour is compared with lean beef. Lacking a knowledge of food values some women may be led to believe that the dessert products are substitutes for milk and that macaroni contains the same complete proteins as lean beef.

A prominent doctor in the field of public health commented that because eating was such a commonplace experience occurring with a certain amount of regularity several times a day, many people developed bad food habits unconsciously. Since good nutrition is so closely allied to good health, no homemaker can afford to consider her family's meals merely as food consumed at regular intervals.

Americans are traveling more and more all the time, and travels sometimes have definite bearing on food habits. Many servicemen stationed in different parts of the United States and foreign countries have brought home demands for different kinds of food, raising nutritional standards in many homes and introducing greater variety in family meals. For example, the sale of sea food was reported stimulated in the Middle West upon the return of servicemen who were stationed in coastal locations. The wise homemaker capitalizes on all such factors in planning family meals. In addition to applying available information about nutrition to the food needs of her family, the homemaker should remember that the food she chooses and prepares must also provide real eating pleasure. Nutritive quality means little without palatability; both are prime requirements to a happy, well-fed family.

Meals that are nutritionally adequate can be planned more easily if the simple food plan on page 21 is used as a yardstick. For the inexperienced buyer with a limited knowledge of food values, checking against these food groups should be done often enough to assure her that she is buying a maximum amount of healthful food for the money expended.

Even when food is planned and prepared with intelligent care, there are times when sickness makes it necessary to adjust family meals.

In some illnesses special diets are essential and should be planned under the guidance of a physician or a nutritionist. In such instances it is extremely important to follow the prescribed diets implicitly. Food allergies also require special dietary treatment and prescribed diets. Proteins are considered to be the main factor in foods causing allergies. Some of the common offenders are wheat, beef, eggs, fish, milk, strawberries, tomatoes, spinach, corn, citrus fruit, and chocolate.

Weight-reduction diets for one or more in a family where others do not have the problem of overweight are a real challenge to the homemaker. Ridicule or intolerance of this problem on the part of any member of the family, particularly the one who plans and prepares the meals, makes it difficult if not impossible to carry on a successful program of reducing. Since weight reduction is usually achieved by increased consumption of protective foods and decreased intake of energy foods, the entire family may benefit from such a program, thereby making the weight loss of one or more members a *family* project. Caloric requirements could be met by size and number of servings.

Low-sodium diets are frequently prescribed by doctors for certain organic disturbances. Carrying out such a prescription is sometimes tedious in a family situation, but with a little experience one can soon learn to relate the "special" foods and preparation techniques to the rest of the cooking. Self imposed low-sodium diets are likely to be dangerous and should not be followed.

The influence of income. Our national economy has direct bearing on the standards of living of every American family. While high taxes coupled with inflation are factors affecting all areas of our living, it is the money spent for food that we hear mentioned most frequently when the cost of living is being discussed. It is unfortunate that many women who spend food money are not fully aware of their great responsibility, nor do these women always relate this expenditure to the health of their families. The fact that in the United States there are millions of families who are not well fed is accepted by some people as applicable only to families of low income or those of relief status. Many individuals take the attitude that "It can't happen here," and are inclined to exclude themselves or their families from the category of the underfed, yet in reality the families having poor diets are living in every community in the United States. They include white as well as Negro families, farm as well as city families, and rich as well as poor families.

In Unit 2 the factors influencing the choice of food are discussed. While no two families, free to choose, would probably make the same selection of food, available money, especially in the lower-income groups, is possibly the most important factor involved in the selection of a family food supply. In many families money is the controlling factor; however, the amount of money spent for food and the nutritional adequacy of the diet are not always related. "It is possible to spend a lot of money without buying all of the foods needed for good nutrition. High-priced foods may be no more nutritious than the cheap. Appetite is not a safe guide. Malnutrition may exist in the midst of plenty if food is wasted or if well-balanced meals are refused by members of the family because of poor cooking, bad eating habits, or faddist ideas." [1]

According to the U. S. Department of Agriculture,[2] surveys indicate that (except among families whose incomes are very low) the nutritional quality of food supplies may be associated more closely with food habits and patterns of food purchases than with other social and economic factors.

Periodically, the U. S. Department of Agriculture estimates the cost of a week's supply of food for individuals of different ages, sex, and types of activity. These estimates are based on three food plans—a low-cost, a moderate-cost, and a liberal plan. All three plans meet the nutritional recommendation of the National Research Council (see Appendix A). In general, the low-cost plan contains more of the less expensive foods such as grain products and potatoes than do the other plans.

The two market orders below are based on prices in a supermarket in October, 1959. Order A reflects foods in plentiful supply. The orders have basically the same food value and Order B has less weight on some items. Order A is representative of what a careful shopper might purchase, while Order B makes up the market basket of a hit-and-miss shopper.

Order A		*Order B*	
3 lbs. pork shoulder chops	$1.47	3 lbs. loin pork chops	$ 2.25
4½ lbs. pot roast (boneless chuck)	3.11	4½ pot roast (bottom round)	4.30
2 lbs. codfish steak	.78	2 lbs. halibut steak	1.18
2 doz. small Grade A eggs	.59	2 doz. large Grade A eggs	1.27
1 16-oz. pkg. cottage cheese	.29	1 8-oz. pkg. Cr. cheese	.35
1 16-oz. can pink salmon	.59	1 16-oz. can red salmon	.89
10 lbs. Maine Grade A potatoes	.37	10 lbs. Russet baking potatoes	.69
4 lbs. sweet potatoes	.29	4 lbs. southern yams	.58
1 1-lb. 1-oz. can whole kernel corn	.18	1 10 oz. pkg. frozen whole kernel corn	.18
3 lbs. yellow onions	.19	3 lbs. red Spanish onions	.69
1 lb. escarole	.11	1 head iceberg lettuce	.29
8 oz. salted peanuts	.25	8 oz. salted cashew nuts	.49
TOTAL	$8.22	TOTAL	$13.16

[1] Hazel K. Stiebeling, *Are We Well Fed?* Misc. Pub. 430, U.S.D.A. (1941), p. 14.
[2] U. S. Department of Agriculture, *Food, Yearbook of Agriculture,* 1959, Washington, D. C.

In many communities local newspapers run a weekly column based on U.S.D.A. marketing information. Such columns not only have marketing tips but often include recipes for using foods in plentiful supply.

The three dinner menus below have comparable food value but vary considerably in cost. Menu I cannot be termed "low cost," but it includes foods that, regardless of price levels, are nutritionally economical. Menu III is made up almost entirely of luxury items, while Menu II is representative of a type that might be included on a moderately liberal food allowance.

Menu I

Canned Citrus Juice
Creole Beef Liver
Yellow Turnips Escalloped Potatoes
Corn Muffins Margarine
Chocolate Pudding Coffee

Menu II

Fresh Citrus Fruit
Beef Stroganoff
Spinach with Lemon New Potatoes
Bran Muffins Margarine
Chocolate Ice Cream Coffee

Menu III

Honeydew Melon
Broiled Loin Lamb Chops
Frozen Asparagus with Hollandaise Wild Rice
Blueberry Muffins Butter
Chocolate Mousse Coffee

MANAGING THE FAMILY'S MEALS

What is meal management? "Meal Management" is an awesome term to many homemakers, yet good management of family meals might be defined as the skillful combination of a number of comparatively simple operations. Some will challenge such a statement and inquire, "What is simple about the continuous job of planning meals, or buying groceries and putting them away, and cooking and serving three meals a day every day, to say nothing of the clean-up required?" Yet, singly, each of these operations is fairly free of complexities. Some people interpret a "good manager" as one who conducts household affairs (especially those concerning foods) in an economical manner. This is a short-sighted appraisal. The pressures of today's living mean that the human resources involved in family meals are of equal or greater importance than the money or other material resources. It is when these factors are reversed in importance that dissension is likely to occur.

When several members of the same family are sharing the responsibilities connected with family meals, management becomes more intricate since it involves the direction and control of activities of one or more people. In business or industry this would be a simple operation, but in a family it sometimes causes a crisis. Many difficulties can be avoided if there is a well regulated plan for accomplishing the various jobs. Such a plan would be made cooperatively by all of the members involved, and it would give consideration to the time, interests, and energies of each. The "workable" plan is not a "law." It is a flexible guide. Over-planning in connection with family meals does not contribute to harmonious family relationships. It can be even more detrimental than no plan.

The ideal of a family planning together in a spirit of give and take with everyone's interests and tastes being taken into account is not enjoyed by all families. Sometimes domination by one member (usually the mother or father) supplants *family* planning. Under such circumstances it is impossible to reap the rewards that are characteristic of a group endeavor. Money is not always the cause for domination. It is sometimes related to taste preferences.

There is no one right way to manage family meals. What is right for one family may be all wrong for another. Young homemakers are often handicapped in effecting successful plans for managing meals because they attempt to employ habits and practices of their mothers. It is unrealistic to suppose that in today's rapidly changing world the tools, techniques, and general practices involved in family meals do not change from generation to generation.

Planning ahead. Even the most insignificant job needs to be planned. Certainly feeding a family is not insignificant, yet many families never plan meals. They are all spur-of-the-moment affairs. "Planning" does not mean merely the writing down of menus for a week, or several days, or a single day. It simply means that the person in charge is conscious of the necessity and desirability of having the foods consumed meet the nutritional needs of the body and does something about it in terms of serving enjoyable meals to the family. It is questionable whether this can be achieved without planning. In Unit 1 (pp. 3 to 22) basic material on nutrition is presented. The food groups on p. 21 provide a simple guide for implementing this scientific information into family meals.

Whether meals are formally planned "on paper" or informally planned at a family caucus, the time unit will vary. A week at a time may not be workable; several days may be more practical. A meal-at-a-time may even be successful in instances where facilities permit the storage of a variety of supplies.

Modern equipment and techniques make it relatively simple not only to plan ahead but also to cook ahead for both anticipated needs and unexpected situations. This greatly simplifies family meals. For those who have food freezers of ample size "cooking today for tomorrow" can be projected to provide for meals several months in advance. Even when only limited freezer space is available as part of the refrigerator, it is possible to take advantage of this technique and simplify meals to some extent.

The high degree of individuality of families means that there will be wide variation in both the way meals are planned and the time units for planning. For the family that does plan ahead, there are many advantages. Chief among these is the sheer joy that comes when a family sits down together to an interesting, nutritious, and palatable meal which has been planned, prepared, and attractively served with affectionate consideration for all members. Other positive values are advantageous use of family talents, food money, equipment, and other resources.

Meal patterns. Many factors enter into the meal patterns of families. Some of these are discussed in Unit 2, pp. 26 to 33. No one family's pattern is *best* even though many families are inclined to believe that people who do not eat as they do are "queer." The type of meals should be suited to the needs of the group.

The foundation of a good diet is outlined in the food plan on p. 21. Within the framework of this plan many different patterns are possible. The table on p. 314 suggests a variety of groupings of food for breakfast, lunch, and dinner. Meals will be more nutritious and interesting if such a guide is used.

Numerous family plans for eating do not take into account the "fourth" meal or snack. Since food consumed at times other than meals supplies a considerable portion of the day's intake of some individuals, it must not be ignored in planning and evaluating food for a family. In families where in-between eating is a routine, it should be planned for as an asset rather than allowing it to become a health hazard.

Unit 1 presents a summary of information concerning food in relation to nutrition. A review of this is desirable before considering over-all meal plans for a family. Type of work, activity, age, and sex are some of the important factors in determining the body's need for food. These are discussed briefly here as they affect the homemaker's plans for family meals.

Type of work and activity. In Unit 1 instructions are given for determining estimated caloric needs for different types of activities. Perhaps you have compared your requirement with that of a student either more or less active than yourself and found a marked difference. So it is with family groups. However, qualitatively the diets will be the same—a family in which all or most of the members are engaged in physical work or active exercise will require the same basic food as a family which is doing sedentary work. Appetite based on activity will take care of the *quantitative* requirements.

The sequence of meals used is usually either breakfast, dinner, and supper, or breakfast, lunch, and dinner. Frequently people doing heavy physical work have their dinner in the middle of the day; however, this varies with occupation and habits of the family. It is often necessary for a worker to carry his lunch. In this case dinner might be served in the evening. The custom of serving dinner in the evening is common among families engaged in sedentary work. The following menus illustrate meals suitable for groups engaged in different types of work.

For Group Doing Active Work

Breakfast

Orange Juice
Hot Cereal Cream
Fried Eggs
Sausage Toast
Butter or Margarine
Coffee Milk

Dinner

Broiled Ham
Glazed Sweet Potatoes Buttered Green Beans
Muffins Butter or Margarine
Waldorf Salad
Milk Chocolate Cake Tea

Supper

Spaghetti with Meat Sauce
Tossed Salad
Rye Bread Butter
Butterscotch Pudding

For Group Doing Sedentary Work

Breakfast

Half Grapefruit
3-Minute Egg Whole-wheat Toast
Butter or Margarine
Milk Coffee

Lunch

Grilled Cheese Sandwich
Fresh Fruit Salad Mayonnaise
Milk Lemon Tart

Dinner

Broiled Chicken
Baked Potato Buttered Asparagus
Corn Sticks Butter or Margarine
Fresh Fruit Compote
Demitasse

TABLE 32. SUGGESTED TYPES OF MEALS

	Light	*Medium*	*Heavy*
Breakfast	Fruit Cereal and Milk, or Egg Bread and Butter Beverage	Fruit Cereal Protein—Main Dish Bread and Butter Beverage	Fruit Cereal Protein—Main Dish Potatoes Bread and Butter Beverage
Lunch	Cheese or Egg Dish Bread and Butter Beverage Fresh Fruit OR Clear Soup Protein Salad Bread and Butter Beverage OR Protein Sandwich Vegetable Salad Beverage Light Dessert	Vegetable Plate with Poached Egg Bread and Butter Beverage Light Dessert OR Cream Soup Protein Sandwich Fruit or Vegetable Salad Beverage OR Protein Salad Bread and Butter Beverage Substantial Dessert	Meat Stew Green Salad Bread and Butter Beverage Substantial Dessert OR Broiled Meat or Fish Potatoes Vegetable Salad Bread and Butter Beverage Light Dessert
Dinner	Protein—Main Dish Potatoes Green Vegetable Light Dessert Beverage OR Light Soup Protein—Main Dish Green Salad Bread and Butter Fruit Dessert	Light Appetizer Protein—Main Dish Potatoes Green Vegetable Substantial Dessert Beverage OR Protein—Main Dish 2 Vegetables Salad Bread and Butter Light Dessert Beverage	Cream Soup Protein—Main Dish Potatoes 2 Vegetables Bread and Butter Beverage Light Dessert OR Light Appetizer Protein—Main Dish 2 Vegetables Salad Bread and Butter Beverage Substantial Dessert

On the surface, the above meals may appear to be unimaginative. However, diversified and creative interpretation of bread and butter, protein main dish, vegetable, appetizer, light or substantial dessert, and beverage, make it possible to use this guide for planning interesting and nutritious meals. Potatoes alone can add distinction to a meal if their preparation is varied. They may appear in many types of soups or salads, as a principal ingredient for any number of traditional main dishes, in breads, and as a vegetable.

Bread offers even more versatility. The breakfast bread has wide possibilities—from plain toast there are many other toast potentials. Other bread suggestions include pancakes, popovers, muffins, biscuits, and coffee cakes.

Composition of group. When people in a family group are about of an age, the family meals are greatly simplified. The presence of infants and very young children still does not complicate the meal situation to any extent. However, when the group is made up of three generations with the ages of the children ranging from very young to adolescent, real skill is required in managing the meals. A good manager who is sympathetic toward the needs and idiosyncrasies of the different ages will be able to use the same food resources for all. Geriatric nutrition has been a boon to families and communities. Older people are more easily absorbed into a family group because of the increased knowledge about all aspects of their health and happiness. We know that while their food habits do not always fall in line with their needs, "they are never too old to learn" even when it comes to changing food habits. The mechanics of handling the food is often the determining factor in whether or not the "senior citizen" in the family can eat the same food that is served to others. Chopping salads, cutting sandwiches in small fingershaped strips and serving chopped beef patties are examples. Separate or extra dishes for anyone in a family group are likely to cause hurt feelings, especially on the part of adolescents or older people. In a group of different ages it is important that the food for all appear to be the same. Extra seasonings or sauces can easily be added at the table, as can dessert toppings and other accessory foods.

The modern homemaker must often cope with the diet craze of some member of the family group. This is likely to be an adolescent and serious consequences can occur, especially if milk consumption is either cut off or greatly reduced. The increased need for calcium may arise during the rapid growth of adolescence, and therefore more than a quart of milk will be required. Liberal use of milk solids in meal preparation can provide for a generous amount of the needed milk. This form of milk has the psychological advantage of not being obvious.

Tolerance, understanding, and cooperation on the part of other family members (rather than ridicule) can usually help to bring the dieting member "back into the fold" with a sane approach to the dieting problem. An alert homemaker may choose such a time to put her whole family on a needed weight-reduction program.

Eating habits and food requirements vary also according to sex, which in turn affects activity. Everyone recognizes the fact that boys and men eat more food and food of a heavier type than girls and women. Some people have the mistaken idea, however, that boys and men are interested only in "meat, potatoes, and bread," and as a result their dietaries are often lacking in interest and variety, as well as in food values, because the person doing the planning believes that he is catering to their food likes. As one observes the male diners in a restaurant, they will be seen often eating large bowls of chef's salad, fruit salad plates, and other popular types of salads.

After choosing the type meals for a family group, it is advisable in general to conform to the same pattern for each day's menus. For example, if the working schedule of the family group requires a light lunch in the middle of the day, such a meal should be served consistently rather than varying it with a medium or heavy type of lunch. The heaviest meal of the day also should be served consistently at the same meal period instead of alternating its time of service. In some families this will be the night meal, while in others the heavy meal will be served in the middle of the day. Departure from routine and meal schedule would occur in most households on holidays and Sundays.

Meal customs. No discussion of meal patterns would be complete without mention of certain customs concerning the American way of eating. Breakfast, for example, is an almost standardized meal. Many people never vary any part of this meal, while others want variety only in the fruit. Some families choose to have the same fruit, but want a frequent change in the bread served or the way the eggs are prepared.

If families enjoy variety for breakfast there are any number of ways of taking favorite breakfast foods—fruits, cereals, eggs and breads—and incorporating them into interesting meals. Breakfast menus which deviate from the routine will sometimes serve to spark interest in eating and enjoying this meal, which otherwise might be skipped. In many families a pancake breakfast can generally be relied upon to pick up sluggish appetites. When accompanied by fruit and milk, pancakes provide a hearty and nutritious meal (see Fig. 49).

Regardless of the type of breakfasts served on busy weekdays, many families indulge in favorite breakfast dishes on Sundays and holidays when breakfast time is more leisurely. Some breakfast favorites which have gained wide popularity for Sunday breakfasts include waffles, combined with crisp bacon, sausage, or creamed chicken; omelets, served with tart jelly, minced ham, or Spanish sauce; sweet rolls or coffee cake; mixed grill of two or more meats, such as lamb chops, chicken livers, bacon, and lamb or veal kidneys; broiled ham or Canadian bacon; broiled fish of different types, including kippered herring or salt mackerel; and chicken prepared in various ways.

Lunch, or the meal eaten in the middle of the day, presents a number of problems for many American families. In some instances both father and children must carry a home-packed lunch. However, since there is a growing tendency to accept the school lunch as an integral part of the educational program, more and more children are receiving a nutritionally adequate lunch at school. Where children have the opportunity of getting such a lunch through the school lunchroom, it simplifies the homemaker's problem of planning for their food requirements. If lunches have to be carried by any family member, they too must be carefully planned so that they will furnish a suitable share of the daily food needs.

Courtesy American Can Company

Fig. 49. A good start for a day's work.

In many families members who are employed eat their lunch away from home. Under these conditions the homemaker, if not employed outside the home, will be confronted with the problem of lunch for herself. This is referred to as a problem because frequently women are inclined either to "skip" this meal rather than eat it alone, or to eat a snack from the refrigerator. Either of these practices makes it difficult for them to meet their daily food needs.

In most rural areas the adult members of the family have their noon meal, which is usually dinner, at home the year around, and during the summer months all members of the family, including the children, have this meal together. Regardless of where the various members of the family eat their noon meal, it is necessary for the persons doing the planning to have a knowledge of the type of meals they are choosing in order that they can plan the other two meals wisely.

The evening meal, whether it be dinner or supper, is usually a time when the entire family assembles. Unfortunately, in some homes it is the only meal which families do eat together. Since it is likely to be the most leisurely meal, it affords opportunities for introducing new food and to prepare familiar foods in new and interesting fashions. "Happy is he who sits down to the dinner provided for him, without thought of what he must leave out, with a mind free for social pleasure, secure in the skill and *knowledge* of his cook."[1]

While the evening meal usually does not present a problem for the family group, it frequently does for the business woman who prepares her own meals. She may live alone or with two or three companions. In any event, when time is short there is an inclination to prepare meals without giving much thought to their food value. It is of course just as important that meals for adult groups have the same careful planning as those for family groups if the daily food needs are to be met.

Season. Some people make the mistake of disregarding the weather in planning meals, while others act unwisely in carrying this consideration to the extreme. It is not a good nutritional practice to serve only cold food in the summer months, and certainly winter meals would be drab without some raw, crisp food. Digestion is nearly always improved when there is at least one hot dish in each meal. Some people shrink from hot bouillon in the summer, yet it stimulates gastric secretion and may be far more refreshing than a cold dish which has a high fat content.

In hot weather digestive disturbances are likely to be more prevalent than at any other time. Special attention should be given to the refrigeration of all foods at this season and particularly meat, milk, fish, and all left-over cooked foods. Occasionally large groups of people become ill from a food served at some community gathering. Many times this happens in the summer, and it is frequently traced to spoilage of a protein food, such as chicken salad or cream pie which has not been properly cooled and refrigerated.

Foods which should generally be avoided in the summer include high calorie foods, especially those rich in fats. Since energy requirements are slightly higher during winter months, these foods are more appropriate for cold weather than for hot.

The season of the year also influences, to some extent, the variety of foods on the market and their cost. In the winter months the variety of fruits and vegetables is likely to be limited, particularly in small towns. The low-income family is especially handicapped at some seasons in certain sections because prices of the protective foods may prohibit purchasing them. Fruits and vegetables should be used in quantities while at the height of their season when they are inexpensive. Seasonable foods offer a particular advantage for the low-income family with a limited food budget. Only families having a liberal food allowance can afford to purchase certain foods out of season.

On most markets eggs are cheaper during the late spring and summer, which is the height of the egg-production season. They should be used frequently during this season either alone or in combination with other foods.

---

[1] Mary Swartz Rose, *Feeding the Family* (New York: Macmillan, 1940), p. 70.

Size of group. Often, members of a family lack consideration for the person who plans and prepares the meals. As an extreme example, one student accounted for her numerous food dislikes by the fact that in her family it was not uncommon for every member to request a different meal. Everybody's likes and dislikes were catered to by the mother who, because of this catering, frequently prepared four different meals instead of one. This was possible only because the group was small. The size of a group should not make a difference in a homemaker's planning, but it does affect the time necessary for marketing and for preparation and service of meals.

Psychological and aesthetic factors in meal planning. Successful meals cannot be assured unless certain psychological and aesthetic factors are taken into consideration. If a family knows that Irish potatoes will always be mashed, that apple sauce will always accompany pork roast, and that codfish balls may be expected every Friday, the person doing the planning has failed to make the meals interesting and attractive.

Monotony in combinations of foods may be avoided by planning for variety in flavor, texture, color, method of preparation, and form or shape of food.

> The aim of the artist is to arrange a meal not only wholesome, but a joy to all the senses. So long as beauty is a part of life, and the spirit more than meat, the housewife will take pride in assembling her family around a board which delights the eye and "makes the mouth water."[1]

Flavor. Certain foods are strong in flavor; others are mild; while still others have a distinct, though not strong, flavor. When several strong or distinctly flavored foods are used in the same meal, the result is not pleasing. It is well to keep in mind general food likes and dislikes when combining flavors. For instance, broiled liver is not as universally liked as broiled steak. Because of this fact, a popular food should be served with liver. Baked bananas and broiled liver at the same meal would be objectionable, because both foods are distinctly flavored, and neither is universally liked. Baked potatoes would be a good substitute for the bananas.

A meal made up entirely of mild-flavored foods lacks zest. Almost everyone has experienced such meals and has had a desire for some flavor which would "pep up" the meal. It is in the interest of improved flavor that certain mild-tasting foods are frequently served with an accompaniment which adds zest. For example, lamb is usually served with either mint sauce or mint jelly; omelets are often accompanied by a Spanish sauce, and lettuce salad served with Roquefort cheese dressing may provide just the right flavor to prevent a meal from being monotonous.

Repeating flavors in a meal is a common mistake in menu planning. Macaroni and cheese, with a salad containing grated cheese; tomato sauce with meat loaf, and tomatoes as a salad; lamb and mint jelly, with mint ice as

[1] *Ibid.*, p. 79.

and cream cheese pink or green in order to carry a party color scheme into her tea sandwiches. Tea sandwiches are attractive and appealing because of their size, shapes, and variety of fillings and breads. It is more appetizing to obtain a green color effect by adding chopped parsley, pickle, or mint to tasty cheese, butter, or fruit fillings; or a pink effect by adding chopped cherries or cherry juice to a cream cheese filling, than it is to use artificial coloring.

For a St. Valentine's bridge luncheon one hostess used artificial coloring to the extent of serving chicken salad colored red, and cookies and a fruit ice colored in the same hue. Good taste would have been shown if the salad, of natural colors, had been garnished with a radish flower; the cookies decorated with tiny seed candies, red predominating; and the fruit ice, uncolored, served with a sprinkling of chopped red cherries over the top. In planning class or club dinners, sorority teas, or any other school or home entertainment, it is a good policy to practice restraint in the use of artificial color added to foods.

Method of preparation. Varying the method of preparation has much to do with the interest of meals. It has already been pointed out in the discussion of texture that too many creamed foods may detract from the appetizing qualities of meals. Repetition of other methods of preparation such as frying, baking, stuffing, sautéing, breading, or escalloping, may be equally monotonous.

Form or shape of food. Form of food is less important than the other aesthetic factors discussed; however, it should not be disregarded in meal planning. It is easy to overlook the shape of food when variety in flavor, texture, color, and method of preparation are being planned. A meal made up of foods in the same or similar forms is likely to be uninteresting. A luncheon consisting of chicken à la king in pastry shells, buttered new potatoes, tomato aspic molded in individual round molds, muffins with butter balls, and cream puffs filled with fresh fruit is an example of a meal which is so "round" as to suggest that it might roll away.

Poor taste is often shown in serving food in realistic forms. A chicken croquette molded in the shape of a chicken, a mock duck made from a leg of lamb; and a peach salad supposedly resembling a jack-o'-lantern are illustrations of realistic foods sometimes served. Realism in foods may be suitable for a child's party, but it should be avoided at other times.

Unexpected situations. If family meals are "affectionately" planned they will be suitable to serve the most discriminating guests, but in spite of careful planning, the homemaker who has the foresight to be prepared for an unexpected guest, a casual afternoon "at home," or an impromptu Sunday-night supper finds entertaining simple and enjoyable. In her household there is likely to be an atmosphere of informal hospitality which delights guests as well as members of the family. It is possible to prepare for such occasions by having on hand reserve supplies from which palatable dishes may easily and quickly be prepared. In homes having home freezers, food sup-

Courtesy American Can Company

Fig. 50. Easy-to-fix appetizer or dessert.

plies are generally ample and adequate to take care of any unplanned occasions. These freezers will usually be found to be stocked with cooked foods as well as those to be prepared, providing almost endless variety for family and guest meals.

Before storing cooked foods in the freezer, thought should be given to packaging them for convenient use, both as to amounts and shape of package. In one family where a grown son must eat his meals at "off" hours his mother freezes a variety of cooked foods in individual portions. These include casserole dishes, soups, and desserts. Such a plan means that no one in the family is eating warmed-over food. It also provides for adding one or two extra servings when necessary. Another homemaker freezes chicken à la king in the top of her double boiler, removes it when frozen and wraps it for storage. The frozen mold slips easily into the double boiler when she is ready to heat and serve the chicken. In addition to frozen foods, some suggestions for reserve supplies and their uses are the following:

1) *Canned fruits.* These are among the most popular processed foods; therefore they can be used with assurance of their acceptance—broiled peach or pear halves, sautéed pineapple or apple slices, fruit salads, dessert compotes and fillings for tart shells are a few of the possibilities for using canned fruits.

In Figure 50 an assortment of canned fruits are combined with a fresh mint garnish for an appetizing first course or dessert.

2) *Canned or bottled fruit juices.* The variety of these is unlimited and there are a number of interesting ways of using them. They may be used alone, or several may be mixed to serve as cocktails at the beginning of a meal, for fruit soups, or as part of the dessert with cookies or plain cake.

3) *Canned soups.* Some of these soups need no further seasoning and make a delicious first course, main course, or base for a tasty sauce for meat and vegetables. Subtle flavors can be obtained by mixing two or more canned soups, such as cream of pea and cream of tomato.

4) *Cheese.* Cheeses or cheese spreads may be used for grilled or tea sandwiches, for hors d'oeuvres, in sauces for main dishes, as accompaniments to salads, or as desserts.

5) *Canned fish.* Shrimp, crab, lobster, tuna, sardines, fish flakes, and salmon have many possibilities for salads, casserole and Creole dishes, and for sandwiches.

6) *Relishes.* A dish of pickles, olives, and mixed relishes will usually serve to "dress up" a meal.

7) *Crackers.* Fancy crackers are acceptable accompaniments for various courses in a meal, and may be used with tea as afternoon refreshments.

8) *Canned meats.* Chicken, ham, and tongue are among the most delectable canned meats. While not inexpensive, there are a variety of ways in which they may be extended in casseroles and creamed dishes by combining with vegetables, cheese, eggs, or other foods.

9) *Canned vegetables.* Baked beans and tomatoes are examples of canned vegetables that have many possibilities for quick meals. Other suggestions are whole-kernel corn, Lima beans, baby beets, and artichoke bottoms.

10) *Canned vegetable juices.* An otherwise plain dinner can be "high-lighted" with an appetizer of tomato juice or a mixture of several vegetable juices. A number of these are on the market, many of them already mixed. They are also tasty to use for sauces and soups.

11) *Prepared mixes for waffles, biscuits, popovers, pastries, and cakes.* Products from these mixes are not always equal in quality to those made entirely in the home kitchen, but they serve the purpose of a quick dessert or hot bread which would not otherwise be possible.

12) *Evaporated, condensed, and dried milk.* Many quick beverages, soups, sauces, and desserts can be made with these as a base.

The extent of entertaining and the available storage space should govern the amounts of the various items kept on hand. As foods are used, they should be replaced, so that the supply is complete at all times. If the homemaker forms the habit of drawing daily on her reserve food supply, the reserve ceases to be a solution to the problem of caring for extra guests and arranging impromptu entertaining.

The creative cook will discover that most popular foods which she counts on as a reserve have multiple uses. In addition to the ever-popular tuna fish salad, sandwiches, and casserole dishes, this versatile item may be made into delectable soufflés, chowders, tuna fish balls, etc. Once the idea for using a food in a new and different way becomes a challenge, many occasions for its use will present themselves, resulting in more imaginative meals.

The student's food. For the trained person, menu planning is more or less a routine matter, and meals are planned successfully with what would seem to an observer to be a minimum amount of effort. It is because of her experience, her knowledge of food values, and her skill in preparation that she has acquired this ability. For the untrained person, a different problem is presented. It is easy for college students to accept as a matter of course the three meals a day served, without realizing the amount of planning essential to make well-balanced meals interesting and attractive.

Some students plan all or part of their meals. Those who are members of student co-operatives or other groups are familiar with some of the difficulties involved, such as buying in suitable quantities, providing suitable storage space, and avoiding the tendency to rely on ready-to-eat foods regardless of the effect on the dietary. Students with a well-rounded knowledge of foods and nutrition will be able to provide adequate meals for their group regardless of what the market offers on a given day. Students who live in apartments and plan and prepare one or more meals daily are confronted with very different problems from those students who plan meals for a sorority, fraternity, or student co-operative house. The chief problems these students encounter are petty complaints and food idiosyncrasies. One may observe in any college dormitory, boarding house, or sorority house students who do not eat the food served them, but substitute fountain drinks, sweets, or sandwiches. One group of dormitory students complained that fried foods were not served frequently enough. They did not appreciate the facts that fried foods should be eaten in moderation and that the dietician had their welfare in mind in not serving such foods too often. These same students, if frequently served fried foods, might have complained that their complexions were not clear because of the meals served them.

Students are often responsible for planning social refreshments for campus organizations. It requires real courage to serve food to any group which deviates from the "standard" pattern. This pattern often leaves much to be desired from the standpoint of nutrition, yet ideas are legion for incorporating familiar, nutritious foods into distinctive party refreshments. Fear of being a nonconformist should not deter one from planning new refreshments.

Economic conditions and individual choice frequently make it necessary for students to do light housekeeping. In an effort to stretch the dollar, many sacrifices in the matter of proper food are often made. For the married veteran-student, particularly the one with children, who is subsisting principally on a very limited allowance, the problem may be one of even more serious proportions. However, food prejudices and ignorance are at least as responsible for poorly balanced diets as is the necessity to economize. A number of prejudices may be traced to lack of training in proper food habits during early childhood, which are carried over as fixed habits into adolescent and adult life. Lack of appreciation of good food, rather than actual service of poor food, is frequently the cause of complaints about meals served at college dormitories and lunchrooms. Meal planning at home and menu choosing in a cafeteria or restaurant are in part the same problem. Hence, everyone faces the need, at some time or other, of a knowledge of how to combine foods into suitable meals.

Today most students in the United States have the opportunity of close association with students from many parts of the world who are enrolled in our colleges and universities. This affords an excellent means of broadening horizons concerning national and cultural food patterns. With the guidance of these visiting students, interesting social affairs can be planned around customs and foods of the different national groups represented on the campus. This is one of the best means of understanding the visiting students and making them feel at home. By the same token many American students are privileged to be enrolled in universities in other countries. Some take advantage of informing themselves about the customs and religious regulations which govern the food patterns of the people of the country. Such an experience is a great aid in helping to disperse smugness about the American way being the "best."

The Japanese dinner service as shown in Fig. 51 is a familiar and picturesque sight to all Americans who have lived in Japan and to those who enjoy dining in Japanese restaurants in this country.

BUYING THE FOOD

Money spent on food is the largest single expenditure-category for most families. Regardless of economic status everyone seems to be aware of the grocery bill and most people believe theirs is too high. What passes for the food bill today is likely to contain all sorts of non-food items. Many supermarkets are becoming one-stop shopping centers where clothing, books, dishes, drugs, shrubbery, and many other types of merchandise can be purchased.

Buying food is a skill that is developed gradually by experience. Today's markets make buying the groceries attractive to individuals as well as to entire families. However, it is not a simple job. Modern shoppers have a difficult time in keeping up with shopping facts. In addition to the ever increasing number of new items appearing on the grocers' shelves, the attractive and skillfully designed packages have brought with them a lack of standardization which tends to confuse the buying public. Olives furnish a good example of the lack of standardization in packaging. In a large market where the display is extensive it takes considerable time to make a rational, intelligent decision as to which jar of olives to buy. Fortunately all foods are not packaged in such wide variety. Butter is in a representative stand-by package. True, its packaging has been modernized for both convenience and eye appeal but it remains as a familiar package to most shoppers.

While most consumers are attracted to and pleased by the packages found in our markets today, they do not realize that the packaging innovation came about as a replacement for the "man behind the counter." In other words, in a self-service market every item must sell itself. There is no one to discuss with the consumer the merits of the different items; hence the eye-catching packages.

The packaging industry has not only greatly influenced the buying habits of the American homemaker but in many cases it also controls what the consumer buys. Not only are an increasing number of foods presented in attractive and easy-to-use packages, but in many instances the packaging increases the keeping qualities of the food.

Prepackaged meats are sold in all super-markets, the customer simply selecting from refrigerated counters various cuts and types of meat and poultry wrapped in pliofilm and labeled as to type of animal, cut, weight, cost per pound, and total cost. For the consumer who is lacking information about meat cuts this gives a chance for on-the-spot comparison as to cost, appearance, and suitability for use.

Cheese is sold in most grocery stores prepackaged. A customer who wants small quantities of a variety of cheeses may select the desired quantity of each already wrapped and marked, just as in the case of meat. The manager of one large chain store noticed that the customers who selected the smaller packages of cheese usually purchased several different kinds of cheese, whereupon a new package containing several varieties was presented and proved to be extremely popular.

New plastic wrappings keep fresh foods from drying out by lessening the escape of moisture and gases. Such materials are a boon to the shipment of certain exotic tropical fruits as well as other highly perishable foods. The frozen-food industry has also made a significant change in the buying habits of many individuals. In addition to a great variety of frozen foods, which are ready to be cooked, most food stores offer prepared frozen foods which need only to be heated or thawed and served. These prepared foods include hors d'oeuvres, fish and fruit cocktails, soups, entrées of all types, vegetables, breads, pastries, cakes, and cookies.

The types of retail markets available to a homemaker have much to do with the meals she plans and serves her family. In cities there is a wide range of markets to choose from, such as the farmers' market in which many types of foods are sold, special fish and meat markets, super-markets, stores in which only imported foods are sold, small and large grocery stores independently owned, delicatessen shops and frozen-food stores. In some metropolitan areas push-cart and curb markets are numerous. Both chain and independent stores have market locations widely scattered in certain residential areas, making it quite convenient for many families to shop at these neighborhood stores.

Markets may be cash-and-carry or charge-and-delivery. The latter will usually be more expensive on most items, since the consumer must pay for the charge-and-delivery service, even though she may pay cash and carry her groceries. Some grocers deliver orders valued at five or more dollars.

In some cities, as well as smaller towns, perishable foods are sold in certain areas by peddlers who sell their wares from house to house. Sometimes farmers peddle their produce, but many of these vendors are hucksters who are small produce dealers, buying their products from wholesale houses. Such a "market" is of great convenience when it is difficult for the homemaker to go out to shop.

Most city markets afford an endless variety of fresh, canned, frozen, and already-prepared food, thereby simplifying the purchase of food when food money is available in moderate or liberal amounts. Sometimes, however, because of the large variety, such a market is confusing to the buyer.

In all small towns one or more of the above types of market will be found. In some instances there may be almost as wide a variation in markets and foods as in the cities, while in other towns buying is limited to one or more grocery stores and meat markets, and perishable foods are available only on certain days.

The rural or suburban homemaker is likely to have her own seasonal supply of fresh fruits and vegetables, and may, from this supply, freeze or can sufficient quantities for use when fresh foods are not available. Many urban families have continued their wartime practice of raising all or part of their vegetables in small garden plots. When fresh foods cannot be obtained, either because of limited marketing facilities or lack of funds, the homemaker must exercise great care in planning for her family in order that the members may receive adequate vitamins and minerals.

Regardless of the type of market used, there are certain requisities in which all homemakers are interested. The question of greatest concern is usually, "Are the prices reasonable?" A price which is reasonable to one family will not be reasonable to another. What the consumer should always keep in mind is that a reasonable or fair price which will permit her to purchase an adequate dietary for her family must also be fair to producer, processor, and distributor. This means that the retail price pays the producer for the cost of production and allows a reasonable profit for him, as well as for the processor and distributor.

Trading stamps have been on the food marketing scene for about five years. In many instances they are a big factor in determining which market a family patronizes. Opinions differ as to who benefits most by the stamps—the store or the consumer. For many shoppers the pricing policy as related to the *quality* available in a store is a greater factor in economical food buying than the question of stamps.

It is a good plan to become acquainted with several stores in the community before deciding to patronize any given one. When prices are being compared, this must be done on the same day, and for the same brand, weight, and grade. The habit of reading labels should be cultivated, and a record should be kept of favorite brands and the stores handling them. This eliminates guesswork in food selection.

In buying at several different stores the consumer must take into account the time lost in buying and also the cost which may be involved in operating her automobile. There are some foods, such as milk, butter, and eggs, for which it may be practical to have a standing order with a dairyman or poultryman.

The accessibility of the market is of great importance to the food buyer. Since it is desirable from the nutritional standpoint to consume some perishable foods in as fresh a state as possible, it is necessary to market more frequently for certain items than others. Many consumers buy all types of food from one market, while others prefer to use specialty shops in the same neighborhood.

Along with the accessibility of the market location, the consumer usually thinks of the convenience of the arrangement of the goods. This is a big factor in saving time and energy if the market list is made out with the thought in mind of how the foods are arranged at the market. It is a good plan to divide the market list into the following groups: milk, cream, cheese, and eggs; meat, fish, and poultry; frozen foods; fresh fruits and vegetables; canned fruits, vegetables, and meats; staples, such as flour, mixes, and cereals; and household cleaning supplies.

Many consumers fail to take into account the sanitary standards of the markets where they buy. Too much stress cannot be placed on the importance of a market that measures up to high sanitary standards. This means that not only the physical surroundings are kept in a clean, orderly, and sanitary condition but that the employees maintain high standards of personal cleanliness in both their dress and their manner of handling food. In some cities, the sanitary regulations, determined by health officials, require persons working in food markets to comply with the same health standards as those established for food handlers in public eating establishments. In more and more cities health departments are putting on periodic cleanup campaigns of all grocery stores and specialty food shops. In many instances violations of the local health codes have been found, subjecting the owners in some cases to severe penalties, such as heavy fines or suspension of licenses.

A sanitary market is free from flies, rats and mice, and other types of vermin. Cats carry germs and should never be allowed to come in contact with any food which is not in a metal container or tightly sealed package. It is the buyer's responsibility to demand a hygienic market. If she accepts an unclean one by continuing to patronize it, she is giving the low standards her approval and she may never have a chance to purchase her food in a sanitary market.

Homemakers are always interested in markets which give them a variety in the choice of foods. Because most large markets and many small ones have such widely diversified selections, the consumer is sometimes at a loss as to what choices to make. Frozen, canned, and dehydrated foods are available in almost endless forms and varieties, and fresh fruits and vegetables are for sale both in and out of season, making many of them available the year round. Apples furnish an interesting illustration of the many different forms in which a single food item may be purchased. They are not only available in fresh, canned, dehydrated, and frozen forms, but can be purchased sliced for pies, canned as juice, sauce, and baked apples. Apple jelly and apple butter are obtainable in all stores and confections made from apple juice are widely sold. Also dehydrated apples are packaged with spices and sugar and a ready-to-mix pastry for a pie.

Because of the wide choice in selection of foods, a homemaker is almost forced to go to market with a list; otherwise, she is likely to be so bewildered that she will not make the wisest selections. Flexibility of the grocery list is necessary. In making the market order, if suggestions are noted as to substitutions for perishables, time will be saved. A young, inexperienced food buyer was heard to remark that she never made a grocery list before going to market because she never knew what she wanted until she saw what was displayed. She went on to say that *her* appetite was the sole basis on which she selected food. Apparently she did not subscribe to the theory that marketing begins at home. Perishables may have to be checked once or twice a week while staples need less frequent checking.

Most food shoppers do not realize that their buying habits are being scrutinized constantly by food store managers. This is particularly true in large chain stores, and is designed to benefit both the customer and the store. There are "tricks in all trades," and the food shopper should be aware that even in the most reputable stores certain promotional "tricks" are carried out purely in the interest of moving unpopular stocks. For example, surveys show that in self-service stores, women shop to the right, stepping over to the left to get items on their list. It is only natural then for grocers to put slow-moving goods on the right-hand shelves, where they are readily accessible. A generally recognized trait in the buying habits of women is that they want items that are scarce, regardless of their value to them. Many stores take advantage of this trait to turn over unpopular goods. One store manager quickly disposed of a large quantity of flat sheets of waxed paper (which he had been unable to sell because, by and large, the rolls are preferred) by display of the paper with a large sign stating, "Limit—2 packages to a customer."

Items that are likely to go unnoticed may be placed in line of vision, with a staple article such as coffee, and lower shelves are frequently used for display of items attractive to children. The latter practice is deplored by many parents.

Some families analyze expenses periodically and make alterations in their buying practices. Others, while talking about how high the food bill is, never make any real attempt to reduce it. The age groups of the family members are among the big factors in the total cost of food. Those in the sixteen to nineteen age group have the highest individual costs. For children under thirteen there is little cost difference between boys and girls. After thirteen the food cost for boys is higher.

One factor which makes the food bill high is that food is available in so many different forms that it is frustrating to the buyer. Chicken furnishes a good example. If it is purchased in a ready-to-eat dinner (such as a T.V. dinner) it will cost approximately $1.00 a pound as against $0.39 a pound ready for the pan. This means that the ready-to-eat chicken in this case costs two and one-half times more than that ready-to-cook.

If consumers discipline themselves to think in terms of cost per serving, it will be a great help in cutting down the food bill.

The cost of dark green and deep-yellow vegetables (see food plan on p. 21) can vary greatly. Kale or spinach may be considerably cheaper than broccoli, and yellow turnips cost several cents per serving less than carrots. Cost per pound is not the sole factor to consider in determining whether food is expensive or not. It must be judged in light of the amount of waste and of the nutrients it furnishes. Cheap foods may actually be expensive because they add so little to the nutritional value of the diet.

On the other hand, some of the inexpensive foods supply liberal amounts of nutritive value. For example, the cost of a day's supply of vitamin A from carrots or sweet potatoes for an average adult, is about one sixth the cost of vitamin A from cantaloupe. Certain vegetables, such as those that are light green or pale yellow are expensive sources of vitamin A. Even though the colors green and yellow are associated with vitamin A, some vegetables would have to be consumed in large quantities in order to obtain a day's supply of this important vitamin. It would take three or four cups of green peas to supply the equivalent in vitamin A of one-fourth cup of carrots. Economical sources of vitamin C are tomatoes, citrus fruits, and cabbage.

Unfortunately a great deal of money is wasted in buying quack diets and false pills. The U.S.D.A.[1] puts the figure at $500 million a year.

Helen S. Mitchell writes that besides being a waste of money a false diet cure may give a person a false sense of security, and he may not see a doctor in time to prevent serious trouble.[2]

What about food additives? There is considerable concern about chemicals in foods and yet the most common food ingredients are chemicals. Fats, carbohydrates, proteins, vitamins, and minerals have a chemical composition.

[1] U.S.D.A. *Food: Yearbook of Food: 1959.* Washington, D. C.

[2] *Ibid.*

Modern food technology is responsible for many new and superior food products. Chemicals and additives perform many different functions in the development of these products. Calcium propionate is a chemical added to bread to retard mold. Its use is permitted by both federal and state authorities, as is the case with most chemicals that are added to foods. In addition to those that are used as preservatives (as is the calcium propionate), others help retain color and appearance or maintain flavor. In some instances they are added to increase nutritional value (such as vitamin D being added to milk).

The Food and Drug Administration, along with state agencies, is continually checking for toxic chemicals or others which will degrade food. Most food and chemical manufacturers test the additives contemplated for use and present their tests to the Food and Drug Administration. This practice prevents the dangers of having chemicals in use until proven harmless. This sometimes takes several years. The following summary of market tips may be helpful for student use.

When buying for maximum nutritive value, keep these points in mind:

1) Be certain that foods are bought which will provide the daily requirements listed in the food guide on page 21.

2) Fresh fruits and vegetables start losing their vitamin content as soon as they are harvested. Therefore, they should be as fresh as possible when purchased.

3) Dark-green leafy vegetables have considerably more food value than do those with bleached leaves, such as iceberg lettuce.

4) Some breads have a higher percentage of milk solids than others. Converted and enriched rice are better buys in food value than plain white rice.

6) If soybean products (flour and cereal) are available, they have exceptional food value.

7) It is an advantage to buy vitamin D milk as well as irradiated evaporated milk.

8) Margarine used for either cooking or the table should be fortified.

9) Remember to buy some of the variety meats, such as liver, heart, or kidneys, at least once a week.

When trying to buy more food for less money, these suggestions may help:

1) Buy fresh fruits and vegetables in season. Regardless of the season, some vegetables are nearly always cheaper than others of the same type: e.g., cabbage is generally cheaper than cauliflower or Brussels sprouts.

2) The thrifty consumer buys canned goods by size of can, brand, and, whenever possible, specific grade in relation to use (see pp. 299–303); meats by cuts (never by dollars or cents), weight, and, whenever possible, specific grade; staples by brand and weight. It pays to watch the scales.

3) Evaporated milk or milk powder may be substituted for fresh milk, and it costs less. Fresh milk is obtainable on some city markets in 2-quart and gallon

containers. Skim milk and buttermilk may be purchased for part of the milk supply if the vitamin A which they lack is provided through increased quantities of other foods rich in this vitamin.

4) In some markets it is possible to buy day-old bread and other baked goods. These are just as good as products which have been kept in the home for a day and have many uses.

5) Dried legumes pay high dividends in nutritive value for the money expended. They need not always be served baked or boiled, since there are numerous other ways of preparing them.

6) Peanuts in various forms should be used frequently in main dishes, sandwiches, and desserts.

7) Fortified margarine can be substituted for butter with little, if any, loss in nutritive value.

8) In buying animal proteins there are a number of ways to cut expenditure. Beef, pork, or lamb liver may be substituted for calf liver at a lower cost; cuts of beef from the brisket, chuck, and neck are cheaper than those from the round and ribs; it is economical and saving of fuel to buy certain cuts of meat, such as roasts, in larger quantities than are needed for one meal; roosters are cheaper than hens, and fryers usually cost less than broilers.

9) Cottage cheese is an excellent buy for low-cost meals. Domestic cheeses are cheaper than imported ones.

10) Sorgo sirup and molasses have a high iron content and should be used frequently instead of sugar.

11) Ready-to-eat cereals cost more than those which require home cooking. Extravagant use of any prepared foods will cause food bills to soar.

12) Canned citrus juices are considerably cheaper than tomato juice.

13) Food bargains should be considered carefully before buying. Brands or quality may be inferior, weight may be short, or the premium may not be worth the price.

When buying with safety and sanitation in mind, remember that:

1) Whether buying fresh milk for drinking from a retail market or a dairy, the consumer must insist on pasteurized milk if she is to get a safe supply. Raw milk is a health hazard unless used for cooking purposes.

2) If butter and cream are purchased from farm homes, be certain that they are pasteurized.

3) Unless cooked foods such as poultry, meats, salads, and custard-type desserts such as are sold in delicatessens are kept under refrigeration they are likely to cause severe cases of food poisoning.

4) Federally inspected meat should be purchased whenever it is available. If home-slaughtered and dressed meat is purchased, it is usually safe if bought direct from the farmer, especially if the slaughtering is done under the supervision of the extension agent or the vocational agriculture teacher. In some cities meat is slaughtered at a local abattoir. Before buying meat from this source, consumers should be certain that the abattoir is managed in accordance with accepted standards.

5) If home-canned foods are bought through a farmers' market or from other sources, it is particularly important that the buyer be certain that all low-acid foods

are processed under pressure. It is a safe practice to heat all such foods by simmering for 20 minutes. This is a precaution to destroy any possible trace of botulinus bacteria. (See p. 283.)

PREPARING THE FAMILY MEALS

Getting meals on the table in modern homes involves much less work than when the homemaker was on the producing end of all or most of the foods she served. Depending on the extent to which she uses ready-prepared foods or those which have been partially processed, and the number of labor saving devices at her disposal, preparation time for meals may be negligible. In spite of the numerous improvements that have come about through technological developments, and the need or desire for many women to work outside of the home, there are still large numbers of homemakers who derive real personal satisfaction from the skillful production of foods for their families. Even though some of this group are employed full time they prefer home cooked foods to those which have come from a commercial assembly line. After reading certain cook books and food advertisements and listening to and watching some radio and television programs, it would appear that many people think all Americans are in a great hurry and want to get their cooking done in a minimum amount of time. These people are generally advocates of the "heating and eating" technique. One television performer who belonged to this group described the can opener as a women's "magic wand."

On the other hand, there are those who believe that there is considerable revival of interest in cooking among both men and women, and they cite as evidence the increasing number of cookbooks published, the enthusiasm for new types of kitchen utensils, and the trend to combine kitchen and living areas.

Even a minimum amount of food preparation requires thoughtful attention if the over-all objective of serving a family nutritionally adequate meals is to be achieved. When the majority of foods are cooked at home, the preparation techniques become even more important.

Conserving maximum nutritive value. Food values, especially vitamins and minerals, are easily destroyed or lost through improper methods of preparation; yet many homemakers still cling to cooking methods which have been handed down through several generations, many of which do not comply with our present knowledge of nutrition. One homemaker solved the problem of getting her family to accept properly cooked vegetables by gradually decreasing the cooking time. She started with cabbage, and instead of cooking it the usual one hour, she lessened the time by 10-minute periods until she was only cooking it 8 minutes. This was not done without comments from her family. When the father complained that he liked his vegetables cooked the "old way," this very clever mother went back to the "old way" but not for long because in a few days the father was complaining again. This time he requested that his wife go back to the new method, because he not only thought they were more palatable but he felt much better when he didn't eat overcooked vegetables!

Proper methods of preparing the different types of food are given in detail in Section 2 but a few points are listed here to re-emphasize their importance.

1) From the point of view of retention of ascorbic acid, tomato and citrus juices should not be left standing in metal containers for even a short time. Juice in excess of that used as the cans are opened should be poured into a clean glass jar and stored in a refrigerator, covered.

2) It is a good plan to buy these juices in amounts that can be used in a short time.

3) Fresh citrus juices may be prepared and stored in covered glass jars in a refrigerator for several hours with negligible loss of ascorbic acid.

4) Fresh fruit juices contain more vitamins and minerals if they are served without straining than if they are strained.

5) Cook all foods in the shortest possible cooking time. This is especially important for fruits and vegetables.

6) Whenever feasible, cook fruits and vegetables whole with their outside covering. When paring them, do so thinly.

7) Cook beet and carrot tops for greens. They are as tasty as any other greens.

8) Use as little water as possible in cooking vegetables and fruits. (See Section 2 for exceptions to this rule.) Use water in which vegetables have been cooked or canned for sauces, gravies, and soups. Use juices from cooking fruit in beverages, desserts, and fruit sauces.

9) Cook dried fruits and legumes in the water in which they have been soaked.

10) Frozen fruits, vegetables, and small cuts of meat should not be thawed before cooking. If fruits are to be used raw, they should be served immediately after thawing.

11) Certain cooking methods, such as long stewing or simmering and frying, should not be used excessively, since vitamins are lost.

12) Soda should never be used in cooking vegetables or to decrease acidity in fruits, since this practice destroys vitamins.

13) Certain manipulatory processes, such as stirring air into food while cooking and putting hot food through a sieve, will cause some loss of vitamin content.

14) Maximum food value is retained through cooking in pressure pans.

Increasing nutritive value. In addition to conserving food values through proper preparation of food, there are a number of ways by which the homemaker can increase the nutritive value of the food she prepares. Some suggestions for doing this are to:

1) Use milk in some form in cooking as much as possible. Fresh, evaporated, and dried milk all have many uses. Cooking cereals in milk not only increases the

food value but increases their palatability and is an excellent way of getting milk into the diet of persons who object to drinking it. Certain vegetables which require only a short cooking time can be cooked in milk or served with a milk sauce. Add dried milk powder to certain dishes, such as ground meat dishes, escalloped dishes, and puddings; and use milk instead of water in making yeast bread and rolls.

2) Add freshly extracted citrus fruit juice to fruit cocktails or fruit cups which are made of canned or dried fruits.

3) Use eggs in yeast bread and roll mixtures, even though the recipe does not call for them.

4) In recipes calling for both canned tomatoes and water, omit the water and substitute tomatoes.

Work simplification. A great deal is heard about work simplification in various fields. Business and industry have traditionally studied jobs being done and then applied principles of work that enabled employees to do better work in less time with less energy.

Homemaking, because of the multiplicity of jobs in such diversified areas, is a natural occupation in which to apply principles of work simplification. The reluctance of some women to analyze the jobs they are doing and the *way* they are doing them makes it impossible for them to learn a *better* way. However, those who sit down and figure out what needs to be done and then develop the *easiest* and most *pleasant* way to do it are not only contributing to efficient management but to harmonious family relationship. There is no better place to develop new and improved methods of work than in the area of preparing family meals. This would include the analysis of such jobs as buying and storing the food; the arrangement of equipment and utensils; actual cooking processes; serving meals; and washing dishes and putting them away. Before deciding on the best method to do any of the above jobs, the homemaker should ask herself several questions: *When* and *Where* should the various tasks be done and *Who* should do them? It is also good to ask *Why* certain jobs are being done. Frequently the latter question will bring into focus the uselessness of certain "chores." After determining what needs to be done it is necessary to do the work in the sequence which is best suited to the needs of the family group. It may be better to do marketing as the homemaker is returning from taking the father to work or the children to school, or if this is not possible because of young children, the shopping may have to be done in the afternoon after some member of the family has returned home to stay with the young children. Sometimes it is more convenient for all concerned for the man of the house to do the marketing either on the weekend or on his way home from work. If children are to assist with meal preparation, conflict can be avoided if there is an even distribution of their jobs. Time allowance is important in a good work plan, and sufficient time should be scheduled to permit each job to be done to the satisfaction of the person doing it. Regardless of plans that are made for doing work they must be sufficiently flexible to allow for adjustments. Tenseness and irritability on the part of one or more members of the family are likely to result from adhering rigidly to a program of work. Unexpected situations are a rule rather than an exception in most families and with a little foresight they can be absorbed before creating a crisis.

In some homes inconvenient kitchens which make meal preparation a fatiguing job are tolerated because it is believed that sweeping improvements, involving considerable expenditures, are necessary in order to correct the old-fashioned layout. In many instances a few simple conveniences will make marked improvements. Sometimes a kitchen can be made more convenient by re-arranging cooking utensils and dishes, and by throwing away those things which are not used and only serve to clutter up the kitchen. The attractive kitchens in Fig. 52 have many work simplification features including peg board and sliding work surfaces.

The importance of simplifying kitchen and other home work is being stressed currently by the American Heart Association in their campaign to help homemakers who have heart disease. "Heart of the Home" kitchens are being established in many cities [1] to show patients how, through simple improvements, they can carry on kitchen work in spite of their heart condition. Also, the patients are being taught that the best way to conserve energy is to use the body correctly. Through correct body mechanics, work is distributed over several sets of muscles, thereby resulting in less fatigue. The Heart Association's program is attracting wide attention from women who do not have any handicap, and who are re-designing their kitchens for easier work.

Cooking today for tomorrow. "Bonus cooking," or the preparation of more food than is needed for serving at any one time, is a boon to families that enjoy the freedom of having spur-of-the-moment parties or extras for family meals. It is also intelligent use of resources—time, energy, fuel, money, and freezer storage facilities. There are peak periods for food-related activities in all families. These are usually around holidays when other activities are also at a peak. Where freezer facilities permit, it may be desirable to prepare food for a special occasion several months in advance. Even for regular family meals bonus cooking is a great convenience. This is particularly true of popular foods that can be used in a versatile fashion. Apple sauce serves as an example. Its uses are many—apple betty, apple snow, apple tarts, apple-sauce cake, etc.

If meals are planned ahead, it is easy to work in some part of tomorrow's preparation. This practice can speed the preparation of many meals. Once such a habit is established it becomes the natural rather than the forced way and contributes greatly to relaxation.

---

[1] *The Heart of The Home,* American Heart Association, New York.

Courtesy Japan Tourist Association

Fig. 51. Dining in Japan. Bowls on a lacquer tray contain soup (dark bowl), rice (in diner's hand), salad (R.), and steamed vegetables with meat or fish (L.). A plate with fish and vegetables is on a separate tray.

It is easy to work in some part of tomorrow's preparation if the meals have been planned for two or more days. Specific suggestions for advance preparation are: make congealed salads and desserts; cook dried fruits and legumes; make mayonnaise or salad dressing; bake cakes, cookies, or pastry shells; make steamed breads; cook fowl which is to be used in creamed or casserole dishes or in salads; prepare certain vegetables, such as pickled beets; cook the eggs that are to be used in such dishes as eggs au gratin; chop foods, such as pickles and nuts, which are to be used in salads or desserts.

Courtesy Armstrong Cork Co., Lancaster, Pa.

U.S.D.A. Human Nutrition and Home Economics Research Bureau

Fig. 52. A modern kitchen provides for work simplification: top, a kitchen with many interesting features; bottom, a convenient U-shaped kitchen including a sliding board at which work may be done while seated.

Courtesy Home Art Department, Pennsylvania State University

Fig. 53. A reserved table for a special family situation.

SERVING THE MEALS

Revolutionary changes have taken place insofar as the kitchen and its equipment is concerned. Architects, builders, home economists, manufacturers of equipment, and many others have studied and analyzed every phase of kitchen activity in order to make food preparation for family meals attractive, pleasant, and less time consuming. In many homes, the kitchen is the "show" place of the house.

By comparison *serving* meals has received much less attention. Yet this phase of family living has also undergone radical change. The efficiency desired in cooking the meals has in many instances also become the goal for serving them. It is evident in some homes that the actual eating of food is considered as a necessary burden, to be gotten over with as quickly as possible. In many homes eating in a group, unhurriedly and in pleasant surroundings, is reserved for company, and it is not considered important, or even desirable, as a day to day, meal to meal activity for the family members. However, meal time is the only daily event which unites a family for a single purpose. The number of meals eaten together is usually narrowed down to one or two a day. It would seem then that the serving and eating of family meals is extremely important in the social and cultural development of family life.

Surprise touches in serving family meals can often be accomplished with little extra effort. A table for two set up in a den or other location adjacent to the other dining area gives privacy for a father-daughter "conference" or a "twosome" for a specially-invited date by either a son or a daughter. The success of such an endeavor is more assured if the table setting is unusual. The "reserved" table in Figure 53, in spite of its simplicity, is dramatic, because of the vivid blue cloth, white china (with blue design), and red tulips.

A spokesman for a well known national welfare agency stated that at least some juvenile delinquency was caused by children eating their meals out of the refrigerator. She suggested a "back to the family dinner table" movement to help counteract the trend of those in the family shifting for themselves at meal times.

Attention to the surroundings in which meals are served, the table appointments, and the method of service, gives rise to important values in group life which we cannot afford to overlook. They contribute materially to individual attitudes, group relationships, and the total quality of family living.

To many homemakers, table service means an elaborate set of "rules"—an arbitrary code—used only when guests are invited and therefore having no place in the scheme of everyday living. What a contrast this attitude is to the one held by other individuals, who consider conventions of table service as a pattern and guide and therefore feel free to adjust them to suit the needs of a given situation. The person with the latter attitude is likely to get far more enjoyment out of living because she is reducing worry, tension, and fatigue.

While the basic conventions of table service are rather clearly defined, there is no one *right* way to serve a meal. The application of the established fundamentals calls for the use of judgment and common sense if family and guest meals are to be served in a casual, convenient, and comfortable manner. Mental flexibility is perhaps one of the chief factors contributing to such service. Nickell and Dorsey, in discussing this factor as it relates to the managerial aspects of feeding the family, say, "Mental flexibility, the attitude of readiness and willingness to face possible change, helps a person to see and plan ahead, and, what is more important, to adjust and control the plan as action takes place. This saves time.

Flexibility in planning is called for in many ways in food management. Situations are constantly arising which make it necessary to change menu patterns, and homemakers must be prepared to make substitutions when the need arises. This involves knowing what foods can be satisfactorily substituted from the standpoint of nutrition and cost as well as combining with the rest of the menu."[1]

Regardless of the attitude which is assumed concerning table service, there is an undeniable satisfaction resulting from meals served with a smooth-running, established order of procedure. A cold supper served attractively

[1] Paulena Nickell and Jean Muir Dorsey, *Management in Family Living* (New York: John Wiley and Sons, 1959), p. 369.

on a summer evening has an appeal which the same supper will not have if eaten from the corner of the kitchen cabinet. A form of service worked out to fit a specific situation soon becomes a matter of routine. A homemaker who serves daily meals to her family in a simple, ceremonious way is not likely to be confronted with the problem of her family's "company manners" when guests are present; instead, she can preside over her table with confidence, ease, and graciousness. A hostess may readily achieve success in meal service if she makes simplicity the keynote.

Table service which is "overdone" is an indication of poor taste. When members of the family or guests are "service conscious" the hostess has failed to attain a gracious, dignified form of service. This point may be illustrated by a custom of serving, popular several years ago, which did not permit a maid to retrace her steps while serving a meal. Obviously this practice was a waste of time as well as energy, often delaying the service of a meal unnecessarily. A maid makes the guests "service conscious" if she keeps walking around and around the table. Someone has likened the feeling to that of being on a merry-go-round. How much better is the present custom of taking the shortest route; this is what the hostess who has no maid does.

It is impossible to draw up a set of hard-and-fast rules for meal service, because customs change here, as in other things. The practices a decade ago of using only white damask cloths for dinner and of placing a large number of pieces of silver on the table; the changing position of the salad; and the increasing use of the continental custom of using the fork in the left hand with the tines down when carrying meat to the mouth are a few examples illustrating how customs change from time to time and how they differ in various countries.

The homemaker today is fortunate in that she is unrestricted in her freedom to adjust and break "rules" in working out a type of table service which fits her needs. However, it is not wise or considerate of family and guests to break the "rules" unless for good reasons. The reason for doing so is usually in the interest of comfort, and the hostess's adjustment of the convention can be made without sacrificing any of the appropriateness or graciousness of the service. "Knowing what you do and why you do it will enable you to sit at the head of your table with poise and grace. Add a warm generous spirit of hospitality, a kindly sense of humor. Then you will have the perfect equipment. Without these qualities, the finest appointments in the world won't be of much use to you. With them all the world will be delighted to come to dinner at your house every time that you will let them. Furthermore, you will have found the key to gracious living."[1]

In the following pages in this unit the conventions of table service, along with adaptations and modifications, are discussed. In presenting the material, an effort is made to include the principal table customs as they are used in

[1] Helen Sprackling, *Setting Your Table* (New York: Barrows, 1941), p. 4.

the United States. A study of these conventions should enable a homemaker to establish a type of service suitable to her own situation. After establishing this service, she should in general be consistent in maintaining it for the comfort, convenience, and pleasure of the entire family.

SETTING THE TABLE

Setting the table. A sixteen-year old girl was heard to inquire of her mother, "Do I have to set the table right?" Because the mother was engaged in conversation, she did not respond. Later when she went into the dining room she instructed her daughter to re-set the table "correctly." In this instance "correctly" meant placing the plates, glasses, silverware, and napkins on the table in an orderly manner with evenly spaced plates, with the silverware divided between the right and left sides of the plate (in conventional fashion), the glasses at the tip of the knife or to the right, and the napkin on the left. The sixteen-year old evidently considered the orderly arrangement a chore as against her method of helter-skelter placement of the various articles, with the silver being more or less placed in a "pile" at the right of the plate.

Reasons for orderly table setting seem quite obvious. They contribute to the comfort, convenience, and pleasure of eating. Orderliness in setting the table provides a basis for giving expression to a sense of beauty and individuality in serving meals. Some homemakers consider setting the table as an opportunity to test their decorating sense. In this endeavor there is no chance to make a costly mistake with colors or design as is possible in some other areas of decorating.

Variety in table settings is far more important to some than to others. This is likely to be related to a desire for variety in the food served. It is fairly simple to satisfy this need in table settings if the individual is not inhibited by a feeling that everything should match. Observation of table settings in museums, clubs, shops, stores, publications, etc., is likely to reveal that the most appealing and distinctive tables are those which display the skillful combination of related textures, colors, and shapes in the appointments used.

In Figure 54, unmatched appointments have been assembled to set a "clean cut" buffet table. This table also illustrates good design from the standpoint of related appointments and their placement.

Setting the table starts with the covering, but in some instances no "cloth" is used when there is a good-looking table top. A wide range of place mats and cloths permits almost endless possibilities for the foundation of a table setting. (See pp. 406 to 418.) The size and shape of the table top along with the type of covering used determines the amount of space available for each place. Places at a table are usually designated as "covers" which include articles for service for one. Figure 55 shows a place setting that combines a

Courtesy Home Art Department, Pennsylvania State University

Fig. 54. In color this table is red, white, gray, and brown. It is both orderly and good-looking because of the attention paid to assembling the appointments and their placement.

woven mat and the bare table top. Since crowded dining is not conducive to comfort it is desirable to allow twenty-four to thirty inches for each person. In today's smaller homes this is often not possible. Perhaps this is one reason for the popularity of buffet meals.

Regardless of available space, the appointments for one cover should be grouped so as to present a unit. It is sometimes difficult to judge where one cover begins and another stops. This gives a cluttered appearance to the table and is confusing to the diners.

The placement of the various table articles is summarized in the following paragraphs. It shows the flexibility that is possible in arranging table appointments.

Knives. Knives are placed at the right of the plate with the cutting edges turned toward the plate. If the menu does not necessitate the use of a knife, it is not placed. Fish knives and salad knives are not commonly used. When they are used, they are placed at the right of the dinner knife unless the fish or salad course follows the main course, in which case they are placed at the left of the dinner knife. Fruit knives may be used when fruit is served as a first course or as a dessert. In the former case, the fruit knife is placed at the right of the dinner knife if no spoon is placed, or at the right of the spoon if the spoon is placed. If three pieces of silver, exclusive of the fruit knife, are

Courtesy B. Altman and Co.

Fig. 55. A place setting which utilizes place mat and the bare table for the individual cover. The appointments illustrate how imports from different countries can be combined for distinction and good looks. (China from England; mat from Switzerland; glass from Sweden; stainless steel from Denmark; salt and pepper and flower bowl from the United States).

placed at the right of the plate, the fruit knife is placed on the fruit plate. If fruit is served as a dessert, the fruit knife may be placed at the right of the cover before the dessert is served, or it may be brought in on the dessert plate. The butter knife is placed across the top of the bread-and-butter plate with the cutting edge toward the center of the plate. The handle is usually turned slightly to the right for convenience in handling. When no bread-and-butter plate is used, no individual butter knife is placed.

Forks. In general, forks are placed at the left of the plate, with the tines turned up. Custom differs as to the order in which forks are placed. Present usage favors placing them in the order in which they are to be used. Some people prefer to place the dinner fork at the left of the plate to balance the knife at the right, and to place the other forks at the left of the dinner fork, in order of their use. Either form is acceptable.

If two forks are used and no knife or spoon is placed, the dinner fork may be placed on the right and the other fork on the left. If a fork and spoon are the only pieces of silver used, the fork is placed on the left of the plate and the spoon on the right. If a fork is the only piece of silver to be used, it is more logical to place it on the right. When a fork is being placed for dessert, it is more convenient when placed at the right of the cover before the dessert is served. In doing this, the forks are brought in on a tray. In family service the dessert silver is usually on the table at the beginning of the meal. An English custom of placing the dessert silver, usually a fork and spoon, on the dessert plate may be used. A cocktail fork is placed in one of two positions: (1) at the right of the knife and spoon, and to the right of the spoon, and (2) on the plate on which the cocktail is served. Special forks for fish, pastry, and fruit are desirable, but the average homemaker, who does not usually own these pieces of silver, uses salad forks for these foods.

Spoons. Spoons are placed at the right of the knife with the bowls up. Spoons, like forks, are usually placed in sequence of their use, but may be placed in order of their size. Spoons that are to be used up to the dessert course are placed when the table is set. Dessert spoons, like dessert forks, are placed at the right of the cover before the dessert is served, or are placed on the dessert plate. For convenience they are sometimes laid along with other silver. After-dinner coffee spoons are always placed on the coffee saucer at the right of the cup, rather than on the table.

Glasses. Water glasses are most conveniently placed slightly above and to the right of the tip of the knife. When place mats are used, the position of the glass will have to be shifted if they are included on the place mat. Fig. 55 shows a cover with the glasses placed directly on the bare table. Iced tea glasses may be adjusted if used along with water glasses: if placed to the right of the water glass, it will not be necessary to reach over this glass to add lemon or sugar to the tea. Placement to the left of the water glass gives better balance to the cover, since iced tea glasses are, as a rule, taller. Fruit juice glasses for breakfast are usually placed directly on the plate or on the table just above the plate.

Beverage cups. Hot beverages are placed at the right of the cover and on a line that is slightly below the center of the plate. The handle of the cup should be slanted slightly for convenience in picking it up. Placing the beverage at the top of the spoons or at the top of the cover, as is frequently done, is not good serving technique. When after-dinner coffee is served as a separate course, the cup and saucer are placed in the center of the cover.

Bread-and-butter plates. Bread-and-butter plates are placed above the forks and to the left. In the event that the same plate is used for both salad and bread and butter, the plate is shifted slightly toward the lower part of the cover.

Salad plates. Salads may be served at several different times during a meal. They may be an accompaniment to the main course, or a separate course served as an appetizer, as the course succeeding the meat or, in some in-

Courtesy New York Times Studio

Fig. 56. Individual luncheon cover showing appointments of traditional design.

stances, as a combination salad and dessert. Salad service at the table is described on pages 365–366.

The most convenient position for the salad plate when it accompanies the main course is often a disputed question. It can be answered by each individual by using judgment and thinking through the particular situation. Books on the subject of table service suggest that the salad plates be placed in one of three positions:

Courtesy New York Times Studio

Fig. 57. Individual breakfast cover showing appointments of contemporary design.

1) At the left and slightly below the bread-and-butter plate. The size of the napkin may necessitate shifting this position.
2) In the position of the bread-and-butter plate, provided, of course, that no bread-and-butter plate is placed.
3) At the right, on a line with the other equipment.

The first two positions have been in use for the longest periods and are perhaps preferred by the majority of individuals for that reason. Those who prefer placing the salad on the left do so because it affords excellent leverage in cutting. The third position is a welcome one for the numerous individuals who have thought it extremely inconvenient to reach across a dinner plate to eat a salad. At best, salad materials are none too easy to eat; consequently, having the plate on the right is conducive to managing a salad gracefully. This position would seem to be the best unless a hot beverage is being served. The effect of the position of the salad plate in the removal of covers is discussed under the methods of serving.

The napkin. The napkin, simply folded in a square or rectangular shape, is placed at the left of the fork so that the open corner nearest the plate is at the lower edge of the cover. This permits opening the napkin with ease when it is taken in the lap. A crowded table sometimes necessitates placing the napkin in the center of the cover, between the knife and fork. For more formal occasions where service plates are used, it is sometimes placed in the plate; however, the position at the left is preferred. Folding the napkin in a fancy shape and placing it in a standing position is a practice of some restaurants. This makes the napkin conspicuous, and therefore it seems out of place in the home.

One hostess who uses round, folding, card tables for serving at her parties, increases table-top space by sewing loops on the napkins and a flat button on the edge of the round cloth at each cover, over which she buttons on the napkins and lets them hang down off the table. Guests "unbutton" the napkins after they are seated.

Cooking devices on the table. Simplified meals of one dish or more are popular in many homes and these may either be prepared at the table or kept warm by the use of chafing dishes, broilers, warmers, and electric trivets. When such equipment is used it may be necessary to adjust the rules of conventional table setting in order that such devices can be used with safety and comfort. It is unwise to attempt their use on small tables.

Placing the accessories. Too many accessory dishes or the careless placing of them sometimes spoils an otherwise perfectly appointed table.

If individual salt and pepper containers are used, they are placed above the plate. Larger salts and peppers should be placed where they can be reached easily. Dishes in which jelly, pickles, butter, and sugar are served should be conveniently placed on the table. The serving silver for these dishes, placed parallel with the edge of the table, should be at the side of each dish, and the handles should be easily accessible to the persons who will pass the food. If a meal is being served by a maid, the accessory foods may be passed on a tray.

Serving silver for the food being served by the host and hostess should be placed in alignment with their personal silver. If space does not permit, the serving silver may be placed above the cover, at the side of the serving dish. The first position is preferred, however.

Placing the chairs. Chairs should be placed directly in front of the covers and far enough from the table so that the line of the cloth is not broken. This makes little or no moving of the chairs necessary when sitting down.

TYPES OF TABLE SERVICE

Types of table service. When homes were more spacious than they are today, and household workers were employed by many more families, and living in general was more leisurely, "table service" was probably more elaborate and formal than it is today. The various types that are presented in books on etiquette and table service allowed a choice of a variety of ways of serving both family and company meals.

In adjusting to changed circumstances, families who once had maids, and even butlers, were faced with the reality of meal service without any "servants." For some of these families this was a welcome release from the rigid schedule which had to be met in order to keep within the working day of employees. While families in moderate circumstances may not have had the problems of learning to get along without a maid, they too have undergone change in serving family and company meals. Regardless of the economic status of families, this change in the way meals are served has resulted in simplified and attractive service, which in many homes is the same for the family as for the guests. This trend is to be commended as it does not give undue emphasis to table service, but instead considers the "service" in the proper perspective with the other factors that combine to make dining pleasant and enjoyable.

For the average person all table service is classified as either formal or informal. Special types such as "English," "Russian," and "Compromise," are meaningless terms. If we accept the two broad categories of formal and informal as a "rule of thumb," we will find that the various types described here (and in other books dealing with table service) will fall in one or the other classification. For home use we need only be concerned with informal service, since it is inappropriate to attempt to serve formal meals (which are at least of five courses) in a home without a staff of employees.

Since ideas for serving food informally are legion, it is impossible to present suggestions that will fit all situations. Just as informal dress is interpreted in many different ways, so is informal table service. In either case the results can be charming and in good taste, or they can be so casual as to be sloppy and distasteful.

Often students are unaware of the many possibilities that are open to them in the area of serving foods. In order to become acquainted with these, it is wise to accumulate background information by studying traditional methods in view of making adaptions to present-day living. While "formal" service is not in keeping with family meals, it is highly desirable for everyone to be acquainted with the methods and "ceremonies" involved, since this type of service is used in elite clubs, hotels, on shipboard, etc.

Informal service. *Family:* this will vary with each family. Some families have "service" at breakfast, which means a regulated breakfast routine of sitting down together at an attractive table and enjoying the first meal. It is the regulated routine (necessary in order to get the family started for the day's activities) that makes the service of breakfast smooth and orderly. Dinner, or the main meal, for most families means two courses—the main course and a dessert. The food, with the exception of a dessert, is usually on the table when the family is seated. One possibility for serving is passing the serving dishes, with each one helping himself. The plates are placed, in this case, at the individual covers. Unless passing is done in some order, confusion is apt to occur. Perhaps you can recall the service of a meal where dishes were being offered you from both the right and the left at the same moment, making serving very awkward. This situation may be avoided by having the serving of the main dishes started at one end and all passing done in the same direction—to the right.

Another possibility is having the plates placed at the cover of the host or hostess, the food being served on the plates by them, and the plates passed to the other members of the family. Accessory foods, such as bread, butter, and jelly, are passed as in the first method. This plan of family service is recommended over the first one for the following reasons: it is less confusing; a meat and one or two vegetables may be served on the same platter, thereby conserving space on the table and also saving dishwashing; accidents are not so likely to occur as when large service dishes are handled by individuals; hot food may be placed in hot service dishes, since they will not have to be passed; the host or hostess can apportion food, such as dark and white meat of chicken.

A tea wagon, service cart, or a small table on rollers is a good "maid" for any household. If it has two shelves, the used plates from a main course may be concealed on the lower one during the dessert, while the upper shelf provides a serving table. Since smaller dining tables are, in many homes, replacing the spacious ones formerly used, a tea cart or small service table placed at the left of the hostess can be one of her greatest helps in establishing an attractive, leisurely form of table service, because it may relieve an overcrowded table, and will save innumerable steps. Using the lower shelf for soiled dishes is particularly recommended at breakfast.

English. English service is given by some writers as "family service." It is also informal, and is a very gracious, hospitable type in which all courses, including soup, salad, and dessert, are served at the table by the host and hostess. Usually the host serves the meat and perhaps one vegetable, and the hostess serves the other vegetables, sauces, etc. The hostess serves the soup, beverage, and dessert. She may also serve the salad, but in some families the man of the house enjoys blending the salad ingredients at the table and then serving the salad. Sometimes the host may serve the dessert while the hostess pours the beverage.

Since much of the charm of English service is due to the fact that the host and hostess personally look after serving members of the family and guests, the menu should be planned to include foods which are attractive to serve at the table. All families have their favorite menus for such occasions, and they are determined to a large extent by the dishes or other equipment available for serving. A beautiful soup tureen, a handsome salad bowl, an antique cake stand, and a smart stainless steel coffee pot of Danish design might be the incentive for the following simple supper (served at the table in English fashion):

Chicken and Corn Chowder
Hard Rolls Butter
Caesar Salad
Swiss Carrot Torte
Coffee

A division of service could be made with the host serving the chowder and (later) the torte and the hostess serving the salad and the coffee. (They might also reverse the service). It is a pleasant practice to dress a salad at the table.

Compromise or combination. This, as the name implies, combines two types of service. It is used by many families. Some of the food is served at the table, as the main course often is, and other dishes are served from the kitchen. The family should not be deprived of the sight of a baked stuffed fish or a crisp brown roast turkey, so these are "naturals" for serving at the table, while a frozen dessert may be more conveniently and attractively served in the kitchen.

Buffet service. This is one of the most popular types of serving. It is discussed in some detail in the unit of social refreshments (pp. 445–467).

Formal service. *Russian.* There are several different ways of executing this formal style of service. The host and hostess do not participate in serving. All of the food is served from the kitchen by employees. This may be done in a variety of ways, but the two most frequently seen are: (1) plate service, in which the food is arranged on individual plates and served by waiters; or (2) platter service, in which the food is arranged on platters or placed in other types of serving dishes and passed by waiters. In some instances the waiter serves the guests from the platters, and the guest is expected to serve other foods himself. If service is strictly formal it usually has these features:

1) Service plates are used. They are sometimes called place plates. These plates are generally highly decorative and are different in design from the dinner plates. No food is ever placed directly on the service plate; on it are placed the dishes holding the food for the courses preceding the main course. It is removed when the dinner plate replaces it.
2) No food is placed on the table until after the guests are seated.
3) Place cards are frequently used.
4) Butter, salt, and pepper are not served. Perhaps the reason for this fact is that the food should be so properly seasoned during the preparation as to make additional seasoning unnecessary.
5) Goblets are always used, and they may be very tall ones.
6) Dessert silver is placed just preceding the serving of the dessert.
7) After-dinner coffee is served without cream.
8) Finger bowls are frequently used.

Courtesy George Jensen, Inc.

Fig. 58. A table set for a formal dinner.

The use of finger bowls. The use of finger bowls at the close of the formal meal is optional. If used, the bowls are filled one-third full of lukewarm water and placed on a small plate which may or may not have a doily on it. Finger bowls are placed after the dessert is removed. The English custom is to place the finger bowl with the dessert, the dessert silver being on the plate which contains the finger bowl. They may be garnished with a flower or a green leaf, in which case cool water is used. It is not considered good taste to perfume the water.

Mechanics of serving. Right or left? Whether to serve from the right or left seems to perplex some people, especially those who are service-conscious. If they seek to have their question answered by looking it up in a book, they will find different opinions, just as is true of other points in meal service. Some writers show more flexibility than others in presenting ideas for ways of serving. It is interesting for students to consult a number of books (both text—and popular) as well as magazines to obtain a cross section of opinion on the controversial subject of table service. Actually concern over whether food should be served, or dishes removed from the right or the left seems insignificant in light of the total values that can be derived from

Courtesy New York Times Studio

Fig. 59. An informal bean supper.

family meals that are served in an "orderly" fashion in pleasant surroundings. What is right for one family may not be suitable for another, and, as in all aspects of table service, comfort and convenience should determine whether right- or left-hand service is used. One is just as correct as the other.

Ideas about serving food are often obtained from restaurant dining. Students who have been employed in summer at resort hotels or other food service establishments frequently have rigid ideas as to so-called "correct" methods of serving. Interesting discussions can result from comparing restaurant service with home service. Very often the former is not suitable for family meals, either from the standpoint of table appointments or serving.

Right-hand service. The procedure for this method of service follows:

1) The person doing the serving—whether a maid, a hostess, or some member of her family—stands at the right of the one being served, and places and removes food or dishes with her right hand.

2) There are exceptions to the above rule, since in serving it is never permissible to reach across the cover of the person being served. In removing or placing the bread-and-butter plate, the serving is done from the left with the left hand.

3) Any food which is being offered for an individual to serve himself is passed from the left with the left hand. This is a convenience for those being served.

Left-hand service. Left-hand service is carried out in the following way:

1) The serving is done from the left of the individual to be served, the food and dishes being placed and removed with the left hand.
2) The exceptions to the above rule are: in filling the water glass, in placing or removing the beverage cup, and in placing or removing the salad if served on the right. In all of these cases the serving is done from the right with the right hand.
3) Food is offered as in right-hand service—from the left with the left hand.

A general rule which will be helpful in remembering these methods of serving is that the hand farther from the one being served is always used. In right-hand service this would, of course, be the right hand; and in left-hand service, it would be the left. Perhaps you have observed a meal being served where food is placed from the right with the left hand, or from the left with the right hand. This method of serving is conspicuous because the elbow of the person serving is awkwardly curved and is placed noticeably close to the one being served.

Since the right-hand method of serving has fewer exceptions, it would seem to be the more convenient; however, the method chosen is a matter of individual preference.

Filling water or beverage glasses. Water glasses are filled three-fourths full of cold water before the family is seated. Ice is usually not served in water glasses; however, in a very warm climate this is sometimes necessary. It is always used in glasses for iced beverages, such as tea. In family service, the water pitcher may be on the table or on a serving table and the glasses refilled by passing them to the person pouring the water. Goblets are not as easily passed as tumblers. If the glasses are to be refilled by a maid, they are left in place, and the water is poured slowly to prevent splashing. The maid holds the pitcher in her right hand and stands at the right of the person. She uses a folded napkin to catch the drip from the pitcher. The glass should not be lifted from the tabie nor drawn to the edge of the table while it is being refilled.

In replenishing ice for beverages, the chipped or cubed ice is placed in a bowl and transferred to the glass by means of a spoon or ice tongs. In family service the bowl may be passed for each one to serve himself, or the glasses may be passed to someone who is serving the ice. If a maid is serving the ice, she may either offer it from a person's left for each individual to serve himself, or she may place it in the glasses with the spoon or tongs, serving from the right side by holding the bowl in her left hand and using the spoon or tongs in her right hand for transferring the ice to the glasses.

Order of serving. In family service, if the food is being served by the host and hostess, a minimum of passing is necessary if the host serves the meat, passing the served plate to the right to the hostess, who serves the vegetables. The plate is then passed to the right of the hostess, to the person seated at the left of the host. If all the serving is being done by the host, the plates are passed to his right, the first one going to the hostess and the next one to the person at her left. This procedure is used until all those on her left have been served. The plates are then passed to the left of the host until all on that side have been served. The host or hostess always specifies who is to receive the first plate.

Who shall be served first? This is a very perplexing question to some individuals. The majority of people writing on the subject of table service say that the hostess should be, and that by so doing, no discourtesy is shown the guests. Most guests will not notice who is served first if the service is well ordered and regulated. If the order of service is conspicuous, the guests are service-conscious and the resulting meal may not be enjoyed by those at the table. At a dinner with a large number of guests, the plates served first are likely to be slightly less desirable because the hot food may have become cool and congealed, or frozen foods may have become soft before all have been served.

The practice of skipping the men in order to serve the women first is not considered a good serving procedure. It was noted on the occasion of a formal dinner that one hostess, before serving the men, served all women guests first, beginning with the one whom she *thought* to be the eldest!

When a maid serves a meal, unless the hostess is doing some of the serving, she is served first and the person to her right is served next and so on until all are served. In English service, the maid places the plates in the same order around the table as is done for family service.

Passing serving dishes. A serving dish is passed by the maid always from the left side. It may be necessary for her to use both hands, depending upon the size of the dish. She uses a folded napkin, which is termed a "service napkin." The dish with the serving silver in it should be held firmly, close to the table, and close enough to the person's plate so that he may serve himself safely. It is not considered the best form to rest the dish on the table. If the serving dish is a very small one, it may be passed on a tray. Hot breads are usually placed on a plate in a folded napkin, and in offering them the maid lifts the corner of the napkin so that a guest may serve himself with ease.

Serving the accompaniments. In any type of service where accompaniments are placed on the table, a hostess may direct the serving of them. For example, she may say to the person nearest the jelly, "Won't you serve yourself to some jelly and pass it?" The passing is done to the right.

Accompaniments which are passed by a maid are offered from the left. Two or three small dishes may be passed at once on a tray.

Removal of dishes. In removing the main course, the table is cleared of all food, accessory dishes, and soiled china before serving the next course. The main platter is taken first, then the vegetable dishes, then the china from individual covers, and last the accessory dishes, these being removed with the use of a tray. Either right- or left-hand service may be used in removing dishes, depending on which method is selected for the service of the meal.

The following directions are given for the removal of dishes with right-hand service:

In removing individual covers, the order of removal is the same, whether it is being done by a maid, a hostess, or a member of her family. Starting with the hostess, the main plate is removed first; this is done from the right with the right hand. If there are no salad plates, bread-and-butter plates, or beverage cups to be removed, the plate is transferred to the left hand and the plate of the person at the right of the hostess is removed next. In family service, several plates may be put on a tray, which is placed on the serving table, and the tray carried to the kitchen. If the family is small, the plates may be stacked on the lower shelf of a tea cart or on a table which is being used for a tea cart rather than taken to the kitchen. In removing a cover where there are several dishes at each place, everything is removed from the right with the exception of the bread-and-butter plate and the salad plate, if placed on the left. In family service, both a salad plate and a bread-and-butter plate are seldom used at the same meal, but instead one plate for the two, which would be placed on the left. This practice is not desirable unless the plate is large enough to prevent crowding. In removing a cover of this kind, it would seem more convenient to do so by taking all of the main plates off first as described above, and then with a tray in the right hand, remove the bread-and-butter plates from the left with the left hand, placing only as many on the tray as can be safely carried to the kitchen. The number would vary, depending upon the size of the tray. Beverage glasses which are taken off along with the main course may be removed with the tray in the same manner, except that in this case the tray is held in the left hand and glasses are removed and placed on the tray with the right hand. It is not good form to stack dishes in front of a person when removing covers. The practice of removing one complete cover at a time may be used, provided the one doing the removing does not reach across a cover.

When silver, such as a knife, has not been used, it is picked up by the person removing the covers and placed on the plate before removing the plate. If the knives are overlooked when taking the plates off, they may be removed later with the use of a tray.

Crumbing the table. After the main course has been removed and preceding the serving of the dessert, the table may be crumbed. A folded napkin and a small plate are used for this purpose and the process should be as inconspicuous as possible. The table is crumbed only where it is necessary.

Placing extra silver. In laying a table for any type of service other than family, the dessert silver is not usually placed until after the clearing of the main course and the crumbing of the table. The dessert silver, or any other

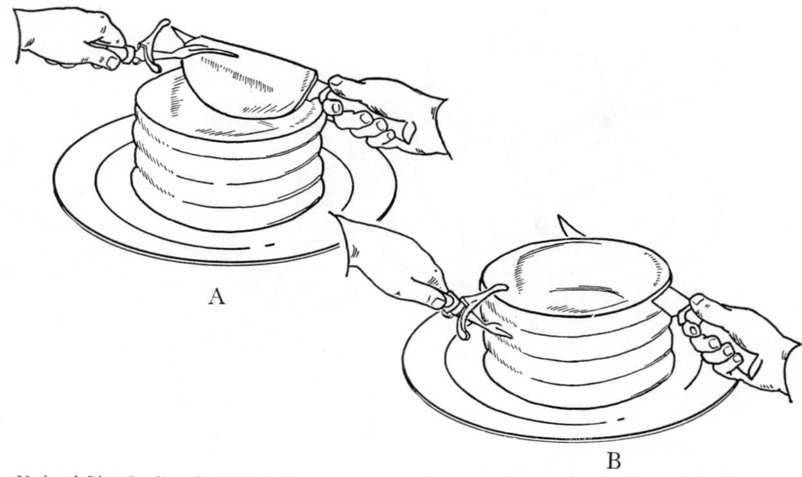

Courtesy National Live Stock and Meat Board

Fig. 60. Carving a rolled rib roast: A, *removing a slive after carving;* B, *position of fork and direction of carving.*

silver which is brought to the table after a meal has started, is brought on a doily-covered tray. Starting with the hostess, the dessert silver is placed from the right with the right hand.

The use of a tray. It is best not to bring a tray to the table except in the instances that have been discussed—in offering accompaniments which are served in small dishes, in removing accessory dishes or small plates and glasses from an individual cover, and in placing extra silver.

The service plate. The service plate, sometimes called a place plate, is used only in formal service and is a decorative plate of a pattern different from that of the dinner plate. No food is ever placed directly on the service plate; on it are placed the dishes for the courses preceding the main course, and it is removed when the dinner plate replaces it. It is not replaced before the dessert is served.

In the practical sense a "place" plate might be described as one in which another dish is placed. This would be the case where a cereal or soup bowl is placed on a plate or where dessert dishes such as parfait or sherbet glasses are served with a plate under them. The desirability of using a place plate (or linen) plate seems clear when one considers the need for protecting table linen from spots which might be caused by placing any of the above mentioned dishes directly on the table without a plate under them. Accidents can frequently be averted by using a plate on which to place accessory dishes.

Special serving at the table. There are several advantages in serving food at the table. When it is done skillfully and gracefully, it adds to the enjoyment of the meal. Some foods are more palatable because they remain hotter,

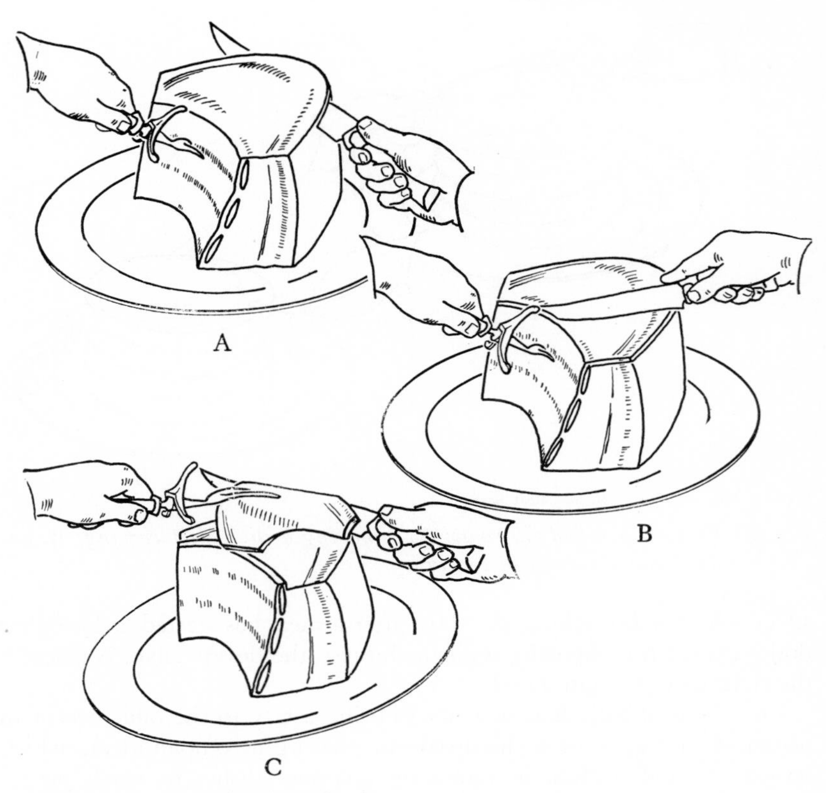

Courtesy National Live Stock and Meat Board

Fig. 61. Carving a standing rib roast: A, *carving the slice;* B, *cutting the meat from the bone;* C, *removing the slice.*

and certain dishes are far more attractive in serving dishes than when served from the kitchen in individual portions.

Carving. "Eating is one of life's greatest pleasures, and next to it, for heightening the enjoyment and taking it beyond mere feeding, stands attractive service. In our very complex and highly keyed world, the average person requires a sense of well-being and pleasure at the table, besides a palatable meal, in order to get the full enjoyment out of his food. And carving, besides acting as one of the finest appetite stimulators, plays no small part in adding to the niceties of service, always provided it is done competently." [1]

Carving is an art which requires a high degree of skill for success, and compliance with a few basic rules. The "rules" are based on common sense, comfort, and convenience. The skill is acquired through study of the art and

[1] M. O. Cullen, *How to Carve Meat, Game and Poultry* (New York: McGraw-Hill, 1941), p. 31.

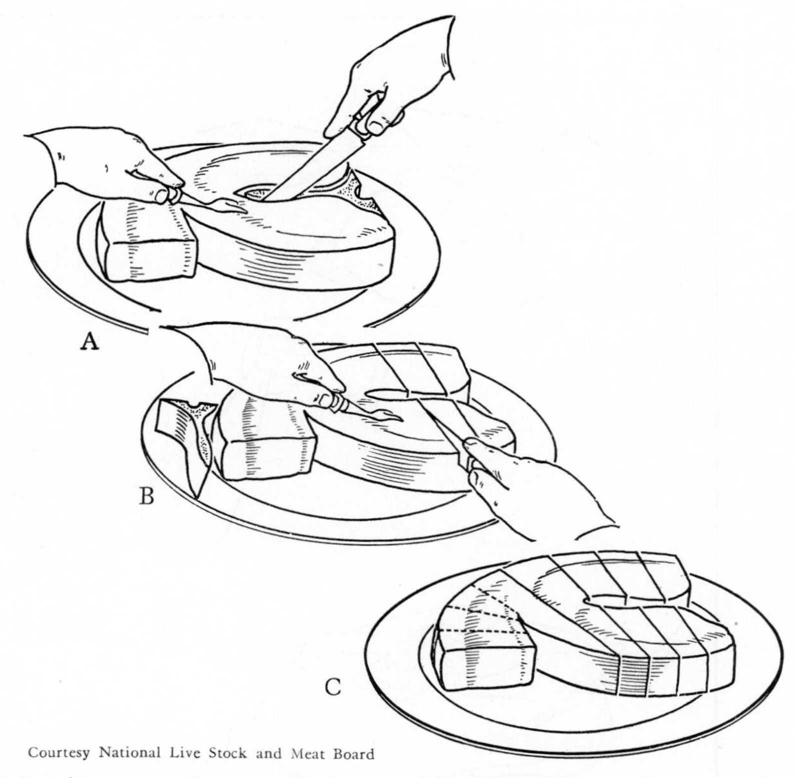

Courtesy National Live Stock and Meat Board

Fig. 62. Carving a porterhouse steak: A, *removing the bone;* B, *carving across the steak;* C, *direction of carving for the whole steak.*

repeated practice in executing it. Cullen suggests that a loaf of bread furnishes very satisfactory experimental material for learning carving technique.

Figures 60 through 63 show the steps in carving some common cuts of meat as well as fowl. It will pay the beginner in this art to study such diagrams before attempting to carve. While it is impossible to gain skill in carving simply by reading written directions, the succeeding suggestions may, if coupled with actual experience, assist in learning the processes of carving.

1) Carving begins at the retail market when the cut of meat or fowl is purcased. No matter how masterful a carver is, unless the meat to be carved has been chosen with intelligence, cut by a skilled meat dealer, and cooked with care, there is always a chance that it cannot be carved properly.

2) A roast or fowl should be allowed to stand at least 30 minutes after it is done before attempting to carve it. This process of "setting" allows the meat to become firm on the inside and will make slicing easier.

3) Good tools are essential for expert carving. "A carver who tolerates a dull knife is just as surely cheating himself, the roast, and therefore the guests, as the

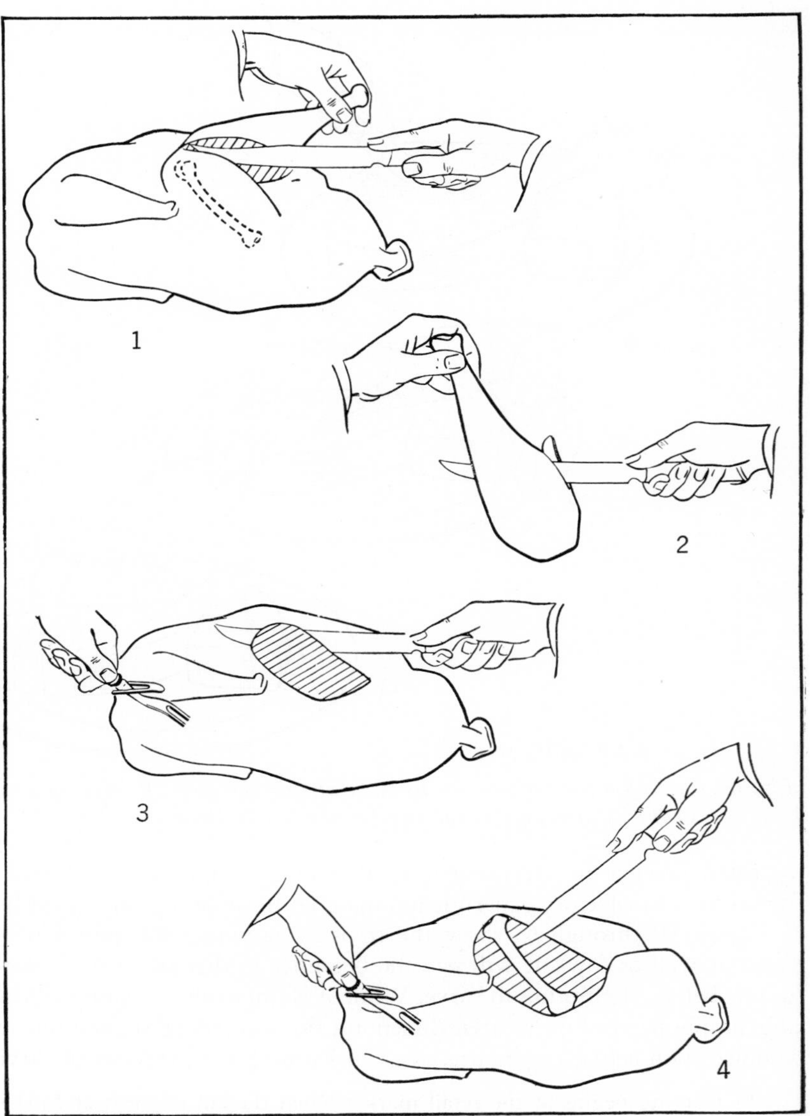

Courtesy National Live Stock and Meat Board

CARVING

Fig. 63. This figure shows the progressive steps in carving turkey: 1) *removing the drumstick;* 2) *carving slices from the drumstick;* 3) *slicing meat from the thigh;* 4) *removing the bone from the thigh;* 5) *slicing the breast with*

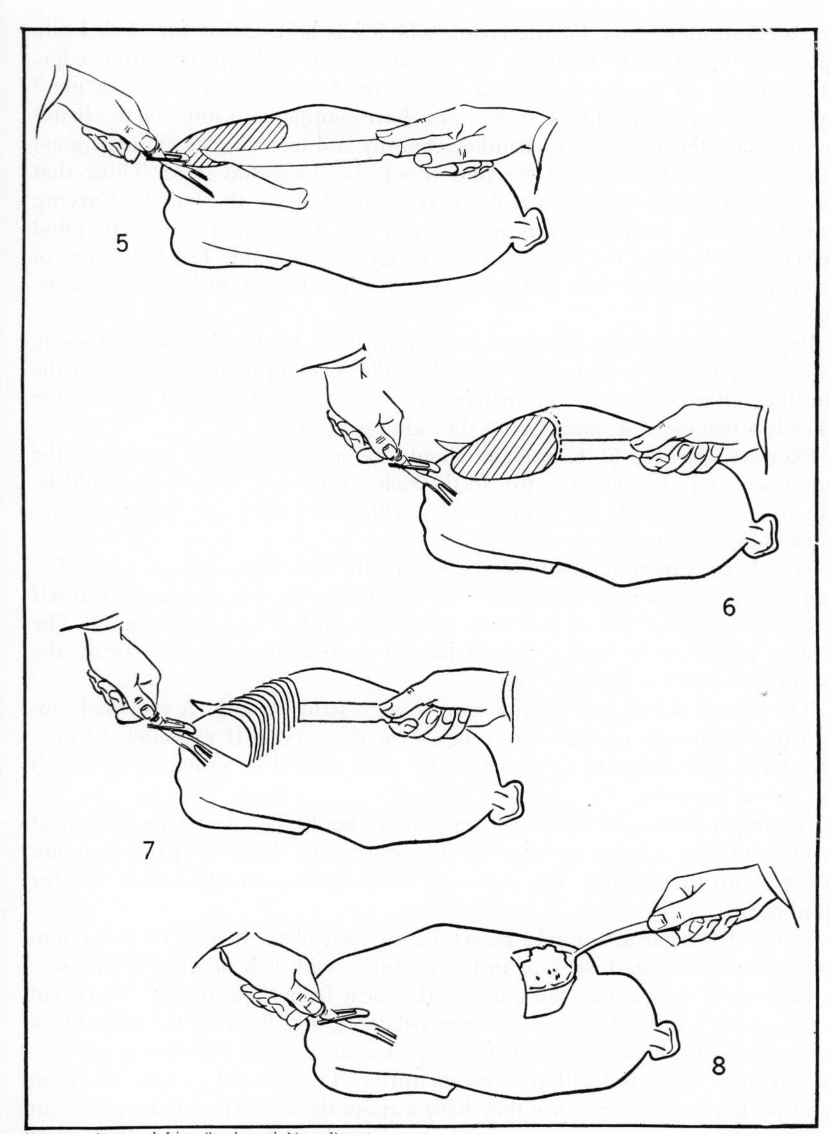

Courtesy National Live Stock and Meat Board

TURKEY

the grain and removing the wing; 6) *slicing the breast after the wing is removed;* 7) *slicing the breast across the grain; and* 8) *removing the stuffing.*

cook who substitutes water for the cream which has been called for."[1] A knife with good quality steel in the blade is necessary if it is to keep its cutting edge. Unless a carving set is very cheap, the steel in the blade is likely to be of good quality. Most good carvers like a stag or real horn handle, and most of the better carving sets have this type. A stag handle is bumpy and uneven, permitting a good grip for the carver. The tines of the fork should be sharp and rigid. Those that are part of a master carving set usually have a guard above the handle. Carving forks are two tined, usually with prongs four to five inches long. There are good 4-piece sets—steak knife and fork, roast knife, and carving aid. The long tines of the latter are strong and with space between them sufficient to hold a roast securely.

4) Regardless of the quality of the steel in the knife blade, it must be properly steeled in order to have a perfect cutting edge. The steeling is usually done in the kitchen, but old-time carvers like to have the steel on the table just in case the blade needs a few extra strokes during the carving process.

5) Skewers, strings, or toothpicks should be removed from meats in the kitchen. There is an exception to this in the rolled rib roast. This roast should be brought to the table with the strings intact. Otherwise the roast will come unrolled while being carved.

6) Whether a carver stands or sits is one of the table conventions which has changed from time to time. Today good serving procedure lets the carver himself decide this. The choice will of course be based on comfort and convenience. The carver who prefers to be seated should have a chair high enough to bring the elbows almost on a line with the table.

7) The size of the platter is important to successful carving. A crowded, undersized platter greatly impedes the progress of the carver. If a household does not afford a platter adequate in size, an extra plate should be provided on which to place carved portions.

8) Accompaniments of fruits or vegetables should be placed on the meat platter only when it is large enough for the presence of the accompaniments not to interfere with the carving. The right end of the platter should be left free for the sliced meat.

9) Some of the garnish should be served on each plate. It may be an accompaniment as well as a garnish—for instance, lemon with fish or mint with lamb.

10) Carving is done *across* the grain of the meat from right to left. When cut across the grain, meat looks better, is more palatable, and is easier to chew. Steak is the exception of not carving meat this way. It is always cut *with* the grain.

The thickness of slicing different meats varies. The general custom is to cut ham and pork in thin slices, since they have a more delicate flavor than when cut thick. Less tender cuts of beef seem more tender when thin or moderately thin. Other cuts of beef, lamb, and veal are usually preferred in moderately thick slices.

11) As a rule, the host carves enough to serve everyone before starting to serve the plates. In serving from a platter which contains vegetables as well as meat, it may be necessary to remove some of the food to the plates before all of the carving is finished.

---

[1] *Ibid.*, p. 17.

Fig. 64. Correct method of holding service silver when serving salad.

12) It is customary for the host to ask guests and members of the family their preference as to light and dark meat of fowl, lean and fat cuts, or rare and well-done pieces of meat.

13) The guests are apt to refuse second servings unless the host carves extra portions before offering them.

Salad service at the table. Salads, because of their freshness, crispness, and color, make an attractive service at the table. Usually they are served by the hostess, who may choose one of the following methods, depending upon the type of salad:

1) The salad may be placed on individual servings of lettuce and arranged on a large platter or chop plate. This service is recommended for individually molded salads or for whole pieces of fruit arranged for a salad.

2) If a large mold of congealed or frozen salad is being served, it is placed on a platter or chop plate and the salad green may be arranged around the outside of the mold, or it may be placed in the center, if a ring mold is used.

3) An unmolded salad may be served in a bowl by first putting in the salad green and then heaping the salad mixture in the center.

4) The salad ingredients may be combined at the table. In this case, the ingredients are in an attractive bowl and the hostess pours the dressing over them and tosses the salad lightly, using the proper servers. Unless the salad green, such as lettuce or water cress, is included in the salad, it is placed in a separate dish at the side of the hostess's cover. Serving salad in this manner requires the greatest amount of skill and should not be attempted without the proper appointments to carry it out attractively. Some men enjoy making the salad dressing and mixing the ingredients.

In serving the salad by any of the methods described, two pieces of serving silver will be needed, and their use will avoid awkward practices, such as balancing a salad on a single server while taking it from the serving dish to the plate, or "chasing" salad materials around a platter in an attempt to serve them with one piece of silver. (See Fig. 64.) In the absence of regular salad servers, a flat piece, such as a tomato server, and a cold meat fork, may be used conveniently. There are also times when a tablespoon may be necessary for the successful serving of some salads.

The salad dressing may be served from a separate bowl by the hostess as she serves the salad, or it may be passed for each one to serve himself. If the hostess is serving it, she may ask if dressing is desired. French dressing is sometimes made at the table. In some European countries the host does this instead of the hostess.

Cooking at the table. The varied possibilities in this area continue to present themselves as equipment manufacturers place more and more portable appliances on the market. From the toaster, which was the first, appliances have been added in succession—waffle bakers, coffee makers, egg cookers, frying pans, casseroles, broilers, sandwich grillers, chafing dishes, and even charcoal burners. It is not likely that in any one family all of these appliances will be used at the table. Certainly the "firsts"—toasters and waffle bakers—continue to be favorites or even "musts" in some families. Even though cooking at the table is on the increase, the smaller dining tables are not conducive to ease of this operation. Neither are electric outlets always in convenient locations for table cooking.

For the devotees of this style of food preparation, a way will usually be found to overcome such problems. However, safety should be the deciding factor in using any table appliance. If there is danger of falls by stepping over electric cords or burns from an overcrowded table, cooking at the table should not be attempted.

One of the most versatile appliances is the electric skillet or "fry pan." Happily, it has many more uses than for frying. Interesting "stews," such as the Japanese *sukiyaki* (see p. 563) are unusual and dramatic dishes to cook at the table in this appliance. Since pancakes are as versatile as the electric skillet they afford many possibilities for cooking at the table. Like waffles, they may provide the basis for either the main dish or the dessert. Whether the pancakes are cooked at the table to be served with creamed ham and mushrooms or for a strawberry "shortcake" as a dessert, the process is sure to be an intriguing one. Hot scrambled eggs have been enjoyed for the first time by some families who cook them at the table, and for the families who enjoy fried eggs, the electric skillet has many possibilities for preparing a variety of foods.

Chafing dishes, which were popular in the Twenties, are again in vogue. For the most part, they are a semi-luxury item because they are made of copper, brass, stainless steel, porcelain, and silver. In addition to making simple dishes as rarebit and Swiss fondue at the table, chafing dishes are excellent for keeping foods hot, such as meat balls, creoles, curries and sauces.

Serving coffee at the table. The coffee pot is no longer a "standard" on the American breakfast table. The instant variety of coffee has taken over in many families with the essential hot water being provided by an electric "tea" kettle or being poured from an appropriate pitcher. If coffee is served at the table from a traditional pot, it is convenient to group the cups at the left of the person serving.

When coffee is served as a separate course at dinner or with the dessert, it is frequently poured at the table, using a coffee service. The coffee service is placed in front of the hostess and the tray has on it, arranged conveniently, the coffee pot, the cups and saucers, the spoons, and perhaps the cream and sugar. The cups are not lifted to the pot but are left on the tray when the coffee is being poured. The hostess places a spoon on each saucer, and if she is serving cream and sugar she asks the guests their preference. The same order of passing is used as for other serving, the hostess specifying to whom the first cup goes. If a maid is serving, she may place the cups and pass the sugar and cream. After serving the coffee, the service is left on the table, and if necessary the pot is replenished so that second servings may be offered.

Serving a dinner course in the living room. Entertaining at dinner sometimes presents a problem in a busy household. Since the hostess must necessarily be in the kitchen just before serving the meal, she may plan to serve the beginning course in the living room, with the host "doing the honors" while she prepares to serve the main course. Appetizers served in the living room for a family dinner are easy and are an acceptable variation. First courses which can be served in the living room are limited. Fruit juice or tomato juice cocktails may be served alone, or they may be accompanied with tasty canapés or assorted hors d'oeuvres of the type which can be eaten with the fingers. The cocktail may be served in a small beverage glass, a sherbet glass, or a cocktail glass. It is not necessary to use a plate under the glass unless the accompaniments include Queen olives, ripe olives, or some other food which contains inedible portions. If plates are used, they may be bread-and-butter plates or salad plates. Individual trays are attractive for this service. The canapés or hors d'oeuvres may be arranged on a large plate or tray and passed for the guests to select their own, or the guests may be invited to serve themselves with cocktail and accompaniments from a small table arranged for this purpose.

Napkins are not essential for this course, but small fingertip or cocktail napkins may be used if the hostess desires.

The English custom of serving after-dinner coffee in the living room is a pleasant way to finish a dinner. This is usually not done if the first course has been served there. If a coffee service is used, it may be placed on one of the living-room tables, on a tea cart, or on a coffee table, and the hostess pours. Coffee service in the living room is more relaxing when the danger of spilling is lessened by using cups that are securely "seated" in saucers.

If a member of the family or a guest assists the hostess, this makes for more relaxation. Coffee may be served in the living room without a coffee service. In this case the coffee is poured in the kitchen and brought into the living room on a tray.

Behavior at meal time. In spite of the changes that have come about in all areas related to family meals, there has been no change in the socially accepted standards for human behavior when it comes to the all-important activity of consuming food. One of the most fortunate attributes a person can possess is knowing the right thing to do at the right moment. To say that this avoids embarrassment is an understatement. It is better to phrase it positively and say that a person need never be embarrassed if he is schooled in the basic rules of conduct (see Fig. 65). For those who receive early training, good manners are a matter of routine and are performed unconsciously.

In the rush of college life students sometimes forget the importance of their behavior at meal times. To say that gracious table manners are an asset is not sufficient; they are essential. Such manners are habitual to an individual of refinement and are not just donned for special occasions.

Table etiquette not only concerns the manner of holding the knife and fork, the way the napkin is used, and the method of eating soup; equally important are consideration for others, the ability to engage in interesting conversation, posture, and general poise.

Class discussion based on observations of behavior in student dining rooms will bring out many peeves held by students against their fellow diners. The attitude of not caring about one's manners at dormitory meals can easily lead to the habit of being careless about behavior at other times.

Students are not always aware of the many variations that exist in customs of dining in other countries. In India, for instance, even those persons belonging to the higher castes may eat all or a part of their food with the fingers. This technique as has been observed is so skillfully and gracefully maneuvered as to not offend in any way. In Chile it is considered "bad" manners to sit at the dining table with hands in the lap, they should be resting on the table. The Chinese custom of lifting the bowl to the mouth in order to facilitate the use of chopsticks is well known to anyone who has eaten in a Chinese home or restaurant. In America some foods such as many types of sandwiches are eaten out of hand, while in Denmark and Sweden the versatile open-face sandwiches are always eaten with a fork. "Knife-fork-and-spoon" soups are characteristic of some countries (the bouillebaisse of France for instance), but our soups are always eaten with a spoon, with the exception of clear broth or consomme which is sometimes drunk.

Nothing is more embarrassing to an individual with polished manners than to be at the table with someone who makes himself conspicuous because of crude manners. In fact, adverse criticism of table manners is (and has been from the time of Henry VIII, for example) usually based on the conspicuous-

Courtesy U. S. Department of Agriculture

Fig. 65. These self-conscious second graders are being taught one of the fundamental rules of dining etiquette.

ness of people who do not comply with accepted forms of table conduct. Often the individuals themselves are the ones least aware of this difference. There is no better way for one to make a check on his table manners than to observe the manners of others. In doing this it will be noticed that people behave differently at the table. Some of those observed will have manners that are above reproach, because they eat food and drink beverages without attracting attention to the operations of eating and drinking.

The spirit of sociability is the principal factor contributing to successful meals; however, the proper method of eating is not neglected by individuals of refinement. Following are some of the points that are of paramount importance:

Promptness. The considerate guest arrives at meals five to ten minutes before the appointed hour. Members of a family should show the same consideration for the person who is responsible for the service of the meals. The principal reason for promptness seems obvious—food which is ready to serve at a specified time is never as palatable if the meal is delayed. In homes where there are household employees, their hours should be considered. Careless dinner guests who are late in arriving may cause a serious disruption in the household.

Fig. 66. Proper method of picking up a goblet.

Conversation. It is the responsibility of everyone at the table to make the conversation bright and interesting. This is particularly important for the host and hostess. At a dinner party your partner may be a delightful conversationalist, but you must not give him your undivided attention. Remember that there is someone on the other side of you, and it is only courteous to divide your attention. A wise hostess will assemble groups she knows to be congenial. At such a party, the conversation is usually not a problem.

Position. Unless the posture is good while dining, a person appears slovenly and crude. Disagreeable practices include lounging in a chair, twisting one's feet around the chair rungs, bending over to eat, and leaning on the table with the arms. The position of elbows is a much discussed point. They should, of course, be kept close to the side while eating or cutting. It is permissible to *rest* them on the table while engaged in conversation between courses. This custom is prevalent in public eating places where the noise makes conversation difficult.

Napkins. The napkin was originated to prevent the clothes of the diner from becoming soiled; however, this purpose should never be apparent. The napkin rests on the lap, folded in half if it is a dinner napkin, and unfolded entirely if it is a luncheon napkin. It should be used as inconspicuously as possible, especially when it is brought above the table. The napkin should be slipped down in the lap and unfolded without display. A guest for one meal does not refold the napkin at the conclusion of the meal, but places it neatly beside the plate.

Use of silver. An individual's manners may be quickly judged by his use of table implements. The knife and fork are perhaps the most misused. The correct position for holding them while cutting, and the proper methods of conveying food to the mouth are shown in Figure 67. The third illustration from the top shows the Continental custom of conveying food to the mouth, which is also common in certain parts of the United States. The second and third illustrations show the correct position of the knife when not in use. The fourth illustration shows the position of the knife and fork at the completion of the main course. The rather common practice of "gang-planking" the knife on the edge of the plate is to be discouraged, as it not only appears awkward but places the knife in a position to be easily knocked off on the cloth. This causes embarrassment and may soil the linen. It is permissible to cut the

Fig. 67. Correct use of knife and fork. Top to bottom: *cutting meat, American method of carrying meat to the mouth, Continental method, knife and fork at end of meal.*

Fig. 68. The correct use of the spoon: top, *placed on the plate at the end of a course;* bottom, *use of the soup spoon.*

salad with a knife. A salad knife is usually not provided for this, and the dinner knife is used.

Any liquid food is eaten from the side of the spoon rather than from the tip. Spoons for beverages are used for stirring and for testing the temperature of the beverage. Sugar may be dissolved and cream or lemon may be added by gently agitating the drink. Vigorous stirring of beverages is not only noisy but unsightly.

Some people have a bad habit of stirring hot cereal vigorously in order to mix it with the cream and sugar. The illustration at the bottom in Figure 68

Courtesy Japan Tourist Association

Fig. 69. Tea Ceremony. Estheticism is the keynote of the mentality of the Japanese people. This is shown in the development in Japan of such unique forms of esthetic accomplishments as tea ceremony, flower arrangement, dancing and music. The tea cult is a "religion of the art of life" in which the Japanese appreciate the artistic atmosphere fostered by the delicate aroma of powdered tea.

shows the proper use of a soup spoon. The illustration at the top in Figure 68 shows the position of a spoon at the completion of a course which has been served in a sherbet glass. At no time should a spoon stand in a sherbet or parfait glass, a beverage cup, a bouillon cup, or a drinking glass. When not in use, it should be placed on the plate or saucer under the glass or cup. When coasters are not provided for ice tea glasses, the spoon is rested on the main plate or on the salad or bread-and-butter plate.

Finger foods. A number of foods are eaten with the fingers. These include olives, some pickles, potato chips, shoestring potatoes, strawberries served with the hulls on, unpeeled fresh pineapple wedges, burr artichokes, radishes, celery, strips of raw carrot, raw cauliflower flowerlets, corn on the cob, crisp, *dry* bacon, hors d'oeuvres of many types, any kind of sandwich that does not have a soft filling (a knife and fork are used for club sandwiches and others of more than one layer), and many kinds of fruit, such as plums, pears, and apples. Regardless of the food being eaten, only one hand should be used. Eating corn from the cob can be very gracefully done if the individual does not appear too eager for the kernels.

Comments about food. A hostess who is apologetic for service, food, and the cooking places her guests in an embarrassing position. Regardless of the food or service, guests will take away a pleasant impression of the hostess who has dispensed gracious hospitality. At an informal meal of an intimate group, it is not out of place to remark on the skill of the hostess concerning the preparation of the food, but it is never wise for a guest to enter into discussion of food likes and dislikes, particularly before the meal. If the menu is not known, this discussion may prove embarrassing.

Finger bowls. Finger bowls may be used at the conclusion of either a formal or an informal meal or following a fruit course. Fingers should be dipped into the water lightly, one hand at a time, and then dried with the napkin.

SUGGESTIONS FOR LABORATORY

Laboratory projects in the area of meal management will be far more challenging if they are planned cooperatively by instructor and students. This will mean that many ideas and philosophies (based on experiences and associations) will be injected into the projects. It will probably mean that they will also be more meaningful.

In executing the laboratory projects it is desirable to make application of subject matter, techniques, and skills learned in preceding courses in foods, nutrition, household equipment, and art.

Some suggested areas for planning projects are: orientation, patterns of eating, meals at different cost levels, exploration of different types of markets including those using trading stamps, visits to real families in the local area, and changing trends in the way of serving meals.

REFERENCES

Cooper, Lenna F., Edith M. Barber, Helen S. Mitchell, and Henderike J. Rynbergen, *Nutrition and Health,* 13th Ed. J. B. Lippincott Co., Philadelphia, 1958.

Cullen, M. O., *How to Carve Meat, Game, and Poultry*. McGraw-Hill Book Company, New York, 1941.

Faulkner, Ray and Sarah, *Inside Today's Home*. Henry Holt and Company, New York, 1954.

Goldmann, Mary E., *Planning and Serving your Meals,* 2nd Edition. McGraw-Hill Book Company, 1959.

Hackwood, Frederick W., *Good Cheer*. Sturgis and Walton, New York, 1941.

Hovey, Helen Stone, and Kay Reynolds, *The Practical Book of Food Shopping*. J. B. Lippincott Co., Philadelphia, 1950.

Kinder, Faye, *Meal Management*. The Macmillan Company, New York, 1956.

Leverton, Ruth, *Food Becomes You*. University of Nebraska Press, 1952.

Nickell, Paulena, and Jean Muir Dorsey, *Management in Family Living,* 3rd. Edition. John Wiley & Sons, New York, 1959.

Rose, Mary Swartz, *Feeding the Family*. The Macmillan Company, New York, 1940.

Sprackling, Helen, *Setting Your Table*. M. Barrows and Company, New York, 1941.

Todoroff, Alexander, *Food Buyer's Information Book*. The Grocery Trade Publishing House, Chicago, 1946.

U.S.D.A., Food, The Yearbook of Agriculture, Washington, D. C., 1959.

U.S.D.A., Marketing, The Yearbook of Agriculture, Washington D. C, 1954.

Wilson, Eva D., Katherine H. Fisher, and Mary E. Fuqua, *Principles of Nutrition*. John Wiley & Sons, Inc., New York, 1959.

UNIT
23

Table Appointments

The modern homemaker has an interesting but difficult problem in selecting her linen, china, silver, and glass. Never before has there been such a varied choice in these articles. The homemakers of two or three generations ago used principally white damask on their tables, because little else was available. Most of their china was white porcelain, imported from France, England, or Germany, and the design was usually a gold band or a dainty floral pattern, as designs were limited on all but the most expensive china. The glass was principally American, but in this field there was a greater choice. The selection of silver, however, was not perplexing, since comparatively few patterns were available.

A different problem confronts homemakers today in purchasing table appointments. Careful buying in department, specialty, hardware, and five-and-ten-cent stores enables a homemaker to secure attractive items even when her income is very modest. No matter what the income, selection will depend upon the ability of the purchaser to assemble appointments which harmonize in form, color, texture, and design.

Knowledge of processes involved in the manufacture of the various table appointments is desirable not only for intelligent selection but for appreciation and continued enjoyment of the articles after they are selected and put into use. Table appointments are as important as furniture in expressing the individuality and culture of the owner. But more important to the person herself and to the members of her family is the pleasure that returns again and again in the consciousness of beauty in ordinary surroundings.

CHINA

History. Ceramics, the potter's art, is one of the oldest of all arts. Its origin dates back to prehistoric times, when plastic mud was used by primitive man as the sole ingredient to fashion vessels and dishes for household purposes. These containers were allowed to bake in the sun until hard enough to use for holding dry substances. Later it was discovered, probably by accident, that after being baked in open fires these bodies had added strength and would hold liquids. Thus gradually the progress of civilization was reflected in the style of the pottery made. Superior clays were discovered and used, as were improved methods of shaping, firing, and hardening the ware. Even before the ancient potter's wheel was conceived, primitive people shaped utensils with their hands, aided by sticks and stones. Indians used corncobs for this purpose, and among some tribes this method of shaping is still practiced. The next method of shaping was by molding clay around frameworks of twigs to obtain desired shapes, the framework being removed after the clay hardened. Succeeding these methods, a stone with a flat bottom was used. This enabled the potter to sit and mold his clay into more perfect shapes by rotating the models in any desired direction. Gourds frequently served both for designs and molds among primitive peoples. The next improvement was the first crude potter's wheel, which was turned by hand. The potter's wheel used in industry today, though scientifically constructed and electrically driven, is a direct outgrowth of this first ancient potter's wheel.

The methods of firing and hardening pottery also improved with the passing of time. First the open fires were used; then crude kilns were built so that the heat could be held in and thus afford higher temperatures. The beehive kiln followed, and later kilns were constructed which protected the pottery from the direct fire and fumes. The modern ones have carefully controlled temperatures permitting the gradual baking of the ware.

The development of pottery has been described as "one of the most romantic and interesting sidelights of history." Since the days of Ancient Egypt, successive generations have contributed to its beauty and technique. Perfection of form and unity of design have never been more apparent than in the vases of the Greeks. The figures painted on these vases still help to keep alive the history and customs of the Greek civilization.

China is the only nation to have given its name to an art and industry. Chinese ceramics were manufactured centuries before the Christian era. "Chinese ceramics are bound up with the literature, the history, and the complicated mythology for which this ancient people is remarkable." [1] The versatility of its scientists and artists was unlimited. The beauty and variety of colors for glazes and enamels produced by the chemists were excelled only by the artists' use of them. The superb forms which they created—the flowers, birds, animals, mythological characters, landscapes, and human figures—have made their designs the envy and despair of the artists of the Western

---

[1] From Frederick Litchfield, *Pottery and Porcelain* (New York: Macmillan, 1925), p. 109.

Courtesy New York Times Studio

Fig. 70. Hand-painted Chinese porcelain showing the traditional Chinese dragon design.

world. For two thousand years the pottery and porcelains of the Chinese were unsurpassed. The wide variety and richness or delicacy of color, the eggshell thinness, the translucency of the first porcelains have never been equaled. We read in Chinese chronicles of vases "blue as the sky after rain, when seen beneath the clouds" and as thin as paper. It is little wonder that the early European navigators brought home amazing tales of the magic and beauty of the art. From the thirteenth to the eighteenth centuries various European countries tried in vain to reproduce it. (See Fig. 70.)

The Italian Majolica ware of the fourteenth to sixteenth centuries was rich in color and varied in design. The metallic glazes added much to the beauty of the ware, but the coarseness of the native clay rendered the products impractical for general use, despite their beauty and popularity.

In the meantime, the Portuguese, the Dutch, and later the English East India Company imported vast quantities of china from China and Japan. "The Japanese potters of the sixteenth century made their most important pieces for export to China, where pottery and porcelain have always been valued, and to Holland where it had a considerable European market." [1]

In spite of every effort on the part of European potters to solve it, the secret of the Chinese formula remained inviolate. In 1715–1716, however, John Böttger, a German chemist who was an experimenter in porcelain-making, under the patronage of the Elector of Saxony manufactured the first true European porcelain from clay which he discovered in Saxony.

For a few years Germany controlled the porcelain market of Europe, but France soon manufactured the beautiful Sèvres ware, made from an artificial but very beautiful paste. English potters were working in many centers in an attempt to rival the continental market. First a soft-paste porcelain was made; then in the early nineteenth century bone china—a hard-paste porcelain—was manufactured by Josiah Spode II.

Modern manufacture of china. The chief materials used for making china are ground sand, clays of many different kinds, feldspar, calcium, and bone. The materials used depend upon the type of china manufactured. Ground sand is used both in the body of china and as the principal ingredient in the glaze. The chemical composition of the clays differs. They are compounds of silica and alumina and may contain lime, magnesium, soda or potash, or metallic oxides. Kaolin, so named for the Chinese hill where it was first found, is the finest type of natural clay and was the first material used for making porcelain. For many years the secret of beautiful Chinese porcelain was not known. The discovery of kaolin in Germany is described by John Spargo in his book *Early American Pottery and China.*[2]

By one of those happy and fortunate coincidences which loom so largely in the romance of history . . . a wealthy German iron founder named John Schnorr, riding in the country near Schneeberg, Saxony, one day observed that his horse was finding it difficult to raise his feet. On making an examination he found that the clay was very white, extremely plastic, and adhesive. He conceived the idea of using it to make hair-powder, then so much in demand. He proceeded to carry this idea into effect. Böttger came across some of this hair-powder and apparently suspecting that it was a powdered clay, experimented with it. Thus was discovered the supply of kaolin which was to make his discovery of the Chinese secret commercially useful and to revolutionize the industry.

[1] *Ibid.*, p. 194.

[2] John Spargo, *Early American Pottery and China,* p. 14. By permission of Appleton-Century-Crofts, Inc., New York, 1926.

Courtesy Towle Silversmiths

Fig. 71. Modern American designers have created pottery of simple elegance, both beautiful and practical.

Feldspar is a mineral which is widely distributed; and since its hardness is little inferior to that of quartz, it naturally makes a superior grade of ware. It has properties capable of imparting translucency to china, due to its fusibility. Bone in a pulverized state is the ingredient responsible for very beautiful translucent "bone china," much of which is imported. Calcium is added to some clay mixtures to fuse with other ingredients in order that the china may be fired.

The principal steps in the manufacture of china are: (1) mixing the ingredients; (2) shaping; (3) firing; (4) decorating; and (5) glazing.

Mixing the ingredients. The correct proportioning of the ingredients is of great importance in this industry, for the ingredients and their proportions determine the type and quality of ware produced. Water is used to blend the thoroughly ground materials, and since clays are stiff and viscid when moist, this blending requires a special type of mixer to make a thoroughly homogeneous mixture. When completely combined, the mixture is of the consistency of thick cream and is called "slip." This slip is next screened in order to remove any coarse particles. Traces of iron are removed by electric magnets. If not removed, they cause the brown specks often seen in inferior china. Following this procedure, most of the water is removed from the mixture by strong pressure. The clay is then put into a pug mill that renders it more plastic and removes any air that may be present. If air is not removed from the clay at this point, the fired china is less dense and consequently less durable, because the air pockets near the surface will break, leaving small pits in the ware. It is not uncommon to see these pits in tableware. When the clay comes out of the pug mill, it is ready to be shaped.

Shaping. The shaping of the prepared clay into plates, cups, pitchers, etc., may be done by one of two different methods—jiggering and casting. Jiggering derives its name from the modern potter's wheel, which is called a jigger. In this method the potter who operates the jigger receives the piece to be shaped on a plaster-of-Paris mold so that the finished shape is formed, one side by the mold as it revolves on the jigger and the other by the potter as he brings down a steel tool which has been accurately shaped for the piece being made. Separate molds and tools are of course used for each individual shape and size. The ware is dried for several hours by a slow oven heat and is then removed from the molds. After the molds are removed, the shapes are finished by smoothing and rounding the edges. Following this process they are ready to be fired.

Casting is a method sometimes used for shaping irregular pieces such as pitchers. In this process the thick creamlike slip is poured into plaster-of-Paris molds, the insides of which are shaped the same as the outside of the piece to be made. Upon standing, the plaster of Paris draws the water from the clay solution which fills the inside of the mold. This leaves a coating of plastic clay of varying thickness, depending upon how many minutes it has stood. The remaining slip is poured out; the mold is removed; and the shape is dried, sponged, inspected, and fired.

Firing. The strength and durability of china are determined by the materials used and by the firing process. All china is either vitrified or vitreous, depending upon the firing. Ware which has been thoroughly fired, leaving no vacant places in the body, is vitrified and is hard, nonporous, and durable. The modern firing of china consists first of placing it in saggers, (cylindrical

Courtesy New York Times Studio

Fig. 72. Antique ironstone china.

cases made of fire clay), or trolleys (long carts with three or four shelves). These move automatically through the kiln. Most of the kilns used today are of a tunnel type in which the temperature is so regulated that the ware is gradually brought to the maximum temperature and then is gradually cooled as it passes through the cooling zones of the kiln. The firing time is from 48 to 72 hours. The term "biscuit" is applied to all ware at the completion of the firing or baking stage. "Chaffers, the distinguished English ceramist, has aptly likened biscuit china to a new clay tobacco-pipe without the least gloss on it."[1] Before biscuit ware is decorated, it is polished. This provides a better surface for taking the glaze as well as the decoration.

Decorating. While china is decorated in various ways, all decorated ware is classed as either underglaze or overglaze. The underglaze decorations are those applied to the biscuit ware and the overglaze decorations are those applied after the biscuit has been glazed.

[1] *Ibid.*

Underglaze decorations are the more permanent type, since they are protected by the glaze. Decorations of this type include the decalcomania process. By this process designs are transferred to the china from paper which has been carefully printed and dusted with dry colors. Other underglazed decorations are applied with a spray gun. This method is used for solid color decorations and for wide bands of color. The portion of the china not to be decorated is protected by covering it. Some underglaze decorations are applied by hand.

Overglaze decorations are much less used because of their perishability. They include gold and silver decorations and some of the raised enamel ones as well as many others. Most overglaze decorations are applied by hand. The cost of this operation added to the cost of gold or silver accounts, in part, for the high prices of china with gold and silver incrustations. Overglaze decorations are also sometimes used on cheaper china because the glaze is inferior and will not permit the use of color under it.

Glazing. This process follows decoration except in overglaze designs, as has been mentioned, in which case it precedes decoration. The glaze is a very finely ground glass suspended in water. It is a thick, transparent liquid which is applied by a glazer. He immerses the ware in the glaze, and on taking it out he shakes each piece in order to remove the surplus glaze. A great deal of skill is required on the part of these operators, since they must know exactly how much glaze to allow to adhere to each piece. After the ware is dipped in the glaze, it is placed in a drying machine for a short time and is then ready for the second and last firing, which is called the "glost" firing. The glost kilns are similar to those used in the first firing, and the process is practically the same except that the heat is less intense. Excessive temperature affects the design to the extent of destroying some colors and injuring others. After the glost firing the china has a smooth, glassy surface and a bright finish.

Selection of china. China is selected for the most part with little appreciation and knowledge of what makes it expensive or inexpensive, attractive or unattractive, durable or not durable. However, the careful consumer stops to analyze the problem and discovers that well-chosen china has the following characteristics:

1) It is attractive because of the material, shape, design, and color.

2) It does not involve the expenditure of too large an amount of money.

3) It is durable because of a nonporous body, a well-applied glaze, and a type of decoration which neither wears nor washes off.

4) It can be replenished as pieces are broken.

5) It is in keeping with the type of home and table appointments with which it is to be used.

Finding china which will measure up to these specifications is not difficult if the purchaser knows simple china terminology. It is necessary to understand the classification of tableware according to the materials from which it is made. While the term "china" is usually applied to all dishes used for the table, in the strict sense of the word this is a misnomer. Pottery, semiporcelain, and porcelain are the terms commonly used to designate certain qualities. Pottery is often spoken of as earthenware. "Semichina" is sometimes used instead of "semiporcelain," and the words "china" and "porcelain" are often used interchangeably. China was the first country to make porcelain; hence the term "china." The word "porcelain" is "derived from the Italian *porcellana,* a cowry-shell, by way of its French adaptation, *porcelaine*. The original Italian is said to have been applied to the cowry-shell as a name because of some fancied resemblance of the shell to a pig's back, *porcella* meaning a small pig. The Ceramic term 'porcelain' is supposed to have been suggested by a fancied resemblance of the quality of the ware to the polished surface of a cowry-shell." [1]

Pottery. Pottery in the broadest sense of the word includes all clay objects which have been molded into shapes from wet clay and then baked or hardened by fire. Since semiporcelain and porcelain may also be made of clay and hardened by heat, the essential differences in these three groups would be in the quality of the clays or materials used, the method of mixing the ingredients, and the degree of heat to which they are subjected in the process of firing. Pottery bodies are not as hard as porcelain and semiporcelain, because the materials used cannot be fired as intensely. Consequently, all pottery is vitreous. The clays are inferior to those of porcelain and semiporcelain. The impurities of the clays are responsible, in part, for the charm of some pottery. The qualities which make pottery beautiful and attractive are not desired in porcelain and semiporcelain. The inaccuracy with which many pieces of pottery are shaped, making them appear hand-molded, and the irregularities in design and color, giving them a craftlike, peasant appearance, would stamp porcelain and semiporcelain as imperfect. Another characteristic which distinguishes pottery is that it is opaque. It may be glazed or unglazed, and while it is often thought of as being highly colored, much of it is neutral in color.

Pottery as it is used for the table today embraces many different kinds and types of dishes. Some of the pottery which is available for table use is of a very crude type. It is extremely fragile because of a soft body and a poor glaze, and is therefore not suitable for constant use. Upon examination it will be found that some of these crude wares are too porous to hold water. On the other hand, pottery may be had which is so refined in type as to resemble porcelain closely. Perhaps the greatest quantity of pottery manufactured is of a type which falls between the groups of crude and highly refined pottery. In this classification we find dishes which give good service and are pleasing

---

[1] Spargo, *op. cit.,* p. 9.

in color, design, and texture, being manufactured by a number of reputable concerns.

Much of the imported pottery, such as Italian, and many domestic potteries are of a very superior quality, having designs, colors, and contours which make it so distinctive that some individuals choose it in preference to porcelain. Pottery of this type has a dignity and charm which makes it possible to achieve beautiful and satisfying table effects in both formal and casual surroundings.

The growing popularity of informal entertaining has been a boon to the pottery manufacturers, especially those in the United States, and attractive services for breakfasts, outdoor meals, buffet suppers, Sunday-night suppers, and such occasions are in vogue at present.

Pottery calls for linen of peasant or homespun character and glass which approximates it in form and texture. It would seem, then, that with its limited use, and its demand for special linens and glass, a complete pottery service might almost be considered a luxury. However, pottery might be used exclusively in a simple home where informal service prevails, or, as has been stated, certain types may constitute a homemaker's best china.

Since a great deal of the pottery made today is highly colored, the purchaser should exercise care in making her selection. Shop displays frequently show several colors combined in one cover—a yellow plate, a blue cup in an orange saucer, and a green mug are not uncommon. Such color combinations have little artistry and would probably grow tiresome after being used a few times. It is possible to combine two or three colors and obtain pleasing, smart effects, which will stand repeated use without becoming dull and uninteresting. Some such combinations include: chartreuse and gray; several tones of brown, shading from a warm leather tan to a dark reddish brown; pale yellow and a light turquoise; and dark red combined with a putty color.

Semiporcelain. Some authorities class as earthenware everything that is not porcelain, thereby eliminating the middle group of semiporcelain. Such a classification makes it difficult for the beginner to learn to know "china." Generally speaking, semiporcelain is a ware superior to pottery because of better materials and longer firing; however, there are different grades of semiporcelain just as there are different grades of pottery. Some of the very finest of domestic and imported "china" is semiporcelain, while the poorest quality of tableware is also semiporcelain. These poorer grades soon craze, and the porous, soft bodies cause them to break easily. It is not uncommon to see dishes in use which are crazed, cracked, and discolored. The discoloration is due to the absorption of grease, food particles and other foreign substances. These dishes are not only unsightly, but are unsanitary and unfit for use. A dish of this type emits an odor of rancid fat. Discolored dishes are frequently noticed in public eating places where inexpensive vitreous semiporcelain is used. Vitrified china will absorb neither food particles nor odors.

Fig. 73. A test for distinguishing porcelain from semiporcelain: left, *porcelain is translucent;* right, *semiporcelain is opaque.*

Another significant fact about semiporcelain is that it is of lighter weight than pottery. It may be either vitreous or vitrified, the better qualities being vitrified. Unlike pottery, it is always glazed. All semiporcelain is opaque, which makes it easily distinguishable from porcelain. (See Fig. 73.)

Many people prefer a good grade of semiporcelain to porcelain because it is better adapted to everyday use and is much less expensive. In buying semiporcelain it is possible to express good taste in china selection for any type of home, because of the wide range of choice in both quality and design.

Porcelain. "Porcelain, though first evolved from pottery, is a thing beyond and apart from it—and pottery is not porcelain. It is quite true that porcelain is made by potters and that a mechanical and decorative kinship exists; that its making is included within the scope of the fictile art along with the making of pottery; and that the ultimate perfection of porcelain's manufacture was developed from the processes of pottery making. But porcelain is the highest, the most precious, and the most highly organized expression of the potter's art." [1]

Porcelain has as its principal ingredients kaolin and feldspar or bone. It is distinguished from all other tableware by its translucency. This is easily tested by holding a piece to the light with the fingers between it and the light, observing that the outline of the fingers is visible through the china. (See Fig. 73.) All porcelain is vitrified, which means that it is hard and nonabsorbent. Porcelain does not chip as easily as earthenware and semiporcelain, but because of the hard, compact body it is more brittle. The purchase of

[1] Harold Donaldson Eberlein and Roger Wearne Ramsdell, *The Practical Book of Chinaware* (Philadelphia: Lippincott, 1925), p. 14.

porcelain involves the expenditure of more money than the average homemaker usually has to invest in china. Aside from the cost of porcelain, the buyer must consider the cost of handsome linen, fine glass, and sterling silver which she will desire to have as appropriate appointments on a table laid with porcelain. Expensive china is frequently a source of great anxiety to the homemaker, and rather than run the risk of having it broken, she keeps it stacked away on the cupboard shelves for use only on special occasions. It is difficult to justify a large investment in china when this is the case. Many persons who live in areas where china is manufactured go directly to the plants and select "seconds" in fine china. Sometimes the flaws are tiny blisters or irregularities in the design which are so slight as to be hardly noticeable. Such "seconds" can often be purchased for a mere fraction of their cost if they were perfect.

Domestic and imported china. For many years the United States lagged far behind other countries in the manufacture of beautiful and serviceable china, and American homemakers had to rely almost entirely on imported wares. Today, however, many domestic "chinas" compare favorably in quality and beauty with the finest of the imported chinas, and since they are also giving excellent service they are most worthy of consideration. American porcelains are particularly beautiful in quality, coloring, and design.

Recently changes in china, both domestic and imported, have been reflected in new shapes, different patterns and deep colors, such as smoky blues and fern greens. Coupe shapes which have been used by certain American manufacturers are now seen in some of the English bone china. Oval shapes with beveled edges are also seen, as are many dishes which are square in shape. Many of the patterns are hand painted and a growing number of contemporary designs are noticed. These are not as symmetrical and precise as some of the motifs which seem to be timeless in appeal.

The demand for imported china has remained great, in many instances exceeding the demand for domestic china. This may be partially due to the prejudice some people hold against domestic china, believing it to be grossly inferior to the imported wares that have been used in their families by preceding generations. It is also true that many inexperienced buyers do not know of the availability of the domestic wares. When making china selections, many individuals have in recent years been pleasantly surprised to find a wide range of choice in superb American-made china.

The person who has made an intensive study of china may be able to identify its origin and distinguish the wares of the leading potters of various countries by characteristic designs, potters' marks, shapes, and colors, but the average consumer, with little knowledge of "china," is faced with a problem of considerable magnitude in selecting wisely. She is assisted to some extent by the manufacturer's marks, but for the most part she must rely upon the dealer for information.

Courtesy Corning Glass

Fig. 74. Space age material used for modern age cooking. China-like utensils can be used directly on the range, and taken to the table for attractive service.

Range-to-table cookware. In addition to imported porcelain utensils which may be used directly on the range top or in the oven, several other materials resembling china are being used for multiple purpose cook-and-serve utensils. Figure 74 shows some of this new ware. These "pans" are made of a super-ceramic which was first developed for use in the nose cones of guided missiles.

Courtesy Corning Glass

Fig. 75. Range-to-table cooking utensils. (*See Fig. 74.*)

Plastic dishes. Plastic dinnerware and eating implements are being widely manufactured. Some of these are well designed, pleasing in color and sturdy at room temperature. However, the plastics used for these items and for certain kitchen ware do not all stand up under hot water. This creates a special problem where a dishwasher is used. One plastic, Melamine, is a virtually unbreakable synthetic which is used for dishes and which resists high heat. Others, such as polyethylene, the "squeeze" material, should be washed with warm water and a mild soap. Figure 77 shows an interesting combination of plastic dishes, textured linen and appropriate table decorations.

Glass dishes. While glass has long been used for certain dishes it is now employed for the making of entire dinner sets. An advantage of this particular type of "china" is that it is heat resistant. In the simple setting in Figure 76 plates and serving dishes are of opaque glass.

Care and storage of china. Careful handling of any kind of tableware prolongs its life. Abusive treatment may not result in breakage but in cracking and chipping, either of which spoils a piece of china for further service. It is not uncommon to see homemakers or household employees handling the "good" china very carefully while the "everyday dishes" receive rather rough treatment; consequently, the families may use, for most of their meals, odds

Courtesy Corning Glass

Fig. 76. A utility service of opaque glass.

and ends of cracked or chipped china, while the "good" china stays on the cupboard shelves awaiting a guest or a holiday dinner.

Dishes must also be handled carefully in order to protect the glaze and the decoration. The following points should be observed in washing and caring for china:

1) Glazes become grazed if dishes are heated by placing in hot ovens or are overchilled by leaving for long periods in the refrigerator.

2) The effect of changing temperature in hot or cold water may cause china to crack. The glaze is likely to be affected by this also.

3) A rubber mat used on a porcelain or other hard-surfaced drainboard is a guard against china breakage.

4) Overglaze decorations are affected by extremely hot water and strong soaps. Gold decorations are particularly sensitive to this treatment. Vinegar and lemon juice affect metallic decorations, and should be rinsed from dishes immediately.

5) A wire dish drainer, preferably a rubber-covered or a plastic one, prevents breakage, as it protects dishes from striking against each other. The dish drainer is also a labor-saver.

6) Accidents are not likely to occur if dishes are carefully stored and systematically arranged on the shelves where they are kept.

The proper storage of china is important if the china is not to be abused. It should be carefully placed on shelves of suitable width for the various pieces. For instance, cups are more safely stored if placed on narrow shelves rather than hung from hooks or arranged in stacks of more than two; platters and other large flat serving dishes are conveniently stored standing on

Courtesy Boonton Moulding Company

Fig. 77. Unbreakable plastic dishes are used in this attractive table setting.

edge in a part of the cupboard which is divided into vertical partitions.

GLASS

The manufacture and making of glass is a very old craft, so old that its origin is not certainly known. Both the Egyptians and the Phoenicians were familiar with it; Egyptian opaque glass of the fourth millennium B.C. exists, as do glass vessels made by Egyptians about 1800 B.C. It is thought probable that these master craftsmen invented glass-making, and the Phoenicians, a traveling people, developed the craft and spread the knowledge of it. There exists Assyrian clear glass of about 700 B.C. and the Greeks are believed to have made glass about 600 B.C. . . . The Romans learned the craft of glass-making, probably from conquered people, mastered most of the technical processes in glass-making, produced pure crystalline glass that was ranked with the precious metals in value, perfected the difficult "Cameo glass" of which the "Portland vase," broken in 1845, was the most famous example, made spun glass and millefiori glass and invented processes of applying gold leaf as ornament.[1]

Glassmaking in Italy reached its zenith in the sixteenth century. The industry was started in Venice. As the furnaces increased in number, they became a fire hazard and were banished from the city in 1291 and moved to the island of Murano. The secrets of the making of exquisite Venetian glass were

[1] From *National Encyclopedia,* Vol. 4, p. 595, 1935. By permission of P. E. Collier and Sons, New York.

carefully guarded by the jealous Venetians, who wished to maintain their supremacy in this fascinating art. In order that these secrets should not be imparted to others, the glass blowers were virtually imprisoned on the island. Departure from Murano was a crime punishable by death. To compensate the workers for their imprisonment, they were given some of the privileges of the nobility. The title of "gentleman" was bestowed on them, and they enjoyed other honors and riches in exchange for their personal liberty. A noble might marry the daughter of a glassworker and, instead of sacrificing his nobility, maintain it. The children of such a union were also noble.

About 1600, Bohemia became an important glass-producing center. Glass-making was introduced in England during the reign of Queen Elizabeth. Before this, most of England's glass had been supplied by the Venetians. England became famous for her beautiful flint glass. America did not enter into the craft extensively before the eighteenth century. The name of Casper Wistar is associated with the earliest glassworks in this country. His factory was established early in the eighteenth century in South Jersey and flourished for more than 40 years. Henry William Stiegel, a German who came from Rotterdam in 1750 and settled in Philadelphia, was one of the earliest followers of the art in America. Today Stiegel glass is rare. A single piece is a cherished possession and may bring a very high price. Perhaps the best known of old American glass is Sandwich. This is made by the famous Sandwich company which was established at Sandwich, Massachusetts, in 1825. There were numerous other glass factories in operation in America before 1850. Early in the nineteenth century glass-making had suffered the same decline as had the other arts. The revival of the art during the late nineteenth century brought into prominence many French artists who have been leaders in the industry. Among these names Réne Lalique, Maurice Marinot, and Emile Gallè are outstanding. An interesting fact concerning some of the French glass artists is that they achieved success in other creative arts before taking up glass-making. Lalique designed and made jewelry, while Marinot was a painter. At the beginning of the twentieth century Sweden came into prominence in the glass industry. The sparkling clearness of some Swedish glass is its chief charm; while the soft tones of the colored glass make it particularly beautiful. In America one of the outstanding contributions in the development of modern glass-making was made by Louis Tiffany, who in 1890 started the manufacture of the well-known Tiffany glass. Within recent years the names of a number of American manufacturers have become identified with beautiful glass.

Manufacture. While glass-making in the broadest sense of the word has always included numerous domestic articles, glass for the table has from the first been among the major items manufactured. It was through the making of articles such as glasses, goblets, bottles, bowls, pitchers, and mugs that glass-making developed into an exquisite art.

The principal ingredients of all glass are sand or silica and some form of alkali, either sodium or potassium. Other ingredients are added, depending upon the kind of glass being made. In regard to quality, the chief kinds of table glass are bottle, crystal, and flint.

The more lime glass contains, the cheaper it is and the harder it is. Bottle glass contains a large percentage of lime. Lead increases fusibility, gives greater luster, and heightens the refractive power. Because of these qualities, the higher the proportion of lead, the greater the beauty and brilliancy of the glass. Both flint and crystal glass contain large quantities of lead. "Rock crystal" is glass of a very fine quality containing a high percentage of lead. The materials for glass are melted and fused at high temperature, and the glass is shaped either by blowing or by pressing while in a melted state.

Colors are obtained by the addition of certain chemicals to the other ingredients. Red may be produced with gold or copper oxide; blue with the oxides of copper and cobalt; violet with manganese dioxide, and amber with charcoal or cadmium sulphide. Milk glass is the result of adding bone ashes or minerals containing aluminum and fluorine.

Blowing was probably the first method of shaping glass. The beauty and quality of the article depend not only upon the materials used, but also on the skill, imagination, and artistic ability of the blower. Briefly, the old method of blowing, and one still in use, is to take a "gathering" of soft hot glass on a blowpipe and (as a child blows soap bubbles) blow it into the desired shape. The pieces are variously fashioned by gently swinging and rotating the pipe. In addition to the blowpipe, an iron rod called a pontil is used to handle the hot glass. This is affixed to the bottom of the piece by a bit of viscous glass and when severed leaves the pontil mark which is characteristic of blown glass. In addition to this method of blowing, glass is also blown into molds. These molds are made in two or more sections, the seams of which may be detected on the finished pieces. The making of glass was revolutionized by a glass-blowing machine which has been in use for a number of years. This machine utilizes compressed air, making possible many things that the breath of a blower cannot accomplish.

The discovery that glass could be shaped by pressure instead of blowing is usually attributed to the Sandwich glassmakers of America; however, the process may be as ancient as blowing, since pressed glass has been found in Egyptian tombs. In making pressed glass two molds are used: an outer mold, which may be in one piece or hinged in sections; and an inner mold or plunger, which forces the soft hot glass into the crevices of the outer mold. The worker who operates the plunger must be skilled in estimating the amount of plastic glass to put into each mold. Too little will leave unfinished places in the piece, while too much will run over the edge of the mold, thereby causing damage to the edge of the piece of glass. Some pieces of pressed glass, because of the shapes, must necessarily be made in two or more sections. The sections are then fused.

The proper cooling of glass objects is an important step in manufacturing.

Courtesy Steuben Glass

Fig. 78. Glass used primarily for its artistic value.

In the annealing process, gradual cooling is done by placing the glass in ovens which are allowed to grow cool slowly. The surface of glass must not be cooled suddenly, on account of the state of activity of the molecules of the inner portion. The result would be that the piece would break the first time it was exposed to a shock.

Pressed glass and glass blown into a mold are often given a finish known as fire polish. The articles are exposed to sufficient heat to melt the surface slightly. This results in a smooth brilliant effect.

Some of the methods used to decorate glass follow:

1) Engraving, in which case the design is applied by means of copper wheels.
2) Etching, a method of securing a design by the action of fluoric acid on the glass; needle etching is also used in applying decorations.
3) Flashing, which consists of superimposing a thin layer of colored glass upon clear glass.
4) Cutting, by which method the design is cut into the glass by means of emery wheels.
5) Pressing, decoration due to the imprint of the design of the mold on the glass.

Selection. Modern glass is of many different kinds and types, making selection rather difficult. In addition to a wide range in quality of American

Courtesy Corning Glass

Fig. 79. Glass used primarily for its practical value.

glass there are also imported glasses from which to choose. Among these, Venetian, Mexican, English, Swedish, Finnish, and Italian are often used for the table.

American. Glassware produced by the reputable manufacturers in the United States is as beautiful in design and as superior in quality as the glass which is made in any other country. Some of this glass represents faithful reproduction of old glass, while in the modern designs great distinction has been attained. American blown glass, especially that which is entirely handmade, is favored by most people because of its uniform thinness, luster, and brilliance. However, certain American glassmakers have reduced the prejudice that pressed glass is thick, heavy, and clumsy by producing pressed glass which is beautiful in proportion and represents grace and logic in design.

American glass embraces the full range of the requirements of good taste. It is available in flawless, uncolored, undecorated Steuben crystal (see Fig. 78); in colors varying from a suggestion of a hue to the deep colors of ruby and cobalt blue; in pieces decorated with enamel and semiprecious metals; and in various other types which will suit the most discriminating taste.

The wide range in American glass is interestingly contrasted by the glass in Figures 78 and 79, both of which are suitable for table use. The water goblet in Figure 78 retails at approximately $12.50, while the utility items in Figure 79 sell for about $1.95 each.

Venetian. This is blown glass which is extremely thin and may be characterized by the presence of tiny bubbles and delicate designs and colors. Fine threadlike strands of glass are often used in decorating. "Sometimes these twine, like the roots of hyacinth bulbs, through their transparent prison, as if they were growing tendrils; and not infrequently . . . a little shiny air-bubble has been artfully left."[1] Venetian glass is fragile and expensive and is therefore not practical for everyday use. A few accessory pieces of Venetian glass, such as a bowl for flowers, or dolphine salts, may be used in combination with another type of thin glass.

Mexican. This is also a blown glass, but has an entirely different texture and character from Venetian. Air bubbles are evident, but they are larger and more irregular than those in Venetian glass. Mexican glass is unmistakably handmade glass, characterized as it is by many irregularities both in sizes and shapes. Unless these irregularities are too exaggerated, they add charm to the glass. Mexican glass, like Venetian, is a thin glass, but owing to the characteristics already mentioned, it is not suitable in texture to use with sophisticated table appointments. It must be used with appointments which approximate it in quality. In Mexico or near the border, Mexican glass is very inexpensive, but in distant shops the cost is greater. The most characteristic color is deep blue. Lighter blues are also used, as are deep red and amber.

English. Most of the English glass found in our shops is what is known as flint glass. It originally took its name from native pebbles, known as flints, which were ground and used with the other ingredients. Today glass containing a large amount of lead is given this name. It is a very brilliant glass and is usually rather heavy. Much of the English flint glass is decorated by flashing. In general, it is a high-priced but very durable glass.

Swedish. Glass from Sweden has an enviable position among the world's fine glass. Much of this glass is characterized by smoky, cloudy color tones which give it a particular kind of distinction. While a great deal of this table glass is undecorated and uncolored, some of it is exquisitely cut, many of the designs being geometric. Much of the Swedish glass is moderately priced.

These are a number of helpful suggestions for the consumer who anticipates buying glassware:

1) Before purchasing, the buyer should be familiar with names of American manufacturers who have well-established reputations for the quality of their wares.

2) It is not wise to invest an excessive amount of money in glassware, since it is easily broken and chipped; neither is it wise to buy the cheapest glass. The latter not only breaks easily but also may lack beauty and distinction.

3) Glassware should be purchased in view of the other appointments with which it is to be used.

---

[1] From Frederick W. Hackwood, *Good Cheer* (New York: Sturgis and Walton, 1941), p. 382.

4) In plain crystal the qualities to be desired are brilliancy, smoothness, freedom from bubbles or other flaws, clearness and evenness of decorations, and transparency. The quality of crystal may be tested by tapping it gently. A clear, bell-like ring is usually a sign of good quality.

5) Blown glass, whether thin or heavy, is more fragile than glass that is molded by pressing.

6) Tumblers, goblets, iced-tea and other glasses should be shaped so that they can be polished easily.

7) The proportions of the different pieces should be carefully considered. Stemware is sometimes so designed that it is top-heavy, making it not only displeasing in appearance but also unsteady.

8) Colored glass is in good taste, but the buyer should recognize that it is likely to grow tiresome if it is the only glass used. Inexpensive colored glass which is in good taste is more difficult to find than low-cost clear glass of good design.

Care of glassware. Glass needs very careful handling to prevent breaking and chipping. Chipped and cracked pieces are dangerous to use and should be discarded. Adequate cabinet space is necessary if glass is to be stored safely. Blown-glass plates should be stored in stacks of four to eight. If more than these are stacked, the weight of the upper ones is likely to cause the bottom ones to break. Glasses are frequently chipped because they are crowded on the shelves. They should be arranged so as not to strike against each other.

Much of the beauty of glass depends upon careful washing and polishing. A sparkling, brilliant glass may be marred by the presence of fingerprints, a greasy film, or lint from a towel. Glassware should be washed in clean, hot, soapy water, rinsed in very hot water, and polished immediately with a towel that is free from lint. During the process of washing, care should be exercised to prevent knocking the pieces against each other. Only a few pieces at a time should be put into the dishpan, and after rinsing they should be placed in a drainer, preferably a plastic or rubber-covered one.

SILVER

Since its use in the sixteenth century, table silver has served to portray the culture and refinement of homelife. It has been handed down from this early date to succeeding generations as a cherished, priceless possession. It is difficult to conceive of people once using crude table implements made of wood, iron, or steel because today we usually consider some form of silver or highly refined stainless steel as the essential material for these implements. The use of table silver not only introduced a period of more gentle living but was indicative of the wealth of the times. During the sixteenth century silverware began to occupy a place of prominence in Great Britain. It was then that the Goldsmiths' Company of London was formed. This was of great significance to the silversmiths because for three centuries this company controlled the silver trade of the civilized world.

Courtesy Towle Silversmiths

Fig. 80. A grouping of traditional sterling silver with pottery of modern design.

The manufacture of silver in America was begun early in the eighteenth century. Among the early silversmiths we find Paul Revere, of Revolutionary fame, who was an admirable craftsman. Silver of the eighteenth century showed the influence of the eras of William and Mary, of Queen Anne, and of the early Georgian period. This influence was seen particularly in the emphasis on curves. About the middle of the eighteenth century the style of silver underwent a complete change, emphasis being laid on straight lines. Tall, slender shapes in hollow-ware took the place of low, sturdily built pieces. Handles of spoons were turned down instead of up and their bowls were tapered. At the beginning of the nineteenth century the Empire influence was seen in silver designs. This period was one of overdecoration, with nondescript and grotesque designs. Fortunately, the art has again gained distinction in the twentieth century.

American manufacturers have come to the front in this century in designing beautiful silver. "Probably no craft in America today is so rich in tradition or has such a well-preserved heritage of its trade as the craft of the silversmith. Undoubtedly the reason for this is that fine silversmithing is as much an art as is it a trade, and regardless of mechanical advancement, a piece of finely wrought silver must always be the work of a master craftsman." [1]

Most American silver is made in Connecticut, Massachusetts, and Rhode

[1] *The Story of Sterling* (New York: The Sterling Silversmiths' Guild of America, 1937), p. 13.

Island. This was where it was produced in colonial times; and because silversmithing is a highly skilled trade and closely knit from one generation to another, it is natural that its development has been largely confined to the states where the art originated in this country.

Types of silver. Silver for the table falls into two classes according to quality—sterling and plated. Silver is also classified as to use. Knives, forks, spoons, and serving pieces are termed "flat" silver, while silver plates, goblets, and serving dishes are called "hollow-ware" or dinnerware. In composition, sterling silver, which is an alloy, contains 925 parts of silver and 75 parts of copper. The copper gives hardness, making the sterling very durable. Before copper was added to silver, the implements made were soft and pliable and therefore not very durable. It is generally conceded that "the word sterling was derived from the name of a North German tribe, the Esterlings, who were noted for the uniform fineness of their silver coins."[1]

Plated silver ranges in quality from excellent to inferior ware. The silver coating is deposited on a metal base by the process of electrolysis. Before it is manufactured the designs are drawn by artists and modeled, first in wax and then in silver. The quality of plated silver is determined by the base metal used and by the number of ounces of silver used in the plating. For the highest quality of plated silver, 6 ounces of silver per gross of teaspoons and 12 ounces per gross of tablespoons are used. The terms single, double, and triple denote the amount of silver that is used for the different qualities of plated ware and do not indicate that the pieces have been dipped once, twice, or three times in silver. Triple plate is the best plated ware made, and if properly cared for it may last a lifetime. Some companies make a quadruple plate, but the same amount of silver is used in coating this ware as is used for triple plate made by other companies. This fact is likely to be misleading to consumers. The trademarks used by different companies to stamp their silver are usually meaningless to the purchaser, and since there is no standardized method of marking, the buyer's best protection is the name of the silversmith.

The most inferior of plated silver is that known to the trade as "flash." It is bright and shiny, as the name implies. The buffing which gives silver a beautiful finish has been omitted on flash silver in order not to remove the thin coat of silver that has been applied. Premium silver is usually "flash" plate.

In the best plated ware the silver is plated on "nickel silver." This metal does not contain silver but is an alloy of copper, nickel, and zinc, the major portion of the alloy being copper. After this alloy is melted down, it is molded into thick bars which are flattened into long, thin, ribbon-like strips by rolling them through machines. The roughly shaped blanks from which spoons,

[1] Howard Pitcher Okie, *Old Silver and Old Sheffield Plate* (Garden City, N. Y., Doubleday, Doran; 1928), p. 1.

knives, and forks are made are cut from these metal strips. The blanks are shorter and thicker than the finished pieces and must be rolled out to the correct proportion. After this step the pieces are shaped as to detail, bowls of spoons, tines of forks, and handles of pieces. This is done by clamping the blanks between steel dies. The design is also imprinted by pressing the forms between dies. The processes which follow are smoothing, polishing, plating, and repolishing. In smoothing, all rough and sharp edges are removed. The absence of this process may be detected in cheap silver by running the fingers over the tines of the forks and noting the rough edges. The polishing or buffing operation must be done carefully, because the slightest defect in the polished surface will be conspicuous after the electroplating. For the electroplating process the pieces are hung in racks which pass slowly through the silver solution, small particles of silver traveling to the various pieces and lodging on their surfaces. A heavier plating is applied at the points of greatest wear, such as the bottom of spoon bowls. This may be done at two different stages: (1) silver inlays are applied to the blanks before electroplating, by making a depression, placing a piece of silver in it, and fusing the two at a high temperature; (2) heavier layers of silver may be added at certain points by sectional plating, this being done after electroplating. The repolishing of the silver adds the finishing touch to its beauty.

"Sheffield Plate" was the original substitute for sterling silver. It was made by fusing sheet silver onto copper, rolling it, and making it into hollowware. The electroplating process used in making silver plate replaced the process of making Sheffield plate, since it is cheaper and the articles produced are of a similar quality. Plated silver is sometimes erroneously advertised as "Sheffield Plate." Consumers should realize that the Sheffield Plate process was abandoned about 1840, making it only barely possible to secure any on the commercial market today. Most of the fine pieces of "Old Sheffield" will be found in museums or in private collections.

Hand-wrought silver is usually sterling which is shaped and decorated from a flat piece of silver by a craftsman using only hand tools, with no mechanical aids. Some of the "hand-wrought" silver today is manufactured by applying many of the mechanical processes used in the normal course of silverware production. This accounts for the fact that "hand-wrought" silver can sometimes be purchased at approximately the same price as ordinary silverware. American "hand-wrought" silver, which is being produced by several well-established silversmiths, is beautifully designed and is gaining wide popularity with a number of people.

Stainless steel and other types of flatware. Silver and different types of silver plate are no longer the exclusive materials used for eating implements. Stainless steel is extensively used for this purpose both in the United States and in a number of foreign countries. Sweden, Denmark, England, and Italy are among the countries which export well designed stainless steel.

American silversmiths are also manufacturing good-looking stainless steel. The hardness of the metal, coupled with its good design, dull sheen, and practicality as well as its contemporary design have made it a preferred flatware.

Handles for this flatware vary. They include different types of wood, reed, stag, and plastics. Figure 82 shows a contemporary design by an American manufacturer.

Less common than stainless steel are certain other materials. Porcelain scoop spoons used in oriental countries are preferred by some Americans for soup spoons, or for serving acid sauces and dressings. Horn is used in France for making certain serving implements such as salad servers, ladles, serving forks, etc. These are available in the United States from shops specializing in imported wares but they are usually very expensive.

Pewter is being used by some manufacturers for the reproduction of early American flatware. These "home-craft" industries will usually be found in the New England states.

Plastic eating and serving implements are widely available. Except for certain serving pieces they are mainly used for picnics and other outdoor eating.

Within the last few years silver with porcelain handles has become more common. Entire sets of silver may be obtained in this fashion but it is most often seen in serving pieces. Needless to say, such silver requires extremely careful handling if the porcelain handles are to wear a reasonable length of time.

Selection. The purchase of silver represents an investment of lifetime duration. The best china and glass have to be replaced because of breakage; linen, no matter what its quality, will wear out; but good silver is permanent. The selection therefore involves a great deal of thought. The first thing to take into consideration is whether sterling or plated silver shall be bought. This will be dependent upon the income and the scale of living. Good plated silver, just as sterling, may be associated with reliable makers, artistry of design, and fine workmanship. There is a wide range in the price of sterling silver but a greater one in plated ware, making a varied choice of silver available to everyone.

The Goldsmiths' Company of England and other "halls" where silver and gold were analyzed stamped an official "Hall" mark on all gold and silver to indicate the purity of the product. The "Hall Mark" which is used on American sterling silver is the word "sterling." This is always accompanied by the name or mark of the manufacturer. Plated silver may be similarly marked, omitting "Sterling."

Important points to consider when selecting silver are:

The maker of the silver. The trademark of a reputable company and a reliable dealer are the purchaser's best guarantees of good silver. The eye cannot safely judge quality in silver. There are a number of old, well-estab-

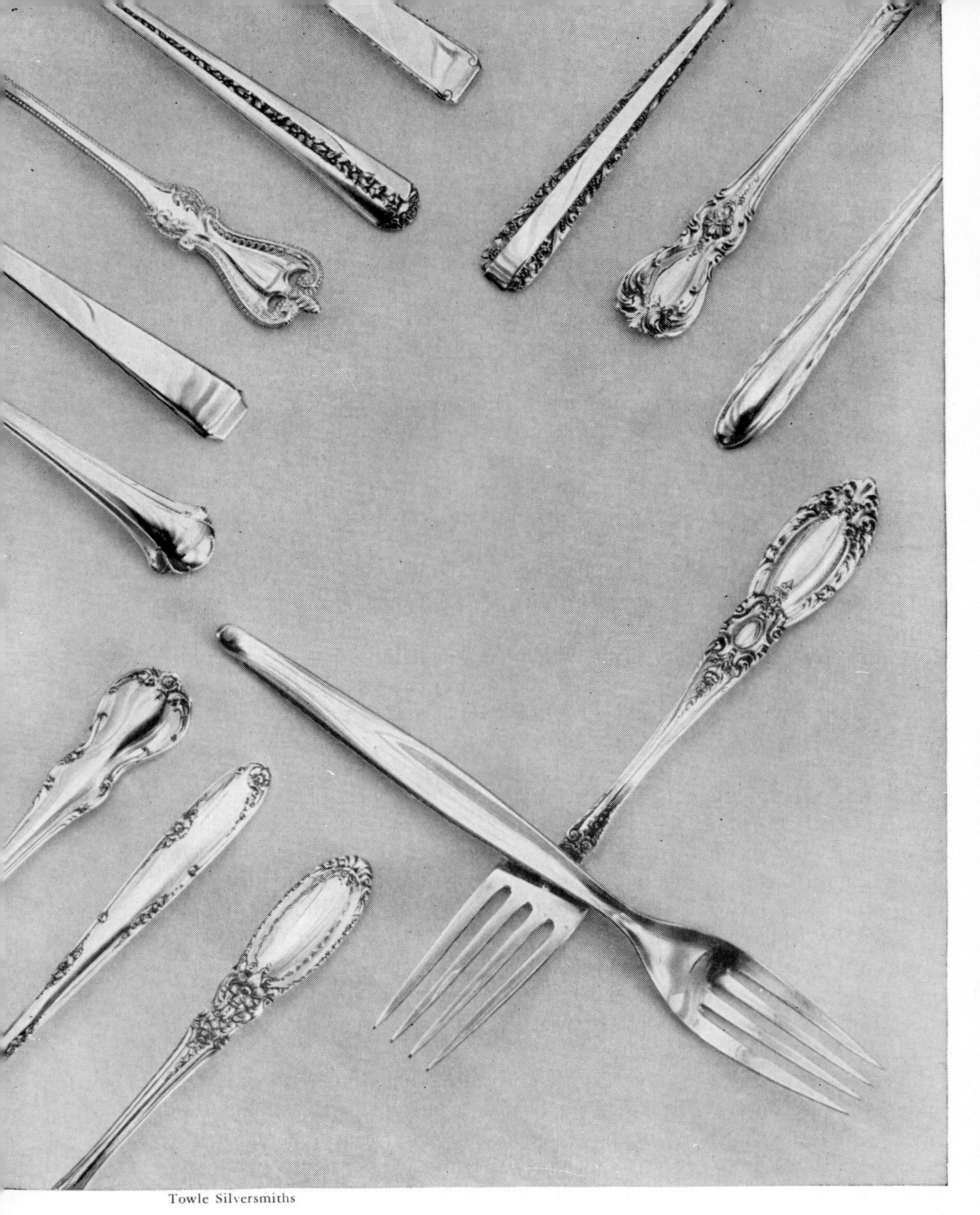

Towle Silversmiths

Fig. 81. Sterling silver flatware showing both traditional and contemporary designs.

Courtesy Gorham Silver

Fig. 82. Stainless steel flatware of contemporary design.

lished companies in America making both sterling and plated silver that is not only excellent in quality but beautiful in design.

The weight of sterling silver. Spoons and forks may be purchased in different weights, while knives come in one weight only. Nearly all companies make two weights of forks. The terms commonly used to indicate these weights are "trade" and "extra." The trade weight is sufficiently heavy to withstand long, hard service and is the one usually purchased. Teaspoons are made in as many as five weights. Different terms are used by the various silversmiths to denote the weights. It is not advisable to buy lightweight teaspoons, since they are in constant use. The cost difference is small and the owner is more than repaid by the satisfaction of the "feel" and by the superior wearing qualities of the heavier spoons.

The quality of plated silver. Thin, poor-quality plated silver is not durable, neither is it sanitary after being used a certain length of time because of the absorbing power of the soft metal on which it is plated. This can be detected by the greasy feel of cheap plated ware after long use. Good service cannot be expected of less than triple plated silver. Replating of old silver is possible, but the cost sometimes exceeds the actual value of the silver.

The design or pattern. This is largely a matter of personal choice; however, ease of care and serviceability should be considered. Some patterns show scratches more readily than others. Patterns with much decoration are harder to keep polished than the plainer ones. Generally elaborate silver patterns are not as serviceable as the less decorative ones because they are not suitable to use with other table appointments of simpler types. When selecting a design in sterling silver it is well to remember that a lifetime purchase is being made and therefore a design having transitory appeal may soon be out of style. Figure 81 shows a variety of designs.

The size of knives and forks. Most reputable silver manufacturers make luncheon or dessert and dinner knives and forks. The luncheon or dessert size are considerably smaller than the dinner size, and they are also less expensive. Unless a liberal amount of money is available for the purchase of silver, the smaller size is perhaps the more practical buy. The two sizes are made in both sterling and plated silver.

The blades of knives. Knife blades of stainless steel are the most desirable. They have good cutting edges and may be kept polished easily. All sterling silver knives have this type of blade, as do the better plated knives. In fine silversmithing the blades are soldered into the hollow handle rather than fastened with cement.

The design of pieces. Well-designed flat silver has good proportion and good contour. Its lines have a feeling of harmony and symmetry. It also has good balance which can be "sensed" by taking the pieces in the hands. The handles of the different pieces should be observed. Some are not comfortable to hold. This point is particularly important in regard to knives. Shapes of knives, forks, spoons, and serving pieces vary slightly according to the maker and the pattern. Before selecting a pattern, the purchaser should notice all pieces to make certain that the shapes are pleasing.

The price. "Bargains" or low-priced sterling silver flatware should be considered carefully before buying. They very often indicate that the pattern is to be discontinued, or the low price may be due to inferior design.

The amount to purchase. It is not necessary to possess a chest of silver before starting in the homemaking profession. Some brides begin with much less and add a piece at a time until their service is complete. The present plan of giving silver is a practical one. After a pattern is chosen, family and friends of the prospective homemaker add the desired pieces at anniversaries, Christmas, and birthdays—a single knife, fork, or spoon being a cherished gift for one who is building up a service of flat silver. When a complete service of silver is not purchased, it seems wise to buy the service in units of four rather than six. The writers know of a number of instances in which this plan is used, and in each case the homemaker has "filled in" her service with an inexpensive silver of a pattern similar to that of her sterling silver service. This provides extra silver for entertaining.

The various items of flat silver are so numerous that it is sometimes bewildering to know which pieces to select. Some pieces of flat silver have very limited use, while others may be used for a number of purposes. Cream soup spoons may also be used for cereal, dessert, or for serving. It is well to consider versatility when making selections of silver.

Very often people have the idea that the height of elegance and distinction in table appointments is a quantity of silver hollow-ware—goblets, service plates, candleholders, and serving dishes. However, this amount of silver makes a cold, formal-looking table which would be more attractive and in complete harmony if set with crystal goblets and china service plates, with perhaps one or two silver serving dishes. A silver meat platter does not necessitate the use of silver vegetable dishes; neither do silver candleholders call for a silver bowl for holding decorations.

Storage and care. The storage and care of silver are often a problem for the homemaker. In many homes the family is deprived of the joy of using the "good" silver every day because it is so stored as to be troublesome to get out and put away. There is no better way to take care of silver than to use it. It is the constant usage that develops soft lustre through handling, washing, and drying.

A specially-made chest, treated to prevent tarnishing, or shallow drawers, partitioned and lined with woolen cloth, are suitable and convenient for storing silver. The cloth not only prevents scratching but absorbs moisture, thereby preventing discoloration. The drawers should be as tight as possible, because exposure to air darkens silver. Chamois bags are suitable for storing silver when it is used at rare intervals only. Large pieces of hollow-ware that are not commonly used should be stored in unbleached cotton flannel bags or cases treated to prevent tarnish. Special chests or shallow drawers with tarnish-preventing lining are best for flatware. If stored elsewhere, a piece of camphor in the storage place retards discoloration.

If silver is properly cared for after each meal, it needs special care only at infrequent intervals. The following procedure should be observed when washing and cleaning silver:

1) Scarring and scratching are lessened if knives, forks, spoons, and serving pieces are separated before washing.

2) Wash each group in clean, hot, soapy water, and rinse with very hot water. Knives that have handles cemented to the blades should not be immersed in hot water, since this will loosen the cement.

3) Silver is often scratched by the treatment it receives after washing. It should not be put down carelessly on hard drainboards, tables, or trays, but should be laid on a towel and dried immediately.

4) Silver used for eggs becomes discolored because of the sulphur content of the egg and should be cleaned at once.

5) A silver cream which is free from abrasives should be used when removing any discoloration from silver.

6) Ornamented silver may be cleaned by applying the silver cream with a soft brush. Brushes should never be used on smooth, plain surfaces.

7) Some silver is ornamented by oxidization, in which case the background or paneling of a design is blackened to provide a contrast. In cleaning this type of silver, care should be taken not to mar this effect.

TABLE COVERINGS

White damask as a covering for the dining table is a tradition that is traceable to our Anglo-Saxon ancestors. Its use succeeded the primitive custom of dining from bare boards. Table coverings and napkins did not come into use simultaneously, and for a time the sides of the cloth were used for wiping the hands and mouth. Since the diners then ate principally with their hands, the condition of the linen must have been deplorable at times. Preceding the use of individual napkins, niceties of table manners demanded that hands be clean before they were dipped into a common dish. Lavers or basins of water were presented to guests for this purpose by servants who carried towels on their arms.

In modern times customs of dining have changed not only as to the type of menus served but in the manner in which they are served. The varied types of tables used for dining illustrate this point. Some of these do not require the use of linen. Also some homemakers choose to use polished wooden or decorated table tops without linen.

The homemaker has a wide range of choice among types of coverings—handsome damasks, either white or colored, hand-embroidered linens of

Photograph by A. Alegri

Fig. 83. This hand-decorated table top provides an interesting background for this chowder supper.

exquisite character or of a peasant type, handmade laces of many kinds, and many interesting novelty linens. Besides the beauty that linen contributes to a table, it serves to protect or to conceal the table top. It is also useful and desirable in deadening noise.

If table linens and other household fabrics are to be wisely chosen, the consumer should have some knowledge of textile fibers and of the construction processes of manufactured materials.

Fibers used for making table linen. Synthetic fibers and the new and interesting treatment of cotton have changed greatly our conception of table linen. The term "linen" which is usually used to indicate any kind of table coverings or mats is sometimes misleading since many modern table coverings are more likely to be made of fibers *other* than linen.

Linen. Linen is the fiber from the flax plant. The fiber is located around the woody pith of the stem and is separated from it by a process of steeping called "retting." In this process the flax stalks are soaked in water and allowed to decay. This releases the bark, which can then be easily removed. In each flax stem there are numerous fibers averaging one thousandth of an inch in diameter. The flax is thoroughly cleaned and combed before it is spun into yarn. In the combing process two grades of flax are produced: (1) the long, fine fibers, called *line* fibers, used for weaving the better linen fabrics; and (2) the short tangled fibers, known as *tow,* used in cheap fabrics. Tow yarn is not as strong, smooth, or lustrous as that made from the long, fine fibers; consequently, the materials woven from it are inferior.

The label "guaranteed all pure linen" may be used on fabrics made of tow as well as on linen fabrics of higher quality, thereby misleading an inexperienced buyer.

The flax fibers may be either wet spun or dry spun. The best grades of linen are wet spun, this making a finer and stronger thread and, consequently, a superior fabric.

Since the flax produced in the United States is grown for the seed rather than the fiber, practically all of our linen is imported. Flax fibers are produced extensively in Belgium, Ireland, France, Russia, Hungary, and Holland. Russia produces a larger quantity than any other country; France and Belgium have always produced the highest quality. During World War I flax culture was discontinued in most countries, and for some years after the war it was extremely costly because of its scarcity. The supply of imported linens was again cut off during World War II, with the result that many table "linens" were made from cotton and synthetic fabrics.

The chief reason why different countries produce different qualities of flax is that there is a difference in the method of retting. In Belgium flax is stream-retted in the river Lys, in the Courtrai district. This is considered to be the most satisfactory type of retting, and produces a fiber that is noted for its strength and color. Several other countries send their flax to Belgium for the retting process. In observing the trademarks on linen fabrics the consumer may sometimes see the words "Belgium," "Lys," or "Courtrai," any one of which indicates that a high grade flax has been used. The flax in Russia is not so satisfactorily retted. It is spread on the ground and allowed to remain for from two to four weeks. This method causes uneven retting and makes a yarn which is strong and coarse, and one which does not bleach easily. Retting in Ireland is done very satisfactorily in pools. This produces a strong fiber but one which is grayish in color.

If colored fabrics are to be made, the dye may be applied (1) to the fibers before they are spun into yarn; (2) to the yarn; or (3) to the woven material. The first two methods are more satisfactory than the third, because the dye penetrates the fiber more thoroughly.

Cotton. Cotton is the fiber that grows on the seed of the cotton plant. As the cotton bolls (the part holding the seed) ripen, they are picked, most often by hand, and then are ginned. The ginning process separates the fiber from the seed. The ginned cotton passes through many processes before it is woven into fabrics. These include (1) cleaning, to remove the heavy dirt; (2) carding, to brush out the fibers, remove the fine dirt and the undesirable short fibers; (3) drawing, to combine the carded fibers, draw them out, and partially twist; (4) spinning, which finally produces the yarn by further drawing out and twisting to give the desired strength.

Cotton is grown in the United States, India, Egypt, China, and Brazil. There are many varieties. The Sea Island variety that is grown on the islands off the coast of North and South Carolina and Georgia is ranked as of the highest quality. It has a staple averaging two inches in length. The quality of cotton is determined by (1) the length of the fibers (the longer the fibers are, the stronger); (2) the softness; (3) the fineness; (4) the color; (5) the luster; and (6) the state of maturity at which the cotton is picked. Fabrics are sometimes marked with the variety of cotton used, as "Sea Island." This, however, would not always indicate a superior fabric, since there are several grades of this variety of cotton.

Cotton may be dyed in the same manner as linen (see p. 412). Cotton fabrics made of both white and colored yarns are available in table coverings. These often give good service, but sometimes the colored yarns are weaker than the white ones.

At one time cotton table coverings were dull, fuzzy, and lifeless in appearance. They are not only treated now to give them characteristics of linen, but many of them have a sheen resembling silk. The latter are called "polished" cottons in the trade and are effective for making "dressy" table coverings. The polished finish is more or less permanent and will withstand repeated washings. Embossed cottons in plain or patterned designs make interesting table covers as do many less expensive cotton prints. (See Fig. 84.) Denim, once considered a "rough" fabric, is featured in designs and a variety of solid colors for "smart" table settings. Turkish toweling mats and napkins are practical as well as attractive for certain occasions. Drip-dry cottons so popular in wearing apparel are also being used for table coverings.

Synthetic fibers. A number of synthetic fibers are used in fabrics that are appropriate for table coverings. While nylon is a more versatile fiber than when first developed, it is still not as widely used for table fabrics as is rayon. One of the chief advantages of certain nylon fabrics is that they do not require ironing. Because rayon is more extensively used in the construction of table linen than other synthetics, it is discussed here. Rayon has been in use in America since 1911. Briefly, the process of making rayon consists of chemically treating cotton linters (short-staple fibers) or wood pulp until they have the consistency of glue. This solution is forced through tiny tubes and, as the filaments come from these tubes, they are coagulated either by exposure to the air or by treatment in a chemical mixture. These filaments are collected and twisted together to form the yarn. After this process is completed, the yarn is washed to remove the chemicals. It then goes through processes of bleaching, solidifying, washing, and oiling, after which it is dried and reeled into skeins.

There are several types of rayon which differ according to the method of manufacture. The quality of rayon fibers ranges from good to poor just as that of cotton and linen fibers does. The use of rayon has been greatly increased since it has been extensively combined with linen and cotton.

Rayon in table fabrics is used principally for damasks. It has a high gloss

Photograph by A. Alegri

Fig. 84. Card table camouflage. A folding card table, covered with a cloth of an inexpensive well-designed cotton print, furnishes an attractive setting for an intimate dinner party for a trio.

which makes a shiny damask that is easily distinguishable as rayon. While the original rayon fabrics had a glassy sheen, today they have been delustered to a marked degree. The removal of this shininess has definitely decreased the consumer's objection to these fabrics for table linens. However, they still have a much higher luster than either linen or cotton.

Union fabrics. When a union fabric is used for table linen, the characteristics of the different fibers may or may not be distinguishable. Rayon mixed with either cotton or linen still makes a damask of high luster. When cotton and linen are mixed, the luster of the linen is dulled to some extent by the cotton; yet the cotton may be treated to resemble the linen, making it difficult to know what the fabric is.

The construction and finish of table fabrics. Regardless of the fiber used, the appearance and durability of table linen are largely determined by the construction of the yarn, the way the yarns are woven into fabrics, and the finishing processes the fabrics receive after weaving.

Weaving. Other things being equal, the tighter the yarn is twisted and the closer it is woven, the more durable the fabric. The closeness of threads in a fabric is spoken of as the thread count, which means the number of lengthwise threads and crosswise threads to the square inch. The lengthwise yarns are called warp and the crosswise, filling or woof. A closely woven material is particularly important in table linens, because most of the yarns for this purpose are only slightly twisted and a firm weave holds them in place and makes the fabric more durable. Since the luster of tightly twisted yarn is dulled, it is not often used for table linen.

Most table linens are made with one of two weaves: plain and damask weaves. In plain weave the filling thread goes *over* one warp thread and *under* the next. Examples of this weave are linen crash, which is made with flat yarn, and art linen, which is made with round yarn. Damask weaves are made on Jacquard looms (so named for the inventor). In this type of weave one set of threads stays on the surface of the fabric longer than in a plain weave. These surface threads are called floats, and since they reflect light, a high luster is produced. Damask with long floats is not as durable as that with short floats.

Damask may be either double or single. Double damask has a higher thread count than single and is therefore stronger. Since the yarns are very close together, double damask is usually more beautiful and the pattern is more distinct on the wrong side. A poor grade of double damask may not be as serviceable as a good grade of single damask.

The numerous patterns in table damask are a result of weaving details, as are patterns obtained by novelty weaving, which is a variation of the plain weave. Damasks may be purchased in designs of an elaborate floral nature or in geometric, conventional, or satin stripe patterns. Patterns with long floats have an added beauty because of the increased reflection of light and luster. The appearance of damask will depend somewhat on whether the cloth has a border across the ends as well as along the sides. When damask is bought by the yard rather than as a finished cloth, it does not have the pattern across the ends.

Some of the most interesting table linens available are hand woven. One of the principal sources of these are craft schools, many of which are located in the Southern States. Other beautiful hand woven linens are obtainable wherever handicraft work of sightless persons is sold.

Bleaching. Many linen and cotton fabrics used for table linen undergo a bleaching process which whitens the natural grayish or cream color of the fibers. Most bleaching is now chemically performed; however, in Ireland grass-bleaching is still used for some of the finer linens. This requires a great deal of time, but materials bleached by this method are stronger than those bleached with chemicals, since chemicals weaken the fibers to some extent. Linen and cotton table fabrics may be purchased fully bleached, in which case they are pure white; partially bleached fabrics are cream colored; and unbleached ones have a deeper cream or tan color. Both partially bleached and unbleached fabrics become white as they are laundered and hung in the sun.

Mercerizing. This is a process by which cotton materials are treated to give them a lustrous appearance. The material is subjected to tension during treatment with a alkaline solution. Fibers are strengthened by the process, and they also attain a greater affinity for dyestuffs. To the inexperienced buyer mercerized cotton damask has the appearance of linen damask; however, this "linen" appearance is not retained after several launderings. Some cotton damask is given a permanent linen or "basco" finish, which makes it superior to other cotton damasks. In this process the yarn is singed, making the fabric smooth and free from lint.

Sizing. Materials of poor quality are often made to resemble better fabrics by sizing, which is a process of filling up the spaces of loosely woven materials with starch, sugar, gum, or other sizing substances. A certain amount of sizing is used in all table linens to give body and prevent them from becoming shopworn. Poor-quality linen and cotton damasks have an excess amount of sizing. This washes out after one or two launderings, leaving a thin, sleazy fabric.

Beetling. By the process of beetling, linen and cotton materials are pounded with heavy blocks in order to increase the natural luster of linen and give the cotton a glossy appearance. The pounding makes the surface of the materials smooth and compact. This process is responsible for the leathery feel of damask.

Dyeing. Until recently dyeing would not have entered into a discussion of table linen. Today, however, colored linen, cotton, and rayon are used for table coverings. Dyeing is most satisfactory if the fiber of the yarn rather than the woven fabric is dyed. Linen does not absorb or retain dye so well as cotton or rayon. Consequently, colored linen damasks or other linen table fabrics fade more quickly than do those made from other fibers. Since faded linens are unattractive, it is not wise to invest in high-priced colored table fabrics made of linen. The color of table linen is one of the chief factors affecting its appearance. It may apply to the degree of whiteness, depending upon how much bleaching the fabric has received, or to the color resulting from dyeing. Colored linens are in vogue at present, and beautiful ones may be obtained in damasks as well as in novelty linens.

Selection of table linen. A careful and discriminating buyer will purchase table linen that has beauty; will be durable and serviceable; can be easily and successfully laundered; is reasonably priced; and is suitable in type to the other table appointments used.

Beauty. The beauty and appearance of table linen are dependent on (1) the fibers used; (2) the weight, quality, and type of yarn; (3) the weave; (4) the finishing processes of the fabric; (5) the color; (6) the decoration; (7) the method of finishing the edges; and (8) the quality of workmanship. The influence of the first five of these factors has been discussed.

Decoration and method of finishing edges. The type and amount of decoration and the methods of finishing the edges contribute materially to the appearance of table linen.

Decorations include monograms, appliqué designs, hand and machine embroidery, cut work, filet treatments, applied bands of contrasting colors and materials, block printing, and woven designs.

The decoration used on table linen depends upon the style of the linen and the type of fabric. Monograms should be used only on damask of high quality; appliqué designs may be used on fine-textured linens (see Fig. 85) or on informal fabrics of a coarser type. Exquisite dinner or tea cloths may be decorated with fine hand embroidery. A coarser embroidery is suitable for heavier linens for informal use.

A modern idea in decoration is to have the napery embroidered with the exact patterns of the china or silver. These matching linens are usually made to special order and are available only in expensive linens of high quality. Machine embroidery detracts from the beauty of table linen and is used only on the inexpensive types. Cut work and filet work frequently decorate table linen; however, they are also used on some luncheon sets. The method of decoration by applied bands is used on breakfast and luncheon linens and is a simple and attractive form of decoration. Block printing is popular for novelty or informal linens. It is used on both linen and cotton fabrics. Regardless of the type of decoration, the amount influences the beauty of table coverings. Linens of excellent quality need little to adorn them.

There are numerous edge finishes for table linens. Some that are commonly used are these: hemstitched and plain hems, both of which may be made by hand; rolled and whipped edges, which may be hand or machine-made; picoted edges; fringed edges (see Fig. 86); lace-trimmed edges, applied by hand or by machine; and rickrack and other commercial trimmings which are sometimes used for novelty edge finishes.

Round tables are used more frequently than they were a few years ago, and many of the round cloths are finished with a wide fringe. This type of finish makes for a graceful, draped effect.

Edge finishes should be suited to the style of the linen and the type of fabric. An edge finish made by machine rather than by hand detracts from the appearance of the linen and therefore decreases its value to a discriminating customer.

Of the various types of edge finishes, the plain and hemstitched hems made by hand are the only ones suitable for a damask cloth. A machine-stitched hem detracts from the beauty of damask and is a mark of low quality.

The hemstitched hem is frequently used as an edge finish for table linens other than damask. There are a number of different kinds—single, double, Italian, and other fancy types. Double hemstitching is one of the most commonly used types.

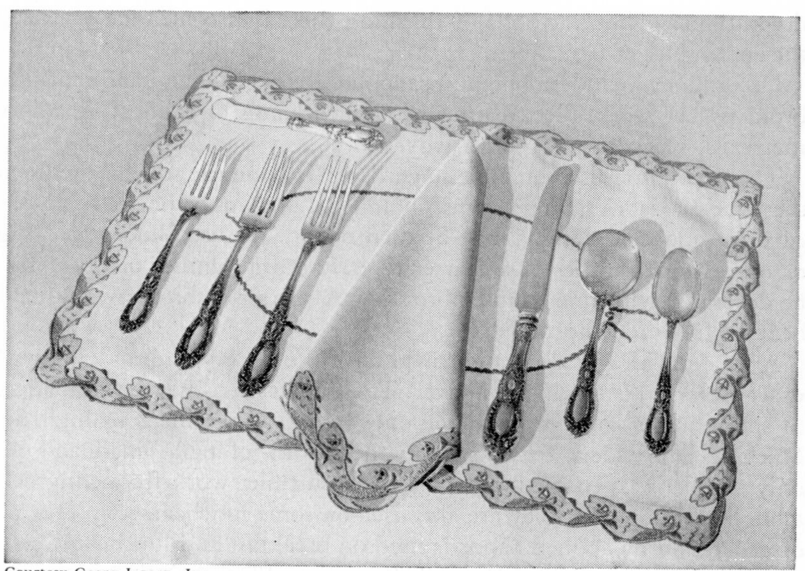

Courtesy Georg Jensen, Inc.

Fig. 85. Exquisite handmade placemats combined with fine sterling silver for this place setting.

Courtesy Georg Jensen, Inc.

Fig. 86. Placemats of peasant-like character furnish an appropriate background for handsome silver.

Rolled and whipped edges are used on sheer table linens when an inconspicuous finish is desired. Picoted edges are unattractive and are seen only on cheaper linens. Fringed edges are attractive on peasant or homespun linens. Their appearance after laundering depends upon the kind of yarn as well as the method of laundering. Lace edge finishes belong on fine handmade linens. Many different laces are used and they may be either hand or machine-made. The type of lace used should suit the fabric to which it is applied if it is to add to the appearance of the linen. Machine-made laces seldom make attractive finishes. Crocheted finishes are sometimes crocheted to the edge of the linen instead of the finished lace being applied. Scalloped edges are among the most decorative types and are used only on the finer linens. The commercial braids afford an endless number of novelty finishes. They are, of course, suitable only for informal linens.

Quality of workmanship. Table coverings of the most attractive types must necessarily display excellent workmanship. Linens of beautiful quality are sometimes marred by decoration or edge finish of inferior workmanship. Good workmanship is partially measured by the weave; the size, evenness, and regularity of stitches; the general neatness of the work; the evenness with which block-print designs or other stamped designs are applied; the evenness of hems; the method of fastening fringed edges; the absence of raw edges when braids or lace are used for finishes; and the evenness of hemstitching.

Durability and serviceability. Durability of a fabric refers to the length of time it will wear, while serviceability indicates its suitability for various occasions. The same factors which influence the appearance of table linen are also responsible for durability.

Whether or not table linen is serviceable depends altogether on the type. Besides linen for the three daily meals, the average homemaker wants in her linen chest extra linens for entertaining. In the list may be included card-table covers, tea cloths, and coverings for porch or garden tables. If carefully selected, the same linen may be used for various occasions. For example, breakfast and luncheon doily sets may be purchased in view of using them for informal guest suppers, while a cloth of embroidered linen, of linen and lace, or of all lace is suitable to use both as a formal dinner cloth and as a tea cloth.

Price. The table linens that are reasonable in price are plentiful in the stores. While nothing specific regarding price can be given, some general statements may be helpful to the consumer.

In table linens of good quality there are no low prices to compete with cotton fabrics, chiefly because of the high production cost of linen. However, low-priced linens of inferior quality do compete with cotton table coverings. Mistakes are sometimes made by consumers in buying linen which is poor in quality when they might make a better selection by buying a good grade of cotton which would have better wearing qualities.

Of the table "linens" made of cotton, the cotton damasks are perhaps the least desirable. However, other cotton table coverings may be purchased which are attractive as well as durable and inexpensive.

Rayon table "linens" are usually priced higher than cotton but are cheaper than linen. Consumers may be misled by the luster of rayon, and purchase it for linen damask. This is particularly true in a union fabric of rayon and linen. The consumer should remember that while the initial cost of rayon table fabrics may not be as great as the cost of linen, the final cost is greater because of the inferior wearing qualities of rayon.

Suitability of table linen to other appointments. Table linen which is suitable in type to other table appointments may be selected if the buyer has an appreciation of quality, materials, and types. To combine linen, china, silver, and glass so that the texture, weight, design, and color of all are comparable in feeling requires thought, but the result is a completely satisfying picture.

Satisfaction. If a consumer has considered the preceding factors in selecting her linen, it will be a source of pleasure and satisfaction to her. Sentiment is an important consideration in buying linen. A homemaker who is appreciative of her table linens derives pleasure from possessing, handling, and using them. They are a means also for creating for her family enjoyment of the beautiful. "A thing of beauty is a joy forever" only when we are conscious that our joy is derived from beauty.

Size. Sizes of table linens are important and should not be overlooked when purchasing. Dining tables today differ so much in type and size that homemakers sometimes find it difficult to suit sizes of made-up linens to their tables. Exact measurements of the table to be fitted should be used in buying cloths. The use of some doily sets rather than all large cloths is economical from the standpoint of cost and saves time and energy in laundering. In the selection of doilies as well as large cloths, measurements of the table should be taken into account.

Damask, whether linen, cotton, rayon, or union, may be purchased by the pattern, in which case the cloth is bordered on all sides, or by the yard. The size of the tablecloth is determined by the size of the table and the number of people to be seated. The cloth should hang from 10 to 12 inches over the sides and ends of the table, depending upon the distance from the table to the seat of the chair.

The amount of table linen to buy. The amount of table linen for a family will vary depending upon the number and personnel of the group, the scale of living, and the amount of entertaining done.

With the present emphasis on informality, it is difficult to suggest the kind or amount of table linen to purchase. A spacious dining room with a large table calls for different types of linen than would be used in a dinette where the table is small. Also, in a combined kitchen-dining area the table linen, if used at all, may be still different from that used in either of the above situations. Regardless of the size of the table or the environment in which meals are served, it is considered advisable to have several changes of everyday linen, as well as one or two sets for entertaining. These may be cloths or mats or both. Most department stores carry standard sizes of cloths ranging in size from 36-inch squares to banquet cloths 90 inches long and of varying widths. Luncheon mats are usually a standard rectangular size and shape. Round individual mats are also available.

Napkins. Napkins may be purchased as part of a "set" of linen or they may be purchased separately in sets or singly. All patterned damask cloths have matching napkins; most luncheon sets consist of a runner, plate mats, and napkins to match.

Napkins vary in size according to their use, most of them being square. Cocktail napkins are usually 5 inches by 8 inches, and some luncheon napkins are rectangular in shape. The most commonly used sizes of napkins are:

Bridge or tea napkins	12 to 14 in. sq.
Breakfast or luncheon napkins	18 to 20 in. sq.
Dinner napkins	22, 24, and 27 in. sq.
Rectangular luncheon napkins	12 in. by 18 in.

The sizes of runners and mats in luncheon sets vary to some extent; however, the runners are usually 18 inches by 36 inches, and mats are either 12 inches by 18 inches or 14 inches by 20 inches. The 14-inch by 20-inch mat is preferred, because it allows room for the entire cover. Round or oval mats are sometimes used, but since it is not possible to set the entire cover on them, they are inconvenient and may not present a pleasing appearance.

In addition to cloths, luncheon sets, and napkins, an adequate linen supply includes mats for trays. The size of the mat selected depends upon the tray on which it is to be used. A silver coffee service, a bread tray, and a tray for service would necessitate mats of three shapes and sizes.

Plastics. Oilcloth has been replaced almost entirely by plastics of various types. The latter range in design from bizarre all-over "lace" and floral patterns to clear plastics which some homemakers use over their linens as a means of reducing laundering.

Where economy and utility are paramount factors many people consider such materials as a satisfactory substitute for other types of table coverings. Plastic table mats have gained increasing popularity. Plastic cloths are sold to fit tables of various sizes. Also, plastics are sold by the yard.

Woven straw. As our trade with foreign countries increases, more and more imports made of straw are seen. Table mats are among the most attractive of these items. In addition to natural straw, they are available in both pastel and deep colors. The traditional rectangular-shape mats have been replaced partially by oval and round ones.

Paper "linens." Cellophane, crepe paper, and heavy waterproofed paper are used for making effective tablecloths, napkins, doily sets, and tray doilies. These paper "linens" are practical to use as tray covers for some family meals and in a summer lodge, or for picnics and other types of informal entertaining. Fascinating place mats and napkins of high-quality paper and excellent design are available for parties—both special occasions and general entertaining. Since paper "linens" constitute a fire hazard, it is necessary to use them cautiously.

Table pads. The table pad serves as a protection for the table top when hot dishes are used, and as a silence cloth. As previously stated, pads are never used under sheer cloths or cloths with cut or openwork. The types commonly used are quilted padding, double-faced outing flannel, and asbestos pads that fit the table leaves. The quilted padding is a good protector, but it frequently shrinks after laundering so that it does not fit the table. Another disadvantage is that unless the cloth is very heavy, the quilting shows through the cloth. Outing flannel is not so heavy as quilted padding, but it launders satisfactorily and protects sufficiently. When it is used, small table asbestos mats should be used under extremely hot dishes. Large asbestos pads made to fit the table provide thorough protection, and are washable on the upper side. However, they stain and discolor easily, are bulky to handle, and frequently present a storage problem. If muslin covers are made to fit these pads, they may be kept clean; but unless the covers fit tightly, they do not make a smooth foundation for the cloth. More and more manufacturers are using durable types of wood finishes on dining tables. These finishes require little or no protection.

Regardless of the type of table pad used, it must fit the table. If the pad is too short and has to be pieced, a ridge is unavoidable. This not only looks bad but also creates an unsteady foundation for table appointments, and a consequent risk of accidents. A silence cloth that is too long may be shortened by turning the edges under as far as the edge of the table.

Marking table linens. Marking is not so essential for table linens as for other household linens, since table linens are not usually sent to commercial laundries. When monograms are used as decoration, they also serve as markers. If marks are to be used, the most satisfactory type are those on tape which should be tacked inconspicuously to the underside of the linen. This method is not so desirable for small pieces, however, as for large cloths. Linens may be marked by stamping initials on the wrong side with marking ink. These marks do not stand repeated laundering and must be renewed as the ink becomes dim.

Caring for table linens. Much of the beauty and durability of table linen depend upon the care it receives. No matter how superior the quality of linen selected, it cannot give continued satisfaction if it is subjected to abusive treatment through laundering and storage. Heirloom linens are prized possessions in some families. Without proper care it would not be possible to hand them down for the enjoyment of future generations.

Storage. In most homes table linen has a separate storage space from other household linens. This space is usually located in the dining room, kitchen, or pantry. It may be a small closet or a built-in cabinet devoted exclusively to the purpose of storing table linen, or it may be a portion of a cabinet or closet which is used principally for china and glassware.

When planning storage space, some individuals fail to provide adequate space for table linens, and count on storing them in buffet or cabinet drawers. In small families such facilities may furnish suitable and sufficient space; but in larger families with greater amounts of table linen to store, additional space will usually be needed. In many homes where modern dining tables have polished wood, glass, tile, marble, or composition tops, storage is not a problem since little linen is used.

Regardless of the type of space used for storing table linens for the average household, it should be planned to permit the storage of the following articles:

1) Large tablecloths, so that they do not have to be creased too many times. Some homemakers prefer to roll their best tablecloths on rollers made of heavy paper and covered with cloth. This prevents creasing. However, unless the rolling is done carefully, the linen is likely to become mussed.

2) Napkins stacked in sets, so that they can be kept in order and are conveniently accessible. This type of storage can be arranged by dividing drawers into the proper size compartments.

3) Place-mats and other types of doilies, *without* folding. Table runners may be folded in half or thirds, or they may be rolled. It is preferable to have enough flat storage space to permit storing each set of mats with matching napkins on a separate tray.

4) Small tablecloths, such as bridge and luncheon types, folded in half or quarters without having too many stacked together. Heavier linens should not be stored on top of these cloths since this causes wrinkles and deep creases.

In addition to storage space for the above items, there should be space for storing linens which are used only occasionally. If these linens are wrapped in dark blue paper to keep out the light, they will not turn yellow. A drawer lined with dark blue cloth or paper will also help to prevent them from yellowing.

Laundering. The laundering of table linen frequently presents a problem for the homemaker, because with few exceptions table linens cannot be sent to the commercial laundry but instead must be carefully hand-laundered. This of course should be considered when buying.

Linen table coverings do not soil as easily as cotton ones, owing to the hardness and smoothness of the linen fibers; but on the other hand they require more frequent pressing to keep them free from wrinkles. Stain removal is easier on linen than on cotton fabrics owing to the long, loosely twisted flax fibers which "give up" stains quickly. Rayon table coverings require more careful handling than do linen and cotton, because rayon fibers are delicate when wet.

The following points should be observed when laundering table fabrics:

1) New linens should be laundered before using.

2) Stains should be removed before laundering, otherwise they become "set" and are not so easily removed.

3) Small tears or worn places should be mended before laundering.

4) Hot water and soap will not injure linen or cotton fabrics. Lukewarm water and mild soap should be used for rayon.

5) Starch should not be used on any table linen.

6) White linens should be dried in the sun, if they are to keep their whiteness. Strong sunlight should be avoided for colored fabrics. Linens may be rolled in heavy towels to absorb the moisture before ironing.

7) Table linen should never be put through a wringer, as the resulting creases may eventually cause breaks in the linen.

8) Cotton and linen table coverings are ironed when damp, first on the wrong side and then on the right side. The iron should move crosswise on the fabric. This keeps linens in shape and produces a high luster in linen damasks. The scorching point of cotton is higher than that of linen, making it possible to use a hotter iron on cotton without danger of scorching. Rayon table fabrics should also be ironed while damp. The iron should be warm rather than hot; otherwise the rayon may melt and disintegrate.

9) Tablecloths should be folded with the right side out and with as few creases as possible. If storage space permits, they may be rolled to avoid creasing. Unless this is done properly, small wrinkles may be rolled in, and these look worse than the creases in a smoothly folded cloth. Napkins are folded with the right side out in square, rectangular, or triangular shapes. Dinner napkins are always folded square, while other napkins may be folded in any of the three shapes. Plate doilies and other doilies are not folded. Table runners may be folded once or rolled.

Removal of stains. Table linens need not remain marred by stains and spots, since almost any type of stain can be removed successfully. A number of factors must be taken into account before attempting removal—the nature of the stain, the kind of fabric, the weave, and the color. Patience is necessary for this process, because repeated applications are often required before the stain disappears.

The nature of the stain must be ascertained before using anything on it. A stain remover for one kind of stain may permanently set one of another character. Many of the stain removers contain strong acids which destroy cotton, linen, and rayon fibers. While these fibers are not easily injured by alkaline removers, they may be harmed to some extent by repeated usage of alkalies, such as strong soap, bleaching powders, washing soda, and ammonia. Materials used for stain removal may be classified as (1) absorbents, (2) solvents, and (3) bleaches. All three classes are used for table linens.

Absorbents such as cornstarch, chalk, fuller's earth, and magnesium are effective on light, freshly made stains, usually of a fatty character. To apply, the absorbent is spread on the stained fabric and allowed to absorb the staining material. It should be worked around gently, and as it absorbs it should be brushed off and a fresh application made. Absorbents do not injure fabrics in any way.

Solvents used on table linens include water, wood alcohol, carbon tetrachloride, and benzol, none of which impairs fibers. Fortunately, many stains on table linen are soluble in water and are fairly easy to remove, since all table fabrics are suitable for water treatment. Solvents that are inflammable must be used carefully. Carbon tetrachloride is noninflammable, but the vapor, inhaled or swallowed, is dangerous; hence it must be used cautiously.

Bleaches make up a large group of stain removers. Those commonly used on table linen are Javelle water,[1] hydrogen peroxide, and lemon juice. Bleaches must be used carefully, since almost all of them remove color as well as stains. If they are used in a concentrated form or too often, they may weaken the fabrics.

The fresher the stain, the easier it is to remove. If stains are allowed to remain in colored linens, it is sometimes impossible to remove them without affecting the color. Gentle rubbing or brushing motions should be used in applying the cleaner, in order that the fabric may not be injured. Hard, brisk rubbing may break the floats in damask and cause other materials to become rough in appearance. When a solvent is being used, a soft cloth or a clean piece of blotting paper may be placed under the linen to absorb the stain. In treating stains, the cleaner should be applied on the wrong side of the linen so that the stain does not have to pass through the fabric. After a spot is treated, it is important to remove the surplus cleaner by thorough rinsing. If a liquid cleaner is being used and the piece of linen being treated is not to be laundered after the stain is removed, care must be taken not to "ring" the fabric with the cleaning reagent. To prevent this, the cleaner should be spread irregularly into the fabric and the linen dried as rapidly as possible. Following are directions for removing some common stains:

a. Chocolate and cocoa. Stains made by either of these beverages are composed of fat, milk solids, resinous coloring matter, starch, and sugar. The

[1] Javelle water: ½ lb. washing soda; 2 c. boiling water; ¼ lb. chloride of lime; 4 c. cold water. Mix soda and boiling water in one mixing bowl. In another, mix lime and cold water. Pour the two mixtures together and let settle. Bottle the clear liquid for use. If the solution turns pink, it is still good to use.

stain should first be washed in cold water to remove the milk. Ordinary laundering may then be all that is necessary to remove it. A persistent stain can be removed with Javelle water. If a chocolate stain is made from cake frosting or candy, the surplus chocolate should be scraped off before trying to remove the spot.

b. Coffee. The brown stains from coffee are soluble in water, and fresh ones are not difficult to remove. Usually this may be done by ordinary laundering with soap and water. If the spots remain after laundering, the stained part should be spread over a bowl, being held in place by string or elastic, and boiling water poured from a height of three or four feet so that it will strike the stain with force. If the stains are old or very heavy, they may be resistant to this treatment; drying in the sun or using a mild bleach may then be effective. If the coffee has cream in it, the stain may necessitate the use of a fat solvent, such as carbon tetrachloride. This should be applied after the coffee stain has been removed.

c. Egg. Egg stains are caused from the albumen of the egg white and from the fat and yellow color pigment of the yolk. Washing in cold water followed by ordinary laundering will remove most egg stains. If hot water is used before the treatment with cold water, the albumen coagulates and is difficult to remove.

d. Fruit. Fruit stains are frequently difficult to remove. Stains from canned fruits are slightly different in character from those made by fresh fruits, and are somewhat more easily removed because they usually contain more sugar, and the color pigments are altered to some extent by the cooking process. Laundering with hot water and soap may be all that is necessary to remove canned fruit spots, while fresh fruit stains need boiling water applied as in removing coffee stains. Stains that do not yield to boiling water may be bleached by moistening with lemon juice and hanging the fabric in the strong sunlight. This method should be used on white linens only. The use of soap should be avoided on fresh fruit stains, as alkalies set them, turning red fruit stains to a greenish blue and making removal difficult. Some fruit stains, such as those from citrus fruits, are not apparent unless they are pressed with a hot iron before being washed. When so handled, the stains become persistent and very often require a bleach.

e. Grease. Grease spots are caused by butter, cream, candle wax, mayonnaise, and bacon or other fat meats. With the exception of candle wax, most grease stains are removable by using warm water and soap and rubbing the particular spot thoroughly. Naphtha soaps are effective for such spots. Grease spots resistant to this treatment may be removed by using a solvent such as carbon tetrachloride. Absorbents may be successfully used on slightly fatty spots. In removing candle wax, the surplus should first be carefully scraped off before using the solvent.

f. Ink. Ink spots are not common on table linen. If the fabric is white, ink eradicator can be used successfully. Ink may be removed from colored linens by soaking in salt and lemon juice or in buttermilk. Exposure to the sun is helpful in this treatment.

g. Iron rust. Iron rust stains on linen are usually the result of careless handling during laundering, being caused by rusty clothes lines and by certain bluing material used on inadequately rinsed fabrics through reaction between soap and bluing. These stains may be removed by sprinkling with salt, moistening with lemon juice, and placing in the sun. Another effective method is boiling in a solution containing four teaspoons of cream of tartar to one pint of water. After this treatment the fabric must be thoroughly rinsed.

h. Mildew. Mildew spots are growth of molds which appear on fabrics that have been allowed to remain damp too long. If these spots are not removed immediately, the mold continues to grow and, instead of remaining on the surface, it eats into the fabric and may destroy the fibers. Very fresh mildew stains are removed by washing in soap and water and drying in the sun. Soaking in sour milk and placing in the sun without rinsing, and moistening with lemon juice and salt and exposing to the sun are methods which are successful on slight stains. Persistent or old mildew stains can be removed from white fabrics by bleaching with Javelle water.

i. Grass. A fresh, light grass stain may be removed by washing in warm water with a naphtha soap. If this fails, treat the spot with ammonia and cold water and repeat the washing.

j. Scorch. Slight scorch stains are easily removed by soap and water and drying in the sun. If the linen is scorched while pressing, placing it in the sun immediately without wetting it may be effective. Rubbing soft bread crumbs over the scorch stain before exposing it to the sun is a method sometimes used.

k. Meat juices. Stains from meat juices should first be soaked in cold water so as not to coagulate the protein and then washed with soap and cold water. If a grease spot remains after the removal, it should be treated with a solvent.

l. Tea. The brown coloring matter of tea stains makes any but the freshest stain difficult to remove. Stains made by clear tea are more difficult to remove than those from tea containing cream or milk. Fresh stains may be successfully removed by soaking in a borax solution of one teaspoon of borax to one cup of water and then rinsing with boiling water. Treatment with lemon juice and exposure to the sun for two or three days proves a satisfactory method for more persistent stains.

m. Indelible lipstick. Indelible lipstick may be removed by working lard or petroleum jelly into the stain. Let stand for about 30 minutes, then sponge with a dry-cleaning fluid. Remove any ring which may be left by laundering.

n. Tomato juice or catsup. These stains should first be thoroughly sponged with cold water after which glycerine should be worked into the stain. Let stand for about 30 minutes and then wash in mild soap suds.

REFERENCES

BOOKS

Autis, Edmund de Forest, *Pottery—Its Craftsmanship and Its Appreciation.* Harper & Brothers, New York, 1940.

Denny, G. G., *Fabrics.* J. B. Lippincott Co., Chicago, 1947.

Dyer, Elizabeth, *Textile Fabrics.* Houghton Mifflin Co., Boston, 1940.

Encyclopedia Britannica. New York Encyclopedia Britannica, Inc., 1940.

Goldmann, Mary E., *Planning and Serving Your Meals.* McGraw-Hill Book Co., Inc., New York, 1950.

Hackwood, Frederick W., *Good Cheer.* Sturgis and Walton, New York, 1911.

Hess, Katherine Paddock, *Textile Fibers and Their Use.* J. B. Lippincott, Chicago, 1948.

Lee, Ruth Webb, *Sandwich Glass.* Published by the Author. Framingham, Mass., 1939.

Lewis, J. Sydney, *Old Glass and How to Collect It.* Dodd, Mead and Co., New York, 1911.

Litchfield, Frederick, *Pottery and Porcelain.* The Macmillan Co., New York, 1925.

Moore, N. Hudson, *The Old China Book.* Tudor Publishing Co., New York, 1935.

National Encyclopedia. P. F. Collier and Sons, New York, 1935.

Northend, Mary Harrod, *American Glass.* Tudor Publishing Co., New York, 1936.

Okie, Howard Pitcher, *Old Silver and Old Sheffield Plate.* Doubleday, Doran and Co., Inc., Garden City, N. Y., 1928.

Plant, James S., *Steuben Glass.* H. Bittner & Co., New York, 1948.

Rathbone, Lucy, and Elizabeth Tarpley, *Fabrics and Dress.* Houghton Mifflin Co., Boston, 1948.

Skelley, Leloise Davis, *Modern Fine Glass.* Richard R. Smith, New York, 1937.

Spargo, John, *Early American Pottery and China.* D. Appleton-Century-Crofts, New York, 1926.

The Story of Sterling. The Sterling Silversmiths' Guild of America, New York, 1937.

Wingate, Isabel, *Textile Fabrics.* Prentice-Hall, New York, 1940.

Wyler, Seymour B., *Old Silver, English, American and Foreign.* Crown Publishers, New York, 1937.

FILMS

Beauty That Lives Forever. International Silver Company.
The Glass Center of Corning. Association Films Regional Libraries:
Ridgefield, New Jersey
Chicago, Ill.
Dallas, Texas
San Francisco, Calif.

UNIT

24

Table Decorations

The traditional theme in table décor is still the dominant one. The centerpiece of roses in Fig. 88 represents a top favorite of many individuals and groups. However, just as other areas related to preparing and serving food have undergone great change, so has the matter of decorating the table. As modern accessories have provided greater decorative possibilities through interesting textures, design, and colors, table decorations as such have become less important. Also the food itself fulfills a more significant function in decorating the table. In some instances it is the only décor. Smaller dining tables do not permit the use of a "centerpiece" in many cases. The design of many of today's modern homes makes it possible to "decorate" the dining area with a beautiful garden scene. When the dining table is placed in relation to a large open or glass area which frames a pleasant outdoor view, table decorations are likely to be lost, detracting rather than contributing to the total effect.

A flower arrangement on the table is not apt to be enthusiastically received when the bird feeders just outside the dining room window are crowded with highly-colored feathered friends. A view of the first garden tulips makes the dried winter bouquet on the table out of place and out of character. Appropriateness stands out as being the most important characteristic of attractive table decorations. This means that the decoration cannot stand alone but must be considered along with the other table appointments, the food, the occasion, and the entire surroundings.

Conformity to cultural traditions is sometimes responsible for trite and unimaginative table decorations. The subtle use of seasonal symbols (pumpkins, bells, hearts, etc.) often makes for more distinctive décor than when they are arranged in an obvious fashion. There is no "rule" that says traditional décor must always be used with traditional china, linen, etc., or that traditional arrangements may not be used in contemporary settings. If handled with restraint, table decorations characteristic of different periods can be adapted to any particular setting. A change in the style of decor is often a pleasant and stimulating accent to enjoyable meals. Of all the items used for decorating tables, flowers are most popular. Their thoughtful use provides endless possibilities for varied settings.

FLOWER ARRANGEMENT

The love of flowers is universal, and the arrangement of them is an international art. In Japan, where the art was created and has been fostered for centuries, it is basic to the feeling that nature and culture are inseparably united. It is only natural that this notion is considered to surpass all others in application of the art. Even in "modern" Japan, flower arrangement continues to be an educational requirement.

Since World War II the West's interest in all forms of oriental art has continuously increased. Large numbers of Americans who have lived and traveled in Japan have introduced into their homes in the United States artistic oriental furnishings and accessories. Many of these people studied and acquired skill in flower arrangement during their association with the Japanese. In most instances our materials, backgrounds, and homes themselves make it necessary to adapt rather than copy Japanese flower arrangements. If perfection in arrangements is the goal, pleasure in this fascinating art is likely to be sacrificed.

Whatever the influence, there is increased and widespread interest in the use of flowers for decorative purposes. Garden clubs, church organizations, horticultural associations, and many other groups sponsor seasonal flower shows. Among the most popular attractions at these shows are the artistic flower arrangements.

Arranging flowers for "show" must be done according to rules, which are very often "hard and fast." The creative person is likely to find arrangement by "prescription" confining in giving expression to her own ideas. Flower arranging is one of the best ways of experimenting with design.

The material which follows is intended for the amateur who is interested in acquiring basic information for assisting her in achieving artistic and satisfying flower arrangements.

Cutting, treating, and preparing flowers. Since fresh flowers are essential for pleasing effects, part of the beauty of an arrangement depends upon the way the flowers are cut, the treatment they receive immediately afterwards, and their preparation for arrangement.

Time and method of cutting. A thoughtless gardener may defeat his whole season's work by cutting flowers at random and at any hour of the day. Both the plant and the flowers will suffer from the shock of cutting unless it is done in the early morning before the sun is hot or in the very late afternoon after the sun has gone down. If flowers are cut during these hours, they will retain

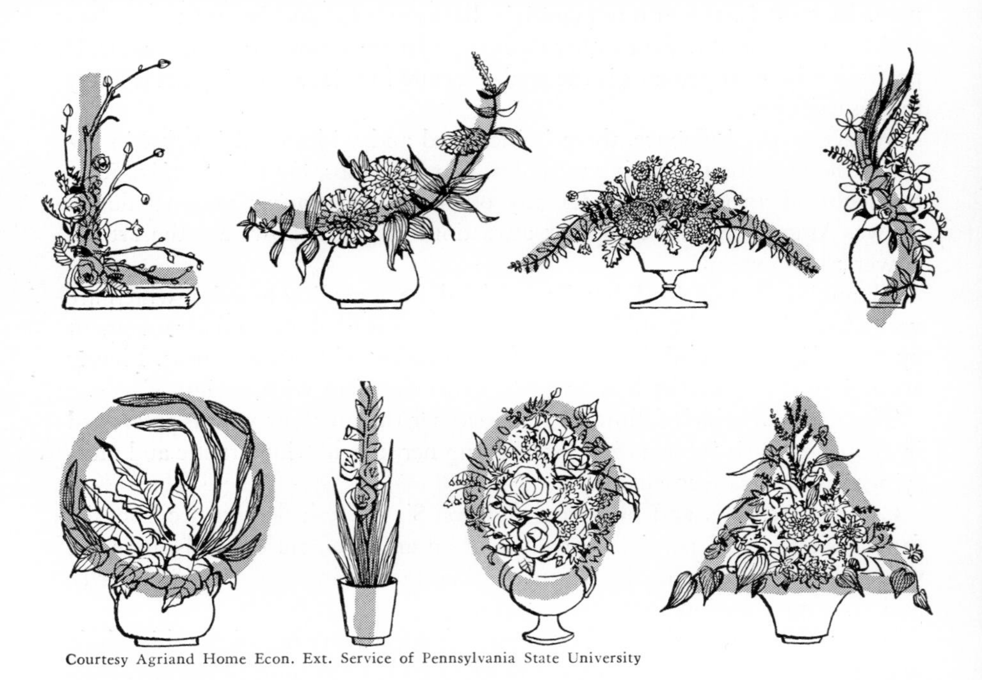

Courtesy Agriand Home Econ. Ext. Service of Pennsylvania State University

Fig. 87. Basic floral designs. Top, Left: *The first sign of spring. Wild cherry and tulips combined.* Right: *Simple beginning for an informal arrangement.* Middle, *Right Angle, Crescent, Horizontal, and Hogarth Line.* Bottom, *Circle, Vertical, Oval, and Triangle.*

Courtesy Towle Silversmiths

Fig. 88. A conventional table setting with a traditional "centerpiece."

their freshness for a much longer time. The stages at which various flowers are most desirable for cutting are somewhat different. For example, morning-glories and poppies will remain open up to two days if the buds which would normally open the next day are cut the night before. These buds should be arranged in the container in which they are to be used, as poppies and morning-glories are extremely fragile and should be handled as little as possible after they have opened. Dahlias, at their best, must be cut when fully opened; while roses, gladioli, irises, and many others may be cut either when in full bloom or as the buds are beginning to open. It is a source of pleasure to watch the buds unfold.

Gardeners differ as to the best method of cutting flowers. While scissors are used in many instances, it is the opinion of most individuals that they crush the stem and squeeze the cells together, thereby impeding the rise of water. For this reason, a sharp knife is often used, making a slanting cut upward. This insures a larger open surface which will permit the passage of water into the stem.

Care after cutting. Immediately upon cutting flowers or receiving them from the florist, they should be placed in a deep receptacle which allows the water to come up to the blossoms. If they are left in this container in a cool, dark place where there is no draft for several hours before arranging them, the plant tissues become filled with water, making the stems more erect and the flowers better able to withstand the dry atmosphere of the interior.

Some flowers and plants require special treatment after cutting. Hardwood stems of flowering shrubs or trees should be split several inches so as to increase the water-absorbing surface, as a large amount of water is required to keep them from wilting. Semi-woody stemmed flowers, such as chrysanthemums, will also benefit by having the ends of the stems split. Other flowers must have their stems sealed before putting them to soak in water. These are the ones which bleed heavily, such as poppies and poinsettias with their milky sap, and some of the hollow-stemmed flowers, of which elderberry is an example. This sealing may be done by plunging the stems into boiling water for a few minutes; searing the ends over a flame; dipping them in a solution of nitric acid (one-tenth of 1 per cent); or placing them in melted paraffin for several minutes. In the process of dipping the stems or charring them, care must be exercised to protect the blossoms from the steam and heat.

Flowers such as water lilies, which stay open only a portion of the day, may be used effectively for decoration by forcing them to stay open. This may be done by pouring a small amount of warm, melted paraffin on the petals at the base of the stamen. The hardening of the paraffin prevents the blossoms from closing for two days or even longer.

Preparation for arrangement. Most flowers need a portion of their foliage removed before arranging them. The purpose of this treatment is threefold:

1) The flowers remain fresh for a longer period if the lower foliage is stripped off, thereby preventing the water from becoming foul. With few exceptions no foliage should be under water in an arrangement. Flowers such as zinnias, daisies, and marigolds are the type which will deteriorate quickly unless their lower leaves are removed. On the other hand, the foliage of some flowers, such as roses, is not affected by being under water, and may be very beautiful in a clear glass container which permits the leaves to spread out in the water. Foliage which shows in this

Fig. 89. Honeysuckle in a pitcher.

manner should not be torn or bruised, since this will detract from rather than add to an arrangement.

2) Removal of foliage prevents overcrowding in the arrangement. Very often the excess foliage interferes with the amount of water absorbed, causing the arrangement to wilt. In stripping off the excess foliage, care should be taken not to injure the stems or to remove all leaves from the same portion of the stem. The thinning should be distributed all along the stem.

3) Many flowers are completely overshadowed, in both color and form, by heavy foliage. Honeysuckle is an example of a flower which lends itself to a graceful arrangement if most of the foliage is removed. Figure 89 shows an effective

small arrangement of this flower which can be enjoyed as much on the breakfast table as is the flower on the garden trellis.

Containers for flowers. Innumerable flower containers of good design in a price range suited to any purse are available in the shops today. The flower container is as much a part of the design of the arrangement as the flowers used in it. "In each instance, the container is almost as important as the blooms themselves. Perfect blossoms artistically arranged in an ill-chosen dish or vase cannot present a fine ensemble. The container may be said to be the 'other half of the arrangement.'"[1] Instead of a container competing with its contents, it should combine to form a complete picture, harmonious in color, texture, shape, and proportion. The ability to choose from flower containers of both good and bad design those which are beautiful as well as useful is apt to be difficult for the inexperienced person, nor will this person find it easy to select the right ones for particular flowers. In choosing flower containers, one should ask these questions: (1) Is it well designed? (2) Is it harmonious with the surroundings in which it will be used? (3) Is it suitable for the flowers it will contain?

Design. Whether or not a container is well designed depends a great deal upon the extent to which the craftsman has utilized the essential characteristics of the material in which he is working. A design which gives a heavy pottery bowl a beauty and distinction of its own would not be suitable for a bowl of fine silver. A Mexican glass container may be admired because it is slightly irregular in shape, but a rock crystal vase must necessarily be perfect in shape to be beautiful.

The decoration of a container should be very simple and definitely a part of the structural lines of the vase. It should follow the basic form and strengthen it rather than be a separate attraction in itself. The decoration should be conventional rather than realistic, for when flowers are placed in a container already decorated with flowers or fruit, the effect is confusing, to say the least. A point that should never be forgotten is that well-chosen fresh flowers, artistically arranged, are sufficient decoration for any container.

Flower containers have a definite function—holding flowers. The opening at the top should be neither too small nor too large. A medium-sized vase with a very small opening is most impractical, for it can hold only a few small flowers. Vases should be well balanced and have a firm base so that they will not tip over easily. The proportion should be pleasing.

Harmony with surroundings. The suitability of the container to the type of background and to other accessories is the first consideration in making a choice of containers. Fine glass, handsome silver, and rare porcelain containers would be entirely out of place in a small, inexpensively furnished home.

---

[1] From F. F. Rockwell and Esther C. Grayson, *Flower Arrangement* (New York: Macmillan, 1936), p. 46.

Here brightly colored peasant pottery would find its greatest beauty. Some containers, such as pewter, brass, or copper, are at home in any surroundings, their beauty depending upon the craftsman's skill in proportioning and shaping them as well as upon the beauty of the metals themselves.

The size of the containers in relation to the size of the room is a point which might be overlooked easily. Very large containers holding large arrangements of flowers are beautifully effective in spacious rooms, but if used in small rooms, they are out of scale to the extent of appearing almost ridiculous.

Flower containers are frequently selected with no thought of one's other accessories. This is particularly true of those chosen for the dining room. It is not necessary for the flower container to match the china, silver, or glass used on a table; in fact, a more interesting effect is likely to result if it does not match the other appointments, but harmonizes with them in both color and texture. Silver candleholders do not necessarily call for a silver bowl nor does blue glass mean that the flower container must also be blue glass. With a dinner service of Italian pottery, a flower bowl of the same ware of a harmonizing color may be used. A Spanish glass bowl would also make a pleasant combination because there would be harmony in the texture of the pottery and the glass. A rock-crystal flower container is as much out of place on a table with the above mentioned china as an earthenware bowl would be on a table where rock crystal glass was used.

Suitability for flowers. The modern French school of art has done much to educate people along the line of suiting the texture of containers to flowers, as is beautifully exemplified by Vincent van Gogh in his "Sunflowers," "Flowers in a Copper Vase," and "Laurier Roses," and by Paul Gauguin in his "Flowers." As a rule, it is best to select containers which can be used with the flowers in the garden, and those native to the surrounding country. It would be an extravagance to purchase a container for roses if roses were only available through a florist at several dollars a dozen at all times of the year.

Metal containers. This group includes containers made of silver, pewter, brass, copper, bronze, stainless steel, etc. In these materials we find some of the most charming old containers and some of the best modern designs. (See Fig. 90.)

In the estimation of many people, copper and brass are most beautiful when they are not highly polished but possess an incrustation, usually greenish, which adds to their charm as flower receptacles. Both of these metals lend themselves to use with many types of flowers—native grasses and blossoms, sturdy garden flowers of the type of zinnias, chrysanthemums, and marigolds, and the more conventional flowers, such as roses, tulips, and gladioli. The weight, both in color and texture, of bronze containers calls for plant materials which are heavy and bold in color and form. Bronze is not

Courtesy New York Times Studio

Fig. 90. Flowers and fruit combine to make this beautiful crescent arrangement in an old pewter pitcher.

suitable for use on the dining table, but may be used effectively on a buffet.

Silver flower containers are perhaps the most misused of all types. Bud vases, bowls, and baskets of sterling or plated silver are used in many homes as the main type of receptacle; and because their use is so common, they seem to be accepted by most individuals as suitable for all types of flowers, when in reality silver is appropriate for very few flowers. "The color and quality of most silver is trying and it is overwhelming to flowers unless they have good color and great character of form in blossoms and foliage. Orchids of almost any variety or fine roses are a good choice for such containers. Either has sufficient character to hold its own against the silver."[1]

Pewter is more difficult to use for flowers than brass or copper, but on the other hand it is usually a better choice than silver because the simplicity of design makes it useful for flowers too unassuming to look well in silver.

Pottery. Pottery embraces a wide variety of flower containers which are appropriate to use in many homes and are suited in texture, form, and color to innumerable flowers. Pottery which is irregular in form and which is either unglazed or coarsely glazed has a somewhat crude, primitive appearance, and is best suited to wild flowers or garden flowers of a vigorous type. Small sunflowers in a crude brown pottery jug make an effective arrangement for a porch or terrace, while roses arranged in the same jug would be incongruous. Some pottery is so refined in form, glaze, and color that it is appropriate to use with any garden flowers which approximate it in quality. Roses in a Rookwood bowl of fine glaze; sweet peas and baby breath in a delicately colored piece of Newcomb pottery; gladioli in a beautifully formed Cowan vase—all of these would be completely satisfying arrangements.

Glass. Glass of all types is used for making flower containers, and they are among the most beautiful ones available. The exquisite clearness of some glass makes it charming to use with flowers which have beautiful stems and foliage. Colored glass is more difficult to use than clear; however, smoked amethyst, a color found in much glass from Czechoslovakia and Sweden; honey, a characteristic color of Spanish glass, and the delicate pinks, greens, and blues of Venetian glass are all colors which lend themselves beautifully to flowers of almost any color. Strong colors, such as the bright blue of Mexican glass or the deep reds of some Bohemian and American glass, have their place with flowers, and if carefully used will serve to create a stunning effect. A geranium-red Venetian bowl filled with scarlet geraniums and small white chrysanthemums and flanked on either side with silver candelabra holding white tapers makes a beautiful and striking centerpiece for a tea table on a wintry afternoon, but a bowl of this type would have an extremely limited use and would be rather an extravagant possession. Highly ornamental or elaborately cut crystal bowls are only appropriate for exotic blossoms.

Baskets. The use of baskets as flower containers is better suited to places of business than to homes. Baskets of honest construction and simple design are appropriate to use for coarse garden flowers or wild grasses.

Unconventional containers. Effective flower arrangements do not necessarily call for a bowl or vase which was designed for the purpose of holding flowers. Original, distinctive, and beautifully satisfying arrangements can be made in soup tureens, pitchers, salad bowls, bean pots, vegetable platters and

[1] Mrs. Walter R. Hines, *The Arrangement of Flowers* (New York: Scribner's, 1933), p. 107.

any other type of utensil which has the requisites of a well-designed container. Artistic arrangements observed in such containers have included:

Wild purple thistles in a blue earthen bean pot.

Red geraniums in a large cream-colored Wedgewood vegetable dish of Queensware.

Long-stemmed red roses in a blue Mexican glass wine bottle.

An all-white arrangement of small ragged chrysanthemums in a white porcelain soup tureen.

Arranging the flowers. Much has been done toward creating an attractive design in flower arrangement if the flowers have been properly selected and prepared for arranging and a suitable container chosen for them. However, the most difficult part is in the combination of various flowers and their arrangement in the receptacle.

The illustrations in Fig. 87 show the variation in designs for flower arrangement. The materials will usually suggest the design most suitable. These designs should not be considered as rules, but rather as guides for experimentation with materials.

The proper combination of flowers requires some knowledge of plant materials. Much of this knowledge can be gained with a little study and through observation of flowers as they grow. If persons made an effort to know more about plant materials, perhaps we would not see asparagus fern combined with roses and gladioli, calendulas used with sweet peas, and many other combinations equally illogical and commonly used. Textural relationship, which is so important between containers and flowers, must also carry over into the combination of flowers for an arrangement. Only those flowers which naturally belong together should be combined in a composition.

When it comes to the arrangement itself, information is needed in order to obtain distinctive designs. Information alone is not all that is necessary, since actual experience in handling and arranging flowers is essential to success in this art. The following points will serve as a guide:

1) Time and thought are the first requisites in arranging flowers. An arrangement should be designed carefully and the flowers handled one at a time in arranging them in the container. One such arrangement will be far more satisfying than many which have had no time and thought given to them.

2) Flowers of horticultural perfection are not necessary for beautiful effects. Large blossoms or blossoms of uniform size, length of stem, and color are seldom desirable. Dahlias as large as dinner plates might justly be a source of pride to a gardener or nurseryman, but it would be impossible to use these giant flowers artistically in the home. Crooked stemmed flowers will give graceful lines to an arrangement that cannot otherwise be obtained. The sacrificing of a few buds in order to cut longer stems is sometimes justifiable, as an arrangement will be more beautiful with the stems of varying length. When long-stemmed roses or other

[1] *Ibid.*, p. 107.

flowers come from the florist with stems all the same length, it is necessary to cut some of them if they are to be used for distinctive arrangements. Uniformity of color is likely to be monotonous in flower composition. An arrangement which has a shading of color from very dark to very light will prove more satisfying than one that is uniform.

3) Arrangements of a few flowers are often more artistic than a mass arrangement. In such arrangements the stems should not all be the same length. Fig. 87 illustrates this with the very short tulip stems.

4) Balance in a flower arrangement need not be symmetrical or precise as seen in many formal arrangements. A symmetrical balance is more informal and many flowers lend themselves to such an arrangement. The three iris leaves in Fig. 87 show the beauty of informal balance.

5) If the container is tall, the flowers used should approximate one-and-a-half times its height. If a very low bowl is used, the height of the flowers should be about one-and-a-half times its diameter. There are no hard-and-fast rules concerning the width of an arrangement—the artist bases this width on experience; however, the actual or apparent weight of the container has some influence on both the height and width of a composition.

6) Many flower arrangements are overcrowded, and the result is confusing and unsatisfying. As has been previously stated, overcrowding is nearly always due to excessive foliage, which may be the foliage of the plant itself or added foliage of ferns. With few exceptions, ferns weaken a composition. The designer should never introduce anything into a flower arrangement which is not a part of the whole design.

7) While color is a factor in every design, it is not the most important consideration. This does not mean that color can be disregarded. It must be carefully handled since it may be the cause of distracting designs as well as distinctive ones. If more than one color is being used in an arrangement, the darker color must be arranged at the base of the composition in order to stabilize and strengthen the design. An even distribution of several colors does not make for as much interest as does the dominance of one of the colors. A carefully designed arrangement in which several colors are used may be more distinctive than one of a single color, unless the flowers in the latter have unusual beauty of color and form. Bold color combinations may prove interesting unless too many liberties are taken with them. Bright orange should be kept away from reds and purples or the result will be quarrelsome, but bright orange combined with bright blue makes a striking effect. Subtle color combinations are likely to be weak unless the container is carefully chosen and the group placed to good advantage.

8) A composition should be viewed from all sides as it is being arranged, to avoid having a one-sided effect. Generally speaking, there are two kinds of flower arrangements—the free-standing arrangement which is to be viewed from all sides and the arrangement that is related to some definite space and is not viewed from all angles. The first type must be so designed as to make a complete picture from all views. Such arrangements are always used on dining tables, while the other type may be used on buffets or chests in dining rooms unless a mirror is behind them, in which case the free-standing arrangement would be used, with the side toward the mirror somewhat flatter.

9) Devices for holding flower stems firmly are essential for practicing this art. There are many different types and some of the most satisfactory are those which are "homemade" or created on the spot. Pin holders, chicken wire, forked branches, clay, lead coils, and paraffin are useful for this purpose.

Artificiality in decoration. Flower lovers who do not wish to disturb their gardens by cutting flowers sometimes decorate the interior of their homes with artificial flowers. With few exceptions, most plants benefit by having their blossoms carefully cut. A garden will be far more beautiful if the flowers are cut regularly, and they may then be enjoyed inside the house as well as outside.

The use of paints and dyes on flowers, leaves, berries, and seed pods is questionable. Pine cones are perhaps most often abused in this respect. They are gilded and silvered or painted bright red or green and used in great profusion during the holiday season. Pine cones are beautiful in their natural state and need no such treatment to make them effective for decoration. In table decoration, more than in any other type, an abundance of artificial materials is used. Pieces of fruit have been wrapped in cellophane of varied colors and heaped in large bowls or trays and used as a centerpiece. It is difficult to understand why anyone would think the color or contour of grapes, oranges, apples, pears, or bananas could be made more beautiful by concealing them in packages of glittering paper.

Winter bouquets. Permanent decorations of nature's materials are frequently quite as beautiful as flowers that fade. After gardens have been ravaged by fall frosts and winter snows, the outlook for flowers for the house is somewhat discouraging. The ingenious and artistic homemaker will not, however, let the end of summer be the end of decorations for her home. Perhaps in her own garden she has evergreens, a few sprays of which will be beautiful arranged in appropriate containers, or there may be seed pods and grasses of distinctive shapes and coloring which will make attractive arrangements. Winter decorations may be planned in advance by planting straw or "everlasting" flowers in the spring garden and drying them for bouquets which will last through the long months when fresh flowers are at a premium.

There are many possibilities for winter arrangements in the use of ivy, wandering Jew, coleus, and other plants, which make graceful centerpieces because they grow beautifully in either water or soil. In water, a glass container makes them more enjoyable because it is interesting to watch the roots grow. Sweet potatoes, carrots, and beets, if allowed to sprout and then placed in a bowl of water, will also make effective centerpieces. Growing bulbs are always a source of great pleasure, and since they are easily grown and very inexpensive, they may be enjoyed in any home.

The best source of materials for winter bouquets is likely to be the surrounding country. In different sections we find such decorative gems as wild rose haws, cat brier, bayberry, bittersweet, sea oats, and pine cones, to say nothing of numerous wild grasses and other interesting and beautiful plant materials. These things should not be gathered carelessly, since most states are attempting to protect their native trees, shrubs, and plants.

An aromatic dried arrangement has added charm. Eucalyptus leaves will keep their fragrance for several years. Dill heads make an airy and delicate bouquet. The pungent smell of this herb will linger from fall to spring when the dry arrangement can be replaced with the fresh yellow green plants from the garden.

Today plant conservation laws are strict in many states, and it is expected they soon will be in others. Without breaking any protective laws, however, or harming any tree, shrub, or plant, it is possible to obtain interesting material for a number of lasting winter arrangements.

DECORATIVE POSSIBILITIES WITH FOOD

Economical aspects. The custom of buying cut flowers at the florist's for use in decorating, especially the dining table, is a routine with many people. Depending upon the season and the flowers selected, this can be costly. However, the same individuals who think nothing of spending several dollars for flowers would probably consider it wasteful to purchase beautiful out-of-season food to use for table decorations. Even if the food is not later consumed it may not be any more expensive than flowers. Some foods such as pineapples and apples are far less perishable than most flowers and at room temperature they have the advantage of providing a pleasant aroma. A "theme" in decorating can often be carried out with food better than with flowers. A head of curly, green savoy cabbage makes a beautiful and appropriate decoration for a St. Patrick's party; red and green chili peppers in a gourd bowl provide an authentic touch for a Mexican supper; fresh pineapples are perfect for an Hawaiian dinner, and for a Chilean meal, large black grapes in a copper bowl would feature two of this country's principal commodities.

Fruits and vegetables. Most fruits and vegetables are beautiful as they grow, as they appear in the markets, and if properly prepared, as they are served. Why, then, should we not enjoy them as table decorations? While fruits are frequently used for this purpose, vegetables are considered by many to be inappropriate as decorative objects for the table. Rich purple eggplants; fresh, shiny, green peppers; slender cucumbers, shading from pale yellow to very dark green; and brilliant yellow squashes are a few of the vegetables which, combined with fruit, make effective centerpieces. Fruit decorations are used throughout the year for both formal and informal occasions. The following points are suggestive of the many ways in which fruit may be arranged for decorative purposes:

1) Red apples, highly polished and arranged with pine cones and twigs of evergreen, make an inexpensive and effective table decoration for the winter months. Brass, copper, pottery, or wooden bowls are appropriate containers for them.

2) Grapes, beautiful to use just as they are, create interesting variation if large clusters of them are dipped in heavy sugar sirup and then rolled in granulated sugar. This gives the grapes a frosty appearance, making them appropriate to use for holiday decorations. They may be used alone or in combination with sprigs of evergreen.

3) Fresh fruit centerpieces may be varied by adding to them nuts, bright-colored candy curls, sprigs of dried berries, such as bittersweet, or cluster raisins.

4) If blackberries or other bush fruits are plentiful, several short canes, having both fruit and foliage, may be cut from the bush and arranged for a breakfast table. Clear glass containers are particularly desirable for such an arrangement in order to show the thorny stem.

5) A few cut surfaces of citrus fruits add interest to a bowl of assorted fruits, as do pomegranates when they are just beginning to break open and show their bright red seeds.

6) Large Japanese persimmons, available on many markets, make a colorful table decoration. They are unusually beautiful when used in brass bowls. In sections where these persimmons are grown it may be possible to pick a cluster of them or a small branch bearing several. Such a cluster or branch placed on a brass plate or tray makes an effective decoration.

7) Bowls or plates of attractively arranged fruits may be used in combination with flowers on a large table. A bowl of flowers in the center of a long table balanced on either side by a plate of fruit makes a pleasing centerpiece for a breakfast or luncheon table.

Other foods. Many times a part of the dinner menu may be arranged to furnish the table decor. This is particularly true of special occasion dinners. A birthday cake or a burning Christmas pudding make effective centerpieces for dessert parties. Also a compote or a pair of compotes holding decorative petits fours or pastries, and arranged with a grouping of candles will furnish color and interest as table decorations. Figure 91 shows a festive holiday mince pie which competes for attention with an all-time favorite table decoration. Platters and bowls of food for a buffet carefully and attractively arranged may serve as the only decoration. When space is limited this will contribute to the ease of serving.

CANDLES AND CANDLEHOLDERS

Candles may be used effectively in many types of table decorations, and since many of them cost only a small amount their use is very common. The conventional grouping of candles on either side of a centerpiece is most often used; there are other possibilities, however: candles in the center of the table and an arrangement of flowers on either side; a decorative candelabrum

Courtesy Corning Glass

Fig. 91. Not only appetizing but an appropriate decoration.

holding two or more candles in the center as the only decoration; a single candle used, as on a small tea table, to balance a bowl of flowers.

Candleholders should, of course, be in harmony with the other table appointments. Dresden china candlesticks would be out of place used on an informal tea table with an earthenware tea set, as would be primitive Spanish glass candlesticks on a table which was laid with fine porcelain. Candleholders of good design that are suitable for table use do not necessarily involve the expenditure of a large amount of money. They are available to fit almost any pocket book, in glass, pottery, china, brass, pewter, copper, silver, chromium, and spun aluminum. Since they are accessory pieces, they should be purchased in relation to the table appointments one already has. Pottery, brass, and pewter candleholders are suitable for informal use, while holders of crystal, silver, and china would be more appropriate for formal occasions.

Candle holders with hurricane shades are popular both for outdoor and indoor dining. Wrought iron, copper, and brass are materials frequently used for these holders. Silver and glass hurricane types continue as favorites for formal settings.

Candle scones are sometimes used in the dining room to supplement the candles used on the table and serving areas. These are often electrified, but many are designed for using wax candles.

As in other items, cost is not a criterion for good design in candle holders. Some of the most expensive ones do not have artistic merit.

Candles for the table are available in many different colors. The soft, subtle colors are more pleasing, as a rule, than the harsh, intense ones. White or ivory-colored candles are always in good taste; it is a mistaken idea, however, that they are the only candles correct for formal use. Candles of any color are permissible if they harmonize with the other decorations and the table appointments.

Within the last few years candles have undergone considerable change. In addition to traditional styles, many other types are available. Twisted and "chunk" candles are seen in many sizes and colors. Sequins, beads, and metallic washes are used for decorating candles for Christmas and other special seasons.

In selecting candles, allowances should be made for the differences in color at night and during the day. If candles are to be used at night, it is a good idea to place them under an electric light in order to get the true color. Sometimes faded candles which are sold as seconds provide a subtle tone which is more effective than the brighter colors.

The following suggestions may be helpful when using candles:

1) Placing candles in the refrigerator for 24 hours before they are to be used will cause them to burn more slowly and evenly. A cold candle, if not placed in a draft, will burn approximately two inches an hour.

2) To prevent candles from burning irregularly, they should be lighted before they are used in order to burn off the long wick. After burning for several minutes, the wick should be clipped short. Candles will burn unevenly if placed in a draft.

3) The height of candles should be adapted to the height of the centerpiece, being in general taller than the other decorations. Very tall candles are effective to use on buffet and tea tables. Candles of varying heights may be used in candelabra holding three, five, or seven candles. If it is necessary to cut a candle, it can be done easily with a heated knife.

4) Candles should be fitted into the holders securely so that they will stand perfectly straight. Crooked candles detract greatly from the appearance of a table. If the candle is too large for the holder it can be shaved off slightly at the bottom, using a paring knife, or it may be dipped in hot water and forced into the holder while the wax is soft. If too small, a little wax may be melted into the candleholder, the candle inserted and held firmly until the wax hardens. The half-inch rubber bands sometimes supplied with candles help to hold them in place. Wrapping the end of a candle with paper is not always satisfactory for holding it securely.

5) Candles are not placed on a table unless they are to be lighted. They should be lighted before guests enter the dining room and allowed to burn throughout the meal.

6) Candles should be extinguished carefully in order to avoid blowing the melted wax on the table linen. To do this, shield the flame with the hand and blow across it. Candle snuffers of various metals can be purchased at the five-and-ten-cent store and are a great convenience.

7) If candles are the only source of light, a sufficient number should be used to light the room adequately.

8) Candles should not be used in very warm weather. They not only burn too rapidly and are unattractive because of the dripping wax, but also add to the discomfort of the guests.

PLACE CARDS, TABLE FAVORS, AND DECORATIVE OBJECTS

Place cards are a convenience when seating a large number of guests, and they may be used for small dinners, luncheons, or breakfasts of a festive type. The kind of card used depends upon the occasion. Small, plain white cards are appropriate at any time, while decorative ones may be used at feature parties. Highly decorative cards do not as a rule add to the attractiveness of the table, because they stand out as so many spots of color or decoration rather than blending in with the whole scheme. Place-card holders of silver, china, or crystal may be purchased, but unless a hostess entertains frequently with large parties they are an unjustifiable expense. The correct position for place cards is on the napkin or at the top of the cover. If place-card holders are used, they are treated as part of the table decorations, and are therefore not to be taken away by the guests.

Table favors may or may not contribute to the attractiveness of the table. Crepe-paper favors and decorations are of the type which have little beauty; however, they have their place at children's parties and may also be used for special occasions such as a Halloween or St. Patrick's Day dinner. Flower favors of small corsages or miniature vases holding one or two flowers may add to the beauty of the table, but the expense involved would, many times, prevent their use. Since there are so many different kinds of objects used for this purpose—some in good taste and others in poor taste—they should be carefully selected if they are to contribute to the attractiveness of a table.

Pottery and glass fruit, crystal trees and flowers, china figurines of all sorts, birds of silver, crystal, or china, and blown-glass bubbles are among the many object sold as table decorations today. Modern art has called for still different types of decorative objects for table use. Cubes and prisms in both clear and frosted crystal and objects of chromium, spun aluminum, and mirrored glass are typical decorations for modern tables. While some of these decorative objects are very beautiful, they may also be difficult to use. Designs which are created with unusual decorative objects should be beautiful and appropriate and not grotesque or bizarre.

Interesting designs in driftwood are often used as table decorations, either alone or in combination with plant materials.

SUGGESTIONS FOR LABORATORY

Every foods laboratory presents an opportunity for the application of art principles to the serving of food. Some students will be more interested in the artistic approach to setting tables and serving food than others. If given the responsibility of leadership in this area, many ideas will be presented which should stimulate the interest of class associates.

Exhibits of table set-ups and accesories arranged in cooperation with the art department are likely to arouse an awareness as to the many possibilities for creating attractive tables for meal service.

REFERENCES

BOOKS

Arms, John Taylor and Dorothy Noyes Arms, *Design in Flower Arrangement.* The Macmillan Co., New York, 1939.

Fort, Marie Johnson, *Flower Arrangements for All Occasions.* Rinehart and Co., Inc., New York, 1952.

Goldmann, Mary E., *Planning and Serving Your Meals,* 2nd Edition. McGraw-Hill Book Co., New York, 1959.

Hines, Mrs. Walter R., *The Arrangement of Flowers.* Charles Scribner's Sons, New York, 1933.

Koehn, Alfred, *The Way of Japanese Flower Arrangement.* Kyo Bun Kwan, Tokyo, 1935.

Rockwell, F. F. and Esther C. Grayson, *Flower Arrangement.* The Macmillan Co., New York, 1934.

Rockwell, F. F. and E. C. Grayson, *Flower Arrangement in Color.* Wise & Co., New York, 1940.

Selected Flower Arrangements of the Ohara School. Yamanaka and Co., Inc., New York, 1934.

Sprackling, Helen, *Setting Your Table.* M. Barrows and Co., New York, 1941.

Spry, Constance, *Flowers in House and Garden.* G. P. Putnam's Sons, New York, 1937.

Spry, Constance, *Flower Decoration.* G. P. Putnam's Sons, New York, 1933.

UNIT 25

Social Refreshments

"Man is a sociable animal and expresses life's sociability by neglecting no opportunity to eat in company. Men seldom fail to come together to eat upon any occasion that can be made to offer the least excuse for so doing."[1]

As delightful as this custom is, it may also be a hazardous one healthwise unless the food served reflects today's trend toward simplification. If social refreshments take into consideration the calorie-conscious public—men, women, and teen-agers—they will be light, attractive, and nutritious. They will be planned around familiar foods, interestingly prepared and presented in a distinctive fashion so as to *enhance* their simplicity. A large kitchen board used as a "platter" for arranging the sandwich ingredients from which a group of teen-agers make their own; chowder served at the table directly from a stainless steel or other attractive sauce pan; allowing guests to cut their own cheese from a sizable wedge placed on a board—these are illustrations of simplified service which guests appreciate.

Refreshments for a party that are good in taste can be as simple as bread and milk. The "bread" being, as an example, one of the many fruit varieties, sliced thin and served plain or as a small bread and butter sandwich, and the "milk" any one of a number of delicious drinks such as café au lait (p. 646), syllabub (p. 533), or other milk beverages found in selected recipe books.

Unfortunately, many people consider the refreshments they plan for company as something entirely apart from what is prepared for the family. This double standard has led, in many instances, to the practice of serving "fussy" food to guests and reserving the simple things for every day meals. In the final analysis the latter would be chosen by a number of individuals as the most "elegant."

To some hostesses food, especially that which is served to guests, is a meas-

[1] Frederick W. Hackwood, *Good Cheer* (New York: Sturgis and Walton, 1911), p. 193.

ure of social and economic status. To them the richer, costlier, and more elaborate the dessert for their dessert party, the more prestige it carries. One homemaker observed that when she made cheesecake for the family she used cottage cheese and milk, but that when she made it for company she did so with *cream* and *cream cheese.* In this case and others where company is supposed to get the "best," it is certainly questionable as to whether they do or not.

The desire to "keep up with the Joneses" in party food causes some individuals to rely on a catering service. (Even in very small communities, women who like to cook have found this activity to be a remunerative one for their interest.) In certain communities, where it is the custom to have parties "catered," a visitor who is being fêted by several hostesses is likely to be served the same varieties and types of open-faced sandwiches and fancy cakes at two or more parties.

Individuality may be expressed through the food that is served just as it is expressed in dress, home furnishings, and other areas. Individuality in social refreshments is the quality which differentiates them from those served by others. It is the skill of an ingenious hostess, not the result of a superficiality such as the making of extra rich desserts for company or the copying of a picture of a fancy cake from a magazine. The courage to be one's self is a great asset in the matter of planning food for any social function. One courageous bride served fresh fruit, assorted crackers, and hot tea at an afternoon bridge party in a community where it was the custom to serve a salad, sandwiches, and beverage as a first course, followed by a dessert, which was usually ice cream and cake. Because she was a leader, this started the practice of serving lighter and more suitable refreshments at afternoon parties.

The fear of what "they will think" can be dispelled easily if the gesture of hospitality is extended in a natural rather than a self-conscious manner. A student from a Pennsylvania Dutch home reported that the favorite family dessert was apple dumplings served in a bowl with milk and eaten with a spoon, but for company apple pie with ice cream was always served (on a plate with a fork). In a class discussion on "company standards" she seemed both amazed and pleased when the majority of the group "voted" for the family dessert (and its service too) over the company apple pie. However, before the discussion concluded, the student remarked, "But my mother wouldn't think they were good enough for company." The tendency to stick strictly to the traditional American pattern is very strong in many instances. It is a secure way and many never depart from it. In the same class, mentioned above, another student related that goulash prepared by her Hungarian grandmother and served with sauerkraut salad was a special meal for the family. Guests in this household were always served the conventional steak, with French fries and head lettuce salad with Thousand Island dressing because this was the company standard.

Courtesy Towle Silversmiths

Fig. 92. A buffet arrangement of the luxury type. The extended service, of both flatware and china, anticipates the availability of accessory tables for seating guests.

With the de-emphasis on exceeding the body requirements for food, social refreshments tend to center around meals instead of in-between meal affairs. Buffets for larger groups, supper and dinner parties for small or large groups, brunches, cook-outs or other outdoor meals, and special Sunday night parties are some of the types of social situations which seem to be popular throughout America. Even refreshments for parties that are not meals are counted on by some guests as part of the meal. This is particularly true of dessert parties and morning coffees. When planning refreshments for either of these parties consideration should be given to the fact that they are being served shortly *after* meal time.

The suggestions given here for eating with family and friends emphasize informality, since for most families this is the only type of food service that fits naturally into their pattern of living. Eating should be a lively and enjoyable part of any social gathering. Preparations for it should also be enjoyable and the whole experience rewarding. If the food is simple and attractive and ritualistic rules are replaced by casual cordiality, with the *comfort* of everyone in mind, the party is bound to be successful.

BUFFET MEALS

Buffet meals have become an American institution in entertaining. They constitute a social formula for a successful party for any age group, in homes of all types. The service is friendly, intimate, easy, and graceful; and its flexibility makes it practicable to use in a variety of ways. It facilitates serving large groups with a minimum expenditure of time and energy and without putting undue strain on the food budget. Buffet service is appropriate to use for breakfasts, luncheons, dinners, or suppers served either as the evening meal or as an after-theater party. Buffet parties may be as informal as the hostess chooses to make them, or, if the surroundings dictate a more formal affair, buffet meals can be made quite elaborate. In many homes where the dining table seats only six to eight people comfortably, buffet meals for entertaining guests have become the accepted standard.

A great deal of the charm of buffet meals lies in the fascinating table appointments which can be assembled for serving the meal. Bright colored mixing bowls, casseroles, wooden bowls, earthen coffee urns and mugs, and other attractive utensils, once confined to the kitchen, may now handsomely grace a buffet table. And for the more elaborate luncheon and dinner parties the table appointments can be the height of elegance and include linen, silver, porcelain, and crystal of the most exquisite quality. The appointments used should be related to the food served, or perhaps it is more practical to start with the menu and choose the dishes and other table accessories around the food. In addition to the beautiful colors and forms of food, they also have texture. Like fabrics, these textures range from very coarse to very fine. With

Courtesy Griswold Manufacturing Company

Fig. 93. A small informal buffet arrangement.

a conscious appreciation of the beauty of food and experience in planning, preparing, and serving it, one soon learns that it is an excellent medium with which to create satisfying and beautiful designs. The buffet table is ideally suited to giving expression to creativity.

The mechanical details of preparing for a buffet are extremely important if the guests are to be comfortable and relaxed.

The buffet table may be covered with a cloth, or, if a handsome table is used, the bare table may provide just the right background for the table decorations and the china. Many hostesses prefer to use table mats, which must be carefully placed if they are to contribute to the design which the table creates.

The plates used should be large enough to hold the food without crowding. If hot and cold foods are served on the same plate, this is especially important. If tables are not used for the guests to place their plates on, the plate should also be large enough to hold safely a glass or cup in addition to the food. In some European countries guests seem perfectly at ease juggling two plates, one holding a beverage, but Americans are not very adept at this practice. When the number of guests is not large, supper trays offer a convenient way of serving buffet meals. Dinner napkins instead of the small luncheon size will be acceptable, particularly to men guests. The buffet table may in reality be a series of *tables*. Such an arrangement is desirable when a three-course meal is being served—appetizer, main course, dessert and beverage. A separate table or surface (desk, low boy, book case, etc.,) for presenting each course will facilitate serving and will be a device for keeping the guests from crowding into one spot.

If the guests number more than ten or twelve it is possible to start the meal before all are assembled. In other words, the guests circulate from one area to the other serving themselves. Some might be eating their dessert when others are having their appetizer or main course. This plan is particularly convenient if all courses are out and ready for service when the guests arrive. Naturally the menu should not include any foods that would deteriorate on standing. (Suggested menus for this type of buffet are given on p. 452.) If the dining room or living room is not large enough for setting up three areas of service, other rooms might be used—the kitchen, a study, porch, etc. This is an excellent way for people to mingle, which they will do if they are responsible for serving themselves. If more than one table is used, whether they are all in one room or scattered, there should be a focal point of service. This might be for any one of the courses, but it is generally the *main* course which is featured by the table arrangement.

Any table used for a buffet arrangement should be large enough to arrange food, dishes, and decorations without giving a cluttered appearance. Careful thought should be given to the placement of the serving dishes and to the "routing" of the guests. A sauce should be placed in relation to the food it is to be served with, the butter by the bread, etc. Since many dishes which are served at buffets necessitate the use of both hands it is a great convenience to have space by the side of each dish served, so that a guest may place his plate *on* the table while he serves himself. The usual custom at a buffet of having guests pick up their plate, silver, and napkin before they serve themselves is really an awkward practice. The plate is the only thing needed until after the

Arranged by authors

Fig. 94. "Wood on wood" with simple pottery plates and interesting glasses is in keeping with the bread, milk, apples, and cheese supper.

guest is served. The silver and napkin may be picked up *last,* resulting in far less confusion. "Mathematical precision" is a good guide when setting the buffet table. This, too, contributes to orderly service.

In the event that only one table is used for serving, the dessert course may be served from the buffet table after the table has been cleared of the main course and the guests' plates have been removed, or it may be served from the kitchen. The former method carries out the spirit of the buffet party and is easier for the hostess.

Regardless of the arrangement for tables, there are a number of ways in which the food can be served at a buffet meal. The most popular practice is to have guests help themselves. In some instances the hostess may wish to serve the main dish. It is only in elaborate buffet service that maids assist with the serving. However, if there is a maid, she may pass second servings and help the hostess in removing the plates before the dessert is served.

When space and numbers permit, it is a convenience to have table space for guests to place their plates. This space might be provided through card tables, end tables, or nests of tables. Attractive individual tray tables are often used for television suppers or for serving on porches and terraces. Men and boys will particularly appreciate having tables, no matter how small, since they usually abhor balancing a plate on their laps. One hostess who entertained frequently with buffet meals established a "rule of the house" which did not permit men guests to eat from their laps. She usually lacked sufficient table space for all guests, but the men were always provided with substantial, flat space on which to place their plates.

Buffet menus require careful planning if they are to be successful. For large groups it is wise to plan for the type of menus which can be mostly prepared ahead. Whether for a large or small group, the food should present an attractive service when placed on the buffet table, and it is important that it be food which is easily served and eaten. Slippery salads, such as whole stuffed tomatoes, and foods such as baked ham or fried chicken are not easy to manage when standing or using the lap for a table. Since at buffet meals fewer dishes are usually served than at other types of meals, it is a good idea to plan for second servings of the main dish, the salad, or both. If men are included in the group, it may be particularly desirable to offer seconds of both.

It may even be desirable to have two main dishes which are similar, such as curried chicken and chicken a la king. This will allow for taste preference. Also, serving assorted breads is a simple and economical way of dressing up and popularizing a buffet menu. A choice of desserts is especially appreciated by persons watching their weight. Fruit is always an acceptable dessert to offer either alone or as a choice. When hot breads are a part of the menu, they should be passed several times, and it is better to have them buttered in the kitchen. Coffee is usually enjoyed throughout the meal, so it should be available in sufficient quantity.

Sample Buffet Menus

Spiced Orange Juice
Cheese Sandies Radish and Cucumber Slices
Chicken Tetrazzini
Pickled Peach Halves Garden Salad
Bread Sticks or Crusty Bread
Assorted Fruit Tarts
Coffee

Beef Stroganoff Hungarian Goulash
Noodles with Poppy Seed
Mexican Fruit Salad
Assorted Breads
(Small Dark Rye Sandwiches, Spice Muffins, Sally Lunns, etc.)
Breaded Custard Pie Strawberry Sauce
Coffee

Either of the two above menus (the top one for a three-course party and the lower planned for a choice of main dishes) illustrate the type of menu which

Fig. 95. Puffy omelet with a variety of fresh vegetables makes an excellent menu combination.

can be prepared and arranged for service at different areas before the guests arrive.

Curried Chicken
Fluffy Rice — Chutney
Grated Coconut — Salted Peanuts
Citrus Salad
Bread Sticks
Ice Box Cake
Coffee

The above menu is illustrated in Fig. 91.

Chile With Beans
Tossed Green Salad — Garlic Bread
Assorted Cheeses — Fresh Fruit
Crackers
Coffee

Courtesy American Can Company

Fig. 96. Making the most of milk. This party punch is old fashioned syllabub. The recipe is given on p. 533. It is shown here in an attractive holiday setting with Swedish Christmas cookies (p. 638) and fudge brownies (p. 636). The refreshing qualities of syllabub make it suitable to serve at any season of the year. For a summer-time punch, fresh fruits are an appropriate accompaniment.

Courtesy American Can Company

Fig. 97. A curry supper served buffet style.

SUNDAY NIGHT PARTIES

Sunday-night entertaining is becoming more and more popular. Some families have established the custom of having Sunday-night suppers every week because they consider this to be the perfect time to enjoy the company of a few intimate friends, and an excellent way of ending the week end. For larger numbers, especially teen-age groups, Sunday-night suppers are an easy and inexpensive way of entertaining.

To make Sunday-night suppers even more enjoyable many hostesses prefer to invite four to six guests at a time and have a series of parties, rather than attempt one large supper which would require the major portion of the day for preparation.

There are no "rules" that govern this or any other type of special party. The most successful parties are those in which the hostess is guided in her selection of food, table appointments, and service by the sense of fitness which is called "taste." Buffet service is convenient to use when a large number of guests are being served on Sunday night. Individual tray service is particularly desirable for these suppers when only a few friends are invited. The trays may be inexpensive enamel ones, and are more convenient if they are large enough to hold the entire cover. Each guest is given a tray holding the main course, and it is not essential to provide tables as the trays are comfortably placed on the lap. The trays may be served to the guests in the living room, on the porch, or in the garden. When serving a two-course supper, the plates from the first course might be removed from the trays and the dessert placed. The dessert silver may be on the tray from the beginning.

Since no hostess wishes to spend Sunday afternoon in the kitchen, the food served must be something which can be easily prepared ahead of time and served in an attractive manner with a minimum expenditure of time and energy. It is wise to dovetail the preparation of the food for supper with the preparation of dinner. Some of the same foods might be served for both meals. For example, if apple sauce used as an accompaniment to the meat served at dinner, might be prepared in sufficient quantity to serve apple tarts for supper.

The Sunday-night supper menus below are illustrative of the type in which most of the preparation can be done in advance.

Chicken Shortcake
Tomato and Pineapple Salad French Dressing
Chocolate Cake Mints
Coffee

Italian Spaghetti
Green Salad Anchovy Dressing
Assorted Crackers
Lemon Ice with Crushed Peppermint Candy
Coffee

Curried Lamb with Rice [1]
Water Cress and Lettuce Salad Roquefort Cheese Dressing
Hard Rolls
Apple Tarts [2] Coffee

[1] Left-over lamb from Sunday dinner roast.
[2] Apple sauce left from Saturday breakfast.

Courtesy American Can Company

Fig. 98. A tempting tureen supper.

Figure 98 shows a tureen supper. The lobster bisque is made by combining canned mushroom soup with milk and canned lobster. Hard rolls and a green salad complete the menu.

The table is arranged for ease in serving.

PICNICS AND OTHER OUTDOOR MEALS

Picnics offer interesting and exciting possibilities for the people who enjoy meals in the open. Picnics in some sections may take the form of a chicken or steak barbecue; in the New England states a clam bake is a favorite kind of outing; corn roasts and fish frys are other popular kinds of picnics. While some people enjoy eating in the open at a favorite picnic spot, they do not relish cooking out of doors and prefer to carry a prepared lunch. However, genuine picnic-goers like to cook all or part of their meal over a campfire. There are available numerous types of "streamlined" camp stoves and cooking utensils for picnicking, but many picnickers confine their equipment to a coffee pot, a broiling rack, a frying pan, and a long-handled fork or two. Some people would include a few broomsticks in their basic picnic equipment in order that they might feast on delectable "stick biscuit." For "stick biscuit" the dough is preferably made at home (see p. 620) but it may be made at the picnic by using a prepared biscuit mix. Each person bakes his own biscuit, and when the baking is finished the biscuit is slipped off the stick and buttered. These biscuits are delicious with any picnic menu and are a welcome change from the conventional bun.

The modern family does not always confine its picnics to those in favorite picnic spots away from home, since many homes are planned with picnic facilities in the yard. These range from completely equipped outdoor living rooms with large fireplaces to crude barbecue pits with a flag-stone terrace and a trestle table and benches near by. If you have no permanent equipment in your own back yard, there are inexpensive, portable grills which are convenient and satisfactory to use. There are also some deluxe types on the tea-wagon order which can be wheeled around with great ease. Some of these not only have grills for broiling but also compartments for warming food, as well as working space of tile or stainless steel. If all of the possibilities of picnic equipment for the yard are investigated, an intriguing assortment of accessories will be found, such as wrought iron toasting forks, potato tongs, barbecue mitts with fireproof padding, all sorts of chef's hats, aprons, and coats, and many other items.

Outdoor meals should be free from responsibility or worry about the dishes which are being used; consequently, the families who do considerable entertaining outside will probably want to use plastic or other unbreakable dishes and stainless steel implements for eating.

The interest in eating in the open has given the "do-it-yourself" enthusiasts a fertile field for operation. Some of the most attractive layouts for outdoor cookery are designed and engineered as family projects. Figure 99 illustrates such a project. This good looking and efficient barbecue unit is on a partially enclosed terrace opening off the living room and kitchen. The small sink to the left with the working surface on either side of the grate, the easily accessible wood supply, and the cupboards to hold equipment and dishes for

Courtesy the Charles Blanford Family, Scarsdale, New York

Fig. 99. An all-weather barbecue pit.

the outdoor meals, provide luxury features not ordinarily found in connection with barbecue pits.

BREAKFASTS

For the average household, guest breakfasts are not possible except on Sundays or holidays. Since many people enjoy leisurely mornings on these days, after a busy work week, a breakfast party must of necessity be served late in the morning. Depending upon the habits of the community, this might be any time between the hours of nine and twelve. These late breakfasts are sometimes referred to as "brunch" since they take the place of both breakfast and lunch. "Brunches" are particularly popular with teen-age groups.

In planning for a guest breakfast, it may be necessary to give the family some attention before the breakfast guests arrive. A pitcher of fruit juice and a pot of coffee or some milk will usually "tide them over" until they get some more substantial food.

Breakfast entertaining need not be expensive, since two courses are likely to be the limit for most guest breakfasts, and numerous dishes which are favorites for this meal are possible, even on the very modest food budget.

The guest breakfast may be served in the dining room, breakfast room, sun room or, if it is winter time, in the living room where there is a fireplace. For summer breakfasts a porch or outdoor terrace might be the place selected to serve.

For the breakfast party the gayest table appointments should be assembled. They should be put together with care; otherwise they might strike a discordant note which would not be conducive to the enjoyment of the meal. The psychological effect of color is especially significant as it relates to the breakfast meal. There seems to be no better way to start the day than to have this meal at a beautiful, colorful, well-ordered table.

Menus served for guest breakfasts do not have to be the conventional fruit, eggs, toast, and coffee. However, those basic items may constitute the framework for a decidedly different and interesting meal. Instead of sliced oranges, the fruit might be blueberries, cantaloupe, fresh pineapple, or any fruit in season; instead of scrambling the eggs, combine them with cheese and serve an egg and cheese timbale directly with a sharp cheese sauce; also include crisp bacon as an accompaniment. Any one of a number of quick breads, such as popovers or muffins, would make an acceptable substitute for the toast, and the coffee would, of course, remain. In the summer the coffee might be iced.

Summer breakfast menus may contain several fruits, and the main dishes should be kept to the lighter ones, such as soufflés, omelets, chicken prepared in various ways, mushrooms, and lamb chops. For breakfasts in cooler weather waffles, sausage, meat pies, and other such hearty dishes would be appropriate.

Sample Breakfast Menus

Dried Fruit Compote
Quiche Lorraine   Crisp Bacon
Coconut Fruit Bread   Whole Wheat Toast
Butter or Margarine
Coffee   Tea   Milk

Orange Juice
Broiled Bananas and Bacon
Scrambled Eggs
Cinnamon Rolls Butter or Margarine
Coffee Milk

Fresh Fruit Plate
Creamed Ham and Eggs
Corn Muffins or Whole Wheat Toast
Butter or Margarine
Coffee Milk

Choice of Fresh Fruit From Fruit Bowl
Broiled Chicken Livers and Mushrooms
Toast and Muffins
Jelly Butter or Margarine
Coffee Tea Milk

THE COFFEE BREAK

Even though it is frowned on by many, the coffee break has become an established institution in contemporary living. Its setting may be either the office (or other piace of business) or the home. The time is generally midmorning and often midafternoon too. Whenever or wherever it occurs it is a highly social time. For some it may mean breakfast (not a good nutritional practice), but to others it is a stimulating break from the day's routine. In business the refreshments are usually of a commercial type. However, some employees (especially women) use the coffee break as a time to show off their culinary successes.

Removed from the business world, the coffee break is a friendly, informal neighborhood gathering with a varying number of participants. While sometimes it is nothing more than a "gossip" session, it is often fruitful in terms of exchange of ideas between friends. While the food is incidental to the coffee break, it can and should make a desirable contribution to the total daily intake. When it is their turn to hostess the coffee break, some neighborhood leaders have used it as an opportunity to introduce new foods or to make an alteration in their own food habits. Instead of the customary doughnut or sweet roll they have offered their "guests" dried or fresh fruit, or a simple *small* sweet such as the spice sticks on p. 657.

MORNING COFFEE

The traditional type of morning coffee differs from the coffee break in that it is a party planned for entertaining either a small or a large group. This type of morning party is particularly popular in the South, and it is preferred by some people to afternoon teas for certain groups because it seems to be more friendly and hospitable. This type of party is especially popular during the summer months because it permits entertaining in the coolest part of the day. However, morning coffee on a cool day by the fireside in the living room suggests intimacy and is a favored way of serving a few friends. For an informal and casual morning coffee, it is not necessary to arrange a special table for the refreshments. The hostess may choose to use two large trays, one for the coffee service, the other for the plates of simple, tasty, refreshments which she may be serving with the coffee. Under such circumstances the trays might be placed on tables in the living room and the guests asked to serve themselves, or, to make the party more personal, the hostess might pour the coffee and pass the accompanying refreshments.

In Figure 100, dried fruit tarts and cinnamon chocolate are arranged on a terrace table for an afternoon committee meeting.

The usual hours for inviting friends for morning coffee are between nine and eleven. The time necessitates the serving of small amounts of simple, tasty foods.

DESSERT PARTIES AND LATE EVENING REFRESHMENTS

Dessert parties are popular in some sections of the country. At the end of a busy workday schedule they offer an opportunity to assemble friends with a minimum amount of preparation. They also make inexpensive entertaining possible. Such parties give young homemakers a chance to "display" their culinary skill by serving a single item. This may be a special pastry, pudding, cake, or frozen dessert served with an appropriate beverage. Figure 101 shows a cake and coffee service for a small dessert party.

"Calorie consciousness" has influenced to some extent the type of refreshments served at certain social functions. However, sweets still prevail as one of the most popular types of refreshments.

Parties after a dance, the theater, or a concert call for food that is light and simple. Hearty suppers in the late evening may be acceptable at the time they are served, but many a guest has left such a party wondering why the hostess did not use better judgment in selecting the food which she served.

Regardless of the number invited for such a gathering, restraint should be practiced in planning the refreshments. An ample cheese board with crackers and raw-vegetable appetizers may be planned for a large group, and tea, coffee, or hot spiced punch served as a beverage. Small toasted cheese sandwiches and tomato or fruit juice is a tasty combination to serve. It is a good plan to have a bowl of fresh fruit available, since some people prefer it to anything else which is served.

This type of party usually takes on characteristics similar to a buffet meal

Courtesy National Dairy Council

Fig. 100. Dried fruit tarts and cinnamon chocolate for a dessert or morning coffee party.

in the table setting. If the group is large, the dining-room table or a large living-room table may be arranged for the occasion. For a small number it may not be necessary to prepare a large table, since any small table or a tea cart will suffice to hold the tray on which the food is served.

AFTERNOON TEA

The hostess who has perfected the friendly custom of serving tea to a casual caller, a small group of intimate friends, or 50 to 100 guests occupies an enviable position in the realm of social entertaining. Anyone having close acquaintance with English families knows the charm and delight that the daily afternoon tea interlude provides. A hot, fragrant tea brew served in the prettiest and thinnest tea cups, and accompanied by a simple tidbit of food, which augments rather than takes from the tea flavor, suggests the acme in afternoon refreshments. Many American families have for years enjoyed the ancient English custom of tea between an early luncheon and a late dinner, and more and more hostesses are using this custom as a basis for entertaining their friends.

Afternoon tea for a few is always an intimate, cozy affair. The very fact

Fig. 101. Coffee and cake for dessert.

that the number is small means that the systematic procedure which is necessary for efficient serving of large groups can be dispensed with. Large teas which call for a more conventional method of serving in perhaps a more formal setting can and should convey friendly spirit and an atmosphere of cordial hospitality. It is unfortunate that some hostesses have not learned that an afternoon tea for a large group need not be a pompous, formal affair. It is such teas as this which have caused many people to look with dread rather than pleasure on this type of entertainment.

College students are sometimes inclined to consider teas as a necessary evil; however, they should avail themselves of the opportunity of attending, since they provide an incentive for making contacts with fellow students and faculty members. This type of party inspires conversation and interchange of thought which students and other guests should find stimulating. Participation may prove an excellent means of overcoming a self-conscious attitude or a feeling of inferiority. Both will aid in the development of social poise. One senior student who thought she did not care for this type of entertaining made herself go to several teas honoring seniors. Much to her surprise, she found them enjoyable. In her case it was a matter of launching into something new and uncertain, and going to the first tea represented a venture.

Tea parties, even those for a few people, afford limitless possibilities for effecting artistic and unusual table arrangements. The accessories used for serv-

Courtesy Corning Glass

Fig. 102. America's number one outdoor food.

ing tea are in themselves so beautiful that any tea table, small or large, can be graciously appointed. The appointments may range in type from sterling silver, crystal, bone china, and fine lace, to brass, earthen tea dishes, and peasant linen.

When serving tea to a small group, a specially prepared tea table need not be arranged, since a tray holding the necessary tea dishes and food may be placed on any small table in the living room, or on a porch or terrace.

Round tables are particularly charming for tea tables. For a large party, instead of using the dining table, the hostess may choose to set up two gateleg tables in the living room, one in either end. It may be possible to use the same idea in the dining room. Such a plan facilitates the serving and avoids congestion. If the tea table is in the living room, the same careful attention should be used in setting it up as in setting the dining table. It may be covered with handsome lace or linen and the other appointments chosen in keeping. But it should all correspond with and fit into the background of the living room.

The arrangement of a tea table is a test of the skill of the hostess. It should be beautiful in every detail, since it is the focal point of the party. In placing the tea services, dishes, decorations, and food on the table a picture is being created which should be executed according to the basic principles of design. Nearly everyone has seen a cluttered, crowded tea table with plates and cups and saucers spread over the table in helter-skelter fashion. The tea and coffee service with cups, plates, and spoons should represent a compact unit. It is desirable to have the trays large enough to hold eight or a dozen cups so they will not have to be spread out around the tray. Additional cups and plates should be arranged on a conveniently accessible buffet or serving table.

The decorations for a tea table can be dramatic and distinctive if the hostess has an imaginative, creative turn of mind. However, any plan for table decoration should be executed so that it contributes to the total design. One point should always be kept in mind—a few flowers carefully selected and thoughtfully arranged can make a far more exciting table decoration than a mass of flowers crowded into a container without any thought of the design. For a large tea table, candles can be used in lavish numbers and they may be very tall ones. If used, they should be lighted.

The décor for a tea or other table need not be used in the *center* of the table. The term centerpiece is misleading since often the flowers or other decorations can be more effectively placed than in the center. They may be used to balance a punch bowl or a coffee service.

Tea service. In addition to tea, other beverages are sometimes served at an afternoon tea. In many instances a preference of tea or coffee is given, or a choice of plain or spiced tea may be offered. In warm weather a tart fruit punch is frequently served. This requires the use of a punch bowl and cups.

The quality of the tea served is much more important than some hostesses consider it to be. In a college community where afternoon teas were frequently given, a man guest was heard to remark at a large party, "I am going to stay out of the dining room because I know I won't get a good cup of tea." That particular hostess would probably have been shocked to learn that the kind of tea she served made that much difference to even one guest. The tea should not only be fine in flavor, but also hot. When coffee is served, it is equally important that its quality is fine and that it is hot. Directions for making tea and coffee are given on pages 644–646.

Refreshments for afternoon tea should be light, attractive, and good-tasting. One should remember that it is not a meal which is being served, and since many times the tea hour precedes dinner by only a short while, the refreshments should be on the order of *appetizers* rather than *stabilizers*. Most tea tidbits are supposed to be eaten with the fingers. Heavily frosted cakes which are sticky are not considered suitable. If molded and frozen salads are served for afternoon tea, the portions should be very small and the salads light. Traditionally, fancy cookies and various types of small decorated sandwiches constitute the mainstay of tea refreshments.

However, some of the most favored tea snacks are the inexpensive foods which are tastily prepared and artistically served. These include thin bread-

and-butter sandwiches, cinnamon toast, ginger cookies, and bites of cheese.

Throughout Section IV numerous recipes will be found that are suitable to use for tea refreshments. These will include both beverages and accompaniments.

Suggestions for serving large groups of tea guests. The serving of tea to large numbers of guests must be carefully planned in order to avoid confusion. Friends of the hostess are usually invited to assist her by pouring the tea and coffee and serving the other refreshments. A maid may be used to keep the tea and coffee replenished as well as the plates of refreshments.

The serving may be done by inviting the guests to the table and pouring them a cup of tea or coffee, which is placed on a small plate rather than a saucer. They then serve themselves to the cakes and sandwiches. While this method is sometimes used, it is somewhat out of place at a large table because it may cause confusion and congestion. A more suitable and convenient way of serving if two beverages are being served, is for those assisting the hostess to ask each guest's preference as to beverage; to give the guest a plate with the beverage on it; and then to pass the cream, sugar, and lemon, placed on a tray, and the plates of sandwiches and cakes. The same person should serve a guest with all of the refreshments so that nothing will be forgotten, rather than for one to pass the sandwiches, another the cake, and so on. The arrangements of the tea table at the beginning of the tea should be observed by those serving, and they should replace the serving dishes in their original positions. This keeps the table equally attractive throughout the tea. The serving dishes should be replenished during the party so that at no time do the refreshments appear to be diminishing.

SUGGESTIONS FOR LABORATORY

Laboratory projects planned around social situations can be just as extensive and varied as the instructor and students wish.

It is not likely that any one type of party will be chosen as a class project. The scope of experience in this area can be extended if groups of three of four students plan and execute their plans for a party to which several guests are invited. This would mean that three or four affairs would be held during one laboratory period. While space for separate parties may be a problem, it presents a challenge and can illustrate the multiple use of space. For example, a corner of the laboratory can be made into an attractive setting for a "neighborhood" coffee break and a near-by office used to set up a small, apartment-sized buffet.

Since many students are social chairman for campus organizations, at least some time should be devoted to social situations connected with student activities.

A different type of social situation is a laboratory open house. This gives members of a class an excellent opportunity to interpret their foods course to students, faculty, and other friends. An open house might include several working exhibits set up in such areas as:

1) Meals at different cost levels.
2) High and low calorie diets.
3) Social refreshments which emphasize good nutrition and good taste.
4) Interesting breakfast combinations.
5) Versatility of kitchen appliances.
6) Distinctive table arrangements.

Pre-planning should allow for some foods to be prepared in sufficient quantities to serve the guests. This type of affair permits guests to circulate from exhibit to exhibit, talking to a number of students. Communicating under these circumstances allows for a broader interpretation of a course than is possible by "entertaining" with a conventional tea.

SECTION 4

Food Preparation

RECIPE INDEX

TABLE 33. TIME TABLE FOR BOILING VEGETABLES

Vegetables	*Time*	*Vegetables*	*Time*
Artichokes, French	15–20 min.	Collard	16–20 min.
Artichokes, Jerusalem	12–15 min.	Corn	8–14 min.
Asparagus	15–20 min.	Cucumber	10–15 min.
Beans, dried *		Cushaw	15–20 min.
Blackeyed peas	1½ hours	Eggplant	8–12 min.
Lentils	1¼ hours	Kohlrabi	8–10 min.
Lima beans	1¼ hours	Mustard greens	30–40 min.
Navy beans	1½ hours	Okra	15–20 min.
Pinto beans	1¼ hours	Onions, quartered	15–20 min.
Split peas	1¼ hours	Onions, whole	20–50 min.
Beans, green Lima	20–45 min.	Parsnips	12–15 min.
Beans, string (1″ cut)	25–45 min.	Peas, black-eyed	30–45 min.
Beet greens	15–30 min.	Peas, crowder	30–40 min.
Beets, new	30–60 min.	Peas, English (new)	12–20 min.
Beets, old	60–120 min.	Peas, English (old)	20–35 min.
Broccoli	9–12 min.	Peas, Lady	30–40 min.
Brussels sprouts	5– 6 min.	Peppers	10–15 min.
Cabbage, Chinese	8–10 min.	Potatoes, Irish	25–35 min.
Cabbage, quartered	12–15 min.	Potatoes, sweet	15–25 min.
Cabbage, red	8–10 min.	Salsify	15–20 min.
Cabbage, shredded	6–12 min.	Spinach	5–15 min.
Carrot tops	30–40 min.	Squash, summer (whole)	15–20 min.
Carrots	15–25 min.	Squash, summer (sliced)	8–12 min.
Cauliflower, flowerets	8–12 min.	Tomatoes	6–15 min.
Cauliflower, whole	10–15 min.	Turnips, sliced	15–30 min.
Celeriac	8–10 min.	Turnip greens	10–40 min.
Celery	12–20 min.	Vegetable marrow	15–20 min.

* All dried legumes were soaked in warm water 3 hrs., then boiled until tender.

TABLE 34. TIME TABLE FOR STEAMING VEGETABLES

Vegetables	*Time*	*Vegetables*	*Time*
Beets, new	40–60 min.	Celery	30–35 min.
Beets, old	60–120 min.	Potatoes, Irish	25–35 min.
Carrots, sliced	20–30 min.	Potatoes, sweet	20–30 min.
Carrots, whole	30–40 min.	Squash, summer	15–30 min.

TABLE 35. TIME TABLE FOR BAKING VEGETABLES

Vegetables	*Time*	*Vegetables*	*Time*
Beets	45–60 min.	Potatoes, Irish	40–60 min.
Cucumbers, stuffed *	20 min.	Potatoes, sweet	40–60 min.
Eggplant, stuffed *	25–30 min.	Squash, stuffed *	20–30 min.
Onions, stuffed *	30–50 min.	Squash, winter	45–75 min.
Peppers, stuffed *	15–25 min.	Tomatoes, stuffed	15–25 min.

* Vegetables were parboiled before being stuffed.

Suggestions For Laboratory

The basic principles of food preparation covered in the preceding text can be "brought to life" in an interesting and practical fashion by applying them to a variety of recipes selected from many different sources. As Americans travel more and more, they have a wider acquaintance with regional United States food as well as with that of other countries.

The recipes that appear in this section are representative of diverse people and places. While many of them are simple, others are more challenging, and all are explicit. Those who use the recipes will find that many choices are possible in the selection of ingredients, choice of cooking utensils, method of preparation, and manner of presenting the prepared food. For example, gingerbread may be baked plain or as an upside down cake in a square or round pan; it can be made into a layer cake and glazed or iced; or it may be baked in muffin pans and served either as cup cakes or ginger muffins. Gingerbread also makes delicious waffles.

There are almost unlimited resources from which to select ideas about food and recipes. However, many homemakers have a tendency to rely on one or two favorite cookbooks to guide them through a life time of preparing food for their families. Indeed, some people are satisfied with their own resources, never seeking information from any outside source.

The more one knows about a subject, the greater the joy in participating in activities related to it. Cooking is no exception. Many college students enrolled in food classes will become professional workers in the field, and all are potential homemakers; therefore an extensive scope of information on food preparation is both necessary and rewarding. Special cookbooks and other references are listed below. It is interesting to compare, from several sources, the same recipe. Wide variation will be found in proportion and number of ingredients, temperature for cooking, etc. This difference will also be found in recipes given in textbooks. The student who understands principles will be able to use a given recipe or take several and make a satisfactory composite. This experience leads to creativity in food preparation from which great pleasure can be derived. Some of the recipes included here are authentic regional United States and national dishes, others have been adapted. Students will find it interesting to make their own adaptations.

The recipes are presented according to basic principles and under headings of the specific foods being emphasized. For example, *soufflé* appears in the fruit group to show the versatility of fruit, in the milk grouping to illustrate the use of a thick white sauce, along with egg recipes as an example of how eggs are used for leavening, and also among those recipes dealing with cheese. As a further illustration of the sequence of the recipes, those using fruit will be found throughout the section but a concentration of fruit recipes are under the heading *fruit*.

The number of recipes given for each food group is sufficiently large to permit *choice* of items to be prepared which will implement the text. In addition, selections may be made from other references. In a single class situation, considerable variety can be displayed through choice of ingredients, cooking method, utensil, and serving. For example, in a laboratory on vegetable cookery, carrots might be cooked whole and served with an herb butter; or they might be teamed with small white onions in a sweet and sour sauce, or used as the ingredient in an exotic Swiss carrot torte. In class, potatoes may be presented as plain mashed, or in a soufflé, or as the classic French potato soup—vichyssoise.

While many of the recipes in this section use convenience foods, it is expected that the instructor and students will want to make comparisons of dishes made from selected recipes with those prepared entirely or partially from the convenience foods. This procedure allows extra experiences for students who do not require the allotted time for completing the laboratory work.

Even though pre-planning for general laboratory organization and work are necessary on the part of the instructor, student participation in making the final plans is highly desirable. When students are *invited* to contribute their ideas for a course they will be exposed to the ideas, experiences, and philosophy not only of the instructor, but also of the entire class group. When given the responsibility of selecting laboratory projects, etc., students meet the challenge in varied and interesting fashion.

Students, too, will be helpful in working out mechanical detail connected with laboratory work. Some experiences will be found best suited to individual work; others are more effective if carried out in groups ranging from two to four. Whatever the detail, most students have a background of experiences to draw on for assisting the instructor with class organization.

If demonstration seems to be the most desirable method of presenting a part or all of a laboratory, students can be counted on either to assist the instructor with the demonstration or carry out portions of it on their own.

Laboratory work connected with a foods course provides continuing experience for becoming aware of the work simplification techniques possible in food preparation. Such an environment is conducive to learning good work habits and safety measures.

A foods laboratory should not be considered complete unless the planning allows time for presenting the food as it is to be served. If the practice of serving food simply and attractively is consistently carried out, it is believed that it will be helpful in developing habits of serving family meals. Such an appreciation will be a great asset to the potential homemakers in a class. "Attractive" service of foods will be interpreted in many different ways by a group. Conscious effort in this direction will enable instructor and students to draw their own criteria for attractiveness after a few laboratory meetings.

It is almost a certainty that when instructor and students gather around a summary table to evaluate and discuss the prepared and attractively served products many spontaneous ideas will be expressed and information gained that are not necessarily a part of the laboratory plan. This is an excellent way in which to "pick up loose ends" and to clarify principles and procedures.

REFERENCES

Beard, James, *Fireside Cook Book*. Simon and Schuster, New York, 1949.

Boni, Ada, *The Talisman Italian Cook Book*. Crown, New York, 1950.

Brown, Robert C., *The Complete Book of Cheese*. Random House, New York, 1955.

Burton, Katherine and Helmut Ripperger, *Feast Day Cook Book*. David McKay Company, New York, 1951.

Donon, Joseph, *The Classic French Cuisine*. Knopf, New York, 1959.

Dorn, Frank, *Good Cooking with Herbs and Spices*. Harvey House, New York, Irvington-on-Hudson, 1958.

Farmer, Fannie M., *The Boston Cooking School Cook Book*. 10th edition. Little, Brown, Boston, 1960.

Heseltine, Marjorie Moulton, *The New Basic Cook Book*. Houghton Mifflin, Boston, 1957.

Hess, O. and A., *Viennese Cooking*. Crown, New York, 1952.

Kander, Mrs. Simon, *The New Settlement Cook Book*. Simon and Schuster, New York, 1954.

LoPinto, Maria and Milo Miloradovich, *The Art of Italian Cooking*. Doubleday, New York, 1948.

Mitchell, Leonard Jan, *Lüchow's German Cookbook*. Doubleday, New York, 1952.

Nichols, Nell Beaubien, *Good Home Cooking Across the U.S.A.* Iowa State College Press, Ames, Iowa, 1952.

Rombauer, Irma S. and Marion Rombauer Becker, *The New Joy of Cooking*. Bobbs-Merrill, New York, 1951.

Roosevelt, Nicholas, *Creative Cooking*. Harper, New York, 1956.
———, *Good Cooking*. Harper, New York, 1959.
Showalter, Mary Emma, *Mennonite Community Cookbook*. Mennonite Community Association, Scottdale, Pa., 1950.
Sullivan, Lenore, *What to Cook for Company*. Iowa State College Press, Ames, Iowa, 1952.
Toklas, Alice B., *The Alice B. Toklas Cook Book*. Harper, New York, 1954.
Tracy, Marian, *The East-West Book of Rice Cookery*. The Viking Press, New York, 1952.

FRUITS

Fruit is an accepted food at any meal. Fresh fruits are popular, but processed fruits extend opportunities to vary the serving. Fruits may be served separately or in combination. Many salads, fruit plates, and desserts have greater appeal if more than one kind of fruit, either fresh or processed, is used or if they are combined. From suggestions in cookbooks and magazines, coupled with the imagination of the person who prepares the food, an appetizing fruit dish may be prepared during any time of the year. Instructor and students will find enjoyment in exploring different methods of preparing fruit. A few recipes and suggestions are included.

Utensils that may be convenient in fruit cookery include a coarse sieve, colander, food mill, blender, apple corer, French potato cutter, pressure pan, oven-to-table and top-of-range-to-table utensils.

Fruit juices. Individually or in combination, fruit juices make an appetizing approach to a meal, as a beverage to be served with a meal or refreshments at a party, or as the basis for frozen dessert.

BEVERAGES

Cider and Orange Juice

(1c. per person)

Ingredients	*For 2*	*For 12*	*For 50*
Cider	1 c.	1½ qt.	6 qts.
Orange juice	1 c.	1½ qt.	6 qts.

1) Combine the ingredients.
2) Serve in iced tea glasses over crushed ice.

Grape Juice and Lime

(1c. per person)

Ingredients	*For 2*	*For 12*	*For 50*
Grape juice	1¾ c.	2 qts. + 2½ c.	10½ qts.
Lime juice	¼ c.	1½ c.	1½ qts.

1) Combine the ingredients.
2) Serve in iced tea glasses over crushed ice.

Fruit Punch
(1c. per person)

Ingredients	*For 2*	*For 12*	*For 50*
Sugar	1/4 c.	1 1/2 c.	2 1/2 lbs.
Water	1/4 c.	1 c.	1 qt.
Lemon juice	1/4 c.	1 1/2 c.	1 1/2 qts.
Orange juice	1/3 c.	2 c.	2 qts.
Strong green tea infusion	1/4 c.	1 1/2 c.	1 1/2 qts.
Salt	dash	1/8 t.	1/2 t.
Ginger ale	2/3 c.	1 qt.	4 qts.
Ice	to chill		
Mint leaves	sprig for each serving		

1) Boil sugar and water slowly for 1 min. and pour over ice in a pitcher or punch bowl.
2) Add the fruit juices, tea, and salt.
3) Add the ginger ale just before serving.
4) Place a sprig of mint in each glass as it is served.

Fruit Punch
(Frozen fruit base)

Ingredients	*For 2*	*For 12*	*For 50*
Orange juice	1/4 c.	1 12-oz. can	4 12-oz. cans
Lemonade	1 1/2 tb.	1 6-oz. can	4 6-oz. cans
Pineapple juice	2 tb.	1 6-oz. can	4 6-oz. cans
Water	1 1/2 c.	2 1/4 qts.	9 qts.
Ginger ale	1/3 c.	1 1/3 c.	1 1/2 qts.

1) Combine the frozen fruit concentrates in a pitcher or punch bowl.
2) Stir to mix and nearly thaw the concentrates.
3) Add the water and stir well. If possible, aerate by pouring the mixture from one container to another several times.
4) Add the ginger ale and serve chilled or with crushed ice.

Spiced Punch

Ingredients	*For 2*	*For 12*	*For 50*
Sugar	1/4 c.	1 1/2 c.	6 1/2 c.
Water	1/3 c.	2 c.	2 qts.
Whole cloves	4	1 t.	4 t.
Stick cinnamon	1/2-in. stick	4-in. stick	four 4-in. sticks
Orange juice	2/3 c.	1 qt.	4 qts.
Lemon juice	1/3 c.	2 c.	2 qts.
Grapefruit juice	1/3 c.	1 1/2 c.	1 1/2 qts.
Pineapple juice	1/3 c.	1 1/2 c.	2 qts.

1) Simmer sugar, water, and spice 10 min.
2) Strain and cool.
3) Add fruit juices.
4) Serve iced in tall glasses or in a punch bowl.

Guava Punch
(Puerto Rican)

Ingredients	*For 2*	*For 12*	*For 50*
Guava juice	1 c.	6 c.	5 10-oz. cans
Salt	dash	¼ t.	¾ t.
Milk	1 c.	6 c.	5 qts.

1) Be sure that juice and milk are cold.
2) Combine ingredients and serve.

Cranberry Punch

Ingredients	*For 2*	*For 12*	*For 50*
Sugar sirup (ratio, ½ c. sugar to 1 c. water)		to taste	
Cranberry juice cocktail	1 c.	1½ qts.	5 qts.
Orange juice	½ c.	3 c.	3½ qts.
Lemon juice	2 tb.	¾ c.	3 c.
Pineapple juice	¼ c.	1½ c.	1½ qts.

1) Make sirup and cool it.
2) Mix the fruit juices in a suitable container.
3) Sweeten to taste.
4) Serve either iced or hot.

FROZEN DESSERTS

Orange Ice

Ingredients	*For 1 qt.*	*For 2 qts.*	*For 1 gal.*
Sugar	1 c.	1 pt.	1 qt.
Water	1 c.	1 pt.	1 qt.
Grated orange rind	1 t.	2 t.	1 tb.
Orange juice	2½ c.	1 qt. + 1 c.	2½ qts.
Lemon juice	¼ c.	½ c.	1 c.
Salt	dash	¼ t.	½ t.

1) Cook the sugar, water, and orange rind, stirring until sugar is dissolved, for about 5 min. Cool.
2) Combine the fruit juices and salt.

3) Add sirup to taste.
4) Pour the mixture into the can of a clean ice cream freezer, and fasten the top.
5) Put ice into the tub to about ¼ of the depth of the freezer; alternate ice and salt in the ratio of 1 part salt to 6 parts ice.
6) Turn the handle slowly and evenly until it begins to turn hard, then more rapidly until it turns very hard. (Add more salt and ice as needed).
7) Drain the brine from the tub, remove the dasher, replace the cover, and close the opening with a stopper.
8) Pack with more salt and ice.

Grape Ice

(1 quart; frozen in refrigerator)

Gelatin	1 t.	Grape juice	2½ c.
Cold water	1 tb.	Lemon juice	¼ c.
Sirup (hot) (See Orange Ice)	½ c.	Salt	dash
Sirup (cold)	to taste		

1) Soften the gelatin in the cold water; add to the hot sirup and stir to dissolve. Cool.
2) Combine the fruit juices and salt.
3) Add the gelatin mixture; add cold sirup to give desired sweetness. Mix well.
4) Having temperature regulator set to coldest (or as specified in manufacturer's directions), pour the mixture into 2 refrigerator trays and freeze to a mush.
5) Transfer to a chilled bowl and beat with a rotary or electric beater and return to refrigerator trays.
6) Continue freezing until the mixture is firm (about 2 hours).

Lemon-Milk Sherbet

Ingredients	*For 1 qt.*	*For 2 qt.*	*For 1 gal.*
Sugar	1 c.	2 c.	4 c.
Lemon juice	¼ c. + 1 tb.	½ c. + 2 tb.	1¼ c.
Milk	2½ c.	1 qt. + 1 c.	2½ qt.

1) Add the sugar to the lemon juice and stir until dissolved.
2) Add the milk *slowly to the lemon juice and sugar,* stirring constantly.
3) Strain.
4) Freeze, using 1 part of salt to 8 parts of ice, following directions for freezing *Orange Ice.*

Raspberry Sherbet
(1 quart; frozen in refrigerator)

Raspberry flavored gelatin	1 pkg.	Sugar................	⅓ c.
Cold water..............	¼ c.	Milk (or half-and-half)	2 c.
Boiling water............	½ c.	Lemon juice..........	2 tb.

1) Soften the gelatin in the cold water and dissolve in the boiling water.
2) Add the sugar and stir to dissolve.
3) Add the other ingredients and mix well.
4) Pour into a refrigerator tray and freeze as directed under *Grape Ice.*

COOKED FRUITS

Spiced Apple Sauce
(About 2 servings)

Tart apples.....	3 med.	Sugar....................	To taste
Water..........	½ c.	Cinnamon or nutmeg.....	dash

1) Wash the apples and cut in eighths.
2) Add water, cover, and cook slowly until the pulp is very soft.
3) Put through a food mill or coarse sieve. Add sugar.

As a Dessert

Put the apple sauce into suitable dishes and sprinkle with selected spice.

As an Accompaniment to Pork

Put the apple sauce into a serving dish and sprinkle with cinnamon.

Apples Baked with Fruit Juice
(2 servings)

Tart apples........	2	Butter or margarine........	½ t.
Sugar.............	1 tb.	Fruit juice................	¼ c.

1) Wash and core the apples; score by cutting, just through the skin *either* around the apples at about the center *or* in 4 or 5 places from the top for about 1 inch.
2) Fill the centers with sugar and butter or margarine.
3) Place the apples in a suitable baking dish and pour the fruit juice over them.
4) Cover and bake until tender at 350° to 400° F. (177° to 204° C.) basting frequently with the fruit juice.

Apple Crunch

Ingredients	*For 2*	*For 4*	*For 6*
Tart apples.........	1 or 2 *	2 to 4 *	3 to 6 *
Water.............	1/4 to 1/3 c.	1/2 to 2/3 c.	3/4 to 1 c.
Cinnamon..........	1/3 t.	2/3 t.	1 t.
Brown sugar........	1/3 c.	2/3 c.	1 c.
Butter or margarine	2 tb.	1/4 c.	1/4 c. + 2 tb.
Corn flakes.........	1/2 c.	1 c.	1 1/2 c.

1) Wash, pare, core, and slice the apples into a baking dish. Add the water.
2) Blend the cinnamon, brown sugar, and butter and add the cornflakes.
3) Scatter this mixture over the apples and stir into the apples gently with a fork.
4) Bake for about 30 min. at 350° F. (177° C.) or until the apples are tender and the crust brown.
5) Serve hot with cream or hot custard.

Broiled Bananas
(1 per person)

1) Peel the bananas and wrap each spirally with a strip of bacon, securing the ends with toothpicks.
2) Place the bananas on an oiled broiling rack and broil, with the fruit about 2 inches below the source of heat.
3) Turn carefully to insure even cooking. When the bacon is crisp, the banana will have cooked sufficiently.

Banana Toast
(for 2)

Thin-sliced firm bread......	2 slices	Bananas........	1 or 2
Butter or margarine........	1 tb.	Cinnamon......	1/2 t.
Sugar..................	1 t.		

1) Toast the bread and spread it with butter or margarine.
2) Cover with thinly sliced bananas, being sure they overlap and come to the edges of the toast.
3) Sprinkle with cinnamon and sugar and broil for 1 or 2 minutes.

Fruit Soufflé
(About 6 servings)

Butter or margarine...	3 tb.	Sugar †..........	to taste
Cornstarch **.........	1/4 c.	Salt..............	dash
Fruit purée...........	1 c.	Egg whites.......	4
Egg yolks............	4	Cream of tartar...	1/4 t.

* Number depends upon size of apples

** If purée or pulp is thick, decrease the cornstarch to 3 tb.

† The amount of sugar depends upon the sweetness of the fruit and personal taste.

1) Melt the butter or margarine in a saucepan.
2) Add the cornstarch and stir to blend.
3) Add the fruit purée slowly and stir until thick.
4) Beat the egg yolks until thick, add the sugar and salt, and add the hot mixture, stirring until well blended.
5) Beat the egg whites until frothy, add the cream of tartar and beat until they hold up in peaks when the beater is removed.
6) Fold the beaten whites into the cooked mixture and bake in a buttered baking dish about 35 minutes at 325° F. (163° C.).
7) Serve at once with fruit sauce or cream.

DRIED FRUITS

Soaking dried fruits decreases cooking time, as does the use of a pressure pan. A choice of fruit, utensil, and cooking method may be made with the following table as a guide. The choice will be determined by the way the fruit is to be used.

TABLE 36. DIRECTIONS FOR COOKING DRIED FRUITS

Fruit	*Water*			*Time* *	
	Amount	*Saucepan*	*Pressure pan* †	*Saucepan*	*Pressure pan*
SOAKED:					
Apples	8 oz.	2 c.	1 c.	12–16 min.	0–1 min.
Apricots	8 oz.	1½ c.	¾ c.	8–12 min.	1½–3 min.
Peaches	8 oz.	2 c.	¾ c.	12–15 min.	2–4 min.
Pears	8 oz.	2 c.	¾ c.	12–15 min.	2–4 min.
Prunes (med.)	8 oz.	3 c.	1 c.	30–40 min.	6–10 min.
UNSOAKED:					
Apples	8 oz.	3 c.	1⅔ c.	20–25 min.	8–10 min.
Apricots	8 oz.	2½ c.	1½ c.	20–25 min.	3–6 min.
Peaches	8 oz.	2¾ c.	1½ c.	25–30 min.	4–8 min.
Pears	8 oz.	2¾ c.	1½ c.	25–30 min.	4–8 min.
Prunes	8 oz.	3 c.	1¼ c.	40–50 min.	10–12 min.

* The shorter time for fruit to be eaten with no further preparation.
† Pressure—15 lb.

DRIED FRUIT COMPOTES

Dried apricots, peaches, pears, and prunes are frequently served as a breakfast fruit. For a change, any two or three may be combined as a dried fruit compote and served as a breakfast fruit or a dessert.

Dried Fruit Whip

Ingredients	*For 2*	*For 4*	*For 6*
Pulp from cooked, dried fruit *	½ c.	1 c.	1½ c.
Egg white	1	2	3
Salt	1/16 t.	⅛ t.	3/16 t.
Sugar **	½ tb.	1 tb.	1½ tb.
Lemon juice	½ t.	1 t.	1½ t.

1) Prepare fruit pulp by chopping fine, including the skin; or rub fruit through a colander, food press, or coarse wire strainer; or whirl in a blender.
2) Beat egg white until it stands in a peak when the beater is lifted. Add salt.
3) Add sugar gradually to beaten white, beating thoroughly.
4) Fold fruit pulp into egg-sugar mixture, using a wooden spoon. Fold in lemon juice.
5) Serve in one of the following ways.
   a) With no further preparation.
   b) Cook over water in a double boiler or over low direct heat, stirring frequently until the whip thickens, but not so long that it is dry.
   c) Bake in a buttered baking dish about 20 min. in a slow oven—250° to 300° F. (121° to 149° C.). If the oven does not have a regulator, the baking dish should be set in a pan of water and this water should not boil.
6) If more than one variety of fruit whip is made, compare as to appearance, texture, and flavor. Whips may be served plain, with a sauce (as caramel, custard, or lemon), or with whipped cream.

Quick Dried Fruit Betty †
(About 4 servings)

Zwieback	8 pieces	Sugar	⅓ c.
or		Flour	2 t.
Rusks	4	Cinnamon	⅔ t.
Cooked dried fruit	to cover	Melted butter or margarine	1⅓ tb.
Salt	light sprinkling		

1) Arrange the zwieback or rusks in a shallow, oven-to-table baking dish.
2) Cover with fruit and sprinkle with salt.

---

* Fruit purée for infant feeding may be used.

** Amount may vary with tartness of fruit and personal taste. Brown sugar may be substituted for granulated sugar.

† As a dessert, this may be served plain, with cream, or with ice cream.

3) Combine the remaining ingredients and sprinkle the mixture over the fruit.
4) Place under broiler about 3 inches from the source of heat for 2 to 5 min., or until the topping melts.
5) Serve at once.

VEGETABLES

The inclusion of vegetables in the daily menu following suggestions made by nutritionists for an adequate diet may seem difficult, but when the variety of vegetables coupled with the many ways in which they may be prepared are considered, this difficulty becomes a challenge to include new and interesting items. A few references and recipes will be helpful in planning the laboratory.

PREPARING VEGETABLES FOR COOKING AND SERVING

Regardless of merchandising methods which enable the homemaker to buy vegetables that are clean, they should be washed before cooking or serving raw. Interest is added to both preparation and appearance of vegetables as served if various forms are used. For instance, green beans may be whole, broken into two or three pieces, cut lengthwise, or cut crosswise in ¼–⅓-inch slices. Carrots may be whole, especially if they are small, cut lengthwise in halves or quarters, sliced, or diced. Certain vegetables—small onions, beets, potatoes, and turnips—are more attractive if cooked whole. Also nutritive value is conserved by cooking the vegetables uncut.

UTENSILS THAT ARE USEFUL IN VEGETABLE COOKERY

Utensils include various slicers, choppers, and shredders, floating-blade peeler, coarse sieves, colander, food mill, blender, graters, garlic press, blending fork, rotary and electric beaters (both portable and attached to a mixer), top-of-range-to-table and oven-to-table dishes, pressure pans, and electric casseroles and frying pans.

Before working in the laboratory, students will benefit by being familiar with what the text and other references include concerning the effect of cooking methods on retention of color, form, flavor, and nutritive value of vegetables. Terms used to identify cookery methods are included in the Glossary. Consulting recipe books, both general and those that deal with regional and national foods, will introduce greater variety in methods of preparation as well as appreciation for delicious foods not familiar to many of us.

Vegetables, individually or mixed, are likely to be served buttered or with a sauce. They are important combined with meat. Processed vegetables add convenience as well as variety to the daily food.

SUGGESTIONS FOR PREPARING AND SERVING VEGETABLES

With no cooking. Many vegetables other than salad plants are popular in the raw state, either for hors d'oeuvres, in salads, or as snacks. These include small, tender green beans, carrot curls and strips, cauliflower flowerlets, celery—plain, curled, or stuffed—onions, radishes, tomatoes, and turnips.

Cooked and served. *Buttered.* Any vegetable may be boiled in the appropriate amount of water until tender, not soft (see Table 33, p. 486), drained, and served with melted butter or margarine. This may be plain or seasoned. Baked vegetables are also served often with plain or seasoned butter or margarine. Seasoned butters may be creamed or melted. Allowing 1 to 2 teaspoonfuls of butter or margarine per serving, the following variations are for four servings. Used plain, the butter allowance is 1 tb. + 1 t. to 2 tb. + 2 t. To this amount, add:

Parsley (fresh) 1 tb., cut fine
Chives (fresh) 2 t., cut fine
Dill (fresh) 2 t., cut fine
Mixed fresh herbs 1–2 t., cut fine
Dried herbs or herb mixture 1 t.
Lemon, 2 t. lemon juice + 1/4 t. grated rind
Anchovy, 1 t. anchovy paste

With a Sauce. Many sauces are used to give interest and variety to the ways in which vegetables are served. A few are included.

WHITE SAUCE *

Ingredients	*For 2*	*For 4*	*For 6*
Butter or margarine	2 t.	1 1/3 tb.	2 tb.
Flour	2 t.	1 1/3 tb.	2 tb.
Salt	dash	1/8 t.	1/4 t.
Pepper	dash	dash	1/8 t.
Milk	1/3 c.	2/3 c.	1 c.

1) Melt the butter or margarine.
2) Add the flour and seasonings and combine thoroughly.
3) Add the cold milk all at once; cook the mixture, stirring until the sauce thickens.

* See p. 523.

VARIATIONS

Change the recipe for white sauce for *4* as follows:

Sauce	*Ingredient*	*Method*
Béchamel	⅔ c. chicken stock ¼ c. and 2 tb. cream	Substitute stock for milk. Add cream when sauce is thick.
Béchamel (Yellow)	1 egg yolk added to Béchamel	Beat yolk and add thickened sauce. Reheat.
Brown	Increase flour to 3 tb.	Stir flour in a frying pan over a low heat until it is light brown in color.
Caper	2 tb. capers	Add to sauce and mix.
Cheese	Use 1 tb. fat. Add ½ c. grated cheese.	Add cheese to sauce and stir until it melts.
Curry	⅓ to ½ tb. curry powder	Add to melted fat before adding flour.
Dill	1 tb.	Cut fresh dill fine and add to cooked sauce.
Herb	¼ t. herb mixture (See p. 659.)	Add to ingredients before adding milk.
Mornay	Béchamel sauce; 1 to 2 tb. grated, highly flavored cheese.	Add cheese to hot sauce; stir to melt.
Pimiento	2 to 3 tb. pimiento	Chop or force through a coarse sieve. Add to sauce.

Hollandaise Sauce

Ingredients	*For 2*	*For 4*	*For 6*
Butter or margarine	2⅔ tb.	¼ c. + 1 tb.	¼ lb. (½ c.)
Vinegar or lemon juice	1 t.	2 t.	1 tb.
Egg yolk (small)	1	2	3
Salt	dash	⅛ t.	¼ t.

1) Divide the butter into 3 pieces.
2) Put one piece with the egg yolk and vinegar or lemon juice into an enamel or thin aluminum saucepan.
3) Place the mixture over hot (not boiling) water in a larger saucepan. Cook until the mixture thickens, stirring constantly with a wooden spoon.
4) Add the second piece of butter; stir until it is combined well with the first mixture.
5) Add the third piece of butter; season, beat, and serve at once.

Mock Hollandaise Sauce

Ingredients	*For 2*	*For 4*	*For 6*
Butter or margarine	½ tb.	1 tb.	1½ tb.
Flour	½ tb.	1 tb.	1½ tb.
Salt	⅛ t.	¼ t.	⅜ t.
Water	⅓ c.	⅔ c.	1 c.
Egg yolk (small)	1	2	3
Lemon juice	1 t.	2 t.	1 tb.

1) Melt the butter in a saucepan.
2) Add the flour and salt, and blend thoroughly.
3) Add the water, stirring constantly, and cook until the mixture thickens.
4) Beat the egg yolk; add some of the mixture; return to the saucepan and cook 2 min.
5) Remove from the fire, add lemon juice, and beat well.

Lemon Sauce

Ingredients	*For 2*	*For 4*	*For 6*
Boiling water	⅓ c.	⅔ c.	1 c.
Flour	½ tb.	1 tb.	1½ tb.
Butter or margarine	1 tb.	2 tb.	3 tb.
Lemon juice	½ tb.	1 tb.	1½ tb.
Salt	dash	1/16 t.	⅛ t.

1) Stir the flour into approximately an equal amount of cold water to form a smooth paste (2 tb. water for 1½ tb. of flour).
2) Add the boiling water and cook until thick, stirring constantly.
3) Remove from the fire; add butter, lemon juice, and salt.
4) Beat well.

Mushroom Sauce

Ingredients	*For 2*	*For 4*	*For 6*
Concentrated mushroom soup	¼ c.	½ c.	¾ c.
Milk or water	2 tb.	¼ c.	¼ c. + 2 tb.

1) Combine the ingredients.
2) Heat, stirring occasionally.
[NOTE: Additional sliced or whole mushrooms may be added for a different texture and more pronounced mushroom flavor.]

ORANGE SAUCE

Ingredients	*For 2*	*For 4*	*For 6*
Butter or margarine	1 t.	2 t.	1 tb.
Cornstarch	1 t.	2 t.	1 tb.
Sugar	1 t.	2 t.	1 tb.
Salt	dash	1/8 t.	1/4 t.
Orange juice	1/3 c.	2/3 c.	1 c.
Lemon juice	1 tb.	1 1/2 tb.	2 tb.

1) Melt butter or margarine in a saucepan.
2) Add the cornstarch and blend well.
3) Add the sugar and salt and blend.
4) Add the fruit juices slowly, stirring until the mixture thickens slightly.

TOMATO SAUCE

Ingredients	*For 2*	*For 4*	*For 6*
Concentrated tomato soup	1/4 c.	1/2 c.	3/4 c.
Bay leaf	bit	1/4 leaf	1/2 leaf
Parsley, cut fine	1/2 t.	1 t.	1 1/2 t.
Cloves, whole	1	2	3

1) Add the seasonings to the soup.
2) Simmer for about 5 min., stirring frequently.
3) Strain.

With Meat, Poultry, and Fish. Cookbooks include main dishes, soups, and salads that combine vegetables with meat. In regional books and those from other countries these are likely to specify small amounts of the more expensive meat ingredients. They are delicious as well as satisfying foods, and the combinations suggest opportunities to use left-overs in unusual ways.

Mixed vegetables. Two or more vegetables are often prepared and served together, and there are many attractive ways to combine left-over vegetables or to use left-over vegetables along with one or two freshly cooked ones. Here, too, the ideas presented in recipes from various sources supplement the knowledge and imagination of the homemaker who wants to make food interesting.

Processed vegetables. Vegetables that have been preserved for future use may be served in the same ways as fresh vegetables. These vegetables also add variety and often save time when preparing a meal.

RECIPES

"Buttered" Green Beans

Ingredients	*For 2*	*For 4*	*For 6*
Green beans........	½ lb.	1 lb.	1½ lb.
Boiling water, salted		to cover	
Butter or margarine.	2 to 4 t.	1 to 2½ tb.	2 to 4 tb.

1) Wash the beans and prepare them for cooking. (Choose size of pieces, from whole to ¼ inch slices).
2) Boil until tender, not soft.
3) Serve with one of the "butter" variations above or one from another source.

Frozen Lima Beans

Ingredients	*For 2*	*For 4*	*For 6*
Frozen lima beans............	½ pkg.	1 pkg.	1½ pkg.
Boiling water, salted.........	as specified on package		
Sauce......................	⅓ c.	⅔ c.	1 c.

1) Cook the beans until tender, not soft.
2) Serve with a sauce described above or one from another source.

Beets

Ingredients	*For 2*	*For 4*	*For 6*
Beets, medium-sized..................	2	4	6
Boiling water, salted................		to cover	
An acid sauce......................	¼ c.	½ c.	¾ c.

1) Cut off the tops of the beets, leaving about 1 in. of stems.
2) Wash thoroughly and boil, unpared, until tender.
3) Cool and peel.
4) Serve with an acid sauce from above or another source.

Baked Beets

Ingredients	*For 2*	*For 4*	*For 6*
Canned *small* beets (No. 303 can)......................	½ can	1 can	1½ can
Chopped onion...............	½ tb.	1 tb.	1½ tb.
Salt.........................		to season	
Beet juice..................	¼ c.	½ c.	¾ c.
Vinegar or lemon juice	1–1½ tb.	2–3 tb.	3–4½ tb.
Butter or margarine...........	1 tb.	2 tb.	3 tb.

1) Put the beets into an oven-to-table baking dish.
2) Scatter the chopped onion over the beets and sprinkle with salt.
3) Add the other ingredients.
4) Bake, covered, for about 15 min. at 350° F. (177° C.) or until the onion is tender and the beets heated through.

Broccoli

Ingredients	*For 2*	*For 4*	*For 6*
Broccoli	about ½ lb.	1 lb.	1½ lb.
Cold water, salted		to cover	
Boiling water, salted		to cover	

1) Remove any tough leaves and woody stems.
2) Soak in salted water for 20 to 30 min.
3) Peel stalks and slit large ones lengthwise about 1 to 2 inches to hasten cooking.
4) Boil, uncovered, until just tender (see table, p. 486). If possible, arrange the stalks so that the flower buds are not submerged.
5) Serve with selected "butter" or sauce.

Cabbage * and Apple
(About 4 servings)

Shredded cabbage	2 c.	Diced, pared apple	1 med.
Water, salted	to cover	Melted butter, margarine or bacon fat	1–2 tb.

1) Cook the cabbage for 8 min. (until just tender).
2) Drain, add apple and fat and stir gently to distribute the apple.

Sweet-and-sour Carrots and Onions
(About 4 servings)

Small carrots	8	Water from carrots plus added water to make	1 c.
Small mild onions	4 to 8	Sugar	2 tb.
Butter or margarine	2 tb.	Vinegar	2 tb.
Flour	2 tb.	Paprika	¼ t.
Salt	¼ t.		

1) Cook the carrots in a small amount of water, covered, until just tender (see table p. 486).
2) Cook the onions in water to cover, in an open saucepan until just tender —about 12 min.

* Red cabbage preferred. If water is hard, the addition of 1 tb. of vinegar will result in cabbage with good color.

3) Drain the vegetables.
4) Make sauce with the remaining ingredients, using method for white sauce (see p. 499).
5) Add the vegetables and let stand over low heat for 15 to 20 min., stirring gently occasionally.

Carrot Torte
(About 12 servings)
(Swiss)

Carrots, grated	⅔ c.	Cloves	¼ t.
Unblanched almonds (measured before grating)	1⅔ c.	Eggs, separated	6
Dry bread crumbs	¾ c.	Sugar	1¼ c.
Cinnamon	½ t.	Lemon juice	1 tb.
		Grated lemon rind	1 t.

1) Put the carrots (packed in measure), almonds, crumbs, and spices into a mixing bowl and mix.
2) Beat the egg yolks, sugar, and lemon diligently with electric or rotary beater, and mix with the dry ingredients.
3) Beat the egg whites until stiff (not dry) and fold into the above.
4) Oil a spring-form pan or deep square cake pan, line with waxed paper, and oil the paper.
5) Sprinkle the bottom and sides of the pan with crumbs and add the torte mixture carefully.
6) Bake 50 to 60 min. at 350° F. (177° C.).
7) Cool in the pan, remove, and glaze the top with the following:

Glaze for Torte

Orange juice	1 c.	Cornstarch	2 t.
Salt	dash	Nutmeg	dash

1) Mix the salt, cornstarch, and nutmeg in a saucepan.
2) Add the juice slowly, stirring, over low heat until the glaze is thickened (should be rather thin).
3) Spread a thin layer over the torte.

Cauliflower

1) Remove leaves, wash, and soak 20 min. in salted water.
2) Cook whole or separated into flowerets in a large quantity of boiling salted water, 10 to 15 min. if cooked whole; 8 to 12 min. if broken into flowerets. Do not cover.
3) Serve with cheese sauce (see p. 500), or parsley butter.

Creamed Celery and Almonds

Ingredients	*For 2*	*For 4*	*For 6*
Celery, cut in 1-in. pieces	¾ c.	1½ c.	2¼ c.
Chicken stock	¾ c.	1 c.	1½ c.
Salt	⅛ t.	¼ t.	⅜ t.
Almonds	2 tb.	¼ c.	¼ c. + 2 tb.

1) Boil celery in salted chicken stock for 12 min. Drain.
2) Blanch almonds by placing in boiling water; remove from fire and let stand 2 min. Drain, add cold water, and remove brown skins. Brown almonds in the oven.
3) Combine the cooked celery and browned almonds, and serve with Béchamel sauce (see p. 500).

Corn Pudding
(6 servings)

Eggs	2	Pepper	½ t.
Corn, cream style	2 c.	Milk	2 c.
Flour	¼ c.	Chopped chives	½ t.
Salt	1 t.	Butter or margarine	2 tb.

1) Beat the eggs.
2) Add all other ingredients except fat and mix well.
3) Pour into an oiled casserole and dot with butter or margarine.
4) Bake for about 1 hr. at 350° F. (177° C.). Serve hot.

Eggplant Stew
(Arabic) *
(4 servings)
(Yakhni)

Lamb meat	1 lb.	Garlic (mashed)	1 sm. clove
Eggplant (med.)	3	Salt	1 t.
Onion (lg.)	1	Pepper	¼ t.
Butter	¼ c.	Tomato sauce	1 c.
Water	2 c.		

1) Cut the meat into small cubes.
2) Pare the eggplant and cut it into small cubes.
3) Chop the onion and fry it gently in the butter for about 5 min.

* Carmen Ferris, *Arabic Food*. Unpublished Thesis, University of Texas, 1952.

4) Add the meat and cook 15 min., turning frequently.
5) Add the eggplant, garlic, and seasonings, and turn lightly a few times.
6) Add the tomato sauce and water, and simmer until done (about 10 min.).

Lentil Soup

(About 4 servings)
(Adapted from an English recipe)

Lentils	½ c.	Herb mixture (p. 659)	¼ t.
Meat stock *	2 c.	Salt and pepper	to taste
Salt pork	1 in. cube	Butter or margarine	1 tb.
Onion	½ sm.	Flour	1 tb.
Carrot	1 med.	Milk	1 c.

1) Wash the lentils and soak them about 2 hours. Drain.
2) Cook with pork, onion, carrot, and herb mixture (tied in cheese cloth) in the meat stock, until the lentils are very tender (about 1 hr.).
3) Remove pork, onion, carrot, and herb mixture.
4) Make purée from the lentils using a blender, food mill, or coarse sieve.
5) Add liquid and season with salt and pepper.
6) Melt the butter, blend in the flour, and add the milk, stirring until slightly thickened.
7) Add the purée slowly and stir to blend.

Baked Onions

(About 4 servings)
(Italian)

Very small onions	1 lb.	Pepper	¼ t.
Olive oil	¼ c.	Wine vinegar	1 tb.
Salt	½ t.	Garlic	¼ sm. clove

1) Bake the onions, without removing skins, for 15 to 30 min. (until tender) at 375° F. (191° C.).
2) Remove from the oven, peel, and put into a serving dish with the remaining ingredients.
3) Mix well and serve hot or cold.

Okra and Eggplant

(About 4 servings)

Okra, small pods	12	Onion, med.	1
Egg plant, med.	1	Salt and pepper	to taste
Tomatoes, med.	3	Parsley, cut fine	1 tb.

* A beef bouillon cube dissolved in 2 c. water may be used.

1) Wash the vegetables.
2) Slice the okra, pare and cut the eggplant, quarter the tomatoes, and slice the onion.
3) Cook vegetables in a very small amount of water, covered, for 30 min.
4) Season, put into a serving dish, and sprinkle with parsley.

Peas
(About 4 servings)

Fresh peas *..... 1 lb. Boiling, salted water....... to cover
Butter or margarine........ 2 tb.

1) Shell the peas, wash them and remove any foreign particles.
2) Boil without cover until just tender (see table, p. 486).
3) Drain and serve buttered.

Frozen peas *...... 1 pkg. Butter or margarine........ 2 tb.

1) Cook the peas as directed on the package until just tender.
2) Drain and serve buttered.

Canned peas *... No. 303 can Butter or margarine..... 2 tb.

1) Heat the peas in a saucepan.
2) Drain and serve buttered.

Ham with Peas
(Italian)

Ingredients	*For 2*	*For 4*	*For 6*
Cooked ham	⅓ lb.	⅔ lb.	1 lb.
Fat	1 tb.	2 tb.	3 tb.
Onion, sliced	½ sm.	1 sm.	1 med.
Parsley, minced	½ tb.	1 tb.	1½ tb.
Fresh peas, shelled	1 c.	2 c.	3 c.
Broth or water	1 c.	2 c.	3 c.
Salt	¼ t.	½ t.	¾ t.
Pepper	dash	⅛ t.	¼ t.

1) Cut the ham into small cubes.
2) Cook the onion and parsley in the fat in a frying pan for about 2 min., without browning the onion.
3) Add the ham, and continue to cook, stirring frequently.
4) Add the peas, liquid, and seasonings, and cook until the peas are tender—about 15 min.
5) Drain, evaporate the liquid about half, pour it over the mixture, and serve.

---

* As an example of color of a green vegetable it is interesting to compare and account for the color of the peas suggested above

POTATOES

Boiled Potatoes
(About 4 servings)

Potatoes (firm)...... 1 lb. Boiling, salted water...... to cover
Choice of "butter" or sauce

1) Wash the potatoes. They need not be pared.*
2) Boil until just tender (see table, p. 486).
3) Serve with your choice of "butters" or sauces.

Sweet Potatoes on the Half Shell
(4 servings) **

Sweet potatoes............	4	Sugar...........	3 tb.
Raisins (seedless)...........	⅓ c.	Salt.............	½ t.

Butter or margarine........ 1 tb.

1) Bake the potatoes about 1 hour at 375° F. (191° C.)
2) Cut lengthwise and scoop out pulp.
3) Mash the pulp, add other ingredients, and mix well.
4) Pile lightly into the shells and brown at 425° F. (218° C.)

Mashed Potatoes
(About 4 servings)

Boiled potatoes †.....	1 lb.	Salt and pepper	to season
Butter or margarine..	about 2 tb.	Milk.............	about ¼ c.

1) Drain the potatoes and mash with potato masher, blending fork, or portable electric beater, leaving the potatoes in the saucepan over low or warm heat. Add the butter, seasonings, and milk (gradually) and beat until light and fluffy.

Potato Soufflé
(About 4 servings)

Mashed potato.........	about 3 c.	Onion, grated......	½ t.
Eggs, separated........	2	Salt and pepper....	to taste
Butter or margarine....	1½ tb.	Milk..............	1 c.
Parsley, finely cut......	1 t.	Cream of tartar....	⅛ t.

Grated cheese (optional)......¼ c.

1) To hot mashed potato add beaten egg yolks.
2) Add seasonings and mix to blend.

---

* If not pared, peel before serving.

** Adapted. By permission, Lena Sturges, Food Editor Staff, Progressive Farmer.

† Mealy potatoes are good for mashing.

3) Add milk gradually and mix well.
4) Beat the egg whites until frothy, add cream of tartar and continue beating until the whites are stiff (not dry); fold them into the mixture.
5) Put into a well oiled oven-to-table dish and bake about 15 min. at 375° F. (191° C.). (20 min. if cheese is not added).
6) If cheese is used, remove the soufflé and sprinkle with cheese; bake about 5 min. longer or until cheese is melted and golden brown.

Baked Potatoes

1) Wash medium-sized baking potatoes thoroughly, using a brush.
2) Place potatoes on a baking sheet or utility pan and bake 45 min. to 1 hr. in a hot oven—425° F. (218° C.). (May be baked while roasting meat at 300° F. (149° C.) for 1½ to 2 hrs).
3) Remove from the oven.
4) May be served in several ways, including:
   a. Cut skin on one side to allow steam to escape and prevent sogginess.
   b. Cut skin lengthwise and crosswise about half the dimensions of the potatoes and push gently to make the pulp fluffy. Serve with butter or margarine, crumbled crisp bacon, or sour cream sauce (see p. 531).
   c. Cut out a portion of the skin, remove the pulp, and mash (see above). Refill the shells and brown under a broiler.
   d. To the potato cut as in *b,* above, add 2 or 3 slices of sharp cheese, pressing the cheese into the potato so that it will melt partially.

[Note: Stuffed potatoes (c above) may be cooled, wrapped in foil, and frozen, to be heated for some future meal.]

Potato Chips
(About 4 servings)

Firm potatoes.................. 1 lb.
Ice water
Fat or oil for frying

1) Wash and pare the potatoes.
2) Slice very thin, using a vegetable slicer or very sharp knife, and chill in salted ice water about ½ hr.
3) Dry thoroughly on a towel or absorbent paper.
4) Fry in deep fat at 390° to 395° F. (199° to 202° C.) until brown, stirring as needed to brown evenly. *Caution:* Care should be taken not to put too many into the fat; the temperature is lowered too much and even browning is not easy.
5) Drain and put onto unglazed paper; sprinkle with salt if needed. (Salt from the water in which the chips were soaked may be sufficient.)

Vichyssoise
(French Potato Soup)

Ingredients	*For 2*	*For 4*	*For 6*
Butter or margarine	1 tb.	2 tb.	3 tb.
Onions, sliced	½ c.	1 c.	1½ c.
Potatoes, thinly sliced	1 c.	2 c.	3 c.
Chicken stock *	½ c.	1 c.	1½ c.
Milk, hot	½ c.	1 c.	1½ c.
Salt	½ t.	1 t.	1½ t.
Pepper	dash	⅛ t.	¼ t.
Paprika	dash	⅛ t.	¼ t.
Cream, light	⅓ c.	⅔ c.	1 c.
Parsley or chives, chopped	1 tb.	2 tb.	3 tb.

1) Melt butter or margarine over low heat in a heavy saucepan; add onions, cover, and cook slowly until onions are yellow.
2) Add potatoes and chicken stock and cook until potatoes are tender (about 8 minutes).
3) Press onions, potatoes, and liquid through a sieve; add seasonings and cream to the puréed mixture.
4) Serve hot or *thoroughly* chilled, topped with chives or parsley.

Spinach

Ingredients	*For 2*	*For 4*	*For 6*
Fresh spinach	½ lb.	1 lb.	1½ lb.
Salt	¼ t.	½ t.	¾ t.
Tart "butter" or sauce	2 tb.	¼ c.	¼ c. + 2 tb.

1) Cut the roots and large tough stems from the spinach and remove any wilted leaves.
2) Wash thoroughly, using a large amount of water. (Change water several times.)
3) Cook covered over low heat with no added water until the leaves are wilted; then remove the cover and add ¼ t. salt. Continue cooking until tender.
4) Serve with chosen tart "butter" or sauce.

Summer Squash en Casserole
(About 4 servings)

Summer squash	about 1 lb.	Condensed celery soup	⅓ can
Chopped onion	2–3 t.	Condensed mushroom soup	⅓ can
Salt	¼–½ t.	Milk	½ c.

Buttered bread crumbs . . . . ½–¾ c.

* May be made by dissolving a chicken bouillon cube in hot water.

1) Wash the squash and slice crosswise in slices about ½ inch thick.
2) Cook in boiling, salted water for 3 min.; drain.
3) Oil a casserole (or individual ramekins) and put a layer of squash on the bottom.
4) Sprinkle with chopped onion and salt.
5) Combine the soups and milk and add to the above mixture to nearly cover.
6) Continue these layers until all the squash is used.
7) Cover with buttered crumbs,* and bake about 15 min. (until heated and brown) at 350° F. (177° C.).

Baked Acorn Squash
(4 servings)

Acorn squash (med.)	2	Butter or margarine	1½ tb.
Salt	to season	Brown sugar or molasses	1½ tb.

1) Wash the squash, cut in half, and remove the seeds.
2) Sprinkle with salt; put about 1 t. of butter or margarine and sugar or molasses into each half, and put the squash into a suitable baking dish.
3) Bake about 15 min., or until tender, at 350° F. (177° C.).

Zucchini Sweet and Sour
(About 4 servings)

Zucchini	2 med.	Wine vinegar	1 t.
Cooking oil	2 tb.	Sugar	1½ t.
Salt and pepper	to taste	Sweet basil	to taste

1) Wash and pare the zucchini and cut in lengthwise slices about ½ in. thick.
2) Brown in oil**; sprinkle with salt and pepper.
3) Add the vinegar and sugar and sprinkle with the basil.
4) Bake about 15 min. at 350° F. (177° C.), basting the squash with the liquid 2 or 3 times during the cooking.

Zucchini with Mint
(About 4 servings)
(Italian)

Zucchini (5–6 in.)	4	Salt	½ t.
Olive oil	2 tb.	Pepper	¼ t.

Chopped mint leaves

* At this point the product may be covered with foil and frozen for future use.
** A top-of-the-range-to-table utensil is desirable.

1) Wash and parboil the zucchini (about 10 min.) and cut into strips.
2) Put into a frying pan with the other ingredients and cook 5 min., stirring frequently.
3) Transfer to serving dish and serve at once.

SWEET POTATOES

Baked

(follow directions for baked Irish potatoes.)

Orange Sweet Potatoes

(About 4 servings)
(Southern)

Sweet potatoes (med.)	3	Butter or margarine	2 tb.
Orange juice	⅔ c.	White sugar	3 tb.
Grated orange rind	1 t.	Brown sugar	3 tb.
Cornstarch	2 t.	Salt	⅔ t.

1) Wash the potatoes and cook in boiling, salted water until tender.
2) Remove the skins and cut in quarters lengthwise.
3) Combine other ingredients and cook until thickened, stirring constantly.
4) Arrange the potatoes in an oven-to-table dish, pour the sauce over them, and bake about 30 min. at 350° F. (177° C.).

Broiled Sweet Potatoes

(4 servings)

Boiled or baked sweet potatoes	3	Brown sugar	about 2 tb.
Melted butter or margarine	about 2 tb.		

1) Remove the skins and cut the potatoes in 3 or 4 slices, lengthwise.
2) Arrange the potatoes in an oven-to-table dish, brush with melted butter or margarine, and sprinkle with sugar.
3) Brown under broiler and serve at once.

Broiled Tomatoes

(4 servings)

Tomatoes	4 to 6	Salt, pepper, and onion salt	to season
Butter or margarine	about 1½ tb.		

1) Wash the tomatoes, remove the stems, and cut them in half crosswise.
2) Arrange the tomatoes on a broiling pan, sprinkle with seasonings, and dot with butter.
3) Set in the broiler 2 to 3 in. below the source of heat and broil about 6 min.

Gaspacho Andaluz
(About 4 servings)
(Adapted from a Spanish recipe)

Tomatoes	4 med.	Salt and pepper	to taste
Cucumber	1 sm.	Fine, dry crumbs	1 c.
Sweet red pepper	1	Oil	about 3 tb.
Onion	1 med.	Wine vinegar	½ c.
Garlic	1–2 cloves	Ice	

1) Chop the tomatoes, cucumber, red pepper, and onion fine.
2) Press the garlic through a garlic press (or mince it) into a mixing bowl and add salt, pepper, and crumbs. Mix well.
3) Add the oil a few drops at a time and stir until a thick paste is formed.
4) Add the vinegar very slowly, stirring to combine thoroughly.
5) Put the mixture into a mixing bowl, add the vegetables, and blend. *OR* make purée from the whole mixture, using a blender.
6) Characteristically, the soup is served in a soup tureen set into a bowl of ice.

Turnips en Casserole
(About 4 servings)

Turnips	1 bnch.	Butter or margarine	about 2 tb.
Consommé	about ½ c.	Salt and sugar	to season

1) Wash the turnips and cube them. (They need not be pared.)
2) Put them into an oven-to-table baking dish, add consommé, dot turnips with butter or margarine and sprinkle with salt and sugar.
3) Bake 20 to 30 min. (until tender) at 350° F. (177° C.).

SALADS

Salads rate high with some individuals and to others they are merely "rabbit food." In some families where they are popular, variety is important and in others there is only *one*—the green salad, also known as "garden" and "tossed." Regardless of its name, this salad is usually based on one or a mixture of salad greens and is dressed with oil, vinegar, and seasonings. It may or may not be embellished with other ingredients such as tomato, radishes, cheese, etc. The green salad is called by some the "gourmets' salad," and indeed it does seem to be identified with elite restaurants. Many variations will be found in recipes for green salad. The Caesar salad given below is, in effect, such a salad with a different twist. Devotees of green salads generally agree that they must be made of a mixture of crisp, flavorful *green* salad plants. Iceberg lettuce as such is frowned on for this type of salad since it is more or less tasteless and often is colorless too.

For those who enjoy variety in salads there are a number of variations. The following recipes are suggestive of some interesting combinations. More will be found in the references.

Mexican Fruit Salad
(About 6 servings)

Avocados, sectioned...	3	Mint, fresh, chopped.	1–2 sprigs
Pineapple, cubed......	1 c.	French dressing......	¼ c.
Oranges, sectioned....	3	Salad greens, assorted.	6 servings

1) Marinate the fruits and mint in the French dressing for about 20 minutes.
2) Place the salad greens on a platter so as to present interesting contour (not flat).
3) Drain fruit mixture and arrange in a casual manner on the greens.

Guacamole (Avocado) Salad
(4 servings)
(Mexican)

Avocado, ripe..........	1 large	Salt............	½ t.
Onion, grated..........	2 t.	Chili powder....	⅛ t.
Lemon juice...........	1 tb.	Tomatoes.......	4
Worcestershire sauce....	½ t.	Salad greens.....	4 servings
French dressing..........	4 tb.		

1) Peel and mash the avocado; add seasonings and blend well.
2) Wash and dry greens and arrange on individual salad plates; wash and core the tomatoes and cut them in half.
3) Place two pieces of tomato on each salad plate and heap the avocado mixture on the cut tomatoes. Pour 1 tb. of dressing over each salad. [Note: A mixture of water cress and lettuce is an excellent combination to use for this salad.]

Caesar Salad
(About 6 to 8 servings)

Garlic.........	1 clove	Salt..............	½ t.
Olive oil.......	½ c.	Pepper...........	⅛ t.
Croutons......	1 c.	Sugar.............	½ t.
Romaine, or other salad green........	2 medium heads	Parmesan cheese, grated..........	½ c.
		Lemons...........	juice of 2
Egg, raw..........	1		

1) Split garlic clove, add to oil and let stand several hours.
2) Make croutons by taking bread slices ½-inch thick and cutting into ½-inch cubes; place on a baking sheet in a slow oven (300° F.) and bake for about 20 minutes or until croutons are thoroughly crisp and brown.
3) Wash and dry greens; tear into bits and heap in a large salad bowl. Sprinkle seasoning, sugar, and cheese over greens.
4) Remove garlic from oil, add ¼-c. of the oil and the lemon juice to the salad greens; put croutons in remaining oil.
5) Break the egg into a bowl and beat *slightly* with a fork; pour the egg over the greens and mix gently with a wooden spoon and fork until well blended.
6) Just before serving add the croutons and toss again.

Chef's Salad Bowl
(2 servings)

Salad greens	2 servings	Swiss	¼ c.
Ham, chicken, tongue or roast beef*	½ c.	Hard cooked eggs, sliced	2
Cheese, Cheddar or		Anchovies	4 fillets
		French dressing	4 tb.

1) Wash and dry salad greens; tear into pieces and arrange in two individual salad bowls.
2) Cut the ham or other meat and the cheese into match-shaped pieces, (scissors are good for this) and arrange in neat piles over the greens.
3) Place the egg and the anchovies on the beds of greens and pour the dressing over the salads.

Pennsylvania Dutch Hot Cabbage Slaw
(About 6 servings)

Bacon	6 slices	Mustard, dry	1 t.
Flour	2 tb.	Egg, beaten	1
Sugar	⅓ c.	Milk	1½ c.
Salt	½ t.	Vinegar	2 tb.
Pepper	⅛ t.	Cabbage, finely shredded	2½–3 c.

1) Fry bacon until crisp and remove from pan.
2) Mix flour and sugar with seasonings and add to the bacon fat.
3) Mix the beaten egg with the milk and add; cook until thick.
4) Just before removing from heat, stir in the vinegar.
5) Mix with cabbage, sprinkle crumbled bacon over the top, and serve hot.

* This is an excellent way to use small amounts of left-over meats.

Sauerkraut Salad
(About 6 servings)
(Vienna)

Sauerkraut, (fresh or canned), drained	2½–3 c.
Onion, chopped	2 tb.
Garlic, minced very fine	½ sm. clove
Parsley, chopped	¼ c.
Sugar	2 t.
Caraway seed	½ t.
French dressing	½ c.

1) Mix all ingredients well and chill.
2) Serve on water cress or other salad green.

German Potato Salad
(4 servings)

Potatoes	4 medium	Celery, chopped	½ c.
Salt	½ t.	Vinegar (garlic or tarragon)	¼ c.
Pepper	¼ t.	Lemon	1 thick slice
Paprika	½ t.	Bacon, crisp	4 slices
Parsley, chopped	1 tb.		

1) Cook potatoes whole; cool and slice thin into a glass or earthenware baking dish, season with salt, pepper, and paprika and sprinkle the parsley and celery over the potatoes.
2) Heat the bacon fat, vinegar, and lemon slice to the boiling point. Remove lemon and pour dressing over potatoes.
3) Cover and heat over a low flame until potatoes are thoroughly warm, or place in a moderate oven and heat.
4) Just before serving, crumble the bacon over the top of the salad.

Chicken Timbale Salad
(About 6 servings)

Gelatin, plain	1 tb.	Salt	½ t.
Cold water	¼ c.	Tarragon or other seasoning	⅛ t.
Chicken broth, fat free	¾ c.	Eggs, hard cooked, chopped	3
Chicken, cooked and diced	1½ c.	Sour cream	1 c.
Pimiento, chopped	2 tb.		
Parsley, chopped	2 tb.		

1) Soak the gelatin in the cold water.
2) Heat the chicken broth; dissolve the soaked gelatin in the hot broth and chill mixture slightly.
3) Add all ingredients *except* sour cream, blend well and chill again until thick, but not set. Then add sour cream.

4) Mold in individual molds or one large mold. Refrigerate for several hours.
5) Serve on water cress or other salad greens.

Molded Cranberry and Orange Salad
(Serves 6 to 8)

Lemon gelatin	1 pkg. (3½ oz.)	Water, cold	¾ c.
Water, hot	1 c.	Cranberries, raw	4 c.
Oranges, unpeeled	2 small		

1) Dissolve the gelatin in the hot water, add the cold water and cool.
2) Wash the cranberries and oranges; cut the oranges in quarters and remove seeds; put the cranberries and oranges through a food chopper, reserving the juice.
3) Add the fruit and juice to the cooled gelatin. Put the mixture into a wet mold or into individual molds and place in refrigerator until thoroughly cold and set.
4) Turn mold out on a bed of salad greens and serve with mayonnaise or a cooked dressing.

Grapefruit and Water Cress Salad

Water cress	1 serving	Pomegranate seed	1 tb.
Grapefruit	½	French dressing	2 tb.

1) Wash and dry cress and place on salad plate.
2) Section grapefruit and arrange sections on water cress.
3) Sprinkle with pomegranate seed and pour dressing over the salad.

SALAD PLATTERS

Instead of chopping and mixing salad ingredients with a dressing, "personalized" salads may be made by arranging the ingredients on a platter and allowing each individual to choose his own salad. This gives leeway for likes and dislikes. A choice of dressing might also be allowed, such as a French type and one with a mayonnaise base. Two suggestions for "Choose-your-own salad" are:

Fish, Egg and Vegetable Platter
(About 6 servings)

Tuna fish, crab or salmon, chilled	1 can (6–8 oz.)
Sardines, chilled	1–2 cans
Eggs, hard cooked	3–4
Beets, pickled	1½–2 c.
Green pepper, sliced in rings	6–8 rings
Onions, sliced in rings	6–8 rings
Salad greens, assorted	6 servings

1) Arrange salad greens on a large serving plate.
2) Drain the juice or oil from canned fish. Turn fish out on salad greens. Fish is more attractive if not broken or separated.
3) Place other ingredients on greens, grouping each rather than scattering them over the platter.
4) Offer a choice of French or Roquefort salad dressings.

Fruit and Cheese Platter
(About 6 servings)

Bananas, cut in lengthwise quarters	2–3
Pineapple, fresh or canned, diced	2 c.
Plums, whole, fresh or canned	12–15
Peaches, halves, fresh or canned	6–8
Grapes, snipped into small clusters	1 lb.
Cheese, cottage	1 c.
Cheese, Cheddar, brick, etc. (cut in wedges)	½ lb.
Salad greens	6 servings

1) Arrange salad greens on a large serving plate.
2) Place the chilled fruits and cheeses on the salad greens, grouping each rather than scattering them over the platter.
3) Offer a choice of poppy seed or mayonnaise dressing.

SALAD DRESSINGS

French Dressing
(About 1 c.)

Salt	½ t.	Vinegar	2 tb.
Paprika	½ t.	Salad oil	6 tb.
Sugar	½ t.		

Combine ingredients by beating in a small bowl, shaking in a tightly closed bottle or jar, or whirling in an electric blender.

Mayonnaise
(About 2 c.)

Salt	½ t.	Egg	1 whole or 2 yolks
Paprika	¼ t.	Vinegar	⅓ c.
Salad oil	2 c.		

1) Select a deep bowl that is narrow and rounded at the bottom.
2) Add seasonings (except vinegar) to egg and beat.
3) Add the oil slowly until the mixture thickens.
4) Alternate the oil and vinegar until all are added.

Cooked "Sour Cream" Dressing

(About ¾ cup)

Dry mustard	1 t.	Cayenne pepper	few grains
Salt	¼ t.	Salad oil	1 tb.
Flour	1 t.	Egg	1
Sugar	2 t.	Vinegar	¼ c.
Evaporated milk, undiluted	½ c.		

1) Put the dry ingredients in the top of a double boiler, add the oil and blend.
2) Beat the egg and add half of the vinegar, mixing well; add this to the oil mixture and cook over *hot* water for about 5 minutes, then allow to cool.
3) Add the remaining vinegar to the milk, stirring to blend; beat the milk into the cooked mixture until the dressing is smooth.

Piquante Dressing

(Cooked)

(Makes 1½ c.)

Flour	⅛ c.	Eggs, beaten	1
Dry mustard	¾ t.	Buttermilk	1 c.
Salt	¾ t.	Vinegar	¼ c.
Pepper	dash	Butter or margarine	1 tb.
Sugar	2 tb.		

1) Combine the dry ingredients in an appropriate utensil.
2) Add the eggs and buttermilk and blend.
3) Add the vinegar slowly and mix well.
4) Place over low heat and cook, stirring until thick.
5) Add the butter or margarine and stir.
6) Strain into a glass or earthenware bowl and beat for a few seconds with a rotary beater.

Sour Cream Salad Dressing

(Uncooked)

(About 1½ cups)

Sour cream, cultured	1 c.	Onion, minced	2 t.
Salt	¼ t.	Vinegar	2 tb.
Sugar	1 tb.	Hard cooked eggs, chopped	2
Paprika	½ t.		
Dry mustard	½ t.		

Put all ingredients into a bowl and blend thoroughly. This dressing may be stored in a jar in the refrigerator for a week to ten days.

TABLE 37. STANDARD SALAD DRESSINGS AND SOME VARIATIONS

FRENCH 1 t. salt — 3 tb. vinegar 1/3 t. paprika — 1/2 c. oil *Herb* Use herb vinegar—basil, tarragon, garlic, etc.—in place of the vinegar. *Citrus* Use lemon, lime, or grapefruit juice in place of the vinegar. Add 1 tb. sugar.	*Spanish* To French Dressing add: 1 tb. horseradish 2 tb. chili sauce *Chiffonade* To French Dressing add the following finely chopped: 1 tb. parsley 1/2 tb. green pepper 1/2 tb. red pepper 1 tb. shallot 2 olives 2 sweet pickles 1 tb. hard-cooked egg	*Cream Cheese* To French Dressing add: 1 pkg. Philadelphia cream cheese. Beat well. *Poppy Seed* Omit paprika. Add 2 tb. sugar, 1/2 t. mustard, 3/4 tb. onion juice, and 1/2 tb. poppy seed. Mix dry ingredients. Add vinegar and onion juice. Add oil gradually. When well mixed, add poppy seed.	*Roquefort* To French Dressing add: 2 tb. Roquefort cheese broken into small pieces. *Tomato* To French Dressing add: 1/4 c. tomato juice. Mix dressing in a bowl that has been rubbed with a clove of garlic.
MAYONNAISE 1/2 t. salt — 2 egg yolks 1/4 t. pepper — 2 tb. vinegar 1/4 t. paprika — 2 c. oil	*Russian* To 1 c. mayonnaise add: 1 1/2 tb. lemon juice 1 tb. A-1 sauce 2 t. chili sauce	*Thousand Island* To 1 c. mayonnaise add: 1/4 c. chili sauce 1 tb. chopped green pepper 1/2 t. tarragon 1 tb. chopped chives 1 tb. chopped red pepper	*Caper* To 1 c. mayonnaise add: 2 tb. capers 2 tb. chopped parsley or water cress 1 tb. chopped pimiento
COOKED 1/2 t. salt — 1 egg, beaten 2 tb. flour — 3/4 c. milk 2 tb. sugar — 1/4 c. vinegar 1 t. dry mustard — 2 tb. melted butter dash cayenne	*Whipped Cream* To 1 c. cooked dressing add: 1 c. whipped cream. *Sour Cream* To 1 c. cooked dressing add: 1 c. sour cream	*Horseradish* To 1 c. cooked dressing add: 1/2 t. horseradish *Pimiento* To 1 c. cooked dressing add: 1 tb. chopped pimiento	*Citrus* In place of vinegar use 1 tb. lemon juice and 3 tb. orange juice.

Buttermilk Dressing
(Uncooked)
(About ¾ cup)

Sugar	1 t.	Celery seed	½ t.
Salt	½ t.	Vinegar	1 tb.
Dry mustard	½ t.	Chopped pickle	2 tb.
Paprika	¼ t.	Chili sauce	1 tb.
Buttermilk	¾ c.		
Egg, hard cooked, chopped	1		

Put dry ingredients in a bowl and blend. Add other ingredients and mix thoroughly.

Tomato Juice Dressing
(Uncooked)
(About 1 cup)

Basil	⅛ t.	Chili powder	⅛ t.
Salt	¼ t.	Garlic vinegar	2 tb.
Sugar	½ t.	Poppy seed	½ t.
Tomato juice	1 c.		

Put all ingredients in a screw-top bottle and shake well. Let stand an hour before using. Use the same as French dressing.

MILK

Choice of utensil and methods for milk cooking. Most recipes call for a double boiler for preparing such dishes as milk sauces, puddings, and custards. However, since modern ranges have heat controls for surface units, it is not necessary to use a double boiler for successful custards, etc. In the absence of temperature controls, asbestos mats or flame spreaders may be used to lower the temperature of the surface unit. If a double boiler is used, there is no assurance that it will prevent curdling of the custard if the water is allowed to boil, because a double boiler also requires control of the heat. When milk is placed over direct heat, the type of utensil used is important; stainless steel or other substantial materials are preferred for the purpose. Light weight utensils should be avoided since they do not allow enough protection and the milk may scorch.

Utensils for baking custards, puddings, etc. can be varied. Even though recipes for baked custard often specify individual custard cups, shallow glass pie pans, individual casseroles, or deep baking dishes may also be used.

Modern appliances such as electric frying pans permit flexibility in cooking. Any custard can be steamed in this versatile utensil by following the manufacturer's directions. Custards can also be steamed in pressure saucepans. Booklets which come with the pans give recipes for this method.

Kind of milk to use. The milk in any of the following recipes may be: fresh fluid whole or skim, reconstituted dried milk or evaporated milk.

Basic White Sauce

	Milk	*Flour*	*Fat*	*Salt*
Thin	1 c.	1 tb.	1 tb.	1/4 t.
Medium	1 c.	2 tb.	2 tb.	1/4 t.
Thick	1 c.	3 tb.	2–3 tb.	1/4 t.

1) Melt fat in selected utensil over *low* heat.
2) Add flour and salt to the fat and blend well.
3) Add the cold milk all at once; cook the mixture until the sauce thickens, stirring occasionally to prevent lumping and sticking.

[Note: Individual taste determines the amount of flour used in any sauce.]

If considered alone the above sauces are not particularly interesting. However, each of them can form the basis for many delicious dishes. These include chowders, bisques, seafood newburgs and soufflés. In fact, if a recipe for American ice cream (see p. 528) is appraised it will be noted that this favorite is also based on a white sauce recipe!

A few examples are given here for using the three types of sauces. Numerous recipes for their use can be found from other sources.

Cream of Corn Soup

Ingredients	*For 2*	*For 4*	*For 6*
Butter or margarine	1 1/2 tb.	3 tb.	1/4 c.
Flour	1 tb.	2 tb.	3 tb.
Milk	1 c.	2 c.	3 c.
Onion	1 slice	2 slices	3 slices
Salt	1/2 t.	1 t.	1 1/2 t.
Bay leaf	bit	bit	bit
Corn (cream style)	1/2 c.	1 c.	1 1/2 c.

1) Make white sauce as directed above, adding the onion and bay leaf along with the milk.
2) When sauce is thick add corn and blend well. Pour into serving bowls and garnish with paprika, chopped parsley, or grated cheese.

Cream of Spinach Soup

Ingredients	For 2	For 4	For 6
Butter or margarine	1½ tb.	3 tb.	¼ c.
Flour	1½ tb.	3 tb.	¼ c. + ½ tb.
Milk	1 c.	2 c.	3 c
Salt	½ t.	1 t.	1½ t.
Pepper	1/16 t.	⅛ t.	3/16 t.
Spinach, raw chopped	⅓ c.	⅔ c.	1 c

1) Make white sauce as above.
2) Cut spinach fairly fine, using scissors, and add to the sauce. Continue cooking *slowly* about 5 min. The spinach should be fairly crisp when the soup is served.
3) Pour into serving bowls and garnish with a grated cheese, paprika, or chopped hard-cooked egg.

Pretzel Soup
(Pennsylvania Dutch)

	For 2	For 4	For 6
Butter or Margarine	2 tb.	¼ c.	¼ c. + 2 tb.
Flour	1 tb.	2 tb.	3 tb.
Milk	2 c.	4 c.	6 c.
Salt	⅛ t.	¼ t.	½ t.
Pepper		to taste	
Parsley, chopped	1 tb.	2 tb.	3 tb.
Pretzels, broken in pieces	1/16 lb.	⅛ lb.	¼ lb.

1) Make a white sauce of the first five ingredients according to directions on p. 499.
2) Add parsley to the sauce and pour over the pretzels which have been placed in individual bowls.

Scalloped Fish au Gratin

Ingredients	For 2	For 4	For 6
Butter or margarine	1½ tb.	3 tb.	¼ c.
Flour	2 tb.	¼ c.	¼ c. + 2 tb.
Milk	1 c.	2 c.	3 c.
Salt	¼ t.	½ t.	¾ t.
Rosemary	⅛ t.	¼ t.	½ t.
Parsley, chopped	1 tb.	2 tb.	3 tb.
Grated cheese	½ c.	¾ c.	1 c.
Fish fillets	¾ lb.	1½ lbs.	2 lbs.
Herb vinegar	1 t.	2 t.	1 tb.
Buttered crumbs	2 tb.	3 tb.	¼ c.

1) Make white sauce of the first four ingredients according to directions on p. 523.
2) Stir in rosemary, parsley, and cheese, retaining a small amount of cheese to sprinkle on top.
3) Cut the fillets in small cubes and stir into the sauce; add vinegar.
4) Place in a well-oiled, shallow baking dish and sprinkle with grated cheese and buttered crumbs.
5) Bake for about 40 min. at 350° F. (177° C.).

Chicken à la King

Ingredients	*For 2*	*For 4*	*For 6*
Butter or margarine	1½ tb.	3 tb.	¼ c.
Flour	2 tb.	4 tb.	6 tb.
Milk	1 c.	2 c.	3 c.
Salt	¼ t.	½ t.	¾ t.
Onion, grated	1 t.	2 t.	1 tb.
Basil	⅛ t.	¼ t.	½ t.
Pepper	dash	⅛ t.	¼ t.
Cooked chicken, diced	¾ c.	1½ c.	2 c.
Mushrooms, chopped	¼ c.	½ c.	¾ c.
Pimiento, chopped	1 tb.	2 tb.	3 tb.

1) Make *medium* white sauce of the first four ingredients according to directions on p. 499.
2) Stir in all other ingredients and heat thoroughly.
3) Choice includes serving (1) on toast, waffles, rice, or noodles or (2) in large or individual casserole or patty shells.
[Note: To make an Hawaiian type dish add diced pineapple to the above ingredients in the same amounts as given for mushrooms.]

Broccoli Soufflé
(About 4 servings)

Butter or Margarine	2–3 tb.
Flour	3 tb.
Milk	2 c.
Salt	½ t.
Pepper	¼ t.
Other seasonings, as liked	¼ t.
Egg yolks	3–4
Broccoli, chopped *	1 c.
Egg whites	3–4
Cream of tartar	½ t.

* If frozen broccoli is used it need not be cooked; fresh broccoli will be sufficiently cooked for this purpose if boiling water is poured over the tender stalks before chopping.

1) Make a *thick* white sauce of the first four ingredients according to directions on p. 499, adding other seasonings.
2) Beat the egg yolks; pour a little of the hot sauce into them before adding to the rest of the sauce. Continue cooking for a few minutes.
3) Add the broccoli to sauce and blend well.
4) Beat the egg whites until frothy, add the cream of tartar, and continue beating until they form a peak that bends over slightly when the beater is lifted.
5) Fold the sauce into the egg whites.
6) Pour into an oiled baking dish or mold and bake about 30 minutes or until firm at 350° F. (177° C.).
7) Serve at once either in the baking dish or turn out on serving dish.

Custard

Ingredients	*For 2*	*For 4*	*For 6*
Milk	1 c.	2 c.	3 c.
Eggs	1 to 2	2 to 4	3 to 6
Sugar	1 tb.	2 tb.	3 tb.
Salt	1/16 t.	1/8 t.	3/16 t.
Vanilla or other flavoring	1/4 t.	1/2 t.	3/4 t.

Soft Custard
(Stirred)

1) The milk may be scalded or used cold.
2) Beat the eggs slightly and add the sugar and salt; stir to blend.
3) Add milk to the egg-sugar mixture slowly, stirring to mix well.
4) Cook over low heat, stirring occasionally until the mixture coats the spoon.
5) Add flavoring. Pour into a bowl *at once* for chilling.

Floating Island

Make soft custard as above *except* separate egg yolks from whites of *half* the number eggs. Beat reserved egg whites until stiff and then add 2 tablespoons of extra sugar for each white, beating until well mixed. Butter a large mold or baking dish or individual molds, and sprinkle with granulated sugar. Place beaten egg whites in the mold and bake at 300° F. until set and slightly browned. Cool and turn out.

Pour the chilled custard into an appropriate serving dish and float the "island" on the custard. Sirup from left-over canned berries, maraschino cherries, etc., may be poured over the "island." This provides both color and flavor.

English Trifle

Make soft custard as on page 526. Choose attractive serving bowls and alternate layers of sliced sponge type cake with sliced fruit, processed or fresh, or berries (allow ¼ cup of fruit per serving). Make two or three layers, depending on the size of the bowl. Pour chilled soft custard over the cake and fruit and refrigerate for several hours.

Baked Custard

1) Follow steps 1, 2, and 3 for making soft custard.
2) Pour the mixture into selected baking dish or custard cups and set in a pan of water. Bake for about 30 minutes at 325° F. (163° C.). The custard is done when the blade of a thin knife, inserted at the center, comes out clean.
3) Chill and serve in the custard cups or turn the molds out onto a serving dish.

Breaded Custard "Pie"

(About 4 servings)

Follow steps 1, 2, and 3 for making soft (stirred) custard for four. Pour into a buttered glass pie pan. Make three slices of toast, butter, cut toast into cubes, and place over top of custard mixture. Set the pie pan in a pan of water and bake for about 25 minutes or until firm at 325° F. (163° C.). (See test for baked custard above.) Take custard out of hot water as soon as it comes from the oven and chill thoroughly before serving. To serve, cut in pie-shape wedges and serve plain or with a fruit sauce.

Spanish Flan

(About 6 servings)

Sugar	1 c.	Milk	3 c.
Eggs	6	Sugar	½ c.
Vanilla	1 t.		

1) Caramelize 1 cup of sugar by putting it into (1) a small frying pan of substantial material and placing it over direct, moderate heat and stirring until the sugar is melted *or* (2) top-of-the-range-to-table utensil in which the flan is to be baked. If the former utensil is used, the caramelized sugar should be poured at once into the container in which the flan will be baked.
2) While sugar is caramelizing, beat the eggs and add milk, the ½ c. of sugar, and vanilla.
3) Pour into baking dish containing caramel mixture and place dish in a pan of hot water.

4) Bake until firm (about 35 minutes) at 325° F. (163° C.). Chill before serving.
5) The flan may either be served from the dish in which it was baked or turned out on a serving dish.

[NOTE: If individual molds are desired the caramelized sugar should be placed in custard cups and the mixture poured over it.]

FRENCH ICE CREAM

Ingredients	*For 1 qt.*	*For 2 qt.*	*For 1 gal.*
Egg yolks	5	10	20
Sugar	¾ c.	1½ c.	3 c.
Salt	¼ t.	½ t.	1 t.
Milk	1½ c.	3 c.	1½ qt.
Thin cream	1½ c.	3 c.	1½ qt.
Vanilla	1½ t.	1 tb.	2 tb.

1) Select a substantial pan for cooking over direct heat.
2) Beat the egg yolks until thick and add the sugar and salt.
3) Add the milk and cook over *low* heat, stirring frequently, until the mixture coats a spoon.
4) Cool, add the cream and flavoring and stir to mix thoroughly.
5) Cool to 50° F. (10° C.) before freezing.
6) Fill the freezer can ¾ full with the mixture; close, put in freezing tub or bucket and fasten.
7) Fill tub ¼ full of ice and then fill with ice and salt used in the ratio of 1 part of salt to 8 parts of ice.
8) Turn handle slowly and evenly about 5 min. or until it begins to turn with difficulty; then turn rapidly until the mixture is hard.
9) Drain the brine from the tub, remove the dasher, and replace the cover, putting a stopper into the opening of the cover.
10) Fill the tub and cover the top of the can with a mixture of 1 part salt to 4 parts ice and let stand until ready to serve.

AMERICAN ICE CREAM

Ingredients	*For 1 qt.*	*For 2 qt.*	*For 1 gal.*
Milk	1½ c.	1½ pt.	1½ qt.
Flour	1 tb.	2 tb.	¼ c.
Salt	1/16 t.	⅛ t.	¼ t.
Egg yolks	2 sm.	3 med.	6 med.
Sugar	½ c.	1 c.	2 c.
Thin cream	1½ c.	1½ pt.	1½ qt.
Vanilla or other flavoring	¾ tb.	1½ tb.	3 tb.

1) Put the flour and salt into an appropriate utensil; add the milk a little at a time at first to avoid lumping.
2) Cook mixture over *low* heat until it thickens slightly.
3) Beat the egg yolks thoroughly; add sugar and mix well.
4) Add a small amount of the hot milk mixture to the egg yolks; pour into the remaining milk and continue cooking over low heat for several minutes until the mixture coats a spoon.
5) Cool and add cream and flavoring.
6) Follow directions for freezing French ice cream, steps 6 through 10.

Butterscotch Pudding

Ingredients	*For 2*	*For 4*	*For 6*
Milk	1 c.	2 c.	3 c.
Cornstarch	2 tb.	¼ c.	¼ c. + 2 tb.
Salt	⅛ t.	¼ t.	⅜ t.
Butter or margarine	1½ tb.	3 tb.	¼ c.
Brown sugar	½ c.	1 c.	1½ c.
Eggs	1	2	3

1) In an appropriate utensil combine the salt and cornstarch with about ¼ of the milk; add the remaining milk and stir until smooth.
2) Place mixture over low heat. Cook, stirring slowly until mixture is slightly thickened.
3) Cover and cook 10 minutes longer, stirring occasionally.
4) Heat the butter or margarine and brown sugar in a separate pan, stirring frequently until the mixture is bubbly. Add to the cooked mixture and blend.
5) Beat the eggs and add hot mixture gradually, blending well. The hot mixture will cook the egg sufficiently.
6) Chill and serve plain, with custard sauce, or cream.

Buttermilk Pie
(One 9-in. pie)

Sugar	⅔ c.	Buttermilk	2 c.
Flour	⅓ c.	Egg yolks, beaten	3
Salt	¼ t.	Lemon juice	3 tb.
Nutmeg	⅛ t.	Egg whites	3
Lemon rind	½ t.	Sugar	⅓ c.

1) In an appropriate utensil combine the ⅔ c. sugar, flour, salt, nutmeg, and lemon rind. Mix well.
2) Add buttermilk slowly, blending thoroughly; cook over hot water until thick, stirring occasionally.

3) Add beaten egg yolks which have been mixed with a little of the hot buttermilk mixture; cook for about 2 min.
4) Remove from heat and chill. When cold, add lemon juice and pour into baked pastry shell.
5) Make meringue by beating egg whites until stiff and then beating in the sugar slowly.
6) Heap meringue on the pie and bake at 350° F. (177° C.) for 8–10 min.
7) Chill thoroughly before serving.
   [NOTE: An excellent pudding may be made by placing the cold filling in a small buttered casserole, putting the meringue on top, and baking the same as for the pie.]

BEEF STROGANOFF
(About 6 servings)
(Adapted from a Russian recipe)

Ingredient	Amount	Ingredient	Amount
Olive oil	¼ c.	Tomato sauce	2 tb.
Onion, thin sliced	1 c.	Salt	1 t.
Lean beef, cooked (cut in 1½ in. strips)	2 to 3 c.	Nutmeg	⅛ t.
Mushrooms, sliced	1½ c.	Sour Cream	1½ c.

1) Put the olive oil in a pan of substantial material and place over medium heat.
2) Add the onions; cook and stir until they are transparent.
3) Add all other ingredients *except* sour cream, cover and cook for about 10 minutes.
4) Add sour cream and blend lightly. Continue cooking only until hot through. Do not boil.
5) Serve over fluffy rice or noodles. If the latter are used the dish is more interesting if the noodles are sprinkled liberally with poppy seed.

CUCUMBERS IN SOUR CREAM
(About 4 servings)

Ingredient	Amount	Ingredient	Amount
Cucumbers, tender, firm	1½–2	Pepper	dash
Dill or basil, fresh or dried	1 t. fresh–⅛ t. dried	Sugar	½ t.
Salt	½ t.	Vinegar	2 tb.
		Nutmeg	dash
		Sour cream	½ c.

1) Slice cucumber very thin. Leave the peeling on.
2) Add all ingredients *except* sour cream and mix.
3) Add sour cream and mix lightly. Serve at once.

Sour Cream Sauce for Vegetables
(About 1 cup)

Bacon, crisp and crumbled	3 pieces	Sugar	1 t.
Onion or chives, finely chopped	1 tb.	Salt	¼ t.
Parsley, chopped	1 tb.	Sour cream	1 c.

1) Mix crumbled bacon with other seasonings.
2) Stir lightly into sour cream.
3) Serve over cooked or raw vegetables.

Cocoa

Ingredients	*For 2*	*For 4*	*For 6*
Cocoa	2 tb.	¼ c.	¼ c. + 2 tb.
Sugar	1½ to 2 tb.	3 to 4 tb.	4½ to 6 tb.
Boiling water	⅔ c.	1⅓ c.	2 c.
Milk	1⅓ c.	2⅔ c.	4 c.
Vanilla	½ t.	1 t.	1½ t.

1) Mix the cocoa and sugar together in a saucepan.
2) Add the boiling water all at once and cook to a smooth paste, stirring constantly. Turn the fire low to prevent the cocoa from boiling over.
3) Heat the milk over low heat, then add to cocoa paste, stirring during the addition, until well mixed.
4) Add vanilla. Beat well with a rotary or electric beater. Serve.

Variations in cocoa:

1) "Mexican" cocoa is made like plain cocoa except that a little cinnamon is added to the cocoa and sugar.
2) In "Russian" cocoa, coffee is substituted for the water.
3) Cocoa made with powdered milk. Use 1 c. of water and 5 tb. dried milk to replace the milk and water. Make cocoa paste as in recipe for plain cocoa, using ½ c. water. Add remaining water gradually to powdered milk, stirring constantly to keep the mixture smooth. Add to cocoa paste, heat, and add vanilla. Beat with a rotary beater and serve hot.

Chocolate

Ingredients	*For 2*	*For 4*	*For 6*
Chocolate	1 square	2 squares	3 squares
Sugar	2 tb.	¼ c.	¼ c. + 2 tb.
Milk	2 c.	4 c.	6 c.
Vanilla	½ t.	1 t.	1½ t.

1) Loosen paper around chocolate squares and place (in paper) in a small shallow pan over low heat to *soften*.
2) Scrape the softened chocolate off the paper into sugar and mix.
3) Place milk in utensil over low heat. When hot, add the chocolate and sugar slowly, stirring to blend.
4) Add vanilla, beat, and serve.

Orange-Chocolate Milk Shake

Ingredients	*For 2*	*For 6*	*For 12*
Chocolate sirup	1½ tb.	¼ c. + 1 tb.	½ c.
Orange juice	2 tb.	¼ c. + 2 tb.	¾ c.
Orange rind, grated	1 t.	1 tb.	2 tb.
Milk	1 c.	3 c.	1½ qt.

1) Mix all ingredients and beat or shake thoroughly.
2) Fill glasses half full of chipped ice and pour in the milk mixture.

Banana Milk Shake

Ingredients	*For 2*	*For 6*	*For 12*
Bananas, mashed	1	3	6
Lemon juice	2 t.	2 tb.	¼ c.
Milk	1⅓ c.	4 c.	8 c.
Cinnamon	⅛ t.	½ t.	1 t.
Salt	dash	⅛ t.	¼ t.
Ice cream, vanilla	1 c.	3 c.	6 c.

1) Combine ingredients in an electric mixer or blender, or shake in a jar.
2) Pour into glasses and serve immediately.

Chocolate Malted Milk

Ingredients	*For 2*	*For 6*	*For 12*
Chocolate sirup	½ c.	1½ c.	3 c.
Malted milk	2 tb.	¼ c. + 2 tb.	¾ c.
Milk	1¼ c.	3¾ c.	2 qt.
Cream	⅓ c.	1 c.	1 pt.
Salt	dash	1/16 t.	⅛ t.
Vanilla ice cream	½ pt.	1½ pt.	1½ qt.
Vanilla	3 to 4 drops	8 to 10 drops	⅛ t.

1) Mix all ingredients thoroughly, either by beating or by shaking.
2) Serve at once.

Hot Almond Eggnog

Ingredients	*For 2*	*For 6*	*For 12*
Eggs, separated	2	6	12
Salt	dash	1/8 t.	1/4 t.
Sugar	2 tb.	1/3 c.	2/3 c.
Milk, scalded	2 c.	6 c.	12 c.
Almond extract	1 t.	1 tb.	2 tb.
Vanilla extract	1 t.	1 tb.	2 tb.
Almonds, toasted	1 tb.	1/4 c.	1/2 c.
Nutmeg	dash	1/8 t.	1/4 t.

1) Beat the egg yolks until light; add salt and sugar and blend well.
2) Scald the milk and add to the egg yolks; add flavorings.
3) Beat the egg whites until stiff and fold into the mixture; pour into cups.
4) Chop almonds fine and sprinkle, along with nutmeg, over the top of egg-nog.

[Note: If cold eggnog is preferred, chill the milk and egg yolk mixture before folding in the egg whites.]

Syllabub (Milk Punch)
(Adapted from the English)

Ingredients	*For 2*	*For 6*	*For 12*
Sugar	2 t.	2 tb.	1/4 c.
Cider, cold	1/3 c.	1 c.	2 c.
Lemon juice	1 tb.	3 tb.	1/4 c. + 2 tb.
Lemon rind	2 t.	2 tb.	1/4 c.
Nutmeg	dash	1/4 t.	1/2 t.
Milk, cold	1/2 c.	1 1/2 c.	3 c.
Cream, light, cold	1/4 c.	1/2 c.	1 c.
Egg whites	1	2	4
Sugar	1 tb.	2 tb.	1/4 c.

Additional nutmeg for the top.

1) Mix the first sugar with the cider, lemon juice, lemon rind and nutmeg. Let stand until sugar dissolves.
2) Combine milk and cream.
3) Beat egg whites until stiff and then beat in the other sugar.
4) Add cider mixture to milk and cream and beat with a rotary or electric beater until frothy.

5) Fold in egg whites, pour syllabub into a punch bowl and sprinkle liberally with nutmeg.
[NOTE: The last three steps should be done just before serving.]

CHEESE

The proverb "cheese is the poor man's meat and the gourmet's delight" is illustrated by the selected recipes which follow. The special references for cheese as well as other more general ones will provide many variations of these same recipes.

CHEESE SOUFFLÉ

Ingredients	*For 2*	*For 4*	*For 6*
Butter or margarine	1⅓ tb.	2⅔ tb.	¼ c.
Flour	2 tb.	¼ c.	¼ c. + 2 tb.
Milk	½ c.	1 c.	1½ c.
Salt	⅓ t.	⅔ t.	1 t.
Cayenne	dash	1/16 t.	⅛ t.
Egg yolks	2	4	6
Grated cheese	⅔ c.	1⅓ c.	2 c.
Egg whites	2	4	6
Cream of tartar	¼ t.	½ t.	¾ t.

1) Make a white sauce, using the first 5 ingredients, and stir until thick (see p. 499).
2) Beat the egg yolks, add some of the sauce and mix; stir into the rest of the sauce and continue cooking.
3) Add the grated cheese to the hot mixture and stir until the cheese is melted. Remove from the fire.
4) Beat the egg whites until frothy, add the cream of tartar, and continue beating until they form a peak that bends over slightly when the beater is withdrawn.
5) Fold the egg whites carefully into the cheese sauce.
6) Bake for 15 min. in a moderately slow oven—325° F. (163° C.)—then raise to 375° F. (191° C.) for 20–30 min.
7) *Serve at once.*
[NOTE: A *quick* cheese soufflé may be made by eliminating the white sauce made of the first five ingredients and substituting canned concentrated asparagus soup in the following amounts: for two, ½ c.; for four, 1 c.; for six, 1½ c. The soup should be heated, the beaten egg yolks added, and the mixture cooked for about a minute. The above directions from 3 through 7 should be followed to complete the soufflé.]

Cheese Strata

Ingredients	*For 2*	*For 4*	*For 6*
Bread, buttered	3–4 slices	5–6 slices	7–8 slices
Cheese, grated	½–¾ c.	¾–1 c.	1–1½ c.
Eggs, beaten	2–3	3–4	5–6
Milk	¾–1 c.	1½–2 c.	2½–3 c.
Salt	¼ t.	½ t.	¾ t.
Pepper		to taste	
Other seasoning		as desired	

1) Butter the bread and cut in half or quarter pieces. Select a shallow oven-to-table baking dish of the desired size; oil, and place half the bread flat in the dish.
2) Sprinkle the bread with the cheese and put the rest of the bread on top of the cheese.
3) Mix eggs, milk and seasonings and pour over the bread.
4) Let stand for 30 minutes to one hour.
5) Bake for about 40 min. at 350° F. (177° C.) or until puffed and brown.

Italian Spaghetti
(6 servings)

Onion	⅓ c.	Salt	1 t.
Garlic	1 clove	Pepper	¼ t.
Parsley	3 tb.	Bay leaf	1 large
Celery	⅓ c.	Thyme or basil	¼ t.
Green pepper	3 tb.	Anchovies, minced	8
Olive oil	2 tb.	Spaghetti	1½ 7-oz. boxes
Tomato paste	1 6-oz. can	Butter or margarine	2 tb.
Water	½ c.	Grated cheese	

1) Chop the first 5 ingredients fine; fry lightly in oil.
2) Add water to the tomato paste and add to the above.
3) Add seasonings and simmer until thick.
4) Add the anchovies.
5) Cook the spaghetti in boiling, salted water until *just tender.*
6) Drain and add the butter or margarine.
7) Put the spaghetti into a bowl, pour the sauce over it, and sprinkle generously with grated cheese (Parmesan or Provolone).
8) Serve *immediately*. Serve more grated cheese separately.

French Onion Soup

Ingredients	*For 2*	*For 4*	*For 6*
Onions, sliced	1 c.	2 c.	3 c.
Butter or margarine	2 tb.	1/4 c.	1/3 c.
Consommé, 10 1/2 oz. can	1 can	2 cans	3 cans
Water, hot	1/4 c.	1/2 c.	3/4 c.
Rye bread, toasted	2 pieces	4 pieces	6 pieces
Grated cheese, Parmesan	1/4 c.	1/2 c.	3/4 c.

1) Put onions and butter or margarine in a tightly covered saucepan, place over low heat, and cook until onions are soft.
2) Add consommé and water to onions, and heat.
3) Serve in earthenware bowls; put toast in soup and sprinkle liberally with cheese.

Cheese Soup

Ingredients	*For 2*	*For 4*	*For 6*
Butter or margarine	1 tb.	1 1/2–2 tb.	2–3 tb.
Onion, chopped or thin sliced	1 tb.	2 tb.	1/4 c.
Flour	1 tb.	2 tb.	1/4 c.
Chicken stock	3/4–1 c.	1–1 1/2 c.	1 1/2–2 c.
Milk	3/4–1 c.	1–1 1/2 c.	1 1/2–2 c.
Salt	1/8 t.	1/4 t.	1/2 t.
Paprika		dash	
Pepper		to taste	
Cheese, processed sharp Cheddar	1/2 c.	3/4–1 c.	1–1 1/4 c.
Parsley, chopped	1 tb.	2 tb.	1/4 c.

1) Melt the butter or margarine. Add onion and sauté over *low* heat until onion is limp.
2) Add the flour and mix; add stock, a little at a time at first, continue adding, and cook until slightly thick.
3) Add milk and seasonings and cook for several more minutes.
4) Just before serving add cheese and parsley.

Top-of-Range Potatoes Au Gratin
(About 6 servings)

Potatoes, medium	4 to 6	Water	1/2 c.
Salt	1/2 t.	Cheese, grated	1 c.
Dill, or other seasonings	1/8 t. dry, 2 t. fresh	Milk	1/4 c.

1) Wash potatoes (if new do not pare).
2) Slice *thin* and place in a shallow top-of-the-range utensil of substantial material with a tight-fitting lid.
3) Sprinkle salt and dill over potatoes; add water, cover, and place over low heat for about 15 minutes or until the potatoes are tender. Do not drain.
4) Sprinkle cheese over the top, add milk, and place under broiler for 3–5 minutes.

Open-faced Grilled Frijole-Cheese Sandwich

Ingredients	*For 2*	*For 4*	*For 6*
Bread, firm type	3–4 slices	6–8 slices	9–12 slices
Bean soup, concentrated, 10-oz. can	½ can	1 can	1½ cans
Cheese, Cheddar, grated	½ c.	1 c.	1½ c.
Cheese, cottage	2 tb.	¼ c.	⅓ c.
Salt	⅛ t.	¼ t.	½ t.

1) Toast bread on both sides.
2) Spread thickly with bean soup just as it comes from the can.
3) Mix the two cheeses and the salt and spread on top of the bean mixture.
4) Place the open face sandwiches under the broiler until the cheese is bubbly and slightly brown.

Quiche Lorraine
(About 6 servings)

Pastry, plain	for an 8 to 9 in. pie	Onion, finely chopped	1 tb.
Eggs	3–4	Salt	½ t.
Milk	2 c.	Pepper	⅛ t.
Cheese, grated	1 c.	Nutmeg, grated	dash
Bacon, crisp	6–8 pieces		

1) Make pastry according to recipe on p. 626.
2) Line a glass or earthen pie pan with pastry.
3) Beat eggs *lightly* and add all other ingredients but the bacon.
4) Pour mixture into pastry shell, bake 10 minutes at 450° F. (232° C.) then reduce heat to 350° F. (177° C.) and bake for about 20 minutes or until set. Test as for baked custard on p. 527.
5) Put crisp bacon on top either in whole slices or crumbled.

Cheese Sandies
(Makes 30 1-in. balls)

Butter or margarine, room temperature	¼ c. (½ stick)
Cheese, sharp Cheddar, grated	1 c. (packed)
Salt	¼ t.
Dry mustard	¼ t.
Flour	1 c.
Water	1 tb.
Egg white	1 tb.
Poppy seed	2–3 t.
Sesame seed	2–3 t.

1) Mix the butter or margarine with the cheese; add salt, mustard, flour, and water and combine thoroughly. It will be necessary to knead the flour in with the hands.
2) Make a test sandie by rolling a ball the size of a small walnut and baking for about 15 minutes at 350° F. (177° C.) or until lightly brown. If the sandie spreads, a little more flour should be added; if it cracks or splits, a few drops of water should be added.
3) After the sandies are rolled into balls, dip the top of each ball into unbeaten egg white and then into either the poppy or sesame seed. If half of the sandies are topped with poppy seed and the other half with sesame seed it makes an attractive assortment.

Cheese Puff Canapés
(About 1½ doz. canapés)

Bread, ¾ in. thick	6 slices
Egg white	1
Cheese, American grated	¾–1¼ c.
Baking powder	⅛ t.
Salt	⅛ t.
Mustard, dry	¼ t.

1) Cut bread in round, square, or rectangular shapes and toast on both sides.
2) Beat egg white until stiff but not dry.
3) Mix the baking powder, salt, and mustard with the cheese and add to the beaten egg white.
4) Spread the mixture thickly on the toast, being careful to cover the bread so the edges will not burn.
5) Place under broiler 2–3 minutes or until cheese melts.

Cheese Puff Openface Sandwiches

1) Make as for cheese puff canapés above except leave the bread in whole slices.
2) This variety of cheese sandwich makes a welcome change from the usual grilled type.

Cheese Shortcake

1) Make the same as for quick cheese rolls below except double the amount of cheese and cut it into the dry ingredients along with the fat.
2) Roll out dough and cut in rounds or squares; place on baking sheet and bake the same as cheese rolls.
3) Use as shortcake biscuit for any creamed chicken, fish, or egg dish.

Cottage Cheese-Tuna Spread
(About 1½ cups of spread)

Cottage cheese	1 c.	Celery, pascal, finely chopped	¼–½ c.
Tuna fish, 6½ oz. can	1 can	Eggs, hard-cooked, chopped	2
Onion, chopped fine	1 tb.	Salt	to taste
Pimiento, chopped	1–2 tb.		

1) Blend the cheese and tuna fish with a fork until the cottage cheese is scarcely identifiable.
2) Add other ingredients and mix.
3) Use as a sandwich filling; a salad—plain or in combination with sliced tomatoes, cucumbers, etc.; or a cocktail spread.

Quick Cheese Rolls

Ingredients	*For 2*	*For 4*	*For 6*
Flour	½ c.	1 c.	1½ c.
Baking powder	½ t.	1 t.	1½ t.
Salt	¼ t.	⅜ t.	½ t.
Fat	1⅓ tb.	2⅔ tb.	¼ c.
Milk	¼ c.	½ c.	¾ c.
Melted butter or margarine	¾ tb.	1½ tb.	2¼ tb.
Grated cheese	¼ c.	½ c.	¾ c.
Salt and paprika	to sprinkle over dough		

1) Sift and measure the flour. Add baking powder and salt and sift into a mixing bowl.
2) Cut the fat into the dry ingredients.
3) Add the milk and stir to make a dough. Knead on a lightly floured breadboard; then roll into a rectangular sheet ⅛ inch thick.
4) Brush the rolled dough with the melted butter or margarine, spread the grated cheese evenly over the dough, and sprinkle with salt and paprika.
5) Form the dough into a firm roll; cut into ¾-inch slices.
6) Place the slices in oiled muffin pans and bake for 15 to 20 min. in a hot oven—425° F. (218° C.).

Cottage Cheese Stollen
(A quick sweet bread)

Eggs	2	Butter or margarine	½ c.
Sugar	¾ c.	Flour, all purpose	4 c.
Rum flavoring	2 tb.	Baking powder	4 t.
Milk	¼ c.	Salt	½ t.
Lemon rind, grated	½ lemon	Raisins, seedless	2 c.
Cottage cheese, creamed type	1 c. (an 8 oz. pkg.)	* Almonds, blanched and chopped	½ c.

1) Beat the eggs and add sugar, flavoring, milk, and lemon rind.
2) In a separate bowl, cream the butter or margarine with the cottage cheese, blending thoroughly.
3) Sift together flour, baking powder, and salt; add raisins and almonds to the flour mixture.
4) Make into a soft dough by adding the flour mixture and the cottage cheese mixture alternately to the egg and sugar mixture.
5) Place the dough on an oiled baking sheet, and with the hands or a wooden spoon, shape into a long oval loaf, being careful to have the loaf of uniform thickness to assure even baking. The dough may also be patted into glass pie pans to make a round stollen.
6) Bake in a moderate oven—350° F. (177° C.) 1 to 1¼ hours.
7) While the stollen is still warm, it may be glazed with a mixture of 1½ cups of confectioners' sugar, 2 tablespoons of melted butter, 1 tablespoon milk, and ¼ teaspoon of almond extract.
8) Garnish with chopped cherries or nuts on top of the glaze.
   [Note: This bread improves after standing a day or two. In addition to being an excellent breakfast or luncheon bread, either plain or toasted, it may be sliced very thin and used for tea sandwiches.]

Cheese Cake
(6 to 8 servings)

Zweiback, rusks, or Melba toast	1 c.	Salt	⅓ t.
Butter or margarine	2 tb.	Lemon rind	⅓ t.
Sugar	2 tb.	Lemon juice	1 tb.
Eggs, med.	3	Cream	¾ c.
Sugar	1 c.	Cottage cheese	1½ c.
		Flour	1⅓ tb.

1) Roll the zweiback, rusks, or toast into crumbs.
2) Cream the butter or margarine with the sugar and mix well with the crumbs.

* Unparched, skinned peanuts may be substituted.

3) Line a 9-in. pie pan, pressing down well.
4) Beat the eggs until frothy, add the sugar gradually, and beat well.
5) Add the salt and lemon and stir to blend.
6) Add the cream, then cheese and flour, and stir well.
7) Pour the mixture into the crust and bake for about 1 hour in a slow oven —300°–325° F. (149°–163° C.).
8) Turn off the heat, open the oven door, and allow the cake to cool in the oven.
9) Serve cold with jelly—guava suggested.

Cheese Cake Pudding
(8 to 10 servings)

Gelatin, plain	1½ tb.	Cottage cheese, creamed type	2 c.
Water, cold	½ c.	Sour cream, cultured	½ c.
Sugar	½ c.	Egg whites	2
Milk	½ c.	Sugar	¼ c.
Egg yolks, beaten	2	Maraschino cherries, sliced	⅓ c.
Vanilla	1 t.		

1) Soak gelatin in cold water.
2) Put the ½ cup sugar, milk, and beaten egg yolks into a saucepan and cook over low heat to make a soft custard.
3) Add soaked gelatin to the hot custard and place in the refrigerator to cool slightly. Add the vanilla.
4) Place the cottage cheese and sour cream in a bowl and mix thoroughly.
5) Beat egg whites until stiff and add the ¼ cup sugar gradually.
6) Combine the three mixtures, stirring the custard into the cottage cheese and sour cream, and then folding in the beaten egg whites.
7) Rinse a mold or a glass loaf pan with cold water and place sliced maraschino cherries over the bottom of the mold; pour the mixture carefully into the mold.
8) Chill for 2 or 3 hours or until congealed.
9) Turn pudding out on a serving dish, slice, and serve plain or with whipped cream.

Coeur à la Crème
(Number of servings depends on use)

Cottage cheese	½ lb.	Sugar, confectioners'	1 tb.
Cream cheese, room temperature	¼ lb.	Salt	⅛ t.

1) Put cottage cheese into a blender and turn on and off 2 or 3 times only. Too much blending will liquify the cheese. In the absence of a blender put the cottage cheese through a food mill.

2) Mix the cream cheese, sugar, and salt with the cottage cheese.
3) Pack in a perforated mold or strainer lined with damp cheese cloth and let stand in the refrigerator for 2 or 3 hours.
4) Turn out onto serving dish and serve with strawberry jam or fresh strawberries. The crème may be used as a spread, accompaniment for waffles or pancakes, or as a dessert.
   [NOTE: The French fashion for serving this crème is to mold it in a special heart-shaped basket.]

CHEESE BOARD

A variety of cheeses served on a tray, an ordinary cheese board, or a regular kitchen board has many possibilities. It may be served at an open house as the principal refreshment, at a buffet meal as one of the substantial protein dishes, as a dessert, etc. Bread sticks, crackers of various types, corn chips, dark breads, and assorted fruits are some of the interesting accompaniments to serve with cheese. When cheese is to be a featured menu item or used for social refreshments, the varieties and flavors should be chosen wisely. Natural cheeses that are aged, dry and crumbly or creamy, are the best choices. Processed cheeses should be reserved for cooking. Whatever the choice of cheese, it should be served at room temperature. If served cold, the flavor cannot be savored.

The presentation is more dramatic if the cheeses are placed on the board in their natural state. This might be a whole small cheese, a sizeable wedge of a larger one (rinds left on) and unwrapped individual portions of others.

If fruit accompanies cheese, it is more appealing if served *au naturel*. Pineapples, melons, etc., naturally need to be pre-cut. In the case of apples and pears, serving will be facilitated if small auxiliary boards and knives are placed near the cheese and fruit arrangements.

NUTS

Perhaps the most popular ways of using nuts are to serve them toasted and salted or to include them as an ingredient in cookies, cakes, and candies. Because they are high in food value they should be considered as part of a meal rather than as an accessory. Nuts are palatable and most are expensive. Their popularity can be capitalized on by including them in dishes other than desserts. The recipes which follow are predominantly peanut because they are generally available and are a wise buy from the standpoint of nutrition and cost. Even though most recipes using nuts will specify a special one, it is possible to interchange one for another.

Convenient utensils. Chopping nuts can be a laborious and wasteful process unless special devices are used. These include regular nut choppers (glass jars with a wooden block in the bottom and a cover with chopping blades on a cylindrical spring), small wooden bowls for confining the nuts while using a chopper or food grinder, coarse graters, and electric blenders. If a blender is used, use caution to avoid pulverizing the nuts.

Scissors are convenient for cutting dried fruits such as peaches and apricots.

Coconut Fruit Bread
(12–20 servings depending on use)

Coconut, flaked	1 c. not packed	Baking powder	3 t.
Cranberries,* raw, chopped	1 c.	Soda	1/4 t.
Peaches or apricots, dried (uncooked) sliced thin	1 c.	Sugar	2/3 c.
Flour	3 c.	Salt	3/4 t.
		Egg	1
		Buttermilk	3/4 c.
		Orange juice	3/4 c.
		Oil, cooking	1/4 c.

1) Mix the coconut and fruit.
2) Sift in the dry ingredients and mix thoroughly.
3) Beat the egg and add the other liquid ingredients.
4) Combine the two mixtures until well blended but do not over-stir.
5) Pour into an oiled 6- or 8-in. square pan and bake for about 35 minutes at 325° F. (163° C.).
6) May be served warm, cut in squares, or *chilled* and sliced thin for small sandwiches.

[Note: This bread is excellent for freezing.]

Pecan and Apricot Bread
(About 16 slices)

Dried apricots	1 c.	Egg, beaten	1
Soda	1/2 t.	General utility flour	1 1/2 c.
Boiling water	1 c.	Salt	1/2 t.
Butter or margarine	2 tb.	Baking powder	2 1/4 t.
Sugar	1/2 c.	Pecans, chopped	1/2 c.

1) Wash the apricots and dry on absorbent paper or a clean towel.
2) Chop the apricots and sprinkle soda over them.
3) Pour boiling water over the apricots and cool.
4) Cream the fat, add the sugar and beaten egg.
5) Add the soaked apricots (including the water).
6) Sift the flour, measure, add salt and baking powder, and sift into a mixing bowl.

* Chopped, well-drained maraschino cherries may be substituted.

7) Add the nuts to the dry ingredients.
8) Add the liquid mixture to the dry ingredients.
9) Pour into an oiled loaf pan and bake for about 1¼ hours in a moderately slow oven—325° F. (163° C.).

Peanut Butter Bacon Muffins
(About 12 muffins)

Flour	1 c.	Bacon, crisp crumbled	⅓ c.
Corn meal, yellow	½ c.	Egg	1
Baking powder	1 tb.	Milk	1 c.
Sugar	1 tb.	Peanut butter	⅓ c.
Oil, cooking	2 tb.		

1) Sift dry ingredients and add bacon.
2) Beat the egg and add the milk, peanut butter, and oil.
3) Combine the two mixtures, stirring only enough to blend.
4) Put mixture in well-oiled muffin tins and bake for 20 to 25 min. at 370° F. (191° C.).

Nut Brittle Coffee Cake
(About 6 servings)

Butter or margarine	2–3 tb.
Nut brittle, peanut or other, crushed	½–¾ c.
Coffee cake	(See recipe p. 621.)

1) Select an appropriate baking dish or pan and melt the butter or margarine in it by placing in the heated oven.
2) Sprinkle the nut brittle over the bottom of the pan.
3) Make coffee cake according to recipe and pour the mixture over the brittle.
4) Bake for about 30 min. at 375° F. (191° C.).

Peanut Loaf

Ingredients	*For 4*	*For 6*	*For 8*
Bread crumbs, soft	1 c.	1½ c.	2 c.
Milk	½ c.	¾ c.	1 c.
Peanuts, chopped	¾ c.	1⅛ c.	1½ c.
Celery, chopped	½ c.	¾ c.	1 c.
Eggs, beaten	1	1 lg.	2
Salt	½ t.	¾ t.	1 t.
Mace	¼ t.	⅓ t.	½ t.

1) Soak the bread crumbs in the milk for about 15 min.
2) Add the other ingredients.

3) Pour the mixture into an oiled loaf pan.
4) Set the loaf pan into a pan of water.
5) Bake for about 40 min. in a moderate oven—350° F. (177° C.).
6) Serve with tomato or mushroom sauce. (See pp. 501 and 502.)

Carrot Nut Pudding
(6 to 8 servings)

Ingredient	Amount	Ingredient	Amount
Butter or margarine, room temperature	¼ lb.	Milk or water	¼ c.
Brown sugar	½ c.	Flour	1½ c.
Carrots, raw, grated	1 c.	Baking powder	1 t.
Raisins, seedless	1 c.	Soda	½ t.
Nuts, any kind, chopped	½ c.	Salt	½ t.
Egg, beaten	1	Nutmeg	½ t.
		Cinnamon	½ t.

1) Mix softened butter and sugar.
2) Add carrots, raisins, nuts, egg, and milk; mix thoroughly.
3) Sift in dry ingredients and blend.
4) Put in a buttered oven-to-table baking dish and bake uncovered for about 45 minutes at 375° F. (191° C.).
5) Serve with a tart fruit sauce.

Molasses Pecan Pie
(One 9-inch pie)

Ingredient	Amount	Ingredient	Amount
Eggs	3	Pecans	1 c.
Molasses	¾ c.	Lemon juice	1 t.
Sugar	½ to ¾ c.	Butter or margarine, melted	2 tb.

1) Beat the eggs.
2) Add molasses and sugar. Mix well.
3) Add other ingredients.
4) Pour into an uncooked pastry shell. (See pp. 626–627.)
5) Bake 45 min. in a slow oven—300° to 325° F. (149° to 163° C.) and then 10 min. in a hot oven—425° F. (218° C.).

Nut Brittle Whip
(About 6 servings)

Ingredient	Amount	Ingredient	Amount
Egg whites	2	Coffee, instant powder	1 t.
Heavy cream, whipped	1 c.	Nut brittle, peanut or other, crushed	½–1 c.

1) Beat egg whites until stiff.
2) Add nut brittle and coffee powder and continue beating until well mixed.
3) Fold in the whipped cream; chill for about 30 minutes before serving.

Peanut Butter Confections

(About 2½ doz.)

Egg, small	1	Orange juice	2 tb.
Peanut butter, crunch type	½ c.	Orange or lemon rind, grated	1 tb.
Sugar	⅓ c.	Milk, powdered	1½ c.
Baking powder	1½ t.		

1) Beat the egg and stir in all ingredients except the last two.
2) Sift milk and baking powder into the mixture and stir well.
3) Drop by teaspoon on an oiled baking sheet and bake for about 15 minutes at 325° F. (163° C.).
4) Serve as a "cookie" with milk or a fruit dessert.
   [Note: Bake one test confection first to see if the mixture is the right consistency, since the moisture content of the peanut butter varies. If the confection flattens, a little more milk powder should be added. If the confection seems dry, add another teaspoon of orange juice.]

Nut Pilaf

(About 6 servings)

Rice, cooked	2 c.	Dates, chopped	½ c.
Cream, light	¾ c.	Orange rind, grated	2 tb.
Almonds or pistachio nuts, chopped	½ c.	Sugar	2 tb.

1) Mix all ingredients and place in a shallow baking dish.
2) Place in pan of hot water and bake for about 30 min. at 350° (177° C.).
3) Serve hot or cold as a dessert *or* serve with meat.

Mushroom-Peanut Sauce

Shelled peanuts	½ c.	Butter or margarine	2 tb.
Canned mushrooms	4-oz. can	Flour	2 tb.
Milk	about ⅔ c.	Salt	¼ t.
White pepper	dash		

1) Remove the brown covering from the peanuts and brown them in the oven or broiler.
2) Drain the mushrooms, and measure the juice in a 1-c. measure.
3) Fill the cup with milk.
4) Melt the butter or margarine, add the flour and seasonings, and stir to blend.
5) Add the liquid and cook until the sauce is thickened.

6) Add the mushrooms and browned peanuts.
7) Serve with asparagus or broccoli.

Nut and Fruit Sauce
(About 1 c.)

Cornstarch	1 t.	Fruit juice, left-over canned	1 c.
Nutmeg	dash	Nuts, chopped	¼ c.
Ginger	dash		

Vanilla or other flavoring . . ½ t.

1) Put cornstarch and spices in a small pan of substantial material.
2) Add the fruit juice, a little at a time at first, and mix.
3) Cook over low heat until slightly thick, stirring occasionally.
4) Add nuts and flavoring.
5) Use as a dessert sauce for puddings, ice cream, cake, etc. or for breakfast waffles or pancakes.

Nut Spreads

Chopped nuts add variety and interest to any number of sandwich and cocktail spreads. A few combinations are:

1) *Nut-butter.* Finely chopped nuts are creamed into softened, flavored butter. The flavor may be spices, grated citrus rind, or minced fresh herbs such as mint. If a sweet spread is desired, sugar may be added.
2) *Nut-cheese.* The creamy cheeses such as cottage and cream are best suited to combining with chopped nuts. The two may be used alone or combined with other chopped ingredients such as olives, pimiento, green pepper, preserved fruits, etc.
3) *Nut-dried fruits.* Any chopped dried fruit combines with nuts and softened butter to make delicious spreads. Sugar may be added for a sweeter spread.

EGGS

Preplanning for the laboratory might result in demonstrations (by instructor, students, or both) illustrating certain principles that apply to egg cookery. Some points that might be included are:

1) The effect of low vs. high temperature on appearance and tenderness of the finished product.
2) Methods of cooking that result in scrambled, poached, and/or fried eggs that are not over-cooked and are, therefore, attractive as served.

The preparation of selected products may be examples of the use of eggs in cookery:

1) As leavening material—omelets, soufflés, a sponge-type cake.
2) For thickening—custards, puddings, etc., introducing recipes not previously used in the laboratory when milk is the product emphasized.

3) As stabilizers in emulsions—mayonnaise or a hot emulsion used as a sauce.
4) For color—to vary a sauce, as a garnish, etc.
5) As a mixer (or binder)—in a main-dish loaf; both in croquettes and for dipping croquettes before frying or baking.

Some utensils that are useful in egg cookery. Special utensils are not necessary for the preparation of eggs, but a few are handy. These include an egg steamer (poacher), electric egg cooker, timer, slicer for hard-cooked eggs, and wire whisk. A rotary beater saves time and both range-to-table and oven-to-table utensils save both time and effort.

New standards for grading eggs.

A new "controlled quality" egg grading program has been authorized by the United States Department of Agriculture and became effective in September, 1959. The new grade shield is used on packages of these eggs (see p. 116). In addition, both grade and egg size are stamped on the carton. Requirements for eggs of AA grade bearing this label are:

1) Eggs must be gathered two or three times a day.
2) They must be cooled at once and held throughout the marketing channel at not more than sixty degrees Fahrenheit and a relative humidity of about seventy per cent.
3) Any necessary cleaning must be by approved sanitary methods.
4) Eggs from each flock must be packaged separately and marked as to flock identity. Birds in a flock do not vary in age more than sixty days.
5) To be eligible, a sample of twenty-five eggs must average not less than seventy-three Haugh units in two consecutive weeks and no egg may measure less than fifty-five units. There may be no serious yolk defect.
6) To stay in the program, the flock must maintain an average of seventy-two Haugh units and no weekly average of less than sixty-eight. Not more than one egg in ten may measure less than fifty-five Haugh units.
7) Government graders sample and test eggs each week.
8) Loss eggs may not be included in labeled packages.
9) If not sold within ten days, eggs must be put into different cartons or the grade mark must be obliterated.
10) Government graders are responsible for sampling, testing, and keeping records.

Eggs of Grade A quality may have a lower Haugh unit average and a "flock" includes all birds on the same farm. The new program does not interfere with the grading program which has been in effect for at least thirty years.

Breakfast Eggs

Cooked in the shell. Unless eggs are at room temperature the shells are likely to crack when they are put into hot water and the white will then ooze out. However, if the water is salted, the white will remain in the shell if the egg cracks. If water is kept below boiling, the egg will be tender and, unless it has been stored for some time, the edge of the yolk will not be green in color. Timing determines the degree of cooking—3 min. for soft-cooked eggs and up to 15 min. for hard-cooked eggs. For the person who "forgets," if the egg is hard-cooked, there is a simple test: the hard-cooked egg will spin rapidly on a wood surface if given a brisk turn.

Poached and steamed. For poaching, eggs are broken into a small container and slipped into boiling, salted water in a suitable utensil. The heat is lowered, the eggs are cooked to the desired stage, and removed with perforated spoon or flat wire whip. If the eggs are not fresh, addition of about 1 t. vinegar per pt. of water will hasten coagulation of the white.

In an egg steamer, the eggs are put into the oiled cups of the steamer, set over hot water and covered. Water should be below boiling; time is dependent upon personal taste.

Broiled. Heat about 1 tb. of fat in a flameproof baking dish, break eggs into the dish, and cook over moderate heat until the white begins to coagulate. Put the dish into a broiler, about 2 in. below the source of heat, and broil 2 to 4 min.

Fried. Heat a small amount of fat in a frying pan, break eggs into the pan, cover, and cook over moderate heat until the white is firm and coagulated over the yolk. (Time is dependent upon personal taste).

Scrambled Eggs

Ingredients	*For 2*	*For 4*	*For 6*
Eggs	2 to 4	4 to 8	6 to 12
Milk, water, or cream		1 tb. per egg	
Salt	dash to 1/8 t.	1/3 t.	1/2 t.
Pepper	dash	about 1/8 t.	about 1/4 t.
Fat	1/2 to 1 tb.	1 to 2 tb.	1 1/2 to 3 tb.

1) Beat the eggs slightly, add liquid and seasonings, and mix.
2) Melt the fat in a frying pan, add the eggs, and stir over low heat until the mixture is thick but not dry.
3) Turn onto a serving dish at once.

French Omelet

Ingredients	*For 2*	*For 4*	*For 6*
Eggs	3	6	9
Cream of tartar	1/16 t.	1/8 t.	3/16 t.
Water	3 tb.	1/4 c.	1/3 c.
Salt	1/8 t.	1/4 t.	3/8 t.
Pepper	dash	dash	dash
Fat	2 tb.	3 tb.	3 tb.

[Note: A pinch of basil or sweet marjoram may be added.]

1) Beat the eggs to a froth; add the cream of tartar and beat to mix well.
2) Add the water and seasonings and beat again.
3) Melt the fat in a frying pan and add the eggs.
4) With a fork or spatula, raise the cooked part to let the uncooked part run underneath.
5) When slightly set, allow it to brown *very slightly*.
6) Loosen the edge of half the omelet and fold over the other half.
7) Turn the omelet onto a platter, garnish, and serve at once.
   [NOTE: See cookbooks for variations.]

CURRIED EGGS

Ingredients	*For 2*	*For 4*	*For 6*
Butter or margarine	2 t.	1⅓ tb.	2 tb.
Flour	2 t.	1⅓ tb.	2 tb.
Salt	Dash	⅛ t.	¼ t.
Pepper	Dash	Dash	⅛ t.
Curry powder	½–1 t.	1–2 t.	1½ t.–1 tb.
Chicken stock	¼ c.	½ c.	¾ c.
Cream	2 tb.	¼ c.	¼ c. + 2 tb.
Hard-cooked eggs	2 to 4	4 to 8	6 to 12

1) Using white sauce directions (see p. 499) make a sauce with first 6 ingredients.
2) Add the cream and the eggs, cut in half.
3) Serve with rice.

EGGS BORGHESE
(Adapted from an Italian recipe)

Ingredients	*For 2*	*For 4*	*For 6*
Fat	1 tb.	2 tb.	3 tb.
Onion, sliced thin	½ sm.	1 sm.	1 med.
Flour	1 t.	2 t.	1 tb.
Salt	¼ t.	½ t.	¾ t.
Pepper	dash	⅛ t.	¼ t.
Nutmeg	dash	⅛ t.	¼ t.
Milk	¾ c.	1½ c.	2¼ c.
Hard-cooked eggs	2–3	4–6	6–9

1) Melt the fat in a flame-proof dish or frying pan.
2) Add the onions and cook to brown slightly.
3) Add the flour and seasonings and blend.
4) Add the milk slowly, stirring until the sauce is slightly thick.
5) Cover and simmer 5 to 10 min.

6) Add the eggs, quartered, cover, and simmer to heat through—about 2 min.
7) May be served with one of the alimentary pastes.

Eggs à la Benedict
(4 servings)

English muffins	2	Fat	about 1 tb.
OR		Poached eggs	4
Bread	4 sl.	Hollandaise sauce *	about ½ c.
Boiled ham (¼-in. slices)	4		
Cream	about 2 tb.		

1) Cut the muffins in half and toast them (or toast the bread).
2) Cut circular slices from the ham and sauté them in the fat.
3) Arrange the muffins or bread on a serving dish, put a slice of ham on each, and a poached egg on each slice of ham.
4) Pour the sauce, thinned with cream, around the whole.

"Florentine" Eggs
(4 servings)

Spinach	1 lb.	Toast	4 sl.
Butter or margarine	1 tb.	Poached eggs	4
Salt	⅛ t.	Grated cheese	2–4 tb.
Pepper	dash	Anchovy paste	(optional)

1) Boil, drain, and chop the spinach.
2) Add the butter or margarine and seasonings and cook to season spinach thoroughly, stirring occasionally (about 3 min.).
3) Arrange toast on a serving dish, cover each slice with spinach, and put poached eggs on the spinach. Sprinkle with grated cheese.
4) Bake about 5 min. at 350° F. (177° C.).
5) If desired, garnish with anchovy paste just before serving.

Puffy Omelet

Ingredients	*For 2*	*For 4*	*For 6*
Eggs	2	4	6
Cream of tartar	⅛ t.	¼ t.	⅜ t.
Water or milk	2 tb.	3 tb.	¼ c.
Salt	1/16 t.	⅛ t.	3/16 t.
Pepper	dash	dash	dash

1) Separate the whites and yolks of the eggs.
2) Beat the whites until frothy; add cream of tartar and beat until they form a peak when the beater is lifted.

* Mock Hollandaise sauce may be substituted. (See p. 501.)

3) Beat the egg yolks until thick; add milk or water, salt, and pepper. Beat to mix well.
4) Fold the beaten whites into the yolk mixture.
5) Pour the omelet into a hot, oiled, heavy frying pan. Lower the flame and cook 5 to 8 min. It is a good idea to put an asbestos mat under the frying pan when the flame is lowered.
6) Dry the top of the omelet in a moderate oven—350° F. (177° C.) about 5 min. Crease through the center of the omelet, fold carefully, and serve at once.

Variations of Puffy Omelet

1) Add 2 t. of finely chopped chives, sautéed in butter, and 2 tb. of chopped, cooked chicken livers, also sautéed, to the beaten egg yolk. Garnish with parsley.
2) Add 2 tb. of chopped mushrooms, sautéed in butter, to the beaten egg yolk.
3) Add 2 tb. of finely diced ham and about an equal quantity of fresh peas, which have been cooked with ham, to the beaten egg yolk.
4) Spread other ingredients—such as ¼ c. jam, jelly, or tomato sauce—over one-half of the omelet before it is folded.

Chocolate Soufflé
(6 servings)

Butter or margarine	¼ c.	Egg yolks	3
Chocolate	2 sq.	Sugar, fine granulated	½ c.
Flour	¼ c.	Cinnamon	¼ t.
Salt	¼ t.	Orange flavoring	1 t.
Milk	1 c.	Egg whites	3
Cream of tartar	⅛ t.		

1) Melt the butter or margarine and chocolate over *low heat* in a saucepan of rather heavy material.
2) Add the flour and salt and blend.
3) Add the milk slowly, stirring constantly.
4) Beat the egg yolks, add sugar gradually, add seasonings, and beat until light.
5) Add the sauce and stir to blend.
6) Beat the egg whites until foamy, add the cream of tartar and beat until they form a peak when the beater is lifted, and fold them carefully into the sauce.
7) Pour into a buttered casserole (about 1½ qt.) and set the casserole into a pan. Add hot water to about an inch in depth.

8) Bake 50 to 60 min. at 325° F. (163° C.).
9) Serve at once with a selected sauce.

Crème Caramel

Follow directions for Spanish Flan, p. 527 but put the caramel and custard into individual ramekins.

Orange "Custard"

(About 6 servings)

Orange juice	1½ c.	Eggs	5
Grated orange rind	1 tb.	Sugar	1 c.
Grated lemon rind	1 t.	Orange sections	1 c.

1) Add the rind to the orange juice, cover, and let stand about 15 min. Strain.
2) Beat the eggs, add the sugar gradually, and continue to beat until well mixed but not frothy.
3) Add the orange juice slowly, beating during the addition.
4) Pour into buttered custard cups *or* a suitable baking dish, and set the container into a pan of hot water.
5) Bake 30 to 45 min. at 325° F. (163° C.) or until the custard is set.
6) Chill, garnish with orange sections (Mandarin suggested).

Cornstarch Pudding

Ingredients	*For 2*	*For 4*	*For 6*
Sugar	3 tb.	¼ c. + 2 tb.	½ c. + 1 tb.
Cornstarch	2 tb.	¼ c.	¼ c. + 2 tb.
Salt	⅛ t.	¼ t.	⅜ t.
Egg yolks	1	2	3
Milk	1 c.	2 c.	3 c.
Vanilla	½ t.	1 t.	1½ t.

1) Measure the sugar, cornstarch, and salt into a rather heavy saucepan and stir to mix them well.
2) In a small mixing bowl, beat the egg yolks; add about ¼ of the milk and stir.
3) Add the remaining milk to the dry ingredients and stir to blend.
4) Add the egg mixture to the mixture in the saucepan and cook over low heat, stirring slowly until thickening starts. Then turn heat to "simmer" and continue cooking, stirring rapidly, until the pudding is desirably thick.
5) Add vanilla, beat well, and pour into selected dish to cool.

Fish Loaf
(About 4 servings)

Flaked fish	2 c.	Eggs, beaten slightly	2
Lemon juice	1 t.	Half-and-half	½ c.
Dry mustard	½ t.	Dry bread crumbs	1 c.
Salt and pepper	to taste	Butter or margarine	2 tb.

1) Combine all ingredients except butter or margarine in a mixing bowl.
2) Place in an oiled loaf pan and dot with butter or margarine.
3) Bake about 30 min. (until brown) at 350° F. (177° C.).

Fish Croquettes
(About 4 servings)

Fish loaf mixture	(above)	Egg, beaten	1
Flour	¼ c.	Dry crumbs	⅓ c.

1) Using the loaf mixture, shape croquettes.
2) Roll them in flour, beaten egg, and crumbs.
3) Bake about 15 min. (until brown) at 350° F. (177° C.) or fry in about ½ inch of hot fat until brown, turning to brown all sides. Drain on absorbent paper.

Sponge-type Cakes

Recipes are on pp. 611–613.

MEAT

The main dish to many people means only one thing—meat (red meat)—yet little imagination is used in the preparation of this important dish. In addition to steaks, chops, and hamburger, there are unlimited ways of presenting meat in the meal. Once a homemaker accepts the challenge of breaking away from the standard methods of serving meat, she will discover that the main meat dish can add variety and sheer delight to her family's meals.

The recipes and directions that follow are a mere sampling of what may be found in books, bulletins, etc. The instructor and students may wish to select other recipes to supplement the following.

Utensils. Appliances and utensils that are necessary or convenient for use in meat cookery are numerous. Electric appliances include frying pan, casserole, rôtisserie, and deep-fat fryer. For oven cooking, a shallow roasting pan with rack, one or two broilers not included with the range (used for roasting), covered oven-to-table utensils of suitable sizes, loaf pans, and a meat thermometer are necessary or convenient.

The broilers mentioned are equally useful for broiling. Heavy frying pans are essential and a deep-fat frying pan is very convenient. Kettles and sauce pans of heavy material and/or range-to-table utensils should be provided with covers that fit closely.

Small utensils include knives, a heavy fork, tongs, a cutting board, and wooden spoons.

Roast

1) Choose a cut of suitable size from rib or loin of the selected animal source.
2) Insert a meat thermometer to about the center of the thickest muscle. Avoid touching bone (see p. 147). If a thermometer is not used, see Table 38a for approximate time per lb.
3) Place the meat on the rack of a shallow roasting pan, without cover, and cook in preheated oven (see Table 38a).
4) Transfer the roast to a serving dish and remove the thermometer.

[Note: Salt and pepper may be sprinkled on meat either before or after roasting.]

Roast Beef with Yorkshire Pudding

(English; traditionally associated with the Feast of St. George, April 23rd.)

Choose a roast of beef and cook as directed above.

Yorkshire Pudding

(About 6 servings)
(Adapted)

Flour, sifted	1 c.	Egg	1
Salt	¼ t.	Milk	1 c.

1) Sift the flour and salt into a mixing bowl.
2) Beat the egg, add the milk, and beat again.
3) Add half the liquid to the dry ingredients; stir and beat *thoroughly* to form a very smooth batter. Add remaining liquid and beat.
4) Cover and let stand ½ to 1 hr.
5) Put a thin layer of meat drippings into a 9 x 9-inch pan or into 12 muffin pans. Be sure that all the surface is well coated.
6) Heat the oven to 450° F. (232° C.) and heat the pan or pans.
7) Pour batter about ½ inch thick into the hot pans and bake for about 30 min., or until puffed and brown.

Horseradish Sauce

(Serve with Roast Beef and Yorkshire Pudding)

Thick sour cream	½ c.	Salt	¼ t.
Horseradish *	2 tb.	Paprika	dash
		Lemon juice	½ t.

Mix all ingredients just before serving.

* Fresh grated horseradish is best: if prepared horseradish is used, drain well before measuring.

TABLE 38a. TESTS FOR STAGE OF COOKERY FOR ROASTS

	Beef		*Veal (Leg)*		*Lamb (Leg)*		*Pork (Fresh)*	
	Internal Temperature	*Approximate min. per lb.*	*Internal Temperature*	*Approximate min. per lb.*	*Internal Temperature*	*Approximate min. per lb.*	*Internal Temperature*	*Approximate min. per lb.*
Rare	140° F. (60° C.)	18–32 *	....	.....	....	.....	....	.....
Medium	160° F. (71° C.)	22–38 *	....	.....	....	.....	....	.....
Well-done	170° F. (77° C.)	27–48 *	170° F. (77° C.)	25–30	175° F. (79° C.)	30–35	185° F. (85° C.)	35–45

*Longer time for rolled roast than roast with bone.

TABLE 38b. TESTS FOR STAGE OF COOKERY FOR HAM (Medium size)

	Fresh *		*Smoked* **		*Tenderized* **		*Ready-to-eat* ** *(if heated)*	
	Internal Temperature	*Approximate min. per lb.*	*Internal Temperature*	*Approximate min. per lb.*	*Internal Temperature*	*Approximate min. per lb.*	*Internal Temperature*	*Approximate min. per lb.*
Well-done	185° F. (85° C.)	30–35	170° F. (77° C.)	20–25	160° F. (71° C.)	18–20	130° F. (54° C.)	10–15

*Oven temperatu-e—350° F.(177°C.)
**Oven temperature—325° F.(163°C.)

TABLE 39. INTERNAL TEMPERATURES FOR BROILED STEAKS OR CHOPS

	Turn	*Finish*
Rare	100° F. (38° C.)	135° F. (57° C.)
Medium	110° F. (43° C.)	155° F. (68° C.)
Well-done	120° F. (49° C.)	170° F. (77° C.)

"Roast" on a Spit

1) Choose an eye roast from beef.
2) Run the spit through the middle, lengthwise, and fasten the meat with the prongs of the spit. Place in the rôtisserie.
3) Cook to desired stage. (About 20–25 min. per pound).
4) Remove to a warm serving dish. When serving, slice thin.

Roast Canadian Bacon

1. Place a 2-lb. piece of Canadian bacon on a rack in a roasting pan, leaving the wrapping on the meat.
2. Roast in a slow oven—300° F. (149° C.)—for 2 hrs.
3. Remove the wrapping and pour 1 c. of shredded pineapple or tart apple sauce over the meat. Return to the oven and continue roasting about 30 min.
4. Serve with broiled tomatoes.

Broiled Steaks and Chops

1) Choose a tender-cut steak or chop.
2) Place it on the oiled rack of a broiling pan and set the pan into a preheated broiling oven 3 to 4 in. below the source of heat.
3) Cook until half done (see Table 39); remove the broiling pan, sprinkle the meat with salt and pepper, turn, and broil until done.
4) Sprinkle the steak with salt and pepper and serve it on a warm platter.

Broiled Round or Rump Steak

1) Marinate the steak in French dressing, to which garlic is added, about 12 hours.
2) Remove the steak, and broil (see above).

Broiled Flank Steak

1) Be sure that the steak is at room temperature.
2) With a sharp knife, remove the tough membrane from the surface.
3) Broil about 5 min. on each side and season to taste.
4) Using a very sharp knife held at such an angle that the back of the blade almost touches the meat, slice the steak very thin. Sprinkle with salt and pepper.

Baked Slice of Ham
(Cured)

Slice of ham.......2 in. thick
Brown sugar.....½ c.
Cloves as needed
Canned pineapple, 4 to 6 slices
Sirup from pineapple

1) Place the ham in a baking dish, stick with cloves, and sprinkle with brown sugar.
2) Bake in a moderate oven—350° F. (177° C.)—for about an hour or until tender.
3) Arrange pineapple slices over the ham and continue baking until brown.
4) Baste frequently with the pineapple sirup.

[Note: The pineapple may be omitted. The ham may be basted with juice from sweet pickled peaches several times during the baking.]

Baked Steak or Chops

1) Choose tender-cut steak or chops cut 1 to 1½ inches thick.
2) Preheat the oven to 350° F. (177° C.).
3) Place the meat on a slightly oiled rack in an uncovered roasting pan or broiler and bake to the desired degree (about 20 to 25 minutes).
4) Season when done and serve on a warm platter.

Pan-broiled Steak or Chop

1) Select a tender-cut steak or chop.
2) Heat a heavy frying pan and, if needed, melt enough fat to prevent sticking.
3) Brown the meat on both sides.
4) Reduce the heat to "moderate" and cook the steak to desired stage, turning as needed.
5) Sprinkle with salt and pepper.

Fried Cutlets or Chops
(4 servings)

Veal cutlets or chops.......4
Beaten egg...............1
Seasoned flour.....about ⅓ c.
Seasoned dry crumbs about ⅓ c.
Fat for frying

1) Coat the meat with the flour, dip in beaten egg, and coat with the crumbs.
2) Fry in about ½ in. of fat heated to 370° F. (188° C.), turning as needed, until evenly brown, or fry in deep fat at 375° F. (191° C.) until browned.
3) Drain on unglazed paper.

Swiss Steak

Ingredients	*For 2*	*For 4*	*For 6*
Bottom round or boned chuck steak of beef, 1½ in. thick	⅔ lb.	1⅓ lb.	2 lb.
Flour	3 tb.	⅓ c.	½ c.
Salt	⅓ t.	⅔ t.	1 t.
Pepper	dash	⅙ t.	¼ t.
Bacon fat	2 t.	1 tb.	2 tb.
Onions, small, sliced	1	2	3
Canned tomatoes	½ c.	1 c.	1½ c.
Green pepper rings	2	4	6
Celery, chopped	¼ c.	½ c.	¾ c.
Boiling water	⅓ c.	⅔ c.	1 c.

1) Prepare the meat for cooking.
2) Add the salt and pepper to the flour and pound it into the meat, using the dull edge of a meat cleaver, a heavy knife, a wooden potato masher, or a meat tenderer.
3) Heat the fat in a heavy frying pan. Brown the meat in it.
4) Add the remaining ingredients, and cook for about 1 hr. in a slow oven —300° F. (149° C.)—until tender.

Veal Cutlets Parmesan

(4 servings)

(Adapted from an Italian recipe)

Veal cutlets (¼ lb.)	4	Grated Parmesan cheese	¼ c.
Eggs, beaten	2	Dry bread crumbs	1 c.
Salt	¼ t.	Olive oil (or substitute)	⅓ c.
Pepper	Dash	Tomato sauce	1 can

Mozzarella cheese . . . . . 4 slices

1) Dip the cutlets into egg to which salt and pepper have been added.
2) Mix the Parmesan cheese and crumbs and dip the cutlets into the mixture.
3) Brown in the oil.
4) Put the cutlets into a baking dish, pour the tomato sauce over them, and place a slice of cheese on each.
5) Bake 10 to 15 min. at 350° F. (177° C.).

Braised Beef

1) Select a cut of beef from rump or chuck.
2) Brown in fat in a heavy top-of-range utensil; sprinkle with salt and pepper.
3) Insert a meat thermometer (see Roast).

4) Lift the meat and place a rack under the meat.
5) Add 1 c. of water and, if desired, selected herbs or sliced onion and carrot. Cover.
6) Cook over low heat until the temperature indicates desired stage. (Add water during cooking if needed).
7) Transfer the meat to a serving dish and remove the thermometer.
8) Remove excess fat from the liquid and thicken the gravy.

Pot Roast

1) Proceed as for braised beef.
2) Choose 3 or 4 vegetables to be served with the meat and add them whole or in large pieces, long enough before the meat is done to be cooked. (See vegetable time chart, p. 486).

Brisket of Beef in Horseradish Sauce

(About 4 servings) *

Brisket of beef	1 lb.	Flour	1 tb.
Bay leaf, small	1	Beef stock	1 c.
Onion, sliced	1 med.	Horseradish	½ c.
Carrot, sliced	3 med.	Vinegar	½ c.
Celery, diced	1 stalk	Cloves, whole	2
Salt and pepper	to season	Bay leaf	bit
Boiling water	to cover	Salt and pepper	to taste
Butter or margarine	2 tb.	Sugar	¼ c.
Onion, chopped	1 sm.	Parsley, minced	1 tb.

1) Cook the meat, vegetables, and seasonings in the left column in water over *low* heat until the meat is tender—from 1 to 3 hours.
2) Melt the butter or margarine and brown the onion in it.
3) Add the flour and stir to blend.
4) Add the stock slowly, stirring to thicken slightly.
5) Add the horseradish, vinegar, and other seasonings, and simmer about 10 min.
6) Remove the meat from the broth and slice in rather thin slices. Heat them in the sauce.
7) Transfer the meat and sauce to a serving dish and sprinkle with parsley.

Apricot Steak

(About 4 servings) *

Round steak, 1 inch thick	1 lb.	Onion, chopped	1½ tb.
Flour	3 tb.	Apricot juice	from No. 303 can
Fat	2 tb.	Apricot halves	from No. 303 can

1) Cut the steak into serving pieces and dredge in the flour.
2) Melt the fat in a range-to-table utensil; brown the steak and onion.

* Courtesy, Texas Beef Council

3) Add the apricot juice to the flour remaining after dredging the steak and pour over the steak.
4) Bake, covered, about 45 min. (until tender) at 350° F. (177° C.), adding water, if needed, during the baking.
5) When meat is nearly done, add apricot halves and cook uncovered for 15 min.

Veal Ragout

Ingredients	*For 2*	*For 4*	*For 6*
Veal breast or neck	½ lb.	1 lb.	1½ lb.
Fat	2 tb.	3 tb.	¼ c.
Onion, minced	1 sm.	1 med.	1 lg.
Garlic, minced	½ clove	1 clove	1 clove
Curry powder	⅛ t.	¼ t.	½ t.
Water	¾ c.	1½ c.	2¼ c.
Tomatoes, canned	½ c.	1 c.	1½ c.
Salt	1 t.	1½ t.	2 t.
Mushrooms, canned	2 oz.	3 oz.	4 oz.

1) Cut the meat into cubes—about 1½ in.
2) Brown the onions, garlic, and meat in the fat.
3) Add the curry powder, water, tomatoes, and salt and simmer until the meat is tender (about 40 min.).
4) Add the mushrooms.
5) Drain the stock and thicken, using 1½ tb. of flour per c. of liquid.
6) Make a border of cooked rice (see p. 595) in a deep chop plate or baking dish.
7) Pour the thickened stock over the ragout and put it into the rice-bordered dish.

Hungarian Goulash

Ingredients	*For 2*	*For 4*	*For 6*
Beef	⅓ lb.	⅔ lb.	1 lb.
Veal	⅙ lb.	⅓ lb.	½ lb.
Pork (lean)	⅙ lb.	⅓ lb.	½ lb.
Flour	1 tb.	2 tb.	3 tb.
Paprika	1 tb.	2 tb.	3 tb.
Onion, small	½	1	2
Garlic	⅙ clove	⅓ clove	½ clove
Salt	⅙ t.	⅓ t.	½ t.
Bay leaf	bit	½	1
Canned tomatoes	½ c.	1 c.	1½ c.
Water		enough to cover	
Carrots (small)	1	2	3
Celery	⅔ stalk	1⅓ stalks	2 stalks
Parsley	1 sprig	2 sprigs	3 sprigs

1) Wipe the meat with a damp cloth, cut into cubes 1 to 1½ inches on a side, and sprinkle with flour.
2) Fry a little of the fat from the pork in a frying pan; then add the rest of the meat and brown.
3) Add the onions and garlic; brown and add paprika.
4) Add the salt, tomatoes, bay leaf, and enough water to cover; cook slowly until the meat is slightly tender.
5) Add the vegetables and cook until they are tender. (Cut the carrots and celery in 1½- to 2-in. pieces before adding to the meat). Parsley should be added about ½ hr. before ready to serve.
6) When the stew is nearly ready to serve, add dumplings. Serve as soon as they are cooked.

Dumplings
(Serves 6)

General utility flour	1 c.	Fat	2 tb.
Baking powder	2 t.	Egg	1
Salt	¼ t.	Milk	⅜ c.

1) Sift the flour and measure. Sift again with baking powder and salt.
2) Cut in the fat.
3) Beat the egg and add the milk. Mix well.
4) Add the egg and milk mixture to the dry ingredients.
5) Drop by tablespoonfuls on top of the stew, being careful not to allow the dough to sink into the liquid.
6) Set on an asbestos mat over slow heat. Cover tightly, and cook 12 min. without raising the cover.

Beef Stew

Ingredients	*For 2*	*For 4*	*For 6*
Stew meat, cubed	½ lb.	1 lb.	1½ lb.
Fat	2 tb.	¼ c.	⅓ c.
Boiling water	1 c.	2 c.	3 c.
Salt	½ t.	1 t.	1½ t.
Pepper	dash	⅛ t.	¼ t.
Tarragon	¼ t.	½ t.	¾ t.
Marjoram	¼ t.	½ t.	¾ t.
Potatoes, sm.	2–3	4–6	6–12
Carrots, cut in half, med.	2	4	6
Onions, sm.	2–4	4–8	6–12
Turnips, cut in half	1	2	3
Flour	to thicken gravy		

1) Brown the meat in fat in a heavy top-of-range utensil.
2) Add the water and seasonings, cover, and simmer ¾ to 1 hr.

3) Add the vegetables and cook over medium heat until the vegetables are tender (about 15 min.).
4) Put the meat and vegetables into a heated serving dish and thicken the gravy, using about 1 tb. of flour per c. of liquid.
5) Pour the gravy over the meat and vegetables.

Lamb Curry
(Adapted from Indian recipes)

Ingredients	*For 2*	*For 4*	*For 6*
Lamb, 1-in. cubes	½ lb.	1 lb.	1½ lb.
Fat	2 tb.	3–4 tb.	⅓ c.
Garlic, med. cloves	½	1	1½
Turmeric	½ t.	1 t.	1½ t.
Coriander	½ t.	1 t.	1½ t.
Cardamom (seeds of)	2	3–4	5–6
Ginger	dash	dash	⅛ t.
Cloves	2	3–4	5–6
Cayenne	dash	dash	⅛ t.
Salt		to taste	

1) Melt the fat in a range-to-table utensil and brown the meat in it.
2) Add the garlic (put through garlic press or mince) and the other seasonings.
3) Cover with a tight lid and cook over low heat about 35 min., shaking (but not uncovering) 3 or 4 times to prevent sticking.
4) Serve with rice.

Sukiyaki
(About 4 servings)
(Adapted from Japanese)

Salad oil	2 tb.	Spinach	½ lb.
Lean beef (thinly sliced) *	1¼ lb.	Canned bean sprouts	1 c.
Mild onion, sliced	1 sm.	Green onions	about 8
Celery (sliced diagonally)	2 stalks	Beef stock	1 c.
Mushrooms, fresh	6–8	Soy sauce	2–3 tb.

1) Heat a heavy frying pan and add oil.
2) Add the meat and brown it lightly and quickly.
3) Add the vegetables in order, stirring gently after each is added, then the stock, and soy sauce.
4) Cook over low heat 10 to 15 min., and serve at once. (Be sure that more soy sauce is available).
5) Rice, in a separate dish, is served with the sukiyaki.

* If the beef is put into the freezing compartment and left until firm but not really frozen, it can be sliced more easily.

Ham Loaf
(10 servings)

Ground ham,* lean	1½ lb.	Rolled oats	½ c.
Prepared mustard	1 tb.	Evaporated milk	¾ c.
Onion, minced	1 sm.	Egg, beaten	1
Parsley, minced	1 tb.	Brown sugar **	¼ c.
Sweet basil	¼ t.	Vinegar **	¼ c.

1) Put all the ingredients except the sugar and vinegar into a mixing bowl and mix well.
2) Pack into an oiled loaf pan, about 8½ x 4½ in.
3) Mix the sugar and vinegar in a saucepan, heat until the sugar melts, and pour over the loaf.
4) Bake in a moderate oven—350° F. (177° C.) for 1 hr.
5) Leave the loaf in the pan 15 min., then turn it onto a warm platter and garnish with broiled tomato halves and parsley.

Meat Loaf
(About 8 servings)

Beef, ground	1 lb.	Bread crumbs	1 c.
Veal, ground	½ lb.	Thyme	¼ t.
Pork (lean), ground	½ lb.	Salt	½ t.
Onion, chopped	1 med.	Pepper	⅛ t.
Green pepper, chopped	¼ c.	Horseradish	2 tb.
Tomato catsup	½ c.	Eggs, beaten	2
Stock	about ⅓ c.		

1) Put the meats into a mixing bowl and stir to mix well.
2) Add all other ingredients except stock and mix thoroughly.
3) Add enough stock to make the mixture moist and put it into a suitable baking pan.
4) Bake about 45 min. at 350° F. (177° C.).

Upside-Down Meat Pie
(About 4 servings)

Egg	1	Ground beef (lean)	¾ lb.
Milk *or* tomato sauce	⅓ c.	Green pepper, small	1
Onion, chopped	¼ c.	Pimiento	1
Oregano or other seasoning	½ t.	Paprika	liberal sprinkling
Salt	½–¾ t.	Biscuit mix	2 c.
Nutmeg	dash	Parsley, chopped	½ c.

* May use half ground beef.
** For a dryer loaf, omit.

1) Beat the egg, add milk, onion, oregano, salt, and nutmeg, and mix.
2) Add the meat and blend well.
3) Select and oil an 8–9 inch pie pan or a shallow square baking dish.
4) Decorate the bottom of the pan with green pepper and pimiento rings or strips. Sprinkle liberally with paprika.
5) Put the meat mixture in carefully so as not to displace the decoration.
6) Add the parsley to the dry biscuit mix and make a batter of drop biscuit consistency, following the directions on the package.
7) Spread the batter on top of the meat mixture and bake about 25 min. at 375° F. (191° C.).
8) Serve with tomato or mushroom sauce.

Liver and Vegetable Casserole

(About 4 servings)

(Adapted from a Mennonite recipe)

Liver	1 lb.	Celery, sliced	⅔ c.
Seasoned flour	3 tb.	Carrots, sliced	1 c.
Fat	¼ c.	Salt and pepper	to taste
Onions, chopped	2 med.	Tomatoes	1½ c.

1) Soak the liver in cold water 15–20 min. and dry it on absorbent paper.
2) Roll the liver in seasoned flour and brown it in fat.
3) Remove the liver to a cutting board and cut it into about ½ in. cubes. Put into an oiled baking dish.
4) Brown the onions in the fat, add the celery and carrots, and heat them.
5) Pour the vegetables over the liver, sprinkle with salt and pepper, and add the tomatoes.
6) Bake 45–60 min. (until both liver and vegetables are tender) at 350° F. (177° C.).

Tongue with Herbs

(4 servings)

Tongue, fresh	about 1½ lbs.	Bay leaf	1 sm.
Boiling water	to cover	Peppercorns	6
Salt	1 t.	Cloves	6

1) Scrub the tongue thoroughly.
2) Cover with boiling water in a saucepan, add the seasonings, and cook over low heat until tender (about 2 hours) or about 35 min. in a pressure pan.
3) Remove the skin before slicing the tongue. Serve hot or cold.

OR

1) Put the tongue, 1–2 c. of water, and the seasonings into a pressure pan.
2) Close the pan and cook at 15 lbs. pressure about 20 min. per pound.

Tongue Casserole
(About 4 servings)

Cold cooked tongue	1 lb.	Parsley, chopped	1 t.
Butter or margarine	3 tb.	Chives, chopped	1 tb.
Stock, beef or chicken	1/4 c.	Salt	1/2 t.
Sweet pickle, chopped	3 tb.	Pepper	1/8 t.
Bread crumbs	1/3 c.		

1) Slice the tongue.
2) Oil a casserole with butter or margarine.
3) Combine the other ingredients and put half of the mixture into the casserole.
4) Place the slices of tongue on the mixture and put the remaining mixture over the tongue.
5) Dot with remaining butter or margarine and bake about 30 min. at 300° F. (149° C.).

Heart Cutlets
(About 4 servings)

Heart	about 1 1/2 lbs.	Water	1 c.
Fat	to sauté	Salt	1/2 t.
Bay leaf	bit		

1) Wash the heart thoroughly.
2) Slice the heart crosswise about 1/2 in. thick, and remove tough membrane.
3) Sauté lightly in a heavy saucepan.
4) Add the water and seasonings, cover, and simmer until tender—about 40 min.
5) Serve with a selected sauce.

Brains Sautéed with Bacon
(About 4 servings)

Calf's brains	1 lb.	Ice water	to cover brains
Boiling water	1 qt.	Crisp bacon	8 slices
Salt	1 t.	Bacon fat	about 2 tb.
Vinegar	1 tb.	Water cress	4 portions.

1) Wash the brains carefully, removing membranes.
2) Simmer in salted, acidulated water until tender—about 20 min.
3) Drain and soak in ice water 20–30 min.
4) Broil the bacon until it is crisp.
5) Drain the brains, cut carefully in 1/2-in. slices.
6) Sauté in bacon fat; serve with crisp bacon and water cress.

Sweetbreads and Mushrooms, Béchamel

Ingredients	*For 2*	*For 4*	*For 6*
Sweetbreads	1 sm.	1 lg.	1 pair
Water, boiling	1 pt.	1 qt.	1 qt.
Vinegar	1 tb.	2 tb.	2 tb.
Salt	½ t.	1 t.	1 t.
Mushrooms, canned	⅓ c.	⅔ c.	1 c.
Béchamel sauce (see p. 500)	½ c.	¾ c.	1 c.

1) Parboil the sweetbreads in the boiling water to which the vinegar and salt have been added, cooking slowly 20 min.
2) Let stand in cold water until cool, and drain.
3) Break into pieces, discarding fat and connective tissue.
4) Add mushrooms and sweetbreads to the sauce and reheat.

Broiled Sweetbreads

Sweetbreads	1 lg. or 1 sm. pair per serving
Butter or margarine	1 tb.
Lemon juice	1 t.
Salt	to season
Pepper	to season

1) Prepare the sweetbreads as in the above recipe, Steps 1 and 2.
2) Remove fat and connective tissue from the sweetbreads.
3) Cream the butter or margarine and add a little lemon juice, mixing well.
4) Cut the sweetbreads in half lengthwise.
5) Place the pieces on an oiled broiler, brush with lemon butter and place the rack 2 or 3 in. below the heat.
6) When brown, sprinkle with salt and pepper, turn, and broil the other side in the same way.
7) Remove to a warm platter, brush with lemon butter, and garnish with parsley.

Brown Soup Stock

Shank bone of beef		Salt	1 t.
Onion, chopped	1 med.	Cloves	6
Cold water	2 qts.	Bay leaf	½
Carrots, diced	½ c.	Thyme	¼ t.
Turnips, diced	½ c.	Marjoram	¼ t.
Celery, diced	½ c.	Peppercorns	½ t.

1) Remove the beef from the bone and cut into small pieces. Remove some of the marrow from the bone.

2) Brown the onion and meat in marrow and fat trimmings in the cooking utensil.
3) Add the bone and water, cover, and simmer about 2 hours.
4) Add the vegetables and seasonings and continue to simmer about 1 hour.
5) Strain, cool, and remove the fat.

Consommé

1) Heat 1 qt. of brown soup stock slightly and add the slightly beaten white, and clean, crushed shell of one egg.
2) Stir constantly until the stock begins to boil.
3) Continue boiling without stirring 2 to 5 min.
4) Add a cup of cold water, remove from the fire, and let the soup stand about 15 min. Strain.

White Soup Stock

Knuckle of veal		Onion, diced	1 med.
Cold water	2 qts.	Celery, diced	1 c.
Salt	1 t.	Mixed herbs, (See p. 659.)	1 t.

1) Cut the meat from the bone and soak meat and bone in the cold water for ½ hour.
2) Bring to the boiling point, reduce the temperature, cover, and simmer about 2 hours.
3) Add the vegetables and seasonings and continue to simmer about 1 hour.
4) Strain, cool, and remove fat.

POULTRY

Methods for broiling, frying, roasting, braising, and cooking in a rotisserie have been used in connection with the cookery of meat. In general, these methods apply to preparation of poultry also. Choice of poultry for the laboratory might include several of the domesticated birds and perhaps game. A few recipes are offered as suggestions for preparation of poultry parts and for the use of left-over poultry. Others will probably be suggested by instructor and class members.

Before storing or cooking, it is important to check poultry carefully to be sure that all pinfeathers are removed, giblets (and sometimes neck) taken from the carcass, and lungs and kidneys removed. Poultry may seem very clean when brought from the grocery but it should be washed to be *certain* that it is clean.

Chicken and turkey may be used interchangeably in recipes calling for one or the other.

Some utensils that are handy for the preparation of poultry are: tongs, poultry (or good kitchen) shears, roasting rack that can be adjusted to accommodate the bird being roasted (see Fig. 30, p. 156), poultry thermometer, chicken fryer, electric frying pan or casserole, rotisserie, and top-of-range-to-table utensil of suitable size.

Broiled Poultry

Cut poultry in halves or quarters, place it skin side down on a broiling rack, and brush it with oil or melted fat. Place it in the broiler about 4 inches below the heat. Turn it after 10 min. and again brush with oil or fat. Repeat until the poultry is cooked, approximately 30 to 60 min.—the time depending upon size of pieces. After the last turning, sprinkle with salt and pepper. When poultry is done, juice is clear and does not run freely when the thigh is punctured with a skewer or fork.

Poultry Broiled in Rôtisserie

The secret of success when poultry is cooked by this method is in placing the bird on the spit. For a small bird, e. g., squab or Rock Cornish game hen, the spit is run through from side to side; for a larger bird, it is run from head to tail, securing the heaviest parts. When fastened, the bird will turn evenly during cooking. Melted butter or margarine, seasoned to taste, is used to baste the poultry during cooking. Depending upon size, 30 min. to 1½ hours should be allowed for cooking.

Roasted Poultry

Be sure that the poultry is clean and that all pinfeathers are removed and hairs singed off. Sprinkle the inside with salt and pepper and fill with any desired stuffing. (Stuffing may be omitted.) Tie the neck, wings, and legs close to the body. The following directions for roasting poultry give excellent results:

1. Use a shallow roasting pan without a cover.
2. Place the prepared bird breast down on an adjustable rack.
3. Insert a poultry (or nonmetal meat) thermometer to the center of the thickest portion of the thigh *or* to the center of the stuffing through the opening at the back.
4. Cover the bird with a cloth well moistened with fat.
5. Roast at low temperature (see Table 40).
6. If a thermometer has been placed in the thigh, cook to 185°–190° F. (85°–88° C.); if in the stuffing, to 158°–176° F. (70°–80° C.). Approximate times required for roasting are listed in Table 40, p. 570.
7. When nearly done, the bird may be turned breast up for browning.
8. If a special rack is not used, the bird may be placed as nearly breast down as possible on the rack of the roasting pan. It may be turned at about

half the time needed and again—breast up—about ½ hour before it is done. This insures desirable browning of the breast. The cloth is removed during the last period. When done, the leg is moved easily when the end of the drumstick is held and the leg moved.

Rock Cornish Game Hens
(4 servings)

Game hens (frozen)	4	Stock and butter or margarine (hot)	to baste
Toasted bread cubes	2 c.	Currant jelly	½ c.
Celery, diced	½ c.	Lemon juice	1 tb.
Mushrooms, chopped	½ c.	Salt	Dash
Salt	½ t.	Cornstarch	½ tb.
White pepper	¼ t.	Water	2 tb.
Chicken stock or water	to moisten	Butter or margarine	1 tb.

1) Partially thaw the game hens, remove giblets, wash, and check for pinfeathers.
2) Mix the crumbs, celery, mushrooms, and seasonings and *moisten* with stock or water.
3) Stuff the birds lightly; tie wings and legs to bodies.
4) Place the birds on a rack in a shallow baking pan and baste with stock and butter or margarine.
5) Roast about 40 min. (until legs can be moved easily) at 325° F. (163° C.).
6) Make glaze by heating jelly, lemon juice, and salt, and thickening it with cornstarch stirred into the water. Add butter or margarine and stir.
7) Remove the game hens from the oven, pour the glaze over them evenly, and return them to the oven for 5 to 10 min.

TABLE 40. TIME AND TEMPERATURE FOR ROASTING POULTRY

	Weight (Pounds)	*Temperature* (Degrees F.)	*Minutes per Pound*	*Approximate Total Time*	*Temperature* (if thermometer used)
Chicken	4–5	325	40–35	2½ to 3 hrs.	190°–195° F. (88°–91° C.)
	More than 5	325	35–30	3 to 4 hrs.	
Duck	5–6	350	30–25	2 to 2½ hrs.	
Goose	10–12	325	20–18	3 to 4 hrs.	
Guinea	2–2½	350	40–35	1⅓ to 1¾ hrs.	
Rock Cornish game hens	1	325	40	40 min.	
Turkey	8–10	325	25–20	3 to 3½ hrs.	
	10–18	300	20–15	3½ to 5 hrs.	
	20	300	15–13	5 to 6 hrs.	

Fried Chicken

(For quantity, see p. 155.)

1) Roll pieces for frying in seasoned flour or meal.
2) Fry, a few pieces at a time, in deep fat heated to 350° F. (182° C.) until nicely browned, turning occasionally.
3) Drain on unglazed paper.

or

1) As above.
2) Brown in about ½ inch of fat in a heavy frying pan, chicken fryer, or electric frying pan.
3) Cover and continue cooking, using low heat. (Total time, 30–45 min.).

or

1) As above.
2) Brown in shallow fat (¼–⅓ in.).
3) Transfer the pieces to an oven-to-table dish, pour about 2 tb. per chicken of the fat and broth over them, and bake 30–40 min. (until tender) at 325° F. (163° C.).

Chicken Dinner

(About 4 servings)

Chicken legs and thighs	6 to 8 pieces	Onions, ¼-in. slices	4 sm.
Oil	3 to 4 tb.	Carrots, cut in half lengthwise	4 sm.
Salt	½ t.	Potatoes, ¼-in. slices	4 med.
Pepper	¼ t.	Mushrooms, sm. whole or sliced	1 c.
Tarragon or other seasoning	¼ t.	Water	½ c.

1) Select an electric frying pan or a top-of-the-range shallow utensil of substantial material with a close-fitting lid.
2) Put the oil in the frying pan and set control at 325° F. When slightly hot, put the *unfloured* chicken in, add ½ of the seasonings, cover and cook for 15 minutes. (In using a utensil other than the electric frying pan use low to moderate heat).
3) Turn chicken, add vegetables and remaining seasonings, cover and continue cooking for 15 minutes.
4) Turn off heat, add water, cover, and let stand for 10 minutes before serving.

Chicken Fricassee
(About 8 servings)

Fowl (about 4 lb.)	1	Fat	for browning
Seasoned flour		Water	2 c.
Herbs	to season		

1) Cut the fowl into serving pieces; roll them in seasoned flour and brown in fat (range-to-table utensil suggested).
2) Drain excess fat, add water, and herbs tied in a piece of thin cloth.
3) Cover and simmer until the chicken is tender—about 1½ hrs.

Baked Chicken Breasts
(4 servings)

Chicken breasts	4	Water	About ⅓ c.
Seasoned flour		Sweet basil	¼ t.
Fat	for browning	Rosemary	¼ t.

1) Roll the chicken in the flour and brown it lightly in fat (range-to-table utensil suggested).
2) Add water and herbs, cover, and bake 45–60 min. at 325° F. (163° C.).

Chicken Breasts, Suprême
(4 servings)

Chicken breasts, cooked	4	Canadian bacon (¼ in.)	4 sl.
Mushroom caps *	½ sm. can	Rusks (or toast)	4
Fat	2 tb.	Sauce Suprême	

1) Cut meat from the bones and brown meat and the mushroom caps lightly in the fat.
2) Pan-broil the bacon.
3) Heat rusks (or use toast hot) and arrange them on a serving dish.
4) Put bacon, chicken, and mushrooms on the rusks and pour sauce over each serving (or serve sauce separately).

Sauce Suprême

To yellow Béchamel sauce for 4 (see p. 500) add ¾ t. lemon juice and stir to blend.

Baked Turkey Steaks
(1 per person)

1) Place the steaks on a rack in a shallow baking dish and baste each with 2 tb. of orange juice *or* citrus French dressing.

* Fresh mushrooms, if available.

2) Bake in a slow oven—300° F. (149° C.) for 20 min.
3) Turn the steaks, baste with 2 tb. of the juice or dressing, and continue to bake for 15 min.
4) Serve immediately.

Poultry Loaf
(About 6 servings)

Cooked chicken or turkey, chopped	3 c.	Parsley, cut fine	1 t.
Cooked rice	2½ c.	Marjoram	½ t.
Salt	1 t.	Celery, chopped	¼ c.
Pepper	⅛ t.	Chicken stock	1 c.
		Milk	1 c.
Eggs, beaten	3		

1) Mix all the ingredients except liquids.
2) Add the liquids and stir to blend.
3) Bake in an oiled loaf pan about 1 hr. at 350° F. (177° C.).
4) Serve with selected sauce.

Turkey Béchamel
(About 4 servings)

Butter or margarine	2 tb.	Milk	½ c.
Flour	3 tb.	Cooked turkey or chicken, diced	1½ c.
Salt	½ t.	Boiled ham, diced	¼ c.
Pepper	⅛ t.	Water chestnuts, sliced	½ c.
Mace	dash	Parsley, cut	1 tb.
Chicken stock	½ c.		

1) Make a sauce, using the first seven ingredients. (See p. 500).
2) Add the remaining ingredients and heat thoroughly over low heat.
3) May be served with corn bread (see p. 600) as a short cake, with waffles, rice, or one of the alimentary pastes, or in timbale cases or patty shells.

Broiled Chicken Livers and Mushrooms
(About 4 servings)

Chicken livers	½ to ¾ lb.	Cooking oil	about 1 tb.
Mushrooms, fresh	¼ to ⅓ lb.	Tarragon	¼ t.
Salt and pepper	to taste		

1) Wash and dry the chicken livers and mushrooms.
2) Oil a shallow baking dish, place the livers and mushrooms in the dish, and sprinkle with seasonings and oil.
3) Broil (4 in. below source of heat) about 8 min., turn, and broil the other side.

Poultry in Sour Cream
(8 to 10 servings)

Celery, diced	1 c.	Poultry stock	2 c.
Onion, chopped	1 sm.	Flour	1/3 c.
Salad oil	1/4 c.	Cooked poultry, diced	2 c.
Salt	1/2 t.	Mushrooms, sliced	1/2 c.
Sugar	2 t.	Sour cream, cultured	1 c.
Rosemary	1 t.		

1) Sauté the celery and onion in oil until slightly tender.
2) Add seasonings and 1/4 c. of stock; cover and simmer 5 min.
3) Add the flour and stir rapidly, blending well.
4) Add the remaining stock and stir until well blended.
5) Add the poultry and mushrooms and continue cooking about 5 min.
6) Add the sour cream and stir until the mixture is hot.
7) Serve over flaky rice or toast.

Chicken Tetrazzini
(6 servings)

Noodles or spaghetti	1/2 lb.	Paprika	1/2 t.
Bacon	1 1/2 sl.	Canned mushrooms and liquid	8 oz. can
Sweet onion, chopped	1 sm.	Grated cheese (Provolone)	1/2 lb.
Green pepper, chopped	1/2 sm.	Cooked chicken, cut into small pieces	1 1/2 c.
Salt	1/2 t.		
Cayenne	dash		

1) Cook the noodles or spaghetti in chicken broth until tender; drain.
2) Brown the bacon in a frying pan or heavy sauce pan and remove the bacon.
3) Brown the onion and green pepper lightly in the fat.
4) Add the seasonings, mushrooms, cheese, and bacon broken into pieces, and stir gently until the cheese is melted.

5) Add the chicken and noodles or spaghetti and stir slowly over low heat until all are thoroughly heated.
6) Pour into a warm serving dish and serve very hot.

PAPRIKA CHICKEN (Adapted)
(Hungarian; especially for Feast of St. Stephen)

Ingredients	*For 2*	*For 4*	*For 6*
Broilers or fryers	1	2	3
Fat	2 tb.	¼ c.	¼ c. + 2 tb.
Onion, chopped	¼ c.	½ c.	¾ c.
Flour	1 tb.	2 tb.	3 tb.
Salt	½ t.	1 t.	1½ t.
Chicken stock	¼ c.	½ c.	¾ c.
Paprika	½–1 t.	1–2 t.	1½ t.–1 tb.
Sour cream	½ c.	1 c.	1½ c.

1) Cut the chicken in quarters or smaller serving pieces.
2) Melt the fat, cook the onion, over medium heat, until very lightly browned.
3) Add the chicken and sauté, turning frequently, about 15 min.
4) Remove the chicken, add flour and salt, and stir to blend.
5) Add chicken stock gradually, stirring to mix well.
6) Add the chicken, cover, and continue cooking slowly until chicken is very tender (about 15 to 20 min.).
7) Remove from the heat, add paprika to taste (sauce should have a decidedly pink color).
8) Place the chicken on a serving-dish, blend the sour cream into the sauce, and pour sauce over the chicken.
9) Serve with noodles.

SEAFOOD

Americans generally are not enthusiastic about fish. True, there are a few fish products and dishes which are widely used. These include canned tuna, fish sticks, and a variety of deep-fat-fried fish. A foods laboratory dealing with fish and the diverse ways in which it can be included in family meals is a challenge to instructor and students. Because of the short time required to cook fish, laboratory projects may be selected to cover a number of fish dishes. If references are especially selected on the basis of European recipes as well as those from the regions of the United States where fresh fish is a standard item in the diet, students can gain a better appreciation for this delicate, delicious, and nutritious food. The recipes which follow are indicative of the versatility of seafood.

Poached Fish
(4 to 6 servings)

Fish steaks or fillets	4–6 servings	Salt	½ t.
Water	1½–3 c.	Bay leaf	½ sm.
Lemon, sliced	1	Peppercorns	3–4
Onion, sliced	1 medium		

1) Select thick steaks or fillets; if frozen fillets are used, do not thaw.
2) Select a shallow utensil with a close-fitting cover for poaching.
3) Put water and all other ingredients in pan and heat to just under boiling. The water need not cover the fish, since it can be turned over.
4) Place fish steaks in water (do not stack); if frozen fillets are being used, put the unwrapped package "block" of fish in the water.
5) Poach the fish (keeping the water under boiling) until flaky. Time will vary, depending on thickness of fish and whether it is fresh or frozen.
6) Remove fish to plates or platter, sprinkle with paprika, and serve hot or cold with any appropriate sauce or salad dressing.

Broiled Fish Steaks
(1 steak per person)

Swordfish or salmon steaks	1 per serving	Paprika	sprinkling
Olive oil	sufficient to brush steak	Salt	sprinkling
		Pepper	sprinkling
Tarragon or other herb	sprinkling		

1) Place the steaks on a broiling rack, brush with the oil, and sprinkle with the seasonings.
2) Pre-heat broiler and set rack 2–4 inches from heat, depending upon the thickness of the steak.
3) *Thin* steaks should be broiled 10–15 minutes or until slightly brown and can be flaked with a fork. They do not need turning. Thick steaks should be turned with a broad spatula, brushed with oil, seasoned, and then browned and cooked on the other side.
4) Remove to hot plates or platter, serve with lemon wedges and a desired sauce.

Boiled Shrimp
(3–4 servings)

Shrimp, raw, in shell	1 lb.	Peppercorns	4
Water	1 qt.	Celery, stalk and leaves	1 stalk
Salt	½ t.	Onion, sliced	1 medium
Vinegar	1 tb.	Bay leaf	1 sm.

1) Wash shrimp, bring water to boil, add shrimp and all other ingredients and cook for 10 min.
2) Shell and de-vein shrimp.
3) Serve hot or cold with any desired sauce.
[NOTE: The water the shrimp is cooked in can be used as a part of the liquid in any hot sauce.]

SCALLOP STEW
(About 4 servings)

Scallops	1 pt.	Salt	½ t.
Butter	2 tb.	Pepper	to taste

Milk and cream, half-and-half ...... 1 pt.

1) If scallops are large, cut in two.
2) Simmer scallops in butter and seasonings for about 5 minutes.
3) Add half-and-half and continue cooking over *low* heat for about 10 minutes.
4) Serve with crackers or crusty bread.
[NOTE: Clams may be substituted for the scallops.]

CRAB "PANCAKE"
(Serves 4)

Eggs	4	Crab meat	1 c.
Salt	¼ t.	Celery, cut fine	½ c.
White pepper	⅛ t.	Minced onion	1 tb.

Cooking oil .... 3 tb.

1) Beat the eggs and add the other ingredients.
2) Heat the oil in a heavy frying pan and add the crab mixture.
3) Cook over low heat until the mixture is set.
4) Cut into fourths and turn carefully.
5) Cook 1 minute and serve at once with mushroom sauce. (See p. 584.)

CRAB FLAKE TIMBALES
(Serves 6 to 8)

White sauce, thick	1 c.	Paprika	⅛ t.
Crab flakes	1½ c.	Eggs	2
Salt	½ t.	Whipping cream	1 c.

1) Make the white sauce (see p. 499).
2) Add the crab meat and the additional seasonings.
3) Cook until heated thoroughly, and then cool the mixture.
4) Beat the egg yolks and fold them into the mixture.
5) Beat the egg whites stiff and fold them in.

6) Whip the cream and fold it in.
7) Put the mixture into buttered timbale molds or custard cups, place them in a pan containing hot water, and bake for about 12 min. in a moderately slow oven—325° F. (163° C.).

Shrimp and Chicken Jambalaya
(4 to 6 servings)

Butter or margarine	2 tb.	Shrimp, boiled (see pp. 576–577)	1 lb.
Onion, sliced	1 medium	Shrimp broth or chicken stock	2 c.
Tomatoes, canned	2 c.	Rice, uncooked	1 c.
Garlic, minced	1 clove	Chicken, cooked and cut coarsely	1–1½ c.
Thyme	¼ t.		
Chili powder	1 t.		
Salt	½ t.		
Parsley, chopped	¼ c.		

1) Select an appropriate-sized utensil of substantial material that has a close-fitting cover.
2) Melt the butter or margarine in the utensil, add the onion, and cook until soft.
3) Add all other ingredients, bring to a boil, reduce to *low* heat, cover and cook for about 40 minutes or until rice is tender but not mushy. The jambalaya should be rather dry and flaky—not wet and sticky.

Kedgeree
(About 6 servings)

Fish, any white (cooked & flaked)	1½ c.	Cream, light	⅓ c.
Eggs, hard-cooked and chopped	4	Salt	½ t.
Rice, cooked	2 c.	Pepper	to taste
Parsley, chopped	¼ c.	Curry powder	1 t.

Mix all ingredients and either heat over low heat on top of the range or place in a shallow baking dish and bake for about 20 min. at 350° F. (177° C.).

Scallops Newburg
(About 4 servings)

Butter or margarine	2 tb.	Mustard, dry	¼ t.
Scallops, frozen	1 10-oz. pkg.	Milk, rich	1½ c.
Mushrooms, sliced, fresh	¼ lb.	Catsup	1 tb.
Flour	¼ c.	Sherry flavoring	1 t.

1) Put butter or margarine, scallops, and mushrooms in utensil of substantial material, cover, and cook over *low* heat for about 10 minutes.

2) Add flour and mustard and mix well; add milk, catsup, and flavoring and continue cooking for about 5 minutes.
3) Serve with crisp toast or rice.

Scalloped Oysters Au Gratin
(About 4 servings)

Crackers, (saltines or other plain)	12 to 15	Tarragon	1/4 t.
Oysters, drained	1 pt.	Salt	1/2 t.
Lemon juice	1 tb.	Cheese, Cheddar, grated	1/2 c.
		Cheese, cottage	1/4 c.
Paprika	dash		

1) Use a shallow range-to-table baking dish and place the crackers (unbroken), on the bottom of the dish.
2) Put oysters over the crackers and sprinkle them with lemon juice, tarragon, and salt.
3) Mix the two cheeses thoroughly and spread over the oysters; sprinkle with paprika.
4) Place under broiler about 6 inches from heat for about 12 minutes or until oysters are curled at the edges and the cheese is melted.

Boiled Lobster

1) Use 2 tb. of salt for each quart of water used. When the water boils, plunge the live lobster into it. If more than one lobster is to be cooked, *allow the water to come to a boil after each lobster is added.*
2) Cover and boil 20 min.
3) Remove the lobster from the water and cool in cold water.
4) Split and place on a hot platter.
5) Sprinkle with salt and pepper.
6) Serve with melted butter or margarine.

   [Note: A nut cracker for cracking the claws and an oyster fork for removing the meat should be provided for each person.]

Directions for splitting lobster to broil or bake: Sever the spinal cord. Place the lobster shell side down; cross the large claws and hold them firmly. Using a sharp, pointed knife, begin at the mouth and make a deep incision. Draw the knife quickly through the body and the entire length of the tail. Open, remove the intestinal vein, lungs, and stomach.

Broiled Lobster

1) Place a split lobster on an oiled broiling rack.
2) Broil 8 to 10 min. on the flesh side, having the lobster 2 or 3 inches below the source of heat.

3) Turn and broil 6 to 8 min. on the shell side.
4) Place on a hot platter, and season with salt and pepper.
5) Serve with melted butter or margarine.

Baked Lobster

1) Place a split lobster shell side down on a rack in a roasting pan.
2) Sprinkle with salt and pepper and dot with butter.
3) Bake from 20 to 30 min. in a moderately hot oven—375° to 400° F. (190° to 205° C.).
4) Remove to a hot platter.
5) Serve with melted butter or margarine.

Broiled Lobster Tails

1) Choose lobster tails of about equal size, and buy one weighing 6 to 9 oz. for each person to be served.
2) Thaw, either in the refrigerator or at room temperature.
3) With kitchen shears cut through the center of the entire shell.
4) With a sharp knife cut through the meat almost to the under-shell membrane.
5) Loosen the flesh from the shell, but not from the under-shell membrane.
6) Press the sections thus made apart so that the whole lies as flat as possible, and secure with one or two skewers.
7) Sprinkle with salt and place the tails on an oiled broiling rack with the under-shell membrane side up.
8) Place the rack about 3 in. below the heat and broil for 5 min.; turn, brush with butter or margarine, and broil for 6 to 9 min., depending upon the size of the tails.
9) Serve hot with melted butter or margarine.

Mackerel Loaf

(About 6 servings)

Mackerel, canned	1 15–16 oz. can	Tarragon, dill or other seasoning	¼ t.
Carrots, raw, grated	1 c. packed	Pimiento, chopped	2 tb.
Eggs, beaten	2	Milk, buttermilk or sweet	¾ c.
Lemon juice	2 tb.	Rolled oats, quick, uncooked	1 c.
Onion, chopped	¼ c.		
Salt	½ t.		

1) Put mackerel into a bowl and flake with fork.
2) Add all other ingredients and mix well, put into an oiled small loaf pan or individual custard cups and bake for about 40 min. at 350° F. (177° C.).

Shrimp Creole

Ingredients	*For 2*	*For 4*	*For 6*
Fat	1 tb.	2 tb.	3 tb.
Onion, chopped	1 tb.	2 tb.	3 tb.
Celery, chopped	1/4 c.	1/3 c.	1/2 c.
Green pepper, chopped	1 tb.	2 tb.	3 tb.
Flour	1 t.	2 t.	1 tb.
Salt	1/3 t.	2/3 t.	1 t.
Chili powder	1 t.	2 t.	1 tb.
Tomato juice	1 c.	1 1/2 c.	2 c.
Vinegar	1 t.	2 t.	1 tb.
Sugar	1/3 t.	2/3 t.	1 t.
Cooked shrimp	1 c.	2 c.	3 c.

1) Melt the fat in a frying pan; cook the onions, celery, and green pepper in the fat for about 5 min.
2) Add the flour, salt, and chili powder to the fat and blend.
3) Add the tomato juice and cook about 3 min.
4) Stir the vinegar and sugar into the mixture.
5) Add the cooked shrimp to the sauce. Serve with rice.

New England Fish Chowder

(About 4 servings)

Haddock fillet (or other white fish)	1 lb.	Salt pork or bacon, diced fine	1–2 tb.
Water	2 c.	Onion, diced	1 med.
Potatoes, diced	2 c.	Milk and cream (half-and-half)	1 pt.
Salt	1/2 t.		
Pepper	to taste		

1) Cook the fish slowly in the water until it flakes when tested with a fork.
2) Remove fish and separate into flakes.
3) Add potatoes and salt to the water the fish was cooked in and cook about 10 min. or until the potatoes are tender but not soft.
4) Sauté the salt pork or bacon until crisp, add onion and cook until it is slightly brown. Add fish and keep over heat for about a minute.
5) Add fish mixture to potatoes, add half-and-half and continue cooking only until the chowder is hot. Do not boil.
6) Add pepper and additional salt to taste.

[Note: The chowder is even better if it is made the day before it is served. In re-heating it should not be boiled.]

Manhattan Clam Chowder
(About 4 servings)

Salt pork, chopped	1 tb.	Water	1½ c.
Onion, sliced thin	1 medium	Salt	½ t.
Potatoes, raw, cubed	1 c.	Tomatoes, canned	2 c.
		Thyme	¼ t.
Bay leaf	½ sm.		

1) Sauté salt pork until brown.
2) Add onions and cook for a few minutes over low heat.
3) Add potatoes, water, and salt and cook for about 5 minutes or until potatoes are partially tender.
4) Add tomatoes and seasonings and continue cooking until potatoes are done (about 5 minutes).

Louisiana Oyster Loaf
(3 to 4 servings)

Oysters	2–3 doz.	Garlic salt	⅛ t.
Corn meal	1 c.	Bread, French type	1 loaf
Paprika	1 t.	Butter, room temperature	2–4 tb.
Salt	1 t.	Pickles, sour, slivered	½ c.
Pepper	¼ t.		
Cocktail sauce (see p. 585)	½ c.		

1) Drain the oysters; mix corn meal and seasonings and roll the oysters in the mixture.
2) Fry oysters in hot fat until coating is crisp. Drain on absorbent paper.
3) Cut loaf of bread lengthwise about one inch from top to make a lid.
4) Remove the soft part of the bread from the loaf and place the shell and the top in the oven to toast slightly.
5) Butter the inside of the loaf and the top; put the oysters in the bread shell, sprinkle with the pickle, and pour the cocktail sauce over the oysters.
6) Put the lid on the bread and return to oven for a few minutes or until warm through.
7) Remove to serving platter and cut in thick diagonal slices. Serve with an ample supply of lemon wedges.

SAUCES FOR SEAFOOD

Drawn Butter
(About 2¼ c.)

Butter or margarine	½ c.	Pepper	⅛ t.
Flour	3 tb.	Hot water	1½ c.
Salt	½ t.	Lemon juice	1 t.

1) Melt half of the butter, add flour and seasonings, and blend.
2) Add the water, stirring constantly, and cook 5 min.
3) Add the lemon juice, then the remaining butter in small pieces. Blend. A bit of tarragon, marjoram, or chives may be added.

Béarnaise
(About 1 c.)

Onion	1 tb.	Egg yolks, beaten	2
Tarragon vinegar	$\frac{1}{4}$ c.	Parsley, chopped	1 tb.
Butter or margarine	$\frac{1}{2}$ c.	Salt	to taste
Cayenne			

1) Cook the chopped onion in the tarragon vinegar until the volume is reduced to about 1 tb. Cool.
2) Add one third of the butter and the egg yolks.
3) Stir over hot (not boiling) water.
4) When the mixture thickens, add half of the remaining butter and blend.
5) Add the remaining butter and blend.
6) Add the chopped parsley, season with salt and a dash of cayenne, and serve hot.

Bercy
(About 1$\frac{1}{3}$ c.)

Butter or margarine	3 tb.	Flour	2 tb.
Chopped shallot or chives	1 tb.	Fish or chicken stock	1 c.
Salt	$\frac{1}{8}$ t.		

1) Melt 1 tb. of butter and cook the shallots or chives in it 3 or 4 min.
2) Add the flour and blend.
3) Add the stock slowly, stirring to prevent lumping, and cook until the sauce has thickened.
4) Add the remaining butter and salt.

Tartare
(About 1$\frac{1}{4}$ c.)

Mayonnaise	1 c.	Olives, chopped	1 tb.
Parsley, chopped	1 tb.	Capers	1 tb.
Cucumber pickle, chopped	1 tb.	Onion juice	$\frac{1}{4}$ t.

1) Mix all the ingredients except the mayonnaise.
2) Combine the mayonnaise with the mixed ingredients.

Green Condiment Mayonnaise

(About 1 c.)

Mayonnaise	1 c.	Chopped chives or green onions	1 t.
Chopped parsley	1 t.	Chopped spinach	1 tb.

1) Add the finely chopped green condiments to the mayonnaise.
2) Stir carefully to mix evenly.

Mushroom

(About 2 c.)

Butter or margarine	2 tb.	Salt	¼ t.
Flour	3 tb.	Sweet basil	pinch
Mushroom juice and chicken stock	1 c.	White pepper	dash
Mushroom caps	¼ c.	Cream	⅓ c.

1) Melt the fat.
2) Add the flour and stir until well blended.
3) Add the liquid slowly, stirring constantly.
4) Add the seasonings and boil 2 min., stirring slowly but constantly.
5) Add the cream and sliced mushroom caps, and let stand several minutes before serving.

Caper

(About 1 c.)

To 1 c. of thin white sauce (see p. 499), add 2 tb. capers and 1 tb. lemon juice.

Shrimp

(About 1½ c.)

Butter or margarine	1 tb.	Salt	¼ t.
Flour	1 tb.	White pepper	dash
Fish stock	1 c.	Cooked shrimp	⅓ c.

1) Prepare sauce like white sauce (see p. 499).
2) Add the cooked shrimp.

Court Bouillon

(About 1 qt.)

Chopped carrot	1 tb.	Water	1 qt.
Chopped onion	1 tb.	Peppercorns	3
Chopped celery	1 tb.	Cloves	2
Chopped parsley	1 t.	Bay leaf	bit
Butter or margarine	3 tb.	Salt	1 t.
Vinegar	1 tb.		

1) Cook the chopped vegetables gently in the butter or margarine for 3 min.
2) Add the water and all other ingredients, bring to the boiling point, and simmer 15 min.
3) Strain.

Anchovy Sauce
(About 1¼ c.)

Butter or margarine	1½ tb.	Pepper	⅛ t.
Flour	2 tb.	Court bouillon	1 c.
Salt	¼ t.	Anchovy paste	2 t.
Chopped anchovies	2 or 3		

1) Melt the butter or margarine.
2) Add the flour and seasonings and combine thoroughly.
3) Add the court bouillon and stir until the sauce thickens.
4) Add the anchovy paste and stir to blend.
5) Add the chopped anchovies and stir gently.

Cocktail Sauce
(About ½ c.)

Catsup	½ c.	Lemon juice	2 t.
Worcestershire sauce	1–2 t.	Salt	½ t.
Tabasco sauce	few drops	Horseradish	1–2 t.

Mix all ingredients and chill before serving.

FATS AND OILS

Laboratory experiences related to the study of fats and oils can be highlighted to the best advantage in relation to other foods, such as meats, flour mixtures, etc. The use of fat as a cooking medium involves such well-known cookery methods as sautéing, frying, and deep fat frying. (See glossary.) Throughout Sec. IV (Food Preparation), these methods are used for many different foods and dishes. If instructor and students wish to plan for specific projects concerning the use of fats and oils, there are many possibilities. These include:

(1) The interchange of fat and oil in different types of recipes such as flour mixtures, meat and vegetable casseroles, sauces, and sautéed and fried foods.

(2) Experiences with temperature of fat for food being fried. This will present an opportunity to compare results from using automatic fryers with regular deep fat fryers in which the temperature is tested by a thermometer.

(3) Comparing recipes (from different sources) for a familiar fried food such as doughnuts. Since wide variation in the *amount* of fat will be found, it will be interesting to prepare doughnuts from a recipe using a large amount of fat with one using considerably less fat. Palatability, appearance, and cost are some factors to judge in comparison tests.

(4) Criteria for selecting fats and oils for cooking, from the standpoint of cost, ease of use, storage, and palatability.

The following recipes are a few "basics" in which fat or oil figures prominently, either as a cooking medium or as an ingredient.

French Fried Potatoes

1) Wash and pare an Irish potato.
2) Cut lengthwise in ½-inch strips.
3) Soak about 1 hr. in salted ice water and drain between towels.
4) Fry at 380° F. (193° C.) until brown.
5) Drain on unglazed paper and sprinkle lightly with salt.

"Shoestring" Potatoes

1) Wash and pare an Irish potato.
2) Cut lengthwise in ¼-inch to ⅜-inch strips.
3) Soak about 1 hr. in salted ice water.
4) Dry between towels and fry at 390° F. (199° C.).
5) Drain on unglazed paper and sprinkle lightly with salt.

Fish Steaks
(4 servings)

Fish steaks	4	Beaten egg	1
Seasoned flour	½ c.	Dry bread crumbs	½ c.

1) Dip the steaks in flour, then in beaten egg, and then in crumbs.
2) Fry in deep fat at 375° F. (191° C.) to an even, golden brown on both sides.
3) Drain on unglazed paper.

Tuna Fish Balls
(About 4 servings)

Flake tuna	1 7-oz. can
Milk	2–4 tb.
Egg, beaten	1
Salt	⅛ t.
Lemon juice	1 tb.
Parsley, chopped	2 tb.
Bread crumbs	½ c.

1. Mix all ingredients.
2. Drop by teaspoon into deep fat heated to 390° F. (199° C.).
3. Fry to an even, golden brown color and drain on unglazed paper.

Cream Puffs

Ingredients	*For 2*	*For 4*	*For 6*
Water	1/4 c.	1/2 c.	3/4 c.
Butter or margarine	2 tb.	1/4 c.	1/4 c. + 2 tb.
Flour	1/4 c.	1/2 c.	3/4 c.
Salt	Pinch	1/16 t.	1/8 t.
Eggs	1	2	3
Powdered sugar	1/4 c.	1/2 c.	3/4 c.

1) Put the water and butter or margarine together into a saucepan and heat to the boiling point.
2) Sift and measure the flour and add the salt. Add the salt and flour mixture all at once to the boiling water and fat. Stir vigorously. Remove from the fire, but do not cool.
3) Add the eggs, unbeaten, one at a time to the mixture, stirring thoroughly after the addition of each egg.
4) Drop by spoonfuls into fat at 370° F. (188° C.) and fry until brown. Drain.
5) Roll in or dust with powdered sugar.
   [NOTE: These may be served with a fruit sauce for dessert, as an accompaniment for a salad, or as part of a luncheon main course. When used as part of a main course, the sugar may be omitted.]

Deep-dish Apple Pie 1

1) Make *half* of the pastry recipe on p. 626, roll, and cut a design near the center.
2) Choose canned or frozen apples, sweeten if necessary and season to taste.
3) Put the fruit into a suitable baking dish.
4) Fit the crust over the apples and press around the edge of the dish. Trim.
5) Bake about 20 min. at 425° F. (218° C.), reduce temperature to 375° F. (191° C.) and continue baking for about 20 min.

Deep-dish Apple Pie 2

Flour, sifted	1 c.–1 tb.	Oil	1/4 c.
Salt	1/2 t.	Milk	2 tb.

1) Sift the flour with the salt into a mixing bowl.
2) Measure the oil and milk into a small bowl and beat to mix thoroughly.
3) Add liquid to dry ingredients, all at once, and stir rapidly until well, but lightly, mixed. (In warm weather, wrap in waxed paper and chill.)

4) Roll between sheets of waxed paper, cut a design near the center, and fit over apples in a deep dish, as in the preceding recipe.
5) Bake at 425° F. (218° C.), for 20 min., reduce temperature to 375° F. (191° C.) and continue baking for about 20 min.

Corn Muffins 1
(12 medium-sized)

Corn meal	1 c.	Salt	½ t.
Flour, sifted	1 c.	Egg	1
Baking powder	2 t.	Oil	3 tb.
Milk	1 c.		

1) Sift the dry ingredients into a mixing bowl, adding any meal that does not go through the sifter.
2) Beat the egg; add the oil and beat well; add the milk and beat again.
3) Add the liquid to the dry ingredients and stir to moisten the dry ingredients—not until the batter is smooth.
4) Push from a spoon into oiled muffin pans, filling them about ⅔ full.
5) Bake about 20 min. at 400° F. (204° C.).

Corn Muffins 2

Repeat the above, using 3 tb. of melted fat in place of the oil.

CRYSTALLIZATION—SUGAR, JELLY, AND ICE CREAM

Variation in texture of candies, cake frostings, and jellies depends upon techniques used in their preparation and/or ratio of sugar to other ingredients. Crystalline candies are described as "smooth" or "velvety" if the crystals are small; "sugary" or "grainy" if they are large. Noncrystalline candies may owe their texture to the inclusion of a relatively large amount of "foreign substances" or to a combination of high temperature and quick cooling in a thin layer on a cold surface. A recipe may be used as either a candy or a cake frosting recipe by a difference in the temperature to which the sirup is cooked. Influence of acid upon crystallization is also interesting.

Since sugar is an important factor in the formation of the "network" which is a good jelly, the amount used may result in texture varying from too stiff to runny, or in the formation of crystals.

Smoothness of ice cream frozen in a refrigerator may be a matter of the ingredients chosen, stirring while freezing, or both. In any case, the thermostat should be set to "coldest" well ahead of the time the mix is to be put into the container. Some of the techniques that determine the texture of ice cream frozen in a freezer are the temperature of the mix when freezing is started and that of the freezing mixture.

College Fudge 1

(Yield: 1¼ lb.)

Chocolate	2 squares	*or*	
Sugar	2 c.	Cream of tartar	⅛ t.
Milk	⅔ c.	Butter or margarine	2 tb.
Light corn sirup	2 tb.	Vanilla	1 t.

1) Break or shave the chocolate into small pieces so that it will melt easily.
2) Cook together in a saucepan the sugar, milk, chocolate, and corn sirup *or* cream of tartar, stirring until the sugar is dissolved.
3) Continue to cook, stirring occasionally to prevent burning, until the temperature 234° F. (112° C.) is reached.
4) Remove from the fire, add butter or margarine, but *do not stir*. Set aside to cool, placing a thermometer in the pan in such a position that it can be read without moving it. Cool to 110° F. (43° C.).
5) Add vanilla and beat until the fudge loses its shiny look.
6) *Quickly* pour into a slightly buttered pan and, when cool, cut into squares.

College Fudge 2

Ingredients—same as for College Fudge 1.

1) Break or shave the chocolate into small pieces so that it will melt easily.
2) Cook together in a saucepan the sugar, milk, chocolate, and corn sirup *or* cream of tartar, stirring until the sugar is dissolved.
3) Continue to cook, stirring *frequently,* to 234° F. (112° C.).
4) Remove from the fire, add butter or margarine and vanilla, and beat until the fudge loses its glossy look.
5) Pour *quickly* into a slightly buttered pan; when cool, cut into squares.

Make a cake, using a cake mix, *or* frost a commercial unfrosted cake, using the following frosting.

Fudge Frosting

1) Use the recipe for College Fudge *1,* but cook to *232°* F. (111° C.).
2) Beat until fudge loses its shiny look and spread on the cake *quickly*.

Vanilla Divinity

(Yield: 1¼ lb.)

Sugar	2⅓ c.	Water	½ c.
Light corn sirup	½ c.	Salt	¼ t.
or		Egg whites, beaten	2
Cream of tartar	⅔ t.	Vanilla	½ t.
Nut meats	1 c.		

1) Cook together in a saucepan the sugar, corn sirup *or* cream of tartar, salt, and water, stirring until the sugar is completely dissolved.
2) Continue cooking without stirring until the temperature 265° F. (129° C.) is reached. As the mixture cooks, wash away from the sides of the pan any crystals that may form, using thin cloth wound around a fork and dipped into water.
3) Remove from the heat and pour in a fine stream over the stiffly beaten egg whites, beating with a heavy rotary beater during this addition.
4) Beat until the beater turns hard. Continue beating with a wooden spoon.
5) Add vanilla and nuts a short time before the candy is sufficiently beaten. Mix thoroughly. Continue beating until the candy will hold its shape when dropped from a spoon.
6) Drop from the tip of a teaspoon on waxed paper, or turn into a slightly oiled pan and cut in squares.

Make a cake, using a cake mix, *or* use boiled frosting on a commercial unfrosted cake, using the following frosting.

Boiled (Divinity) Frosting

Sugar	2½ c.	Water	½ c.
Light corn sirup	5 tb.	Egg whites	2
or		Flavoring	1½ t.
Cream of tartar	½ t.		

1) Put the sugar, corn sirup *or* cream of tartar, and water together into a saucepan and cook to 240° F. (116° C.).
2) Beat the egg whites until they will hold up in a peak when the beater is lifted.
3) Pour the hot sirup *very slowly* over the beaten eggs, beating constantly during the addition. Add the flavoring.
4) When the frosting becomes stiff, continue the beating with a wooden spoon until it holds its shape when the spoon is lifted.
5) Spread quickly on the cake.

Fondant 1

Sugar	1 c.	Cream of tartar	1/16 t.
Water	½ c. + 2 tb.	Flavoring	½ t.

1) Cook together in a saucepan the sugar, water, and cream of tartar. Stir constantly until the sugar is dissolved. Remove the spoon and do not stir again.
2) Continue cooking and when candy begins to boil, cover the saucepan. Cook for 3 min. with cover on so that the steam which forms will melt sugar crystals from the sides of the pan.

3) Remove the cover and continue cooking until 238° F. (114° C.) is reached. When sugar crystals appear on the sides of the saucepan, wash them down with a cheesecloth-covered fork or clean plastic sponge dipped in cold water.
4) When 238° F. (114° C.) has been reached, remove from the heat and pour at once onto a cold platter that has been rinsed with cold water. Do not try to scrape out the last remaining sirup, as this may cause large crystals.
5) Lay a thermometer in the sirup so that the bulb is at the center of the platter and the temperature can be read without moving the thermometer. Cool to 110° F. (43° C.).
6) Add vanilla and beat with a wooden spoon until it can no longer be beaten.
7) Butter hands and knead candy until no lumps remain.
8) Shape rather small balls.

Fondant 2

Use above recipe, substituting 2½ tb. of light corn sirup for cream of tartar.

Fondant 3

Use above recipe but cook without covering and without washing away crystals as they form at the edge of the boiling sirup. Also, when the candy is poured onto a platter, scrape the saucepan. Cool and beat.

Nut Brittle
(Yield 1¼ lb.)

Granulated sugar	1 c.	Water	¼ c.
Brown sugar	½ c.	Butter or margarine	2 tb.
Light corn sirup	½ c.	Soda	1/16 t.
or		Salt	1/16 t.
Cream of tartar	¼ t.	Nut meats	¾ c.

1) Cook together the sugar, corn sirup *or* cream of tartar, and water to 300° F. (149° C.), stirring only until the sugar is dissolved.
2) Remove from the fire and add butter or margarine, soda, and salt. Stir slightly to mix.
3) Pour a little of the candy into a small warm dish so that it is thick and will not cool quickly.
4) Pour the rest over nut meats on a cold buttered surface, and pull with forks to make a thin, easily broken, candy.
5) Break the brittle into pieces.

Chocolate Caramels
(About 1¼ lbs.)

Chocolate	3 sq.	Condensed milk	½ c.
Sugar	1 c.	Cream	¼ c.
Light corn sirup	½ c.	Milk	½ c.
Vanilla	1 t.		

1) Shave the chocolate, using a vegetable shaver or slicer, into a heavy saucepan.
2) Add sugar, corn sirup, and condensed milk and cook over low heat, stirring frequently, until the mixture is slightly thick.
3) Add the cream and milk slowly, stirring slowly to prevent sticking and cook to 246° F. (119° C.). (Toward the end of the cooking an asbestos mat may be used to advantage.)
4) Add the vanilla, stir to mix, and pour the candy into an oiled pan or dish e.g., a 2 x 4 in. loaf pan).
5) Cool. When cold, loosen around the edges and turn onto a slightly oiled board.
6) Cut into squares, using a sawing motion with a sharp knife (this makes the edges sharp).
7) Wrap each square in waxed paper.

JELLY

To include prevention of crystallization in jelly as well as the influence of ratio of sugar to fruit juice requires preplanning and work in advance of the laboratory period. Desirable fruit for jelly may not be available at the time study of crystallization is scheduled, but fruit juice may be canned or frozen with this and other objectives in mind. Perhaps two interested students would like to prepare the jelly three or four weeks in advance. The following is an example, using plum juice; other juices and suitable directions will be found in books and bulletins which include jelly making.

Plum Jelly

	Fruit Juice	*Sugar*
1)	1 c.	¼ c.
2)	1 c.	¾ c.
3)	1 c.	1¼ c.
4)	1 c.	1½ c.

1) Cook the juice and sugar for jelly 1 to the sheet stage (see pp. 298–299). Check thermometer reading carefully but quickly.
2) Pour the jelly into a scalded, drained jelly glass.
3) Coat with melted paraffin, cover, and store.

Repeat for jellies 2 and 3, being careful to have the same thermometer reading and/or sheet test.

Make jelly 4, cooking to about 10° F. higher than the above jellies and/or past a good sheet test.

Chocolate Ice Cream
(2 quarts)

Chocolate	4 sq.	Egg yolks	2
Milk	1 pt.	Sugar	1½ c.
Stick cinnamon	2-in. stick	Cream	2 c.
Gelatin	1½ t.	Evaporated milk	1¼ c.
Cold water	2 tb.	Vanilla	2 t.

1) Shave the chocolate into a heavy saucepan, using a vegetable shaver or slicer.
2) Add the milk and cinnamon, and heat. Beat to dissolve chocolate. (Use low to moderate heat.) Add half of the sugar.
3) Soak gelatin in water about 5 min., add it to the milk and stir to dissolve.
4) Beat the egg yolks and beat in half of the sugar. Add part of the milk mixture.
5) Stir the egg yolk mixture into the milk in the saucepan and cook until the mixture coats the lifted spoon lightly, stirring slowly. Remove the cinnamon.
6) Remove from the heat, add the cream, evaporated milk, and vanilla and stir to mix thoroughly.
7) Divide the mix among 3 1-qt. freezer cans and freeze, in all cases turning the handle slowly and evenly until it begins to turn hard, then more rapidly until it turns *very* hard.
   (1) Cool the mix to 50° F. (10° C.) and use a freezing mixture of 1 part salt to 8 parts ice.
   (2) Cool the mix to 50° F. (10° C.) and use a freezing mixture of 1 part salt to 3 parts ice.
   (3) Cool the mix to 100° F. (38° C.) and use a freezing mixture of 1 part salt to 8 parts ice.

Grape Frappé

Ingredients	*For 1 qt.*	*For 2 qt.*	*For 1 gal.*
Sugar	¾ c.	1½ c.	3 c.
Water	1½ c.	1½ pt.	1½ qt.
Grape juice	¾ c.	1½ c.	3 c.
Orange juice	3 tb.	¼ c. + 2 tb.	¾ c.
Lemon juice	2 tb.	¼ c.	½ c.

1) Boil the sugar and water 3 min. Chill.
2) Add the fruit juices to the cool sirup and stir.
3) Freeze, using 1 part salt to 3 parts ice, turning the handle slowly at first. The freezing should stop when the mixture is frozen to a mush.

Refrigerator Ice Cream

Gelatin	1/2 t.	Salt	1/8 t.
Cold water	1 tb.	Egg whites	2
Milk	1 c.	Fine sugar	1/3 c.
Egg yolks	2	Heavy cream	1 1/4 c.
Sugar	1/3 c.	Vanilla	1 1/2 t.

1) Soften the gelatin in the cold water.
2) Heat the milk in a heavy saucepan over low heat.
3) Beat the egg yolks; beat in 1/3 c. sugar and the salt.
4) Add some of the milk, and stir the mixture into the milk in the saucepan.
5) Continue stirring until the mixture coats the lifted spoon. Chill thoroughly.
6) Beat the egg whites until they form rounded peaks when the beater is lifted.
7) Add the sugar gradually, beating well after each addition, and fold into the custard mixture.
8) Whip the cream, add the vanilla, and fold it into the above mixture.
9) Pour the mixture into 2 refrigerator trays and put them into the freezing unit.
10) Freeze mix in 1 tray without beating, beat the mix in the other tray after 15 min. and again after 20 min.

Orange Cream Sherbet
(About 1 quart)

Frozen orange juice	2/3 c.	Milk	1 c.
Water	1/3 c.	Cream	1 c.
Sugar	1/2 c.	Salt	dash

1) Blend the frozen juice with water.
2) Add sugar gradually and stir to dissolve.
3) Mix the milk and cream and add salt.
4) Add the sweetened juice gradually, stirring to blend.
5) Pour into an ice tray and place it in the freezing compartment of the refrigerator, set at coldest, *or* in a freezer.
6) Transfer to cold bowl and beat with cold rotary beater after 15 min. and again after 20 min. It should be frozen after about 2 hours.

CEREALS

Custom is responsible for the method used for cooking breakfast cereals. Rolled oats described as "pasty," and undesirable by one person may be called "creamy" by another, and therefore desirable. Awareness of the effect of stirring upon texture of the finished product may well be sharpened by cooking one cereal without and with stirring. The influence of processing methods on rice may be made plain by cooking an equal amount of brown, converted, white, and minute rice. The processors prepare cereals in different forms, from entire grain to finely ground. As the surface exposed to water increases, the amount of water used for a measured quantity of cereal is increased, e. g., more water for finely ground cereals than for flaky ones. Rice is the entire grain most frequently used in our food pattern, though seldom as a breakfast cereal. Time required for cooking varies with the type of processing. A variety of ways in which breakfast cereals are included in cookery will be of interest.

Corn, one of America's contributions to the world's foods, is used extensively in breads, many of which are regional in origin. People from other countries have found cornmeal a welcome cereal product. Perhaps students would like to find recipes to add to those included here and to compare "cornbread" recipes from different parts of the country.

In flour mixtures selected for this laboratory, when the word "oil" is used for preparing a baking utensil, a cooking oil rather than a fat is recommended.

Utensils. For cooking "minute" cereals a fairly heavy saucepan with a close-fitting lid is most desirable. The slight stirring that is necessary is best done with a fork. If longer cooking is preferred, an asbestos mat may be placed under the saucepan after the cereal has cooked for several minutes. A double boiler can also be used for the longer cooking period.

TABLE 41. PROPORTIONS AND TIME FOR COOKING CEREALS OF VARIOUS TYPES

Cereal	*Water*	*Salt*	*Cereal*	*Cooking Time*	
				Boiling (min.)	*Low heat (min.)*
Flaky (partially cooked)	1½ c.	¼ t.	1 c.	3–4	12–15
Granular (partially cooked)	2 c.	¼ t.	1 c.	3–4	15–20
Finely ground (partially cooked)	2½ c.	¼ t.	1 c.	3–4	15–20
Rice:					
Brown	2 c.	¼ t.	1 c.	2–3	30–35
Converted	2½ c.	¼ t.	1 c.	2–3	14
Enriched	2 c.	¼ t.	1 c.	2–3	14
Instant	1 c.	¼ t.	1 c.	Add rice to water, remove from heat, leave covered 5 min.	

1) With Table 41 as a guide, prepare ½ c. of a cereal representative of the types of cereal included—flaky, finely ground, etc.

2) Cook an equal quantity of the flaky cereal, stirring the cereal into the water, and stirring *frequently* as the cereal cooks. (The idea is to exaggerate the stirring to illustrate formation of starch paste.)

Oatmeal-Chocolate Cookies
(About 4 doz.)

Butter or margarine	½ c.	Chocolate bits	1 c.
Vanilla	½ t.	Milk	¼ c.
Sugar	⅓ c.	Flour, sifted	¾ c.
Brown sugar	⅓ c.	Baking powder	2 t.
Egg, unbeaten	1	Salt	½ t.
Nuts, coarsely chopped	½ c.	Rolled oats	½ c.

1) Using butter or margarine at room temperature, add the vanilla, and cream the mixture slightly.
2) Add the sugars and egg and mix thoroughly.
3) Add the nuts and chocolate and stir to mix.
4) Add the milk and stir to blend.
5) Add the baking powder and salt to the flour, sift into the mixture, add the rolled oats, and stir to blend well.
6) Push from teaspoon onto an oiled (*use oil*) baking sheet leaving about 1½ in. between cookies, and bake 10–12 min. at 375° F. (191° C.).
7) Remove to a cooking rack.

Banana-Peanut Crunch Cookies
(About 3 doz.)

Banana, ripe; medium	1	Flour	1 c.
Egg	1	Baking powder	1 t.
Salad oil	2 tb.	Soda	¼ t.
Peanut crunch	⅓ c.	Cinnamon	½ t.
Rolled oats	⅔ c.	Sugar	⅓ c.

1) Mash the banana in a mixing bowl large enough for all ingredients.
2) Add the unbeaten egg, oil, peanut crunch, and rolled oats and mix thoroughly.
3) Sift the flour, measure, sift with the other dry ingredients into the above mixture, and stir to mix well.
4) Drop by teaspoonfuls on an oiled baking sheet, leaving about 1 in. between the cookies.
5) Decorate with sliced maraschino cherries, or multi-colored candy "sprinkles."
6) Bake for 12 to 15 min. in a moderately hot oven—375° F. (191° C.).

Oatmeal Rolls

Yeast	¾ cake	Boiling water	½ c.
Lukewarm water	½ c.	Rolled oats	1 c.
Fat	½ c.	Egg, beaten	1
Sugar	3 tb.	Cardamom seed	½ t.
Salt	¼ t.	Flour	2½ c.

1) Soften the yeast in the lukewarm water.
2) Add the fat, sugar, and salt to the boiling water and stir to mix.
3) Add the rolled oats and mix. Cool to lukewarm.
4) Add the beaten egg and crushed cardamom seed, and stir to blend.
5) Add the yeast.
6) Add flour to make a soft dough and beat well.
7) Let rise to double in bulk.
8) Shape in small balls and place in oiled muffin pans.
9) Cover and leave to double in bulk.
10) Bake for 15 to 20 min. in a very hot oven—450° F. (232° C.).

Cereal Muffins

Rolled wheat or oats	1 c.	Sugar	2 tb.
Flour, sifted	1 c.	Chopped dates	½ c.
Salt	½ t.	Milk	1 c.
Baking powder	2 t.	Egg	1
Oil	3 tb.		

1) Measure the cereal and add ½ of the milk; let it stand about ½ hour.
2) Sift the dry ingredients into a mixing bowl; add the dates and stir to coat and distribute.
3) Add the soaked cereal and stir to blend with dry ingredients.
4) Beat the egg; add the oil and beat; add the remaining milk and beat to mix.
5) Add the liquid to dry ingredients and stir just enough to moisten the dry ingredients.
6) Fill well-oiled muffin pans about ¾ full with the batter.
7) Bake about 20 min. at 425° F. (218° C.).

Lamb Pilaf
(4 servings)

Bacon fat	3 tb.	Rice, uncooked	¾ c.
Lamb, lean, cubed	1½ lb.	Bay leaf	bit
Salt and pepper	to sprinkle	Hot red pepper	1 sm.
Onions, med.	2	Dried prunes, seeded	6–8
Consommé	2½ c.	Lemon	½

1) Melt the bacon fat (range-to-table utensil suggested), add the lamb, and sprinkle with salt and pepper.
2) Add the onions, sliced thin, and sauté until meat and onions are lightly browned.
3) Add 1 c. of consommé, cover, and simmer about 25 min.
4) Add the rest of the consommé; bring to a boil.
5) Add all other ingredients, cover, and continue cooking over moderate heat about 45 min. (Check occasionally and stir if needed).

Boiled Rice Dessert
(4 servings)

Cooked rice	2–3 c.	Milk	1–2 c.

Choice of sugars and/or sirups *

1) Serve the rice in selected dishes.
2) Put milk and 2 or 3 choices of sugar and sirup on the table.

Rice "Pudding"
(4 servings)

Dried figs	¼ lb.	Honey	¼ c.
Cooked rice	2 c.	Preserved ginger	2–3 tb.

Heavy cream ½ c.

1) Simmer the figs until tender and cut them into strips.
2) Combine all ingredients, and put the mixture into serving dishes.
3) Whip the cream and use as a topping.

Cereal "Snacks"

Rice, crisp, bite-size cereal	¼ c.	Peanuts	¼ c.
Wheat, crisp, bite-size cereal	¼ c.	Pretzels (sm.)	¼ c.
Oats, crisp, bite-size cereal	¼ c.	Melted butter or margarine	3 to 4 tb.
Corn, crisp, bite-size cereal	¼ c.		

Cayenne or garlic salt

1) Put the cereals, nuts, and pretzels into a shallow baking pan.
2) Pour the melted butter or margarine over them and mix gently.
3) Bake for 15 min. at 350° F. (177° C.) and turn out onto unglazed paper.
4) Season with cayenne or garlic salt.

[Note: Other ingredients may be chosen.]

* Suggestions: Brown sugar, maple sirup, blackberry sirup.

Wheat-Cheese Toasties
(About 4 servings)

Small shredded wheat biscuits	12–16	Dry mustard	½ t.
Sharp Cheddar cheese, grated	½–¾ c.	Paprika	½ t.

Milk.............to make paste consistency

1) Mix the cheese with seasonings and add milk to make a paste.
2) Spread the shredded wheat with the cheese mixture and place on a baking pan.
3) Set the pan about 3 in. under heat in the broiler and remove when the cheese is melted.
4) Serve as an accompaniment to soup or salad.

Spoon Bread
(4 servings)

Milk	2 c.	Fat	2 tb.
Water	1 c.	Eggs	2 to 4
Corn meal	1 c.	Salt	1 t.

Baking powder.............. 2 t.

1) Heat the milk over low heat until it steams.
2) Mix the corn meal and water, and stir into the hot milk.
3) Cook the mixture until it is thick, stirring occasionally.
4) Add the fat. Cool.
5) Beat the eggs, add salt and baking powder, and fold into the mixture.
6) Pour into an oiled baking dish and bake about 40 min. at 375° F. (191° C.). When done, spoon bread is slightly firmer than cheese soufflé.

Grits Soufflé
(About 4 servings)

Milk	2½ c.	Bacon fat	2 tb.
Water	1 c.	Onion, finely chopped	1 t.
Grits	1 c.	Eggs	2
Salt	¾ t.	Baking powder	1 t.

1) Heat the milk over low heat *or* in a double boiler to steaming.
2) Add the grits and salt to the water; when milk is hot, add the grits.
3) Cook until thick, stirring occasionally; cover and cook slowly (use asbestos mat if saucepan is used) about 1 hour.
4) Add the fat; cool.

5) Beat the eggs, add baking powder and beat to mix.
6) Fold eggs into the cooked grits.
7) Bake in an oiled baking dish for about 40 min. at 375° F. (191° C.).

Apple Corn Bread

(About 16 servings)
(Adapted from a Mennonite recipe)

Flour	¾ c.	Sugar	1 tb.
Corn meal	¾ c.	Egg	1
Baking powder	1½ t.	Oil	2 tb.
Salt	½ t.	Milk	¾ c.
Diced apples	¾ c.		

1) Sift flour, measure ¾ c., add the other dry ingredients, and sift into a mixing bowl.
2) Beat the egg, add oil and milk, and beat again.
3) Add liquid to dry ingredients, along with the apples, and stir to blend.
4) Pour the batter into an oiled 9 x 9 in. pan and bake about 25 min. at 400° F. (204° C.).

Corn Bread

(About 6 servings)

Flour, sifted	½ c.*	Salt	½ t.
Corn meal	1½ c.*	Sugar	1 tb.
Baking powder	¾ t.	Eggs	2
Soda	½ t.	Oil	2 tb.
Sour milk	1 c.		

1) Sift all dry ingredients into a mixing bowl. If all meal does not go through the sifter, add it and stir to mix evenly.
2) Beat the eggs; add the oil and beat again.
3) Add the milk, stir, and add liquid to dry ingredients.
4) Stir to mix evenly.
5) Pour the batter into an oiled pan—8 inch square or large layer cake pan —and bake about 40 min. at 425° F. (218° C.).

Boston Brown Bread

(About 16 slices)

Corn meal	1 c.	Salt	1 t.
Rye flour	1 c.	Soda	1½ t.
Whole wheat flour	1 c.	Molasses	¾ c.
Sour milk	2 c.		

* These proportions may be varied from all corn meal to half meal and half flour.

1) Mix and sift the dry ingredients into a mixing bowl. Do not discard the part of the flour that will not go through the sifter, but add it to the sifted ingredients and mix well.
2) Add the molasses and the milk, beat thoroughly, and turn into molds to about two-thirds full.
3) Cover and steam about 2 hr.
4) Remove from the molds and dry in an oven about 15 min. at 375° F. (191° C.).

Corn Sticks
(About 10 to 30 sticks)

Corn meal	1 c.	Salt	½ t.
Soda	½ t.	Egg	1
Sour milk	1 c.		

1) Sift the dry ingredients together into a mixing bowl. Add the meal that does not go through the sifter and mix well.
2) Beat the egg and add the sour milk.
3) Combine the liquid and dry ingredients.
4) Pour the mixture into hot, well-oiled corn-stick pans, and bake until brown in a hot oven—400° to 425° F. (204° to 218° C.)—using the higher temperature if small pans are used.

Johnnycakes *
(4 servings)
(Adapted from a Rhode Island recipe)

Corn meal (water-ground)	2 c.	Salt	½ t.
Sugar	2 tb.	Boiling water	about 1½ c.

1) Mix the dry ingredients in a mixing bowl.
2) Stir in boiling water to make a batter thick enough to drop from a spoon.
3) Drop onto a hot, well-oiled griddle (or heavy frying pan) and cook until brown.
4) Turn and brown the other side.
5) Serve with meat or fish (or wrap and take on a journey, as used originally).

Hush Puppies

Corn meal	2 c.	Milk	1½ c.
Baking powder	2 t.	Water	1 c.
Salt	1 t.	Onion, chopped	¼ c.

* "Journey" cakes.

1) Sift the dry ingredients into a heavy saucepan.
2) Add the milk and water and mix well.
3) Add the onion; cook over medium heat, stirring slowly, until the mixture is *thick*.
4) Cool; mold into rather small cylindrical shapes.
5) Fry until brown in either shallow or deep fat at 380° F. (193° C.).
6) Drain on unglazed paper.
7) Serve with other appetizers or as one of assorted breads for a luncheon.

Polenta with Chicken Livers

(About 4 servings)
(Adapted from an Italian recipe)

Butter or margarine	½ c.	Pepper	⅛ t.
Bacon, sm. pieces	3 sl.	Chicken stock	1½ c.
Chicken livers	10	Boiling water	1½ qts.
Sage	½ t.	Salt	1 t.
Salt	¼ t.	Corn meal	3–3½ c.

1) Melt butter or margarine in a saucepan.
2) Add bacon, chicken livers, and seasonings; then brown.
3) Add stock, cook 10 min., and set aside.
4) Put water and salt into a heavy saucepan and bring to a boil.
5) Pour the corn meal into it slowly, and stir slowly until the mixture leaves the sides of the pan easily.
6) Pour the mush into a serving dish and pour the chicken liver mixture over it. Serve at once.

FLOUR MIXTURES

Suggestions for laboratory. The various types of flour mixtures have been discussed with no reference to planned laboratory for the preparation of each. No set plan would be feasible for all situations; instructors and students can organize activities possible within time allotment and the interests of the group. For example, in one place a whole laboratory period might be spent with medium batters; in another, both thin and medium batters might be planned for one period.

Prior to student activity, techniques suited to the types of mixtures and the appearance of the batters and doughs may well be demonstrated. Such demonstrations will serve to clarify terminology and give students, especially those with little or no acquaintance with preparation of these foods, a clear idea of how to proceed and of results to be expected. Student participation in planning the items to be prepared and individual choice of those recipes for which each student is to be responsible, will add interest to the preparations.

THIN BATTERS

Popovers
(8 Popovers)

Flour	1 c.	Eggs	2
Salt	⅛ t.	Oil	1 tb.
Milk	1 c.		

1) Sift flour and measure; add salt, and sift again into a mixing bowl.
2) Beat the eggs thoroughly.
3) Add the oil and beat well.
4) Add the milk and beat well.
5) Add the liquid to the dry ingredients and stir and beat the batter until smooth.
6) Fill oiled popover or muffin pans or custard cups about half full with the batter.
7) Bake in a very hot oven—450° F. (232° C.)—for 20 min., then reduce temperature to 350° F. (177° C.) for about 20 min., or until the popovers are dry enough to hold their shape. They slip from the pan easily and are shiny on the bottom when done.

Cream Puffs
(9 to 12 Cream Puffs)

Water	1 c.	Flour	1 c.
Butter or margarine	½ c.	Salt	⅛ t.
Eggs	4		

1) Heat the water and butter or margarine in a saucepan to boiling.
2) Add the flour and salt all at once and stir vigorously to blend the ingredients thoroughly.
3) Remove from the fire, but do not cool.
4) Add the unbeaten eggs, one at a time, and stir to combine well after each egg is added.
5) Drop from the end of a spoon on an oiled baking sheet.
6) Bake in a hot oven—425° F. (218° C.)—for 10 min., then lower the temperature to 375° F. (191° C.) and bake for 20 min., or until the cream puffs are firm enough to hold their shape when removed from the oven.
7) Cool.
8) Cut along the side and fill with cream filling (or a variation), sweetened fruit, or whipped cream.

MEDIUM BATTERS

Basic mix. This mix is suitable, with some adjustments, for griddle cakes, waffles, muffins, and biscuits.

Basic Mix

Flour	6 c.	Baking powder	2 tb. + 1 t.
Salt	1½ t.	Fat	¾ c.

1) Sift the flour, measure, and sift with salt and baking powder 2 or 3 times.
2) Cut in the fat until the mixture resembles coarse meal.
3) Store in a closely covered metal container.

Sweet Milk Griddle Cakes
(4–8 Cakes)

Flour	1½ c.	Egg	1
Baking powder	1¾ t.	Oil	1 tb.
Salt	½ t.	Milk	1 c.

1) Sift and measure the flour; add the leavening material and salt, and sift again into a mixing bowl.
2) Beat the egg thoroughly, and add the oil. Beat well.
3) Add the milk and beat again.
4) Add the liquid to the dry ingredients and stir only enough to mix, leaving the batter rather lumpy.
5) Pour the batter from the end of a large spoon or from a pitcher on a hot griddle, and cook until the cake is puffed and bubbles appear on the surface.
6) Turn the cake and cook the other side. *Do not turn a second time.*

Rosettes

Flour, sifted	1¼ c.	Egg	1
Salt	⅛ t.	Oil	1 tb.
Milk	1 c.		

1) Sift the flour and salt into a mixing bowl.
2) Beat the egg; add oil and beat; add milk and beat.
3) Add the liquid to the dry ingredients gradually, stirring to keep the batter smooth; turn the batter into a bowl not much larger than the rosette iron.
4) Heat the rosette iron in the fat while fat for frying is heating to 375° F. (191° C.).
5) Remove the iron from the fat and touch it to unglazed paper to remove possible drops of fat.
6) Dip the iron into the batter to about ¾ its depth and shake gently to remove drops of batter.
7) Cook in the fat until the rosette is evenly browned.
8) Cool, upside down, on unglazed paper.

9) Roll in powdered sugar and serve with fruit as dessert *or* use as a base for a creamed dish, e.g., creamed chicken.

Thin Pancakes

Flour, sifted	1 c.	Egg	1
Salt	½ t.	Oil	1 tb.
Baking powder	¾ t.	Milk	1 c.

1) Sift the flour, salt, and baking powder into a mixing bowl.
2) Beat the egg; add the oil and beat; add the milk and beat.
3) Add the liquid to the dry ingredients about ⅓ at a time and stir to blend well.
4) Pour batter onto a hot griddle to make cakes of desired size.
5) Cook until the cakes have browned on the bottom, turn and brown on the other side.
6) Remove from the griddle, spread with jelly, and roll quickly.
7) Keep the cakes hot in the oven until ready to serve. (May be cooked at the table on a grill for immediate service.)

Sour Milk Griddle Cakes
(4–8 Cakes)

Flour	1⅓ c.	Egg	1
Baking powder	½ t.	Oil	1 tb.
Soda	½ t.	Buttermilk	1 c.
Salt	½ t.		

1) Combine ingredients and cook cakes as directed above.

Griddle Cakes from Basic Mix

Basic mix	1½ c.	Egg	1
Milk	1 c.		

1) Put the mix into a mixing bowl. Cut with knives or fork to break fat in small particles.
2) Beat the egg and add the milk, beating with the egg.
3) Combine the two mixtures and stir to blend, leaving the mixture lumpy.
4) Bake as above.

Variations, using any of the above recipes:

1) Make the cakes small—about 2 in. in diameter—and serve, buttered, as one of two or three breads for tea.
2) Increase the milk in the sweet milk recipe to 1½ c.; use the griddle cakes as the "cake" for short cake, with any fresh or frozen fruit filling. The cakes may be topped with cheese sauce and crisp bacon as a luncheon dish or with creamed chicken or fish.

Sweet Milk Waffles

Flour	1½ c.	Egg yolks	2
Salt	½ t.	Oil	3 tb.
Baking powder	1¼ t.	Milk	1 c.
Egg whites	2		

1) Sift and measure the flour; add leavening material and salt, and sift again into a mixing bowl.
2) Beat the egg yolks thoroughly; add the oil and beat well.
3) Add the milk and beat again.
4) Combine with the dry ingredients.
5) Beat the egg whites until they are stiff but not dry. Fold them into the mixture.
6) When the baker is hot, pour batter quickly into the center until it extends to about 1 in. from the edge, and close the baker.
7) Cook until brown.

Sour Milk Waffles

Flour	1⅓ c.	Egg yolks	2
Salt	½ t.	Oil	3 tb.
Soda	½ t.	Sour milk	1 c.
Baking powder	¼ t.	Egg whites	2

Combine the ingredients by the above method.

Waffles from Basic Mix

Basic mix	1½ c.	Eggs	2
Milk	1 c.		

1) Put the mix into a mixing bowl. Cut with knives or fork to break fat in small particles.
2) Separate the eggs and beat the yolks.
3) Add the milk to the beaten yolks, and beat to mix well.
4) Combine and stir to mix well.
5) Beat the egg whites until they are stiff but not dry and fold them into the above mixture.
6) Cook as above.

Variations. 1) Before closing the baker, distribute one of the following over the batter:

a) Chopped nuts.
b) Shredded coconut.
c) Uncooked bacon in 1-in. pieces.
d) Thin pieces of cheese about 1-in. square.

2) Substitute corn meal for half the flour in either sweet or sour milk waffles. Serve with creamed or curried chicken or meat as a luncheon dish.
3) Put chopped nuts or coconut into the batter and top waffles with a fruit sauce as dessert.
4) Cook ginger bread batter in the waffle baker and top with spiced apple sauce (see p. 494).
5) Add 2 squares of chocolate to cake pattern 1 (see below) and cook in a waffle baker. Serve with raspberry preserves.

CAKE PATTERNS

1.

3 c. flour 4½ t. B.P. (Tar. or Phos.) ½ t. salt	1½ c. sugar	
1 egg	¼ c. fat	1¼ c. milk

1 t. flavoring
Stir ½ min.

2.

3 c. flour 4 t. B.P. (Tar. or Phos.) ½ t. salt	1½ c. sugar	
2 eggs	½ c. fat	1 c. milk

1 t. flavoring
Stir 1 min.

3.

3 c. flour 3½ t. B.P. (Tar. or Phos.) ½ t. salt	1½ c. sugar	
3 eggs	¾ c. fat	¾ c. milk

1 t. flavoring
Stir 1½ min.

4.

3 c. flour 3 t. B.P. (Tar. or Phos.) ½ t. salt	1½ c. sugar	
4 eggs	1 c. fat	½ c. milk

1 t. flavoring
Stir 1½ min.

5.

3 c. flour 2½ t. B.P. (Tar. or Phos.) ½ t. salt	1½ c. sugar	
5 eggs	1¼ c. fat	¼ c. milk

1 t. flavoring
Stir 2 min.

6.

3 c. flour 2 t. B.P. (Tar. or Phos.) ½ t. salt	1½ c. sugar
6 eggs	1½ c. fat

1 t. flavoring
Stir 2 min.

Proportions for cake patterns.

1. Use half as much sugar as flour.
2. Use ¼ c. fat for each egg.
3. Use fat and milk together equal to the amount of sugar.

4. Use 1½ t. quick-acting baking powder per cup of flour.
5. When more than 1 egg is used, decrease the amount of baking powder ½ t. for each added egg.

Method for cake patterns.

1. Cream the fat, adding flavoring while creaming.
2. Add the sugar slowly, and cream thoroughly.
3. Add the beaten egg yolks, and blend well.
4. Sift the flour, measure, and sift again with the salt.
5. Add one-half of the flour and stir to blend.
6. Add the milk and stir to blend.
7. Add the baking powder to the other half of the flour and sift into the batter.
8. Stir the length of time stated below the pattern.
9. Beat the egg whites until stiff but not dry and fold into the batter, using a wooden spoon.
10. Pour into an oiled cake pan and push the batter well to the sides and corners of the pan.
11. Bake at the appropriate temperature:
    Loaf .... 350° F. (177° C.)
    Layer .... 360° F. (182° C.)
    Cup .... 360° F. (182° C.)

Cake pattern variations:

Orange Cake

1) In cake pattern 2, substitute orange juice for the milk and 2 t. of grated orange rind for the vanilla. Instead of the 4 t. of baking powder, use 2 t., and ½ t. of soda.
2) Bake in oiled muffin pans for about 20 min. in a moderate oven—360° F. (182° C.).
3) Frost with orange frosting. (See p. 616.)

Maple-Walnut Cake

1) In cake pattern 3, decrease the fat by 3 tb. and add 1 c. of finely chopped walnut meats.
2) Bake in oiled layer pans for about 35 min. in a moderate oven—360° F. (182° C.).
3) Frost with maple frosting.

Home-made Cake Mix *

Hydrogenated fat........	2 c.	Cake flour............	12 c.
Sugar (superfine)........	6 c.	Baking powder........	5 tb.
Salt..........	2 t.		

* Laboratory work by Mayme Colson and Marialyce Smith.

1) Cream the fat, in the large bowl of a mixer, at medium speed for about 1 min., pushing it from the sides with a rubber spatula.*
2) Add half of the sugar gradually and cream well.
3) Measure the flour and sift once; then sift 3 times with the other half of the sugar, the baking powder, and the salt. Add to the above.
4) Store in a closely covered container in a cool place.

Cake, Using Home-made Mix

Mix	4½ c. + 2 tb.	Vanilla	1 t.
Eggs	2	Milk	1 c.

1) Put the cake mix into the large bowl of a mixer.*
2) Add the unbeaten eggs, vanilla, and half of the milk.
3) Blend at low speed, and beat 1 min. at medium speed.
4) Add the remaining milk and blend at low speed, then beat 2 min. at medium speed.
5) Divide the batter evenly between two 9-in. layer pans which have been lined with waxed paper.
6) Bake for about 35 min. in a moderate oven—350° F. (177° C.).

Plain Cake
(About 16 servings)

Butter or margarine	⅔ c.	Cake flour	2 c.
Vanilla	1 t.	Baking powder	1 t.
Sugar	1 c.	Salt	¼ t.
Eggs	3	Milk	⅓ c.

1) Cream the fat, adding the flavoring during the creaming.
2) Add the sugar gradually, and cream well after each addition.
3) Add the beaten egg yolks, and blend well.
4) Sift the flour, measure; add salt and sift again.
5) Add one half of the flour and salt to the mixture, stirring enough to blend.
6) Add the milk and stir enough to blend.
7) Add the baking powder to the remaining flour, and sift into the batter.
8) Stir the batter 1½ min.
9) Beat the egg whites stiff but not dry, and fold into the batter, using a wooden spoon.
10) Bake in an oiled square cake pan for about 50 min. in a moderate oven —350° F. (177° C.).

* The mixing may be done by hand.

Chocolate Cake
(About 16 servings)

Chocolate	4 squares	Eggs	2
Butter or margarine	½ c.	Cake flour	2 c.
Vanilla	1 t.	Soda	½ t.
Sugar	1 c.	Salt	¼ t.
		Baking powder	½ t.
Sour milk	1 c.		

1) Melt the chocolate over water in a double boiler.
2) Cream the fat, adding the vanilla during the creaming.
3) Add the sugar gradually, creaming well after each addition.
4) Add the unbeaten eggs, one at a time, stirring the mixture after each addition until it is very light.
5) Add the melted chocolate and blend thoroughly.
6) Sift the flour, measure; add soda, salt, and baking powder, and sift twice.
7) Add about one half of the dry ingredients and stir to blend.
8) Add the milk and stir to blend.
9) Add the remaining dry ingredients and stir 1 min.
10) Bake in an oiled square cake pan for about 45 min. in a moderate oven —340° F. (171° C.)—or in layer-cake pans for about 30 min. at 350° F. (177° C.).

Apple Sauce Cake
(About 16 servings)

Shortening	⅓ c.	Soda	½ t.
Sugar *	1 c.	Nutmeg	1 t.
Cold apple sauce (unsweetened)	1 c.	Baking powder	½ t.
General utility flour	2 c.	Cinnamon	1 t.
		Raisins	½ c.
Nut meats, chopped	½ c.		

1) Cream the shortening.
2) Add the sugar gradually and continue creaming.
3) Add the apple sauce and stir to blend.
4) Sift the flour, measure; add baking powder, soda, and spices; and sift twice.
5) Add the raisins and nuts to the flour mixture and stir to coat them.
6) Add to the first mixture and stir ½ min.
7) Bake in a square cake pan for about 40 min. in a moderate oven—350° F. (177° C.).

* Honey may be substituted for half of the sugar.

[NOTE: This mixture may be baked in a larger pan, spreading it thin and baking for about 25 min. in a moderately hot oven—375° F. (191° C.). Cut into squares or strips and serve as cookies.]

WHITE CAKE

Butter or margarine *	¾ c.	Cake flour	3 c.
Flavoring extract	1 t.	Baking powder	2 t.
Sugar	1½ c.	Salt	¼ t.
Milk	1 c.	Egg whites	4

1) Cream the butter or margarine, adding the extract while creaming.
2) Add the sugar gradually, creaming well after each addition.
3) Sift and measure the flour and sift again with the other dry ingredients.
4) Add about ⅓ of the flour to the above mixture and stir to blend.
5) Add the milk and stir to blend.
6) Add the remaining dry ingredients and stir 2 min.
7) Beat the egg whites until they stand in peaks when the beater is withdrawn, and fold them into the batter.
8) Bake in layers for 25 to 30 min. in a moderate oven—360° F. (182° C.).

GOLD CAKE

Butter or margarine	1 c.	Cream of tartar	2 t.
Lemon rind, grated	1 t.	Soda	1 t.
Sugar	1¾ c.	Salt	¼ t.
Egg yolks	7	Nutmeg	½ t.
Cake flour	3¼ c.	Milk	1 c.

1) Cream the fat, adding the lemon rind during the creaming.
2) Add the sugar gradually, creaming well after each addition.
3) Add the egg yolks, unbeaten, one at a time, and blend well.
4) Sift the flour, measure, add other dry ingredients, and sift again.
5) Add about ⅓ of the dry ingredients; stir to blend.
6) Add half of the milk and stir to blend.
7) Alternate dry ingredients and milk, stirring to blend after each addition.
8) Bake for 30 to 35 min. at 350° F. (177° C.).

PLAIN SPONGE CAKE
(About 16 servings)

Eggs	4	Lemon rind, grated	2 t.
Sugar	1 c.	Cake flour	1 c.
Lemon juice	1 tb.	Salt	½ t.

* Hydrogenated fat may be used, substituting ½ c. plus 2½ tb. This gives a whiter cake.

1) Beat the egg yolks until they are thick and light yellow in color.
2) Add the sugar, about 2 tb. at a time, and beat after each addition.
3) Add the lemon juice and rind, and blend well.
4) Sift the flour, measure; add the salt, and sift twice.
5) Beat the egg white until it is stiff enough to stand in a peak when the beater is lifted.
6) Add half of the flour, about 2 tb. at a time, to the batter and fold it in carefully, using a wooden spoon.
7) Add half of the beaten egg white and fold it in carefully.
8) Add the remaining flour and then the remaining egg white, folding in as directed above.
9) Pour the batter into an unoiled tube cake pan.
10) Drop the pan containing the batter to the work surface 3 or 4 times from a height of about 6 in.
11) Bake for from 30 to 40 min. at 350° F. (177° C.).
12) Invert the pan on a wire cake cooler, and remove the cake from the pan when cold.

SIRUP SPONGE CAKE *
(About 16 servings)

Sugar	1 c.	Lemon juice	1½ tb
Water	½ c.	Grated lemon rind	½ t.
Egg whites	6	Cake flour	1 c.
Egg yolks	6	Salt	¼ t.

1) Boil the sugar and water together to 242° F. (117° C.).
2) Beat the egg whites until they form peaks when the beater is lifted.
3) Pour the sirup over the egg whites *slowly,* beating constantly. Cool.
4) Add egg yolks, beaten until thick, and fold in thoroughly.
5) Add lemon rind and juice.
6) Sift the flour, measure, add salt, and sift twice.
7) Add the flour—about 2 tb. at a time—and fold in carefully, using a wooden spoon.
8) Pour the batter into an unoiled tube cake pan.
9) Drop the pan to the work surface 3 or 4 times from a height of about 6 in.
10) Bake for about 30 to 40 min. at 350° F. (177° C.).
11) Invert the pan on a wire cake cooler, and remove the cake when it is cold.

* For sirup sponge cake or sirup angel cake, sirups may be used in place of the sugar. The amount of sirup equals that of the sugar and water, and the temperature to which it is cooked is 4° F. higher than for the sugar and water.

Angel Cake
(About 16 servings)

Cake flour	1 c.	Cream of tartar	1 t.
Egg whites	1 c.	Vanilla	3/4 t.
Salt	1/4 t.	Almond extract	1/4 t.

Granulated sugar (fine) . . 1 1/4 c.

1) Sift the flour, measure, and sift twice.
2) Beat the egg whites until they are foamy; add the salt and cream of tartar, and continue beating until they are stiff enough to hold up in peaks which bend over slightly when the beater is lifted. During the beating, add the flavoring.
3) Fold in the sugar carefully, about 2 tb. at a time, using a wooden spoon.
4) Fold in the flour in the same way.
5) Pour the batter into an unoiled tube cake pan.
6) Drop the pan to the work surface 3 or 4 times from a height of about 6 in.
7) Bake for 30 to 40 min. at 350° F. (177° C.).
8) Remove from the oven, and invert the pan on a wire cake cooler. Remove the cake when cold.

Sirup Angel Cake
(About 16 servings)

Sugar	1 1/4 c.	Salt	1/4 t.
Water	3/4 c.	Cream of tartar	3/4 t.
Egg whites	1 c.	Flavoring	1 t.

Cake flour . . . . .1 c.

1) Sift the flour, measure, and sift twice.
2) Cook the sugar and water to 236° F.
3) Beat the egg whites until they are foamy; add salt and cream of tartar and continue beating until they hold up in peaks which bend over slightly when the beater is lifted. During the beating, add the flavoring.
4) Add the sirup to the egg whites, beating constantly. Beat until cool.
5) Fold in the flour, about 2 tb. at a time.
6) Pour the batter into an unoiled tube cake pan.
7) Drop the pan to the work surface 3 or 4 times from a height of about 6 in.
8) Bake for 30 to 40 min at 350° F. (177° C.).
9) Remove from the oven and invert on a wire cake cooler. Remove the cake when cold.

Orange Chiffon Cake

(About 16 servings)

Cake flour	2¼ c.	Egg yolks	5
Sugar	1 c.	Orange juice	¾ c.
Baking powder	2 t.	Grated orange rind	2 tb.
Salt	1 t.	Egg white	1 c.
Salad oil	½ c.	Cream of tartar	½ t.

1) Sift and measure the flour, and sift it with the other dry ingredients into a mixing bowl.
2) Make a well in the dry ingredients and add the oil, unbeaten egg yolks, liquid, and orange rind.
3) Beat with a spoon until smooth.
4) Beat the egg white until it is foamy and add the cream of tartar.
5) Continue beating until the egg white forms firm peaks when the beater is lifted.
6) Add the first mixture to the egg whites slowly, folding it in gently with a wooden spoon or rubber spatula until just blended. (*Be careful not to mix too much*).
7) Pour the batter into an unoiled 10-in. tube pan and bake for 65 to 70 min. in a moderately low oven—325° F. (163° C.).
8) Invert the pan on a wire cake cooler and allow the cake to cool in the pan.

FROSTINGS

Boiled (Divinity) Frosting

(See p. 590.)

Fudge Frosting

(See p. 589)

Seven-Minute Frosting

Egg whites	2	Water	⅓ c.
Brown sugar	1½ c.	Light corn sirup	1 tb.
Salt	dash	Vanilla	1 t.

1) Combine all ingredients except vanilla in the top of a double boiler; beat to mix.
2) Place over boiling water; beat with a rotary beater until the frosting forms peaks when the beater is lifted (7–10 min.).
3) Remove from water, add vanilla, and beat until frosting is thick enough to spread.
4) Spread on the cake.

Boiled Frosting for Decorating

Sugar	2½ c.	Water	⅔ c.
Light corn sirup	⅓ c.	Egg whites	2
Salt	⅛ t.	Flavoring	1 t.

1) Put the sugar, corn sirup, salt, and water into a saucepan and heat, stirring until the sugar has dissolved.
2) Beat the egg whites until foamy.
3) When the sirup reaches the boiling point, add 3 tb. of it to the egg white, beating during the addition.
4) Continue to cook the sirup to 250° F. (121° C.).
5) While cooking the sirup, continue to beat the egg whites until they hold up in a peak when the beater is lifted. (They should be stiff, but not dry.)
6) Pour the sirup slowly over the beaten egg whites, beating constantly with a rotary beater during the addition, and until the frosting is stiff.
7) Continue to beat, using a wooden spoon, until the frosting begins to lose its gloss. It will hold its shape when the spoon is withdrawn.
8) Add the flavoring and beat to blend.
9) Put frosting into a pastry tube, pastry gun, or parchment cone, choosing the decorating tube desired, and decorate the frosted cake.
   [Note: If the frosting becomes too dry, a drop or two of water may be added.]

Jelly Frosting

Tart jelly	½ c.
Egg white	1
Lemon juice if desired	

1) Put the jelly and unbeaten egg white into the top of a double boiler over boiling water.
2) Beat continuously with a rotary egg beater until the frosting will stand in peaks when the beater is lifted.
3) Spread on the cake.

Mocha Frosting

Butter or margarine	⅓ c.	Salt	¼ t.
Confectioners' sugar	4 c.	Chocolate	1 square
Vanilla	½ t.	Coffee, strong	⅓ c.

1) Cream the butter, add part of the sugar gradually, and blend thoroughly.
2) Add vanilla and salt.
3) Melt chocolate over hot water and add, stirring until well blended.
4) Add sugar, alternating with coffee, until all the sugar has been added and the frosting is of the right consistency to spread.

Orange Frosting

Orange juice	2 tb.	Grated orange rind	2 t.
Lemon juice	1 tb.	Confectioners' sugar	3 c.
Melted butter or margarine	¼ c.		

1) Mix the fruit juices and rind.
2) Add one half of the sugar and the melted butter, and blend.
3) Add the remaining sugar and blend well.
4) Spread on the cake.

Bittersweet Coating

Chocolate	2 squares	Butter or margarine	2 t.

1) Melt the chocolate and butter over hot water and blend. Cool slightly.
2) Pour over cake that has been frosted with boiled frosting. Pour so that the chocolate covers the top and runs down the sides unevenly.

Crumb Topping

Butter or margarine	¼ c.	Flour	½ c.
Sugar	⅓ c.	Spice to flavor	

1) Cream the butter.
2) Add the sugar and cream well.
3) Add the flour and spice, and mix well.
4) Sprinkle over an unbaked loaf cake.
5) Bake at the temperature for that cake.
   [Note: This gives an interesting finish to the top of any loaf cake. It may be sprinkled with chopped nuts or garnished with nut halves if desired.]

Broiled Frosting

Brown sugar	1 c.	Chopped nuts	½ c.
		or	
Cream	2 tb.	Coconut	½ c.
Melted butter or margarine	2 tb.		

1) Mix the ingredients.
2) Spread over a baked cake and set into a broiler, about 2 in. below the heat, until lightly browned and bubbly—2 or 3 min.

Coffee Cream Filling

Milk	1 c.	Salt	¼ t.
Instant coffee	2 t.	Flour	3 tb.
Sugar	¼ c.	Egg	1

1) Heat the milk over low heat in a heavy saucepan and dissolve the coffee in it.
2) Mix the sugar, salt, and flour; stir in the scalded milk, return the mixture to the saucepan, and cook until thick.
3) Beat the egg; add the hot mixture, stirring constantly.
4) Cool.

THICK BATTERS

A. Make muffins by the following recipe:

Muffins
(12 medium sized)

Flour	2 c.	Sugar	3 tb.
Salt	½ t.	Egg	1
Baking powder	2 t.	Oil	3 tb.
Milk	1 c.		

1) Sift and measure the flour; add the other dry ingredients and sift into a mixing bowl.
2) Beat the egg thoroughly.
3) Add the oil and beat well.
4) Add the milk and beat again.
5) Combine the liquid and dry ingredients and stir quickly until the dry ingredients are *just moist*. The batter is still lumpy.
6) Drop quickly into oiled muffin pans, holding the spoon close to the pan and pushing the batter off with a spatula. Fill the pans about ⅔ full.
7) Bake as follows. 5 min. at 375° F. (191° C.); raise to 425° F. (218° C.) for about 15 min.

B. Muffins from Basic Mix

Basic mix	2 c.	Egg	1
Sugar	¼ c.	Milk	1 c.

1) Put the mix into a mixing bowl. Cut with knives or a fork until the fat is broken into small particles.
2) Add the sugar and stir to mix well.
3) Beat the egg, add the milk, and combine with above mixture.
4) Bake as above.

C. Make muffins from a commercial mix, following the directions on the package.

D. Bake frozen muffins.

E. Make one of the varieties listed in Table 42, p. 618, using the muffin method for combining the ingredients.

TABLE 42. MUFFINS OF VARIOUS KINDS

Muffin	*Flour*	*Salt*	*Baking Powder*	*Sugar*	*Eggs*	*Milk*	*Oil*	*Other Ingredients*
Whole wheat	1 c. 1 c. whole wheat	½ t.	2 t.	2 tb.	1	1 c.	3 tb.	½ c. dried fruit or ¼ c. crisp bacon
Rice	2 c. ¾ c. boiled rice	¾ t.	2½ t.	3 tb.	1 + 1 yolk	1 c.	2 tb.	3 tb. grated orange rind
Bran	1¼ c. ¾ c. bran	½ t.	1 tb.	2 t.	1	1 c.	3 tb.	½ c. chopped dates or figs 2 tb. molasses or honey
Corn	1 c. 1 c. corn meal	½ t.	2 t.		1	1 c.	3 tb.	¼ c. crisp bacon
Berry	2 c.	½ t.	2 t.	¼ c.	1	1 c.	3 tb.	½ c. fresh berries (blue, black, or cranberries)
Nut	2 c.	½ t.	2 t.	3 tb.	1	1 c.	3 tb.	½ c. chopped nuts
Spice	2 c.	½ t.	2 t.	3 tb.	1	1 c.	3 tb.	½ t. each—cloves, cinnamon & allspice ½ c. currants
Waikiki	1 c. ¾ c. corn meal	½ t.	1–¾ t.	¼ c.	1	1 c.	3 tb.	½ t. lemon rind ½ c. crushed pineapple (drained)

Sally Lunns
(About 18)
(English)

Butter or margarine	2 tb.	Yeast	1 cake
Sugar	2 tb.	Lukewarm water	1/4 c.
Salt	1 t.	Eggs	3
Milk	1 c.	Flour *	3 3/4 c.

1) Cream the butter or margarine; add the sugar and salt, and cream.
2) Scald the milk and add to the above, stirring to combine well.
3) Soften the yeast in the water and, when the milk is lukewarm, add the yeast and stir to combine.
4) Beat the eggs and add to the mixture.
5) Add about half of the flour and beat thoroughly.
6) Add the remaining flour and beat well. Cover the bowl.
7) Let the mixture rise until light—about 1 hour.
8) Fill oiled muffin pans about 2/3 full, cover, and let the batter rise until it fills the pans—about 30 min.
9) Bake for 30 min. in a moderately hot oven—375° F. (191° C.).

Drop Biscuits
(12 to 15 Biscuits)

Flour	1 1/2 c.	Baking powder	1 2/3 t.
Salt	1/2 t.	Fat	3 tb.
Milk	2/3 c.		

1) Combine the ingredients by the biscuit method.
2) Drop spoonfuls on a lightly oiled baking sheet.
3) Bake for about 15 min. in a hot oven—400° F. (204° C.).

Drop biscuits may be varied by adding the following ingredients to the above recipe:

1) Add 1 t. cinnamon to the dry ingredients.
2) Add 2/3 c. grated cheese, cutting it into the dry ingredients with the fat. Decrease the fat 1 tb.
3) Add 1/2 c. chopped dried fruit.
4) Add 1/2 c. chopped nuts.
5) Add 1/2 t. curry powder and 1/2 t. celery salt to the dry ingredients.

SOFT DOUGHS

Baking Powder Biscuits
(12 to 20 biscuits)

Flour	2 c.	Baking powder	2 1/4 t.
Salt	1/2 t.	Fat	1/4 c.
Milk	2/3 c.		

* Use a relatively hard general utility flour.

1) Sift and measure the flour; add the salt and baking powder; sift again into a mixing bowl.
2) Add the fat, and cut or rub it into the flour, using 2 knives, the fingers, a dough blender, a fork, or a mixing fork. The mixture should have the texture of very coarse meal when it has been combined sufficiently.
3) Add the milk and stir with a fork until the mixture follows the fork around the bowl.
4) Toss on a lightly floured board and knead about 30 strokes.
5) Roll to about half the desired thickness of the finished biscuits, cut, and place the biscuits on a lightly oiled baking sheet.
6) Bake for 10 to 12 min. in a hot oven—425° F. (218° C.).

Basic Mix Biscuits

Basic mix . . . . 2 c. Milk . . . . ⅔ c.

1) Put the mix into a mixing bowl.
2) Add the milk and stir with a fork to combine well.
3) Knead, cut, and bake as above.

Compare the time required to make these biscuits with that required to make the regular biscuit recipe.

TABLE 43. BISCUITS OF VARIOUS KINDS

Biscuit	*Flour*	*Salt*	*Baking Powder*	*Fat*	*Milk*	*Other Ingredients*
Whole wheat	1 c.	½ t.	2¼ t.	¼ c.	⅔ c.	1 c. whole wheat flour
Corn meal	1 c.	½ t.	2¼ t.	¼ c.	⅔ c.	1 c. meal
Cheese	2 c.	½ t.	2¼ t.	3 tb.	⅔ c.	⅓ grated cheese
Herb	2 c.	½ t.	2¼ t.	¼ c.	⅔ c.	½ t. dry herb (selected)
Parsley or chive	2 c.	½ t.	2¼ t.	¼ c.	⅔ c.	2 tb. chive or parsley
Orange	2 c.	½ t.	2¼ t.	¼ c.	⅓ c.	⅓ c. orange juice 1 t. grated orange rind

Stick Biscuits
(About 8 Biscuits)

Bread flour . . . . 3 c. Baking powder . . . . 1 tb.
Salt . . . . ½ t. Fat . . . . 3 tb.
Milk . . . . 1 c.

1) Sift and measure the flour; add the salt and baking powder, and sift again into a mixing bowl.

2) Add the fat, and combine, using two knives, a dough blender, a fork, a mixing fork, or the fingers.
3) Add the milk, and stir with a fork until the mixture follows the fork around the bowl.
4) Toss on a lightly floured board and knead about 30 strokes.
5) Return the dough to the mixing bowl, cover, and let it stand at least 1 hr.
6) Stretch a piece of the dough to make a strip about 6 in. long and 1½ in. wide and wind it over one end of an oiled stick and around the stick, pulling it to make the dough smooth and rather thin. The stick must not be one that will flavor the biscuit.
7) Rotate the biscuit slowly over coals until it has risen and browned.
8) When done, the biscuit slips from the stick easily. The center may be filled with crisp bacon and marmalade, or with fresh fruit.

Shortcake

Flour	2 c.	Baking powder	2¼ t.
Salt	½ t.	Fat	¼ c. + 2 tb.
Milk	⅔ c.		

1) Combine ingredients by the biscuit method.
2) Roll the dough to fit a shallow pan, or roll to about half the desired thickness of the finished shortcakes, and cut with a large biscuit cutter.
3) Bake whole shortcake in a lightly oiled shallow pan for about 20 min. in a hot oven—400° F. (204° C.)—OR bake individual shortcakes on a lightly oiled baking sheet for 12 to 15 min. at 425° F. (218° C.).
4) Split the shortcake, butter the split surfaces, and put sweetened fruit between the layers and on the top. Whipped cream may be added.

Coffee Cake
(6 servings)

Flour	2 c.	Baking powder	2 t.
Salt	½ t.	Milk	1 c.
Sugar	¼ c.	Oil or melted fat	¼ c.

1) Sift the flour and measure; add the other dry ingredients, and sift into a mixing bowl.
2) Add the oil or melted fat to the milk. Mix well.
3) Combine the liquid and dry ingredients and pour into an oiled pan.
4) Sprinkle the following mixture over the top:

Sugar	½ c.	Cinnamon	1 t.
Flour	1 tb.	Melted butter or margarine	2 tb.

5) Bake for about 30 min. at 425° F. (218° C.).

Dutch Apple (or Peach) Cake
(About 8 servings)

Short cake dough (above)		Sugar	½ c.
Tart apples *or* peaches	5-6	Cinnamon *or* nutmeg	½ t.

1) Make the shortcake dough and spread it in an oiled baking dish.
2) Pare and core the apples (or peel peaches and remove pits), slice in eighths, and press the narrow edges into the dough.
3) Sprinkle with the sugar and spice mixture.
4) Bake about 25 min. at 350° F. (177° C.)—until the shortcake is cooked and the fruit tender.

Banana Nut Bread *
(About 16 slices)

Flour	1¾ c.	Dark corn sirup	½ c.
Salt	¾ t.	Eggs	2
Soda	½ t.	Nuts	½ c.
Baking powder	2 t.	Orange rind	1 t.
Fat	⅓ c.	Mashed banana	1 c.

1) Sift the flour and measure; add salt, soda, and baking powder, and sift into a mixing bowl.
2) Cream the fat.
3) Add the corn sirup gradually, beating after each addition.
4) Add about ¼ of the dry ingredients, and stir until smooth.
5) Beat the eggs and add.
6) Add grated orange rind and coarsely chopped nuts and stir to blend.
7) Add the remaining dry ingredients in thirds, alternating with the banana.
8) Pour into an oiled loaf pan, and bake about 55 min. at 350° F. (177° C.).
9) Remove from the pan, but do not cut for at least 4 hr.

Yeast Bread

Milk	1 c.	Yeast	¾ cake
Sugar	1¼ tb.	Lukewarm water	¼ c.
Salt	¾ t.	Flour (hard)	3 to 3¼ c.
Fat	1¼ tb.		

1) Scald the milk.
2) Add the fat, sugar, and salt and stir to dissolve.
3) Cool to lukewarm temperature.
4) Soften the yeast in the water and add it to the milk, stirring to mix thoroughly.

* May be baked in muffin pans.

5) Add about ½ of the flour and beat until smooth.*
6) Add flour to make a soft—not sticky—dough.
7) Turn onto a lightly floured board and knead until smooth. (Bubbles appear under the surface as the dough stands for about a minute and a fairly deep fingerprint disappears slowly.)
8) Place the dough in an oiled bowl, cover with a damp cloth, and set in a warm place to rise to double in bulk (about 1 hr.).
9) Turn the dough onto a lightly floured board and shape the loaf.
10) Place the loaf in an oiled bread pan, cover with a damp cloth, and let rise to double in bulk (about 45 min.).
11) Bake for 15 min. at 425° F. (218° C.), then lower the temperature to 350° F. (177° C.) and continue to bake until done—about 25 min. (For tests of doneness, see above).
12) Cool on a wire cake rack.

Breakfast Toast Bread

Yeast (cake or pkg.)	1	Hot water	1 c. — ⅔ tb.
Lukewarm water	¼ c.	Flour (hard)	about 2¼ c.
Fat	2 tb.	Dry milk solids	½ c.
Sugar (brown or white)	2 tb.	Egg, beaten	1
Salt	1 t.	Wheat germ	½ c.

1) Soften the yeast in the lukewarm water.
2) Measure the fat, sugar, and salt into a large mixing bowl, add the hot water, and stir to dissolve.
3) Cool to lukewarm, add 1 c. of flour sifted with the milk and beat until smooth.
4) Add the beaten egg and yeast and beat until well mixed. Cover and let rise until bubbly (about ½ hr.).
5) Add the wheat germ and enough flour to make a soft (not sticky) dough.
6) Mix thoroughly and knead until the dough is smooth.
7) Put the dough into an oiled mixing bowl, cover with a clean towel wrung from hot water, and let rise to double in bulk (about ¾ hr.).
8) Shape the loaf and put it into an oiled loaf pan; let it rise to about double in bulk (about ½ hr.).
9) Bake at 400° F. (204° C.) for 15 min.; lower the temperature to 350° F. (177° C.) and bake until done—about 30 min.
10) Cool on a wire cooling rack.

---

* At this point, the "sponge" may be allowed to stand until it is bubbly before completing the process. (See sponge method, p. 235.)

Refrigerator Rolls
(About 1¼ doz.)

Milk	¾ c.	Sugar	¼ c.
Yeast	1 cake	Salt	1 t.
Lukewarm water	¼ c.	Egg, beaten	1 sm.
Fat	3 tb.	Flour (hard)	3 to 4 c.

1) Scald the milk.
2) Soften the yeast in the water.
3) Add the fat, sugar, and salt to the milk and cool to lukewarm temperature.
4) Add 1 c. of flour and beat well.
5) Add the yeast and egg and mix thoroughly.
6) Add flour to make a soft—not sticky—dough.
7) Turn the dough onto a lightly floured board and let it stand about 10 min.
8) Knead the dough until it is smooth.
9) Put the dough into a lightly oiled bowl, cover with a damp cloth, and let it rise in a warm place (80 to 85° F.) for about 1 hour, or until the bulk has doubled.
10) Punch the dough down, cover, and put it into the refrigerator. After 8 to 10 hrs., punch it down again.
11) About 1½ hrs. before time to bake rolls, remove the portion of dough needed and let it rise.
12) Turn the dough onto a lightly floured board and shape the rolls, placing them on an oiled baking sheet or in pans appropriate for the shape of the rolls.
13) Set them in a warm place, cover with a clean towel, and let them rise to double in bulk.
14) Bake for about 15 min. at 425° F. (218° C.).

Sweet Rolls
(About 3½ doz.)

Milk	1 c.	Salt	1½ t.
Yeast	1 cake	Eggs, beaten	2
Lukewarm water	¼ c.	Melted fat	⅓ c.
Sugar	½ c.	Flour (hard)	3¼ to 5 c.

1) Scald the milk.
2) Soften the yeast in the water.
3) Add the sugar and salt to the milk and cool to lukewarm.
4) Add 2 c. of flour and beat well.

5) Add the yeast and eggs and beat well.
6) Add the melted fat and mix well.
7) Add flour to make a soft—not sticky—dough.
8) Turn the dough onto a lightly floured board and let it stand about 10 min.
9) Knead until the dough is smooth.
10) Put the dough into a lightly oiled bowl, cover with a damp cloth, and let it rise in a warm place (80 to 85° F.) until doubled in bulk. (If there is time, punch it down and let it rise a second time).
11) Turn the dough onto a lightly floured board and shape the rolls (or tea rings), placing them on an oiled baking sheet or in pans appropriate for the rolls.
12) Set them in a warm place, cover with a clean towel, and let them rise to double in bulk.
13) Bake for 15 to 20 min. at 375° F. (191° C.). (A tea ring requires 30 to 35 min.).

Kolaches
(About 18)
(Bohemian)

Yeast	¾ cake	Sugar	⅓ c.
Lukewarm water	¼ c.	Fat, melted	⅓ c.
Milk	1 c.	Salt	1 t.
Flour (hard)	about 4 c.	Eggs, beaten	2

1) Soften the yeast in the water.
2) Scald the milk over water in a double boiler. Cool to lukewarm.
3) Add the yeast, then 1 c. of flour, and beat thoroughly.
4) Let the mixture stand until it is light.
5) Add the sugar, fat, salt, and eggs and mix well.
6) Add flour to make a soft dough, and knead.
7) Put the dough into an oiled bowl, cover, and let double in bulk.
8) Roll on a lightly floured board to about ½ in. thick.
9) Cut with a biscuit cutter and let rolls rise in an oiled pan.
10) Press the centers down, fill with the following mixture, and brush the edges with melted fat:

Chopped stewed prunes	¾ c.	Sugar	3 tb.
Melted butter	1 tb.	Cinnamon	½ t.

11) Bake at 350°–375° F. (177°–191° C.).
12) Brush the tops with melted butter.

Julekake
(Norwegian)

Milk	2 c.	Flour (hard)	4 c.
Sugar	1/3 c.	Butter or margarine	1/4 c.
Salt	1 t.	Raisins	1 c.
Cardamom (ground)	1 t.	Currants	1 c.
Yeast cake	1	Citron, cut fine	1 c.
Warm water	1/4 c.	Flour	to coat fruit

Melted butter or margarine....about 2 tb.

1) Scald the milk over low heat in a heavy saucepan.
2) Put the sugar, salt, and cardamom into a mixing bowl and add the milk, stirring to dissolve the sugar and salt.
3) Soften the yeast in the warm water and, when the milk is lukewarm, add the yeast and mix.
4) Add the flour and beat thoroughly.
5) Cover, set in a warm place, and let the mixture rise until doubled in bulk.
6) Beat, add the butter, the fruit coated with flour, and enough flour so that the dough can be kneaded.
7) Knead, and set aside to double in bulk.
8) Divide the dough into 4 pieces, shape each into a round loaf, and put on oiled pans. Brush with melted butter or margarine and let rise to double in bulk.
9) Bake about 45 min. at 350° F. (177° C.).

STIFF DOUGHS

A. Pastry for pies (one 9-in., 2-crust pie):

Flour	2 1/4 c.	Fat	3/4 c.
Salt	1 t.	Cold water	5 tb.

1) Sift flour and measure; remove 1/3 c.; add salt, and sift into a mixing bowl.
2) Cut one-half of the fat into the flour until the mixture is as fine as coarse meal.
3) Add the other half and cut until the particles of fat are about the size of navy beans.
4) Add the water to the 1/3 c. of flour, and stir to form a paste.
5) Add the paste to the flour and fat, and mix lightly to combine all ingredients.
6) Toss enough dough for one crust on a lightly floured board or pastry cloth; shape into a ball, and roll lightly from center to edges. Roll it

evenly, so that the dough is as nearly round and as nearly the size of the pan as possible.

a. Placing crusts for a two-crust pie:
   i. Fold the crust at the center, lift and place on the pan so that the fold is along the center of the pan. Raise the folded half and fit it to the pan so that no air is left between the pan and the pastry. Trim ½ in. beyond edge of pan.
   ii. Roll the top crust, and cut a design near the center so that steam may escape from the filling as the pie bakes.
   iii. Put the filling into the lower crust.
   iv. Moisten the edge of the lower crust with water, and place the top crust. Trim even with edge of pan and fold lower crust over top crust. Press the edges together with the floured tines of a fork or handle of a knife.

b. Placing crust for one-crust pie:
   i. Follow the directions above for placing the crust in the pan.
   ii. Trim about ½ in. beyond the edge of the pan, using scissors or a knife.
   iii. Double the pastry edge, making it stand up all around the edge of the pie pan.
   iv. Press this edge into fluted shape, using the floured thumb and forefinger of one hand and the floured forefinger of the other hand.
   v. If the filling is cooked before it is put into the pastry shell, prick the crust with a fork along the sides and bottom to prevent the crust from bulging during baking. *Do not prick if the filling is to be cooked with the pastry.*

c. If the crust is to be used with a cooked filling, bake from 12 to 15 min. in a very hot oven—450° F. (232° C.).

B. Home-prepared pastry mix:

It is convenient to prepare sufficient pastry mix for several pies. The following mix is based on the above pastry recipe and method of combining the ingredients.

PASTRY MIX
(for four 2-crust pies)

Flour	7⅔ c.	Salt	1 tb. + 1 t.
Fat	3 c.		

1) Sift and measure the flour and sift again with the salt.
2) Cut about half of the fat into the flour and salt until the mixture is about like coarse meal.

3) Cut the remainder of the fat into the mixture until the fat is about the size of small navy beans.
4) Store in a covered tin container.

(For a 1-crust pie)

Pastry mix	1 c. + 1 tb.	Flour	2⅔ tb.
Water	2½ tb.		

1) Put the mix into a mixing bowl.
2) Make a paste with the flour and water.
3) Mix the paste with the pastry mix, using a fork.

Apple Pie

Cooking apples	6 or 8	Cinnamon or nutmeg	½ t.
Sugar	⅓ to ¾ c.	Butter or margarine	½ tb.
Salt	¼ t.	Lemon juice	1 tb.

1) Wash, pare, quarter, core, and slice the apples.
2) Measure the sugar. The amount depends upon the tartness of the apples and individual taste.
3) Sprinkle one third of the sugar to be used over the lower crust and add the apples, heaping them in the crust to allow for shrinkage during baking.
   [Note: The apples may be steamed in the top of a double boiler to shrink them before placing in the crust.]
4) Add the salt and cinnamon or nutmeg to the rest of the sugar and sprinkle it over the apples to distribute evenly.
5) Dot with butter or margarine and add the lemon juice.
6) Cover with the top crust (see directions above).
7) Bake 10 min. at 450° F. (232° C.)—then at 425° F. (218° C.) for 30 to 40 min.

Canned-Fruit Pie
(Berries, Cherries, Gooseberries, etc.)

Minute tapioca	2 tb.	Salt	⅛ t.
Sugar	¼ to ¾ c.	Fruit juice	¾ c.
Drained fruit	2½ c.	Lemon juice (with berries)	1 t.

1) Drain the fruit.
2) Sprinkle 1 tb. of tapioca and 2 tb. of sugar over the lower crust.
3) Fill the crust with drained fruit, leaving a small space at the center free from fruit.
4) Add 1 tb. of tapioca, the remaining sugar, and salt.

5) Pour fruit juice and lemon juice, if used, over the fruit.
6) Cover with the top crust (see directions above).
7) Bake at 450° F. (232° C.)—for 10 min.; then at 425° F. (218° C.) for 30 to 40 min.

Plum Pie

Pastry for pie (pp. 626–7)		Eggs, beaten	3
Plums, canned; pitted	15–18	Milk	¾ c.
Sugar, powdered	1½ c.		

1) Line a pie pan with the pastry.
2) Place plums on the pastry.
3) Mix eggs, milk and sugar and pour over plums.
4) Bake for 10 min. at 400° F. (204° C.); reduce heat to 375° F. (191° C.) and bake about 30 min. longer. Test by inserting the point of a knife in the custard. If it comes out clean the pie is done.

Pumpkin Pie *

Prepared pumpkin	1¼ c.	Ginger	1 t.
Sugar	½ c.	Cinnamon	1 t.
Butter or margarine	2 tb.	Salt	½ t.
Molasses	2 tb.	Eggs	2
Milk	1¼ c.		

1) Cook and strain the pumpkin OR use canned pumpkin. If a darker product is desired, the canned pumpkin may be cooked slowly until it is thicker and darker.
2) Add the sugar, fat, molasses, spices, and salt and stir to mix thoroughly.
3) Beat the eggs, add the milk, and add to the above mixture.
4) Pour into an unbaked crust and bake for 10 min. at 450° F.—(232° C.), then lower the temperature to 325° F. (163° C.) and bake until a thin knife blade, inserted at the center, comes out clean—about 35 min.

Lemon Meringue Pie

Sugar	2 c.	Salt	½ t.
Cornstarch	½ c.	Egg yolks	4
Boiling water	2½ c.	Lemon juice	6 tb.
Butter or margarine	1 tb.	Lemon rind, grated	2 t.

1) Mix the sugar and cornstarch; add water, stirring constantly.
2) Add the fat and salt and cook, stirring until the mixture is *very* thick.

* Mashed squash or sweet potato may be used instead of the pumpkin.

3) Beat the egg yolks, and add some of the above mixture. Return to the saucepan and cook 2 min.
4) Cool.
5) Add the lemon juice and rind, mixing it well, and pour the mixture into a baked crust.

Meringue

Egg whites	2	Cream of tartar	1/8 t.
Sugar	1/4 c.		

1) Beat the egg whites until they are frothy; add cream of tartar, and continue beating until the whites hold up in a peak when the beater is lifted.
2) Add 1/4 c. of sugar gradually to the beaten egg whites, beating well after each addition.
3) Cover the pie with this meringue and bake (about 8 min.) at 350° F. (177° C.)—until brown.

Flan

(About 6 servings)
(Adapted from an English recipe)

Short Crust

Flour	2 c.	Butter or margarine	1/4 c.
Salt	1/8 t.	Lard or shortening	1/4 c.
Baking powder	1 t.	Egg yolk	1
Water	1/4 c.		

1) Sift and measure the flour; sift with salt and baking powder into a mixing bowl. Reserve 1/3 c.
2) Cut fat into the dry ingredients until the mixture is about as fine as coarse meal.
3) Beat the egg yolk, add the water, and the 1/3 c. of flour. Stir to form a paste.
4) Add the paste to the above mixture and stir with a fork to form a thick dough. Roll to about 1/4 in. thick.
5) Line pie or cake pan (or flan ring if available), trim the edge, and shape as for a one-crust pie.
6) Prick bottom and sides of the crust; weight it with another pan *or* put waxed paper into the crust and weight with dry beans or rice.
7) Bake 15 to 20 min. at 425° F. (218° C.), checking by raising the weight to judge time. Remove the weight a few minutes before the crust is done for desired brown color.

Filling for Flan

Any fruit or cream filling may be used.

Apple Filling

Tart apples	4 or 5	Nutmeg	dash
Sugar	about 1/3 c.	Butter or margarine	2 t.
Salt	Dash	Egg whites	2
Sugar	1/4 c.		

1) Pare, core, and slice the apples and steam them until tender.
2) Fill the crust with layers of apples sprinkled with sugar, salt and nutmeg and dotted with butter or margarine. (Pile the last apples to make the surface well rounded.)
3) Make meringue (see p. 630) and spread it over the apples.
4) Brown the meringue at 350° F. (218° C.).

Peach-Raspberry Cream Filling

Sugar	2/3 c.	Egg yolks	2
Flour	1/3 c.	Butter or margarine	1 1/2 tb.
Salt	1/8 t.	Sliced peaches	about 1 c.
Milk	2 c.	Raspberry juice	1/2 c.
Cornstarch	2 t.		

1) Put the sugar, flour, and salt into a saucepan and stir to mix well.
2) Add the milk gradually, stirring to keep the mixture smooth.
3) Cook over moderate heat, stirring frequently, until thick.
4) Beat the egg yolks, add the above mixture and stir well.
5) Add the butter or margarine. Cool.
6) Line the crust with sliced fruit (if canned, be sure it is well drained) and fill with the cream filling.
7) Arrange slices of fruit on the top in a pattern.
8) Make glaze by thickening the raspberry juice with cornstarch and glaze the top of the flan.

ROLLED COOKIES

Sugar Cookies

Fat	1/2 c.	Egg, beaten	1
Flavoring	1 t.	Flour	1 3/4 c.
Sugar	3/4 c.	Baking powder	1 t.
Salt	1/4 t.		

1) Cream the fat, adding the flavoring during the creaming.
2) Add the sugar gradually, creaming well.
3) Add the egg and mix well.
4) Sift the flour, measure, and sift with the other dry ingredients.

5) Add the dry ingredients, about ¼ at a time, to the first mixture.
6) Chill thoroughly.
7) Roll very thin on a lightly floured surface and cut with a cookie cutter.
8) Sprinkle with sugar OR press a half pecan into the center of each cookie.
9) Bake on an oiled baking sheet for 6 to 8 min. at 375° F. (191° C.).
10) Store in a tightly covered tin container to retain crispness.

Christmas Cookies
(Swedish)

Molasses	½ c.	Orange rind	1½ tb.
Light brown sugar	¾ c.	Flour	2 c.
Butter or margarine	½ c. + 2 tb.	Cloves	1 t.
Egg, beaten	1	Soda	½ t.
		Baking powder	½ t.
		Flour to knead	about 1¾ c.

1) Warm the molasses over water.
2) Add the sugar and stir to dissolve.
3) Add the fat, egg, and orange rind and beat well.
4) Sift flour, measure 2 c., and sift with cloves, soda, and baking powder into the mixture. Mix thoroughly.
5) Add enough flour to knead; knead until the dough is smooth, and chill the dough.
6) Roll, cut thin in fancy shapes and bake for 10 min. at 375° F. (191° C.).
7) Frost with white frosting.

Stone Jar Ginger Cookies
(About 3 doz.)

Fat	¾ c.	Soda	¾ t.
Molasses	1½ c.	Salt	¼ t.
Boiling water	¼ c. + 1 tb.	Baking powder	2 t.
Flour	4 to 5 c.	Ginger	1½ t.
Cinnamon	½ t.		

1) Cream the fat.
2) Add the molasses and water, and blend.
3) Sift the flour and measure 4 c.; add the other dry ingredients, and sift again.
4) Add the dry ingredients to the above mixture and enough additional flour to make a dough that is soft.
5) Chill thoroughly.
6) Roll ¼-in. thick, cut, and place on a baking sheet.
7) Bake about 12 min. at 350° F. (177° C.).

REFRIGERATOR COOKIES

Chocolate Cookies
(About 7 doz.)

Chocolate	2 squares	Milk	1/4 c.
Fat	1/2 c.	Flour	3 c.
Sugar	1 1/4 c.	Salt	1/2 t.
Egg, beaten	1	Baking powder	2 t.
Vanilla	1 t.		

1) Melt the chocolate over water in a double boiler.
2) Cream the fat.
3) Add the sugar gradually, creaming the mixture well.
4) Add the well-beaten egg, and mix well.
5) Add the milk and then the melted chocolate and vanilla.
6) Sift flour; add salt and baking powder, and sift again.
7) Add dry ingredients gradually to the above mixture.
8) Shape into rolls. Chill thoroughly.
9) Slice about 1/8-in. thick and bake for about 10 min. on an unoiled baking sheet at 375° F. (191° C.).

Cinnamon Cookies
(About 8 doz.)

Flour	3 1/2 c.	Nuts, chopped	1 c.
Soda	1/4 t.	Fat	1 c.
Baking powder	1 t.	Sugar	1 c.
Salt	1/4 t.	Brown sugar	1 c.
Cinnamon	1 tb.	Eggs, beaten	2

1) Sift the flour, measure, and sift with the other dry ingredients.
2) Add the nuts and mix to coat them.
3) Cream the fat, and add the sugars gradually, creaming well.
4) Add the eggs and stir to blend well.
5) Add the dry ingredients, about 1/4 at a time, and blend well.
6) Divide the dough into three parts and shape each into a roll.
7) Wrap the rolls in waxed paper and store in the refrigerator.
8) When ready to bake the cookies, slice in thin slices, using a sharp knife.
9) Bake for 10 to 12 min. at 350° F. (177° C.).

Maple-Walnut Cookies
(About 7 doz.)

Butter or margarine	1/2 c.	Milk *	1/2 c.
Maple sugar	1 c.	Flour	4 c.
Egg, beaten	1	Baking powder	1 tb.
Chopped walnuts	1 c.	Salt	1/4 t.

* Milk may be omitted and maple sirup substituted for the sugar.

1) Cream the fat.
2) Add the sugar gradually, creaming well.
3) Add the beaten egg, and mix well.
4) Sift flour and measure; add baking powder and salt, and sift again. Add one-third of this to the above mixture.
5) Add milk; mix, and add the remaining dry ingredients and nuts.
6) Shape into rolls. Chill thoroughly.
7) Slice about 1/8-in. thick.
8) Bake for about 10 min. at 375° F. (191° C.)—on an unoiled baking sheet.

DROP COOKIES

Sour Cream Drop Cookies

(About 3 doz.)

Fat	1/2 c.	Soda	1/2 t.
Sugar	1 c.	Cinnamon	1/2 t.
Egg, beaten	1	Nutmeg	1/2 t.
Flour	2 c.	Sour cream	1/2 c.
Salt	1/4 t.	Currants	1/2 c.

1) Cream the fat.
2) Add the sugar gradually, creaming after each addition.
3) Add the egg and beat until light.
4) Sift flour, measure, and sift with the other dry ingredients.
5) Add about 1/3 of the dry ingredients to the first mixture and stir to blend.
6) Add the cream and stir to blend.
7) Add the currants to the remaining dry ingredients and stir to coat.
8) Add to the first mixture and mix well.
9) Drop by teaspoonfuls on oiled baking sheets.
10) Bake for about 10 min. at 375° F. (191° C.).

Fruit Drop Cookies

(About 60)

Flour	2 1/2 c.	Dates, chopped	7 1/4-oz. pkg.
Baking powder	3/4 t.	Butter or margarine	1/2 c.
Soda	1/4 t.	Sugar	1 1/2 c.
Salt	1/2 t.	Eggs, beaten	2
Nuts, chopped	1 c.		
Hot water	2 to 3 tb.		

1) Sift and measure the flour; sift again with other dry ingredients.
2) Add the nuts and fruit and mix to coat them.
3) Cream the fat; add the sugar gradually and cream well.

4) Add the eggs and stir to blend.
5) Add the dry ingredients, about 1/4 at a time, alternating with enough water to make the dough moist enough to drop, and mix well.
6) Drop by teaspoonfuls on an oiled baking sheet.
7) Bake for 10 to 12 min. at 375° F. (191° C.).

Chocolate Chip Cookies
(About 50)

Chocolate, semisweet	1/2 lb.	Egg	1
Butter or margarine	1/2 c.	Flour	1 c.
Vanilla	1 t.	Salt	1/2 t.
Sugar	1/2 c.	Soda	1/2 t.
Brown sugar	1/4 c.	Nuts, chopped	1/2 c.

1) Cut chocolate into small pieces.
2) Cream fat, adding vanilla while creaming. Add sugar gradually.
3) Add the unbeaten egg, and beat to mix thoroughly.
4) Sift flour and measure; add salt and soda, and sift again. Add to the above mixture. Add nuts and chocolate and blend well.
5) Drop on an unoiled baking sheet 2 in. apart. Bake for 10 to 12 min. at 375° F. (191° C.).

ASSORTED COOKIES

Lebkuchen
(About 80)
(Christmas cookies developed from a German recipe)

Egg yolks	6	Soda	1 t.
Eggs	2	Cinnamon	1 t.
Sugar	1 c.	Allspice	1 t.
Honey (or dark sirup)	1 c.	Cloves	1 t.
Sweet chocolate, grated	1/2 lb.	Nutmeg	1 t.
Flour	3 c.	Citron, cut thin	2 c.
Salt	1/2 t.	Nuts, chopped	1 c.

1) Beat the egg yolks and eggs until they are very light.
2) Fold in the sugar gradually, alternating with honey or sirup.
3) Fold in the chocolate.
4) Sift the flour, measure, and sift again with the other dry ingredients.
5) Dredge the citron and nuts with a little of the dry ingredients.
6) Fold the dry ingredients into the first mixture.
7) Fold in the citron and nuts.
8) Line 2 cake pans about 8 x 12 in. with wax paper, and oil the paper.

9) Pour the batter into the pans and spread it evenly.
10) Bake for 35 min. at 350° F. (177° C.).
11) Turn onto waxed paper sprinkled lightly with sugar. Cool.
12) Ice with any boiled frosting and cut into squares.

White Lebkuchen
(About 60)
(Adapted from a German recipe)

Eggs	4	Grated lemon rind	1 lemon
Sugar	2 c.	Cinnamon	½ t.
Pecans, chopped	2 c.	Cloves	¼ t.
Citron, cut fine	⅓ c.	Flour	4 c.
Baking powder	2 tb.		

1) Beat the eggs and add the sugar, mixing thoroughly.
2) Add the nuts, citron, lemon rind, and spices and mix well.
3) Sift the flour and baking powder and add, about 1 c. at a time.
4) Work the dough and roll to ⅜ in. thickness.
5) Cut in diagonals and bake for about 20 min. at 350° F. (177° C.).
6) Cover with a cloth (not in an air-tight container) and allow to mellow several days before serving.

Date Sticks
(About 24)

Flour	½ c.	Butter or margarine	2 tb.
Baking powder	½ tb.	Sugar	½ c.
Nuts, chopped	¼ c.	Egg	1
Dates, chopped	½ lb.	Hot water	½ tb.

1) Sift the flour, measure, and sift again with the baking powder.
2) Mix dates and nuts, and add to the dry ingredients. Mix well.
3) Cream the fat; add sugar, beaten egg, and water.
4) Add the first mixture and mix well.
5) Spread the mixture evenly over a shallow pan that is oiled and floured or lined with waxed paper.
6) Bake for 30 min. in a moderate oven—350° F. (177° C.).
7) Cool.
8) Cut in strips and roll in granulated sugar.

Fudge Brownies
(About 18)

Chocolate	2 squares	Egg	1
Fat	¼ c.	Flour	½ c.
Vanilla	½ t.	Salt	½ t.
Sugar	1 c.	Nuts, chopped	½ c.

1) Melt the chocolate and fat over water in a double boiler.
2) Add vanilla and remove from heat.
3) Add the sugar, and blend well.
4) Add unbeaten egg, and beat well.
5) Sprinkle 2 tb. of sifted flour over the nuts, coating them well.
6) Add the remaining flour and salt to the above mixture; then add floured nuts. Blend thoroughly.
7) Spread the mixture in a slightly oiled pan, and bake about 30 min. at 350° F. (177° C.).
   [NOTE: They do not appear to be done when removed from the oven.]
8) Mark in squares or strips with a sharp knife and cool in the pan.
9) Remove and finish cutting.

FRUIT BARS
(About 3 doz.)

Eggs	2	Salt	½ t.
Brown sugar	1 c.	Baking powder	1 t.
Vanilla	1 t.	Nuts and candied or dried fruits	2⅔ c.
Flour	1 c.		

Powdered sugar

1) Beat the eggs until they are thick.
2) Beat in the sugar gradually.
3) Add the vanilla.
4) Sift flour, measure, and sift into the above mixture with the salt and baking powder.
5) Chop the nuts and fruit and fold them into the batter.
6) Spread in a pan, lined with oiled waxed paper, to about ½ in. in thickness.
7) Bake for about 25 min. at 350° F. (177° C.).
8) Remove from the pan while warm.
9) Cool, cut in bars, and roll in powdered sugar.

YULE SPICE CAKES
(About 60)
(English)

Flour	3½ c.	Butter or margarine	1 c.
Baking powder	3 t.	Sugar	1 c.
Salt	¼ t.	Lemon juice	3 tb.
Nutmeg	½ t.	Lemon rind, grated	½ t.
Currants	1 c.	Egg yolks	2
Seedless raisins	1 c.	Milk	½ c.
Mixed candied fruits	¼ c.	Egg whites	2

1) Sift and measure the flour and sift again with the other dry ingredients.
2) Add the dried and candied fruits and stir to coat them.
3) Cream the butter or margarine.
4) Add the sugar gradually, creaming well.
5) Add the lemon juice and rind and stir to blend.
6) Add the beaten egg yolks and stir to blend.
7) Add the dry ingredients and fruit alternately with the milk, about ¼ at a time, stirring to blend.
8) Beat the egg whites until they stand in a peak when the beater is lifted, and fold them into the mixture.
9) Pour the batter into a square cake pan lined with oiled waxed paper.
10) Bake for about 1 hour at 325° F. (163° C.).
11) Cut in squares.

Sand Tarts
(About 24)

Butter	1 c.	Powdered sugar	¼ c.
Vanilla	1 t.	Flour	2 c.
Ground nuts	1 c.		

1) Cream the butter, adding the vanilla during the creaming.
2) Add the sugar, and cream well.
3) Add the flour and nuts. Mix well.
4) Divide the dough into pieces about the size of a walnut, and shape into crescents.
5) Bake on an unoiled baking sheet for 40 min. at 300° F. (149° C.). The tarts will not be brown when done. Roll in powdered sugar while warm.

Spritz Kranser
(About 24)
(Swedish)

Butter	⅓ lb.	Egg	1
Sugar	1 c.	Flour	2 c.
Lemon rind	½ t.	Salt	½ t.

1) Cream the butter.
2) Add sugar gradually, creaming thoroughly after each addition. Add the lemon rind.
3) Add the unbeaten egg and stir well.
4) Sift flour; add salt, and sift into the above mixture. Mix well.
5) Put dough into a cookie press and shape.

6) Bake for about 10 min. at 325° F. (163° C.).
[NOTE: 1/4 c. of cocoa may be substituted for 1/4 c. of the flour.]

CINNAMON CRISPIES
(About 30)

Butter or margarine	1 c.	Egg yolk	1
Vanilla	1 t.	Flour	2 c.
Brown sugar	1 c.	Cinnamon	1 tb.
Chopped pecans	1/2 c.		

1) Cream the fat, adding the vanilla during the creaming.
2) Add the sugar gradually, and cream well.
3) Add unbeaten egg yolk, and beat until thoroughly mixed.
4) Sift flour and measure; add the cinnamon, and sift again. Add to the above mixture, and blend well.
5) Spread in a thin layer on an unoiled baking sheet.
6) Brush the top with slightly beaten egg white, and sprinkle with chopped nuts.
7) Bake for about 10 min. at 375° F. (191° C.). Mark in squares while warm. Cool and break.

APPETIZERS

The multiplicity of foods served as appetizers is so great and varied as to be confusing, especially to beginners. Words which are used to indicate an appetizer are also numerous: "cocktail," "hors-d'oeuvre," "antipasto," "canape" and "savory" are perhaps the most widely used. Within each of these categories there is unlimited variety, as any reference will show. More important than what an appetizer is called is the choice of an appropriate one. If the food served as a first course is to fulfill its accepted function (see p. 245), certain limitations are imposed in the selection of *what* to serve before the main meal. The meal itself should be the guide for choosing the appetizer, or the appetizer used as the guide for the meal to follow. In other words, if one desires to serve a rather extensive appetizer course, using some hearty and substantial foods, a light meal would be in order. If the meal is to be heavy, a delicate appetizer should precede it. Sometimes diners in restaurants prefer to make the beginning course their entire meal. The Italian Antipasto is ideal for such a dinner.

Recipes suitable for appetizers will be found under the heading of *Fruits, Cheese, Seasonings,* and other groupings. However, selected ones are included here for added interest.

Miniature Oriental Meat Balls

- Crab, flaked, fresh or canned .... 1 c.
- Beef, lean, ground ..... ½ lb.
- Soy sauce .... ¼ c.
- Ginger, powdered ...... ¼ t.
- Onion, chopped fine .... 1 medium
- Salt .... ¼ t.
- Sugar .... 1 t.
- Water chestnuts, chopped .... ½–¾ c.

1) Mix all ingredients thoroughly.
2) Shape into small balls (1 to 1½ inches).
3) Place on rack and broil for about 12 minutes, turning to brown on all sides.

Tomato Chicken Savory
(4 servings)

- Onion, chopped .... 1 sm.
- Green pepper, chopped 2 tb.
- Butter or margarine ... 2 tb.
- Pimiento .... 1 tb.
- Salt .... ¼ t.
- Chicken, finely chopped .... 1 c.
- Bread crumbs (or crumbled crisp cereal) .... 2 tb.
- Sour cream .... 2 tb.
- Tarragon or other herb .... ⅛ t.
- Tomatoes, fresh ...... 2 med.

1) Sauté the onion and green pepper in the butter; add all other ingredients (except tomatoes) and mix well.
2) Cut tomatoes in two, crosswise, salt and pepper them, and heap chicken mixture on top of each half.
3) Place tomatoes under broiler about 6 in. from heat and broil for about 10 minutes.
4) Serve hot as an appetizer course or as part of a luncheon meal.

Liverwurst Spread

- Liverwurst .... ½ lb.
- Horseradish .... 1–2 t.
- Salt .... to taste
- Sour cream .... 2–3 tb.
- Onion, finely chopped .... ½ sm.
- Egg, hard-cooked, chopped 1–2

1) Blend all ingredients until well combined. Chill.
2) Use as a cocktail spread for small crackers or on toast strips.

Jellied Soups

There are a number of brands of commercial canned consommés and madrilènes on the market, which, if refrigerated for 3 or 4 hours, will congeal and be ready for serving as a cold appetizer. They can be varied by the garnish or accompaniments that are served with them. In addition to lemon, which is usually served with a jellied soup, other suggestions include:

(a) Cultured sour cream or mayonnaise—allowing one to two teaspoons per serving. Season cream or mayonnaise with salt and pepper, fresh dill, capers, minced onion, or herb vinegar, and serve on top of the jellied soup.

(b) Chopped parsley, chives, water cress, celery, fresh basil or dill—sprinkle any one of these over the soup after it has been put into individual serving dishes.

(c) Cottage cheese—blend cottage cheese with a small amount of well-seasoned French dressing and top each serving of soup with a small mound of the cheese.

Jellied Orange Soup
(About 4 servings)

Gelatin	1½ t.	Orange juice	1 c.
Water, cold	2 tb.	Lemon juice	1 tb.
Water, boiling	⅓ c.	Salt	⅛ t.
Sugar	¼ c.	Strawberries, fresh or frozen	1 c.

1) Soften the gelatin in cold water.
2) Dissolve in boiling water.
3) Add sugar and other ingredients, except strawberries, and stir until sugar is dissolved.
4) Chill and serve in bouillon cups with strawberries over the top.

Asparagus and Chicken Soup

For each part of water from freshly cooked or canned asparagus, add one part of chicken stock, either canned or made from a bouillon cube, and one part of milk. Make combined liquids into a thin sauce (see white sauce, p. 499), adding 1 teaspoon of minced onion for each cup of liquid. Sprinkle each serving of soup with paprika and either chopped hard-cooked egg or grated cheese.

Mushroom Bouillon

Use liquid from canned mushrooms or obtain the liquid by cooking stems of mushrooms in boiling salted water. Bring the mushroom liquid to a boil with chopped onion (½ teaspoon per cup) and caraway seed (¼ teaspoon per cup). Allow to stand for about 30 minutes. Strain and reheat before serving; serve with a sprinkling of chopped chives or parsley.

Borsch

(Serves 6 to 8)

Beets, medium	4	Bay leaf	½ small leaf
Potato, medium	1	Salt	1 t.
Onion, large	1	Sugar	2 tb.
Garlic	½ clove	Pepper	½ t.
Beef consommé, 10 oz. can	2 cans	Lemon juice	¼ c.
Hot water	¾ c.	Sour cream, cultured	¾ c.

1) Remove the skin from the raw beets and potato and grate coarsely.
2) Remove the skin from the onion and chop coarsely; chop garlic very fine.
3) Put the vegetables, along with all other ingredients except lemon juice and sour cream, into a saucepan which has a tight-fitting lid; bring to a full boil, reduce the heat, and continue cooking for about 10 minutes. (When done the vegetables should retain the chopped or grated appearance and should not be mashed.)
4) Pour the soup into an earthenware bowl to cool; add lemon juice and refrigerate over night.
5) Serve cold with a spoonful of sour cream in the center of each bowl. [Note: If the borsch is made in a pressure pan it should be cooked 1½ minutes at 15 lbs. pressure; the pressure should then be reduced by putting the cooker under running cold water.]

Tomato and Clam Juice Cocktail

Use equal parts of tomato juice and clam juice. Season to taste with salt, pepper, lemon juice, and Worcestershire sauce. Serve cold.

Orange-Cranberry Juice Cocktail

Use equal parts of fresh or frozen orange juice and canned cranberry cocktail. Blend and chill; just before serving add unsweetened carbonated water in the proportion of ⅓ cup to each cup of the fruit juice.

Relishes

Relishes are an important part of certain appetizer courses. In some instances they are the appetizer. In many restaurants assorted relishes are presented on a large dish or tray from which diners may choose as many as they like. In addition to certain raw vegetables such as celery, carrots, cucumber, cauliflower, and radishes, olives, pickles, and chutney are appropriate to use on a relish tray. Cottage cheese is an excellent food to accompany relish appetizers.

Antipasto

The Italians' "before meal" course may be arranged on individual plates or a large plate from which the family or guests make their own choice of tidbits. All or part of the following foods are suggestive of what might be used:

Italian salami	Tomato wedges or slices
Anchovy fillets, or sardines	Tuna fish (chunk style)
Celery hearts	Pimiento (cut in strips)
Green and ripe olives	Pickled beets (sliced)

The Italians usually dress antipasto with olive oil and vinegar. Salad greens are optional.

Caper-Curry Eggs

Cut hard-cooked eggs lengthwise, remove yolks and mash as for deviled eggs. Season with salt, pepper, and curry powder (1/4 teaspoon for 4 eggs), add capers (1 tablespoon for 4 eggs), and enough mayonnaise or milk to combine yolks into a thick mixture. Heap into whites and chill. Serve on a bed of crisp greens with whole or sliced pickled beets.

Piquante Seafood
(4 servings)

Lobster or crab meat (fresh or canned)	1 c.	Tarragon	1/8 t.
Lemon juice	2 tb.	Butter	2 tbs.
Tabasco sauce	dash	Toast, buttered	4 squares
Chili sauce	2 tb.	Bacon, crisp	4 slices
Capers	1 tb.	Parsley or water cress	4 sprigs

1) Flake the lobster or crab; add other ingredients, with the exception of toast, bacon, and parsley, and heat thoroughly.
2) Heap the hot seafood mixture on thin pieces of buttered toast, top with crisp bacon, and garnish with a sprig of parsley or water cress.

Sardine Appetizer

Toast thin-sliced bread on one side. On untoasted side arrange small sardines, sprinkle generously with grated cheese, and place under a broiler until the sardines are hot and the cheese melted. Serve with tomato and lemon slices.

Pickled Eggs
(Serves 6 to 8)
(Pennsylvania Dutch)

Beet juice	1 c.	Cinnamon	1/2 t.
Vinegar, mild	1 c.	Sugar	1/4 c.
Salt	1 t.	Beets, canned, small,	
Cloves	1/2 t.	whole or sliced	2 c.
Eggs, hard-cooked	6 to 8		

1) Mix the beet juice and vinegar, add the seasonings; simmer for 5 min.
2) Remove shells from eggs; put them and the beets into a suitable container, and pour the juice over them.
3) Let stand over night.
4) Serve on an appetizer tray or as an accompaniment to fish or potato salad.

BEVERAGES

Tea and coffee. The tea and coffee drinking habits of families vary greatly, as do the methods for making these beverages. National backgrounds are a big factor in both choosing the kind of tea and coffee to buy and the method of making.

The following methods are suggestive of some of the numerous ways in which these beverages may be made. References will give others.

TEA

Allow ¼ to ¾ t. of tea for each cup of water (8 oz.).

A. Steeping.
   1. Scald an earthenware or glass teapot.
   2. Put tea into an enamel or glass saucepan and add boiling water.
   3. Allow it to stand for 3 min., and strain into the teapot.

B. Pouring water through the leaves.
   1. Scald an earthenware or glass teapot.
   2. Put tea into a small strainer and set the strainer over the teapot.
   3. Pour boiling water through the leaves slowly.

C. Using a teaball or teabag.
   1. Pour boiling water into a scalded earthenware or glass teapot.
   2. Drop a teaball containing tea, or a teabag, into the water and keep it moving until the beverage is the desired color.

D. Using soluble tea.
   1. Put desired amount of tea in cup.
   2. Add hot water and stir.

ICED TEA

A. Make tea by one of the methods above, using double the proportion of tea.

B. Fill iced tea glasses ¾ full of chipped ice and pour the tea over it.

C. Serve with lemon, sugar, and a sprig of mint.

METHODS OF MAKING COFFEE

A. Using ground coffee.
   1. Boiling; clearing with cold water.

a. Put ¼ c. of coarsely ground coffee into a scalded enamel coffee pot and add 2 c. of boiling water.
b. Boil gently 3 min.
c. Add 2 tb. of cold water and let it stand 10 min.
d. Strain.

2. Boiling; clearing with egg white.
   a. To ¼ c. of coarsely ground coffee add 1 tb. of slightly beaten egg white and stir until well mixed.
   b. Put the coffee into a scalded enamel coffee pot and add 2 c. of boiling water.
   c. Boil gently 3 min.
   d. Let it stand 5 min. and strain.
3. Percolating; nonautomatic percolator.
   a. Put ¼ c. of coffee of medium grind into the coffee compartment of a percolator.
   b. Pour 2 c. of boiling water into the lower part of the percolator, add the coffee compartment, cover, and percolate 7 min. after the water bubbles over the coffee.
4. Percolating; automatic percolator.
   a. Put ¼ c. of coffee of medium grind into the coffee compartment of an automatic percolator.
   b. Pour 2 c. of cold water into the lower part, add the coffee compartment, and cover. The percolation will stop automatically.
5. Filtering; using a dripolator.
   a. Put filter paper into the coffee compartment of a dripolator and add 3 tb. of finely ground coffee.
   b. Add the upper compartment and pour 2 c. of boiling water into it.
   c. Leave it until the water has dripped through the coffee.
6. Filtering; using a Chemex coffee maker.
   a. Put filter paper into the upper part of the Chemex.
   b. Put 3 tb. of coffee on the filter paper and pour 2 c. of water below boiling—about 185° F. (85° C.)—through the coffee slowly.
7. Filtering; using a vacuum-type coffee maker.
   a. Put 2 c. of hot water into the lower compartment of a 1-qt. vacuum coffee maker.
   b. Adjust the upper compartment and straining cloth or rod and set the coffee maker over medium heat.
   c. Put ¼ c. of finely ground coffee into the upper compartment.
   d. When the water has risen into the upper part, stir slightly and turn the heat down so that the water bubbles gently.
   e. After 3 min. remove the coffee maker from the heat.
   f. When the coffee has gone down to the lower compartment, remove the upper part.

B. Using soluble coffee.
   1. Put ¾ t. of soluble coffee into a cup.
   2. Add boiling water and stir.

C. Using frozen coffee.
   1. Put 1 t. of frozen coffee into a cup.
   2. Add boiling water and stir to dissolve the coffee.

ICED COFFEE

A. Make coffee by one of the methods above, using double the proportion of coffee.

B. Fill iced tea glasses ¾ full of chipped ice and pour the hot coffee over it.

C. Serve with sugar and cream, either plain or whipped.

Café au Lait

Mix equal parts of strong coffee and hot milk. They may be mixed ahead of serving time or poured simultaneously into individual cups.

Coffee Velvet

Put 1 to 2 tablespoons of vanilla ice cream into a cup and pour hot or cold coffee over it. Serve at mealtime or as a social refreshment.

DESSERTS

It is not likely that laboratory time will be devoted to the preparation of desserts only, but since they are a popular part of the American pattern of eating, the instructor and students should give consideration to the nutritional contribution that is possible through desserts. While recipes for delicious, nutritious desserts will be found grouped under *Fruits, Milk, Eggs, Cheese, Sugar Cookery,* and *Flour Mixtures,* some additional ones are given here for convenience in use. They were selected on the basis of food value, interest, palatability, and they illustrate a variety of cookery principles in the preceding text.

Orange Omelet

(4 servings)

Eggs	6	Orange juice, frozen,	
Salt	½ t.	undiluted	2 tb.

1) Separate the eggs, beat yolks until thick, and add orange juice and salt.
2) Beat whites until stiff; fold yolks into whites.
3) Heat a frying pan with sloping sides and butter well.
4) Pour the omelet into the pan and cook over *low* heat.

5) When puffy and a delicate brown around the edges, place in the broiler 6 inches away from the heat and leave for a few minutes or until the top is slightly browned.
6) Sprinkle with powdered sugar and fold, or leave not folded. Serve plain or with a fruit sauce as a dessert.

Hawaiian Bananas
(4 servings)

Butter or margarine	3–4 tb.	Guava jelly (or juice)	3–4 tb.
Bananas, peeled and left whole	4	Lemon juice	1 tb.
		Pineapple juice	¼ c.

1) Put butter in frying pan and place over *low* heat.
2) Add whole bananas and sauté until light brown, being careful not to break them.
3) Add guava jelly and when melted add lemon and pineapple juice.
4) Continue the cooking over low heat (basting the bananas with the juice) for about 2 minutes. The bananas should be firm when served.
5) Serve as a dessert or as an accompaniment to meat or a curry dish.

Open-Face Dessert Sandwiches
(About 4 servings)

Fruit, fresh, frozen or canned, sliced or puréed	1½–2 c.	Rusk or zwieback, commercial variety	4 to 8 pieces
Ice cream, vanilla	½ pt.	Sugar (for fresh fruit)	to taste

1) Heap fruit (drained from sirup) on rusk or zwieback, using one piece of rusk or two of zwieback per serving.
2) Top fruit with ice cream.

Cranberry Crisp
(About 10 servings)

Rolled oats, uncooked, minute	1 c.	Sugar, brown	⅔ c.
Flour	½ c.	Orange rind, grated	1 tb.
Salt	¼ t.	Butter, room temperature	⅓ c.
Cranberry sauce	1 lb. can		

1) Mix all ingredients except cranberry sauce until crumbly.
2) Place half of the mixture in a buttered 8–9 in.-square pan.
3) Cover with cranberry sauce and put the remaining crumb mixture over the top.

4) Bake for about 40 minutes at 325° F. (163° C.).
5) Cool slightly and cut into squares.

Apple Butter Tarts
(6–8 tarts)

Pastry (see p. 626) sufficient for 2 crust		Sugar	½ c.
Apple butter	½ c.	Cinnamon	1 t.
Cornstarch	1½ tb.	Eggs, beaten	2
		Milk	2 c.

1) Roll out pastry and make individual tarts by fitting circular pieces of pastry into custard cups or other individual tart molds.
2) Mix all ingredients and pour into unbaked tart shells.
3) Bake for about 40 minutes at 350° F. (177° C.) or until the custard is set.

Quick Indian Pudding
(About 4 servings)

Cornmeal	½ c.	Cinnamon	¼ t.
Salt	½ t.	Milk	3 c.
Ginger	½ t.	Molasses, light or dark	½ c.
Ice cream	½ pt.		

1) Mix the dry ingredients; add the milk slowly, stirring to prevent lumping.
2) Place over *low* heat and cook for about 30 minutes; stir to avoid lumping.
3) Stir in the molasses, pour pudding into a baking dish, and bake, uncovered, for about 1 hour at 325° F. (163° C.).
4) Serve warm with vanilla ice cream or cream.

Tapioca Cream
(6 servings)

Milk	2 c.	Salt	⅛ t.
Tapioca (quick-cooking)	2½ tb.	Sugar	⅓ c.
Egg yolks	2	Vanilla	½ t.
		Egg whites	2

1) Scald the milk.
2) Sprinkle the tapioca over the milk and cook in the double boiler until the tapioca is translucent, stirring occasionally.
3) Beat the egg yolks and add the salt and half of the sugar.
4) Stir part of the tapioca mixture into the egg; return to the double boiler; and cook until the mixture coats the spoon, stirring slowly but constantly.
5) Remove from the heat and add the vanilla.
6) Beat the egg whites until fairly stiff and beat in the remaining sugar.

7) Fold the egg whites into the tapioca mixture and pour the pudding into serving dish or dishes.
8) Chill.

Steamed Cranberry Pudding
(About 6 servings)

Butter or margarine, softened	1/3 c.	Flour	2 1/2 c.
Sugar	2/3 c.	Baking powder	3 t.
Eggs, well beaten	2	Milk	1/2 c.
Cranberries, fresh, whole	1 c.		

1) Cream the butter or margarine with the sugar; add the eggs.
2) Sift in the flour and baking powder, adding the milk alternately.
3) Stir in the berries and pour into buttered mold. This may be a special pudding mold with a tight-fitting cover or individual custard cups or a large mold covered securely with aluminum foil.
4) Fill the mold about 2/3 full to allow for rising. Set mold on rack in a pan provided for steaming, add hot water until it comes halfway up on the mold. Put cover on steamer and steam for about 1 1/2 hours. (The length of time required will depend on the size and depth of the mold.)
5) Serve with hard sauce or other selection.
   [Note: A double boiler may be used as a steamer. Butter the top part, fill about 2/3 full, and set over lower part to steam. Add more water as it boils away.]

Hard Sauce
(About 1 c.)

Butter or margarine	1/3 c.	Lemon extract	2/3 t.
Sugar, granulated	3/4 c.	Cinnamon	dash
Nutmeg	dash		

1) Cream the fat.
2) Add the sugar gradually, creaming thoroughly after each addition.
3) Add the extract and spices.
4) Pile the sauce on a serving dish and sprinkle with nutmeg.
5) Allow to chill slightly before serving.

Fruit Sponge
(6 servings)

Gelatin	1 tb.	Fruit juice or nectar	1 c.
Cold water	1/2 c.	Lemon juice *	2 to 4 tb.
Sugar *	1/4 to 1/2 c.	Egg whites	3

* The quantity of sugar and lemon juice should vary with the sweetness of the fruit juice or nectar, the larger amount of sugar and smaller amount of lemon juice being used with unsweetened juice.

1) Soak the gelatin in the water in the top of a double boiler for about 5 min.
2) Stir over boiling water until the gelatin has dissolved.
3) Add the sugar and stir until it has dissolved.
4) Remove from the heat, add the fruit juices, and chill until the mixture is thick but not congealed.
5) Beat the egg whites until they form peaks when the beater is lifted.
6) Beat the jelly until it is light.
7) Add the egg white to the jelly and beat until the mixture forms peaks when the beater is lifted.
8) Pour into a mold or molds, rinsed in cold water but not dried, and set in a refrigerator until ready to serve. (Allow 2 to 4 hrs., depending upon the size of the molds.)

Spanish Cream

(6 servings)

Milk	1¾ c.	Gelatin	1 tb.
Sugar	⅓ c.	Cold milk	¼ c.
Salt	Dash	Flavoring	½ t.
Egg yolks	2	Egg whites	2

1) Scald the milk in a double boiler.
2) Add the sugar and salt and stir to dissolve.
3) Beat the egg yolks, add some of the above mixture slowly, and return to the double boiler.
4) Cook over water that is just below the boiling point until the mixture coats the spoon. Stir slowly but constantly during cooking.
5) Soak the gelatin in the cold milk for about 5 min.
6) Add the soaked gelatin to the custard and stir until it has disoslved. Add the flavoring.
7) Remove the mixture from the heat and chill until it is thick but not congealed.
8) Beat the egg whites until they form peaks when the beater is lifted.
9) Fold the egg whites into the other mixture and pour into a mold or molds, rinsed with cold water but not dried, and set in a refrigerator until ready to serve.
10) Serve with whipped cream or sweetened crushed fruit.

Eggnog Pie

Eggs, separated	4	Water, cold	¼ c.
Sugar	½	Sugar	½ c.
Salt	½	Rum extract or other flavoring	1 t.
Water, hot	½ c.		
Gelatin, plain	1 envelope	Pie shell, baked *	9-inch

Nutmeg to sprinkle

* See p. 626.

1) Beat egg yolks slightly; add ½ cup sugar, salt, and hot water.
2) Cook over *low* heat until thick.
3) Soften the gelatin by soaking in cold water.
4) Add to hot custard and stir until dissolved; cool.
5) Beat egg whites until stiff but not dry; add the other ½ c. of sugar and beat until stiff; add the flavoring.
6) Fold meringue mixture into cooled custard and pour into the baked pie shell.
7) Sprinkle with nutmeg and chill several hours before serving.

Chocolate Ice-Box Pudding

(6 servings)

Gelatin	1 tb.	Water, boiling	3 tb.
Water, cold	3 tb.	Milk	¼ c. + 2 tb.
Chocolate	1½ sq.	Vanilla	1 t.
Sugar, powdered	½ c.	Whipping cream	¾ c.
Lady fingers *	8 to 12		

1) Soak the gelatin in cold water.
2) Melt the chocolate in the top of a double boiler.
3) Add about half the sugar, the boiling water, and milk to the melted chocolate.
4) Add the softened gelatin, and stir until it is dissolved.
5) Add the remaining sugar and vanilla.
6) Cool until the mixture begins to thicken, stirring occasionally.
7) Whip the cream and fold into the mixture.
8) Line a mold with lady fingers, pour the mixture into the mold, and chill for several hours before serving.

Orange Bread Pudding

(About 4 servings)

Milk, scalded	¾ c.	Eggs	3
Bread cubes, toasted	1–1½ c.	Sugar	½ c.
Orange juice	¾ c.	Salt	⅛ t.
Orange rind, grated	1 orange	Nutmeg	dash

1) Pour milk over bread cubes and soak for about 10 min.
2) Add all other ingredients and stir until sugar is dissolved.
3) Pour into individual or large buttered mold and set into pan of hot water.
4) Bake for about 30 min. at 350° F. (177° C.).
5) Chill or serve warm with desired sauce.

* Vanilla wafers or sponge cake may be used.

Bread Pudding

(Serves 6)

Milk	3 c.	Eggs	2
Butter or margarine	2 tb.	Sugar	1/3 c.
Soft bread cubes	2 c.	Salt	1/2 t.
Vanilla	1 t.		

1) Scald the milk to which the butter or margarine is added.
2) Add the bread cubes and soak about 10 min.
3) Beat the eggs and add the remaining ingredients.
4) Combine the two mixtures and pour into a buttered baking dish.
5) Bake in a moderately slow oven—325° F. (163° C.) for 1 hr.
6) Serve plain or with cream or any desired sauce.

MERINGUES

Basic Recipe

Egg whites	3	Cream of tartar	1/4 t.
Salt	1/4 t.	Sugar, superfine	3/4 c.
Flavoring	1/2 t.		

1) Beat the egg whites until foamy. Add salt and cream of tartar and continue beating until egg whites are stiff and dry.
2) Sift the sugar and gradually beat it into the egg whites; add flavoring.

Meringue Shells

(6 servings)

1) Cover a baking sheet with waxed paper and place mounds of the meringue mixture on the paper to make individual shells about 2 in. in diameter, depressing the center of each mound with the back of a spoon *or* shape shells with a pastry tube.
2) Bake at 275° F. (135° C.) for approximately 1 hr. or until thoroughly dry; leave in the oven to cool slightly.
3) Remove from the paper while warm.
4) Serve filled with ice cream or fresh fruit.

Meringue Pie

(6 servings)

1) Butter an 8-in. pie plate and spread the meringue in it, making it higher around the edge.
2) Bake for about 1 hour in a slow oven—275° F. (135° C.). (The meringue should be firm and dry but not brown.)
3) Cool.
4) Whip 1 c. of heavy cream, adding about 1 tb. of sugar and 1/4 t. of flavoring during the whipping.

5) Spread about half of the cream over the meringue; add a layer of fresh fruit, sprinkled with sugar, or a layer of any desired filling; and spread the remaining whipped cream over the top.

Fruit Meringue

1) Make the basic meringue, decreasing the sugar to ½ c.
2) Line a square cake pan with waxed paper and pour the meringue into it, making it even in thickness.
3) Bake for about 30 min. in a slow oven—250° to 275° F. (121° to 135° C.). It should be firm but not brown.
4) Serve with crushed sweetened fruit, and garnish with whipped cream.

Peppermint Ice Cream

Ingredients	*For 1 qt.*	*For 2 qt.*	*For 1 gal.*
Milk	1½ c.	3 c.	1½ qt.
Gelatin	1 t.	2 t.	1 tb.
Peppermint-stick candy	⅜ lb.	¾ lb.	1½ lb.
Heavy cream (or light)	1½ c.	3 c.	1½ qt.

1) Soak gelatin in about 1 (or 2 or 3) tb. of the cold milk.
2) Scald milk over *low* heat.
3) Add softened gelatin to the milk and stir to dissolve.
4) Break the candy into small pieces.
5) Remove the milk from the heat and cool slightly; add the candy and cool rapidly. Some pieces of candy should remain undissolved.
6) Add the cream and stir.
7) Cool to 50° F. (10° C.) and freeze, following directions 6 through 10 under French Ice Cream, see p. 528.

Fresh Peach or Raspberry Ice Cream

1) In the American ice cream recipe (see pp. 528–529), make the following changes:
   a) Substitute puréed fruit for ⅓ of the combined milk and cream.
   b) Add 2 tb. sugar.
   c) Omit the vanilla.
2) Combine the ingredients as directed, and freeze the cream without the fruit for about 5 minutes, or to a mush.
3) Open the freezer and add the fruit, mixing it slightly with the cream.
4) Close the freezer and complete the freezing and packing.

Canned Green-Gage Plum Ice Cream

1) In the American ice cream recipe (see pp. 528–529), make the following changes:

a) Substitute puréed plums, without sirup, for 1/3 of the combined milk and cream.
b) Decrease the sugar to 1/3 c.
c) Omit the vanilla.
2) Combine the ingredients as directed, and freeze the cream without the fruit for about 5 minutes, or to a mush.
3) Open the freezer and add the fruit, mixing it slightly with the cream.
4) Close the freezer and complete the freezing and packing.

Orange Sherbet
(With Gelatin)

Ingredients	*For 1 qt.*	*For 2 qt.*	*For 1 gal.*
Gelatin	1 tb.	2 tb.	1/4 c.
Cold water	2 tb.	1/4 c.	1/2 c.
Boiling water	1/2 c.	1 c.	1 pt.
Sugar	1 c.	2 c.	4 c.
Orange juice	2 1/2 c.	5 c.	2 1/2 qt.
Lemon juice	1/4 c.	1/2 c.	1 c.

1) Soak the gelatin in cold water for about 5 min.
2) Add the softened gelatin to the boiling water and stir to dissolve.
3) Add sugar, and stir to dissolve. Chill.
4) Add fruit juices; stir, and strain.
5) Freeze, using 1 part of salt to 8 parts of ice.

Loganberry-Pear Ice *

Ingredients	*For 1 qt.*	*For 2 qt.*	*For 1 gal.*
Loganberry juice	1 3/4 c.	3 1/2 c.	7 c.
Pear nectar	3/4 c.	3 1/2 c.	7 c.
Salt	1/8 t.	1/4 t.	1/2 t.

1) Combine the ingredients and stir to mix well.
2) Freeze, using 1 part of salt to 6 parts of ice.

Sicilian Sorbet **

Ingredients	*For 1 qt.*	*For 2 qt.*	*For 1 gal.*
Canned peaches	1 1/2 c.	3 c.	1 1/2 qt.
Sugar	3/4 c.	1 1/2 c.	3 c.
Orange juice	1 1/2 c.	3 c.	1 1/2 qt.
Lemon juice	1 1/2 tb.	3 tb.	1/4 c. + 2 tb.

1) Press the peaches through a coarse sieve, using pulp and juice to measure.
2) Add the sugar to the peach pulp and juice and stir to dissolve.

* Other fruit juice and/or nectars may be used.
** Apricot sorbet may be made by using canned apricots in place of the peaches.

3) Add the other juices and stir.
4) Freeze, using 1 part of salt to 8 parts of ice.

Chocolate Mousse
(6 servings)

Bitter chocolate...	1 square (1 oz.)	Sugar................	7 tb.
		Egg yolks............	2
Evaporated milk	1¼ c.	Salt.................	1/16 t.
Water............	¼ c.	Vanilla..............	½ t.

1) Melt chocolate over hot water.
2) Put ¼ cup of milk, water, and sugar in the top part of a double boiler, and heat over boiling water to the scalding point.
3) Pour milk mixture over well-beaten egg yolks, stirring vigorously to keep smooth.
4) Add salt, and return to the double boiler.
5) Cook 5 min., stirring continuously to keep smooth.
6) *Add the mixture gradually to the melted chocolate,* beating well until the mass is thoroughly blended.
7) Cool.
8) Chill the other cup of milk in a bowl surrounded by chipped ice and salt.
9) Whip until stiff.
10) Fold the chocolate mixture into the whipped milk lightly but thoroughly.
11) Add vanilla.
12) Turn into a cold freezing pan and place in the refrigerator freezing compartment. Requires 3 to 4 hrs. to freeze.

Refrigerator Banana-Pineapple Sherbet
(6 servings)

Crushed pineapple.....	1½ c.	Orange juice...........	½ c.
Confectioners' sugar....	¾ c.	Lemon juice...........	¼ c.
Mashed banana........	1½ c.	Egg whites............	2
Salt.....................	¼ t.		

1) Stir the sugar into the pineapple to dissolve.
2) Add the banana and juices and put into refrigerator freezing compartment or freezer until it begins to stiffen.
3) Beat the egg whites and salt until they form a peak that bends over slightly when the beater is withdrawn.
4) Fold in the fruit mixture, pour into freezing trays, and freeze, removing to stir after it starts freezing (about 20 min.).

Refrigerator Avocado Sherbet
(About 8 servings)

In the recipe for 1 qt. of orange sherbet (p. 654):
1) Substitute milk for orange juice and decrease gelatin to 1 t.
2) Add ¾ c. of finely sieved avocado pulp and ⅛ t. salt.
3) Pour into refrigerator trays and freeze without stirring (about 2½ hrs.).

SEASONINGS

"Seasoning makes the difference" is a remark often heard in connection with food. In fact, it is the *seasoning* that transforms ordinary ingredients into distinguished meals, meals that can be culinary delights at modest cost. The subtle use of seasonings is an art, and through practice it can be learned along with the scientific principles of cooking. Failure to introduce beginners to the interesting possibilities of using herbs, spices, and other seasonings deprives them of one of the great pleasures of the kitchen. Fear of not liking a new flavor can be overcome if the unfamiliar seasoning is used with discretion. The Pizza "craze" in the United States and the wide-spread acceptance of its characteristic herb—oregano—is an example of keen interest in a different seasoning.

Some herbs are so closely identified with one product that suggestions for using them in other ways is "heresy." Dill in pickles is popular but when used with butter as a sauce for boiled potatoes it is likely to be rejected by many. However, the same individuals will enjoy dill pickles in potato salad!

Rye bread with caraway is a standard item in bakeries and bread departments of grocery stores but the use of caraway seed in other foods is very limited. Vanilla is so closely identified with baked custard that if *almond* is used instead it is likely to bring forth queries about the "interesting flavor."

Recipes throughout this section have taken into consideration the "new" interest in the use of herbs. However, additional recipes are grouped here in order to emphasize the many possibilities in seasoning everyday foods.

Cinnamon-Orange Punch
(About 6 servings)

Water	1½ c.	Orange juice, frozen	1-6-oz. can
Cinnamon	3 in. stick	Sparkling water	½ pt.

1) Simmer the water and stick cinnamon in covered pan for about 5 minutes and chill.
2) Reconstitute orange juice with cinnamon water and just before serving add the chilled sparkling water.

GINGER-PINEAPPLE JUICE
(About 6 servings)

Ginger, powdered	1 t.	Pineapple juice, frozen concentrate	1-6-oz can
Sugar, granulated	1 tb.	Sparkling water, chilled	½ pt.

1) Mix the sugar and ginger and add to the pineapple concentrate before adding the water to dilute.
2) Add sparkling water just before serving.

SPICE STICKS
(3–4 doz. half-inch sticks)

Orange-Nutmeg

Bread, white, firm type	4–6 sl.	Sugar	2–3 tb.
Butter or margarine	¼–⅓ c.	Orange rind	1 tb.
		Nutmeg	⅛ t.

1) Toast the bread on both sides.
2) Cream the other ingredients and spread liberally on one side of the toast.
3) Using a sharp knife or scissors, cut the toast into ½ in. sticks (about 8 sticks to the slice), being careful not to break them.
4) Place on a baking sheet, put in oven and dry out for about 30 minutes, at 250° F. (121° C.).
5) Cool on a cake rack and serve as a social refreshment or instead of cookies at meal time.
   [NOTE: These hold well in the freezer if placed in a cannister or wrapped carefully to prevent breaking.]

Cinnamon-Clove

Follow directions for Orange-Nutmeg sticks using whole wheat bread instead of white and substituting 1 t. of cinnamon and ⅛ t. ground clove for the orange rind and nutmeg.

If a mixture of the light (orange-nutmeg) and dark (cinnamon-clove) sticks are served it makes an interesting contrast in color and flavor.

HERB TOAST STICKS
(About 1 doz. 1-in. sticks)

Bread	2–4 slices	Basil	⅛ t.
Butter or margarine, room temp.	¼ c.	Sesame seed	1 t.
Curry powder	⅛ t.	Paprika	⅛ t.
		Salt	⅛ t.
		Cayenne pepper	dash

1) Toast the bread on both sides.
2) Cream the butter with the herbs to mix thoroughly.
3) Spread herb butter on toast, cut in inch strips, put on baking sheet in oven and dry out for about 20 minutes at 250° F. (121° C.).
4) Serve with salads, soups, or as a social refreshment.
[NOTE: Any herb mixture may be used for the toast sticks.]

Cottage Cheese-Caraway Muffins
(About 18, 2 in. muffins)

Butter or margarine, room temp.	¼ c.	Egg, beaten	1
Sugar	⅓ c.	Flour	2 c.
Lemon rind	1 t.	Salt	¼ t.
Caraway seed	2 t.	Soda	⅛ t.
Cottage cheese	½ c.	Baking powder	2½ t.
		Milk	½ c.

1) Cream butter or margarine with the sugar; add lemon rind, caraway seed, cottage cheese, and egg and blend well.
2) Sift in the dry ingredients, adding the milk alternately, and stir to mix.
3) Bake in oiled muffin rings about 25 minutes at 400° F. (204° C.).
4) Serve as a social refreshment, as a simple dessert, or for a breakfast or luncheon bread.

Parsley Dumplings

Add ¼ c. of chopped parsley to dumpling recipe on p. 562. The parsley should be added to the dry ingredients.

Saffron Rice
(4–6 servings)

Rice, converted	1 c.	Salt	½ t.
Water, cold	2 c.	Saffron	1⁄16 t.

1) Select a utensil of substantial material with a close-fitting lid.
2) Put rice and other ingredients into utensil and mix.
3) Place over medium heat until water boils, then reduce to *low* or *simmer* heat, cover, and cook for about 35–40 minutes. If rice is kept covered, and the heat low, stirring will not be necessary. The rice should be dry and flaky when done. Stir rice with a fork before serving.
4) Serve plain or with a parsley butter or tomato sauce.

Curried Scalloped Potatoes
(About 6 servings)

Potatoes, pared	4 medium	Salt	½–¾ t.
Coconut, shredded	1 c.	Curry powder	1–2 t.
Onions, finely chopped	2 medium	Milk	1 c.
		Swiss cheese, grated	½ c.

1) Cut the potatoes on a coarse shredder.
2) Mix potatoes with all other ingredients *except* cheese.
3) Put the mixture into a shallow utensil with a close-fitting cover, preferably of the range-to-table type.
4) Cook over *low* heat for about 15 min. or until potatoes are tender.
5) Sprinkle cheese over the top and place under broiler until browned slightly. (If the potatoes are not cooked in a table utensil, transfer to a baking dish before sprinkling the cheese over the top.)

Fresh Mint Sauce

Mint leaves, packed	1 c.	Lemon juice	2–3 tb.
Onion	¼–½ small	Salt	½ t.
Parsley	¼ c.	Sugar	2 tb.
		Cayenne	¼ t.

1) Put all ingredients into a blender and turn on and off several times or until finely minced.
2) Serve with lamb or other meats.

Herb Mixtures

For Vegetables	*For Egg and Chicken Dishes*	*For Lamb or Veal*
1 tb. summer savory	1 tb. tarragon	1 tb. rosemary
1 tb. sweet basil	1 tb. summer savory	1 tb. parsley
1 tb. marjoram	1 tb. chives	1 tb. marjoram

Cocktail Mushrooms
(About 1 c.)

Salt	¼ t.	Olive oil	¼ c.
Sugar	1 t.	Vinegar, garlic (or plain)	1–2 tb.
Paprika	½ t.	Mushrooms, raw and sliced	⅛ lb.
Curry powder	¼ t.		
Sesame seed	1 t.		

1) Mix dry ingredients, add oil and vinegar, and blend well.
2) Add sliced mushrooms and marinate for several hours before serving.
3) Serve as a relish with meat, egg, or cheese dishes.

Rose Geranium Apple Sauce

(About 1 pt.)

Apples, tart	8–10	Rose geranium leaves	4–6
Water	¾ c.	Sugar	¼ c.
Lemon, sliced	½ lemon	Nutmeg	dash

1) Slice apples; do not pare.
2) Add water, lemon, and rose geranium to apples and cook over low heat in a covered saucepan about 20 minutes or until apples are tender.
3) Put the mixture through a food mill, turning until all pulp has passed through the strainer.
4) Add sugar and nutmeg and chill before serving.
5) Serve as a dessert or as an accompaniment to meat or fowl.

Indian Carrot Dessert

(4–6 servings)

Carrots, coarsely grated	1½ c. packed	Saffron	large pinch
Milk	3–4 c.	Cardamom seed	2–3 seed
Sugar	½ c.	Butter or margarine	2 tb.
Raisins	¼ c.	Almonds, blanched and slivered	¼ c.

1) Add carrots to milk and cook over low heat, stirring frequently, until the milk has almost evaporated.
2) Add all other ingredients except almonds and continue cooking until almost dry.
3) Serve hot or cold with the almonds sprinkled over the top.

Poppy Seed Cookies

Butter or margarine, room temp.	½ c.	Egg	1
Sugar	⅓ c.	Lemon rind	1 t.
Almond extract, or other flavoring	½ t.	Salt	¼ t.
		Poppy seed	2 tb.
		Flour	1–1¼ c.

1) Blend the butter and sugar.
2) Add other ingredients and blend thoroughly. It may be necessary to use the hands.
3) Flour the hands lightly and roll dough into 1-in. balls.
4) Flatten balls and place on lightly oiled baking sheet.
5) Bake about 12 minutes at 375° F. (191° C.).

[Note: Bake a test cookie before shaping them all. If the dough is to thin, add a little more flour; if too thick, a few drops of water can be added.]

Rosemary Jelly

Rosemary, dried	1 t.	Orange juice	2½ c.
Water	1 c.	Lemon juice	¼ c.
Pectin	½ bottle		

1) Simmer the rosemary and water in a covered saucepan for about 5 minutes. Remove and discard the rosemary by straining through a fine sieve, filter or cheesecloth.
2) Mix water with all other ingredients and make jelly by following manufacturer's directions on pectin bottle.

FOOD PRESERVATION

Plans for laboratory activities may include any or all of the following, depending upon location, time of year, and emphasis on preservation techniques. Sources for recipes and suitable methods include bulletins from both federal and state agencies. Regional favorites may be of special interest, for example, beech plum or mayhaw jelly may be of interest both as a jelly for home use and as a gift possibility.

1) Canning:
   - Fruit and/or tomatoes—processing by hot water or steam bath.
   - Low-acid vegetables—processing by pressure cooker.
   - A high-protein food (meat or poultry)—processing by pressure cooker.
2) Freezing:
   - Fruit with no sugar, dry sugar, light sirup, and heavy sirup.
   - Vegetables that require different techniques.
   - Poultry, meat, and perhaps fish.
   - Eggs.
   - Ready-to-heat-and-eat foods, e.g., stews; chicken à la king.
   - Ready-to-thaw-and-eat foods, e.g., cakes and baked cookies.
   - Partially-prepared foods, e.g., rolls and muffins to be browned as they thaw and are heated.
3) Drying:
   - Fruit—including scalding and sulphuring.
   - Herbs.
4) Brining and pickling:
   - Kraut—dry salting.
   - Long-process pickles—brining.
   - Short-process pickles.
   - Relishes.
5) Preserves:
   - Preserves.
   - Jams.
   - Marmalades.
   - Conserves.

6) Jellies:
   Without added pectin.
   With added pectin.

Corn Relish

Yellow whole kernel corn	No. 2 can	Onions, chopped	1 c.
Cucumbers, diced	1 pt.	Celery, cut fine	1 pt.
Ripe tomatoes, diced	1 qt.	Cider vinegar	1 pt.
Red and/or green peppers cut in strips	3 med.	Sugar	2 c.
		Salt	¼ c.
		Celery seed	1 t.
		Mustard seed	1 t.
		Turmeric powder	¼ t.

1) Heat the vinegar and dissolve the sugar in it.
2) Add the fresh vegetables and cook rapidly until nearly tender.
3) Add the corn and continue cooking until the vegetables are tender and the corn is thoroughly heated.
4) Add the salt and spices and fill sterilized jars. Seal.

Crisp Sweet Dill Pickles

Medium dill pickles	6	Mixed pickling spices	1 t.
Seeded raisins	½ c.	Whole cloves	1 t.
Sugar	2 c.	*or*	
Liquid from pickles	¼ c.	Ground cloves	½ t.
Vinegar	¼ c.	Cassia buds	1 t.

1) Cut the dill pickles in slices about ⅓-in. thick.
2) Put them in layers in a suitable container, scattering raisins over each layer.
3) Make a sirup with the remaining ingredients; tie spices in a cloth.
4) Pour the sirup over the pickle slices and raisins and let stand at least 24 hours. (The pickles are crisper if they stand longer.)

English Chutney

Ripe tomatoes	2 lbs.	Salt	1 oz.
Sour apples	2 lbs.	Brown sugar	1 lb.
Seeded raisins	1 lb.	Ground ginger	1½ tb.
Large white onion	1	Cayenne	¼ tb.
Celery	4 stalks	Allspice	½ tb.
Lemon juice	3 tb.	Nutmeg	½ t.
Lemon rind, grated	1 t.	Cider vinegar	1½ c.

1) Chop the tomatoes, apples, raisins, onion, and celery fairly fine.
2) Combine all ingredients in a large kettle or saucepot and boil until thick, stirring frequently, especially when the mixture tends to settle on the bottom of the utensil.
3) Pour into sterilized jars and seal.

Strawberry Purée *

Strawberries	1 qt.	Sugar	½ to ¾ c.

1) Wash, hull, and mash the berries.
2) Add the sugar and stir until it is thoroughly dissolved.
3) Pour into a freezer container and freeze.

Raspberry Purée *

Frozen raspberries.................... 2 12-oz. packages

1) Thaw the berries slightly and force through a strainer or sieve.
2) Use as a fruit sauce for puddings or ice cream.

Orange-Grapefruit Jelly **

Sugar	3¼ c.	Lemon juice	3 tb.
Water	1 c.	Liquid pectin	½ bottle

Frozen concentrated orange-grapefruit...... 6-oz. can

1) Put the sugar and water into a large saucepan and stir to melt and bring to a boil.
2) Add the lemon juice and boil hard for 1 min.
3) Remove from the heat and stir in the pectin.
4) Add the thawed juice and stir to mix well.
5) Pour into hot jelly glasses and seal with paraffin.

---

* Adapted from Pauline Paul, *Fruit Purées*. Michigan State College Agricultural Experiment Station, East Lansing, Mich., Circular Bulletin 200, 1946.

** Other concentrated juices may be used.

APPENDIX A

FOOD AND NUTRITION BOARD, NATIONAL RESEARCH COUNCIL RECOMMENDED DAILY DIETARY ALLOWANCES,* REVISED 1958

Designed for the maintenance of good nutrition of healthy persons in the U. S. A.
(Allowances are intended for persons normally active in a temperate climate.)

Age and Sex	*Weight*	*Height*	*Calories***	*Protein* †	*Calcium*	*Iron*	*Vitamin A*	*Thiamine*	*Riboflavin*	*Niacin Equivalents* ††	*Ascorbic Acid*	*Vitamin D*
Adults												
	Kg. (lb.)	cm. (in.)		gm.	gm.	mg.	I.U.	mg.	mg.	mg.	mg.	I.U.
MEN												
25 years	70 (154)	175 (69)	3200	70	0.8	10	5000	1.6	1.8	21	75	
45 years	70 (154)	175 (69)	3000	70	0.8	10	5000	1.5	1.8	20	75	
65 years	70 (154)	175 (69)	2550	70	0.8	10	5000	1.3	1.8	18	75	
WOMEN												
25 years	58 (128)	163 (64)	2300	58	0.8	12	5000	1.2	1.5	17	70	
45 years	58 (128)	163 (64)	2200	58	0.8	12	5000	1.1	1.5	17	70	
65 years	58 (128)	163 (64)	1800	58	0.8	12	5000	1.0	1.5	17	70	
Pregnancy (3rd trimester)			+300	+20	1.5	15	6000	1.3	2.0	+3	100	400
Lactation (850 ml. milk daily)			+1000	+40	2.0	15	8000	1.7	2.5	+2	150	400

Children up to Twelve Years

INFANTS													
0 to 1 month													
1 to 6 months	6 (13)	60 (24)	kg. × 120		0.6	5	1500	0.4	0.5	6	30	400
7 to 12 months	9 (20)	70 (28)	kg. × 100		0.8	7	1500	0.5	0.8	7	30	400
1 to 3 years	12 (27)	87 (34)	1300	40	1.0	7	2000	0.7	1.0	8	35	400
4 to 6 years	18 (40)	109 (43)	1700	50	1.0	8	2500	0.9	1.3	11	50	400
7 to 9 years	27 (60)	129 (51)	2100	60	1.0	10	3500	1.1	1.5	14	60	400
10 to 12 years	36 (79)	144 (57)	2500	70	1.2	12	4500	1.3	1.8	17	75	400

Children Thirteen to Nineteen Years

BOYS												
13 to 15 years	49 (108)	163 (64)	3100	85	1.4	15	5000	1.6	2.1	21	90	400
16 to 19 years	63 (130)	175 (69)	3600	100	1.4	15	5000	1.8	2.5	25	100	400
GIRLS												
13 to 15 years	49 (108)	160 (63)	2600	80	1.3	15	5000	1.3	2.0	17	80	400
16 to 19 years	54 (120)	162 (64)	2400	75	1.3	15	5000	~~1.2~~ .9	1.9	16	80	400

* The allowance levels are intended to cover variations among most normal persons as they live in the United States under usual environmental stresses. The recommended allowances can be attained with a variety of common foods, providing other nutrients for which human requirements have been less well defined.

** Calorie allowances apply to individuals usually engaged in moderate physical activity. For office workers or others in sedentary occupations, they are excessive. Adjustments must be made for variations in body size, age, physical activity, and environmental temperature.

† The Board recognizes that human milk is the natural food for infants and feels that this is the best and desired procedure for meeting nutrient requirements in the first months of life. No allowances are stated for the first month of life. Breast feeding is particularly indicated during the first month when infants show handicaps in homeostasis due to different rates of maturation of digestive, excretory, and endocrine functions. Recommendations as listed pertain to nutrient intake as afforded by cow's milk formulas and supplementary foods given the infant when breast feeding is terminated. Allowances are not given for protein during infancy.

†† Niacin equivalents include dietary sources of the preformed vitamin and the precursor, tryptophan; 60 mg. tryptophan are counted as being equivalent to 1 mg. niacin.

APPENDIX B

NUTRIENTS IN AVERAGE SERVINGS OF FOOD *

Food	*Approximate Measure*	*Calories*	*Protein* (gm.)	*Calcium* (mg.)	*Phosphorus* (mg.)	*Iron* (mg.)	*Vitamin A* (I.U.)	*Thiamine* (mg.)	*Riboflavin* (mg.)	*Niacin* (mg.)	*Ascorbic Acid* (mg.)
MILK											
Buttermilk	1 c.	86	8.5	(288)	227	0.2	10	.09	.43	.3	3
Chocolate-flavored	1 c.	185	8.0	272	228	.2	230	.08	.40	.2	2
Condensed	½ c.	490	12.4	417	349	.31	650	.08	.59	.3	3
Dried, whole	5 tb.	195	10.5	380	290	—	550	.10	.48	.05	5
Evaporated	½ c.	173	8.8	306	246	.2	505	.06	.46	.3	2
Fluid, whole †	1 c.	166	8.5	288	227	.2	(390)	.09	.42	.3	3
Nonfat solid (skim)	5 tb.	140	13.5	490	385	—	tr.	.15	.45	.5	5
CHEESE											
Cheddar	1 oz.	113	7.1	206	140	.3	400	.01	.12	tr.	—
Cottage	1 oz.	27	5.5	27	54	.1	(10)	.01	.09	tr.	—
Cream	1 oz.	106	2.6	19	27	.1	(410)	tr.	.06	tr.	—
FRUITS											
Apples, fresh	1 med.	76	.4	8	13	.4	120	.05	.04	.2	6
Apricots, canned	4 med. halves & 2 tb. sirup	97	.7	12	18	.4	1,650	.02	.03	.4	5
Apricots, dried, cooked unsweetened	½ c.	121	2.8	40	55	2.3	3,450	.005	.07	1.4	4.5
Avocado	½ peeled	279	1.9	11	43	.7	330	.07	.15	1.3	18
Banana	1 med.	88	1.2	8	28	.6	430	.04	.05	.7	10
Berries, fresh:											
Blueberries	½ c.	43	.4	11	9	.6	200	.02	.02	.2	11
Blackberries	½ c.	41	.9	23	23	.7	140	.03	.03	.3	15
Raspberries	½ c.	35	.8	25	23	.6	80	.02	.04	.2	15
Strawberries	½ c.	27	.6	21	20	.6	45	.02	.05	.2	45

* Adapted from *COMPOSITION OF FOODS—RAW, PROCESSED, PREPARED*, U. S. Department of Agriculture, Agriculture Handbook No. 8.
[NOTE: Parentheses indicate imputed value.]
† Pasteurized.

NUTRIENTS IN AVERAGE SERVINGS OF FOOD (Continued)

Food	*Approximate Measure*	*Cal-ories*	*Pro-tein* (gm.)	*Cal-cium* (mg.)	*Phos-phorus* (mg.)	*Iron* (mg.)	*Vita-min A* (I.U.)	*Thia-mine* (mg.)	*Ribo-flavin* (mg.)	*Nia-cin* (mg.)	*Ascor-bic Acid* (mg.)
Cherries, red, canned in sirup	½ c.	61	1.0	14	15	.4	920	.03	.02	.2	7
Grapefruit	½ med.	75	.9	41	34	.4	20	.07	.04	.4	76
Grapes, American	1 bunch	55	1.1	13	16	.5	60	.05	.03	.2	3
Grapes, European	1 c.	102	1.2	26	33	.9	120	.09	.06	.4	6
Melons:											
Cantaloupe	½ med.	37	1.1	31	29	.7	6,190	.09	.07	.9	59
Watermelon	½ slice ¾ × 10 in.	45	.8	11	19	.3	950	.08	.08	.3	10
Orange	1 med.	70	1.4	51	36	.6	(290)	.12	.04	.4	77
Orange juice, canned unsweetened	1 c.	109	2	25	44	.7	(240)	.17	.04	.6	103
Orange juice concentrate, frozen, unsweetened	2 oz.	100	1.8	23	40	.7	(223)	.16	.04	.5	95
Peaches, canned	2 med. halves & 2 tb. sirup	79	.5	6	16	.5	530	.01	.02	.8	5
Peaches, fresh	1 med.	46	.5	8	22	.6	880	.02	.05	.9	8
Pears, canned	2 med. halves & 2 tb. sirup	79	.2	9	12	.2	tr.	.01	.02	.2	2
Pears, fresh	1 med.	95	1.1	20	24	.5	30	.03	.06	.2	6
Pineapple:											
Canned	1 large slice & 2 tb. sirup	95	.5	35	9	.7	100	.09	.02	.2	11
Fresh	1 slice, 3½ in. diameter	44	.3	13	9	.3	110	.07	.02	.2	20
Juice	½ c.	60	.4	18	10	.6	100	.06	.02	.2	11
Plums, fresh	3 med.	77	1.2	30	33	.9	600	.12	.06	.09	9
Prunes, dried	4 med.	73	.6	15	23	1.1	510	.03	.04	.5	1
Raisins	¼ c.	107	.9	31	51	1.4	20	.06	.03	.2	tr.
Rhubarb, stewed with sugar	½ c.	191	.06	56	27	.6	35	.01	—	.1	8.5

NUTRIENTS IN AVERAGE SERVINGS OF FOOD (Continued)

Food	*Approximate Measure*	*Calories*	*Protein* (gm.)	*Calcium* (mg.)	*Phosphorus* (mg.)	*Iron* (mg.)	*Vitamin A* (I.U.)	*Thiamine* (mg.)	*Riboflavin* (mg.)	*Niacin* (mg.)	*Ascorbic Acid* (mg.)
Tomatoes:											
Canned	½ c.	23	1.2	13	32	.7	1,270	.07	.04	.8	20
Fresh	1 med.	30	1.5	16	40	.9	1,640	.08	.06	.8	35
Juice, canned	½ c.	25	1.2	8	18	.5	1,270	.06	.04	.9	19
VEGETABLES **											
Green and yellow:											
Asparagus:											
Canned with liquid	½ c. cut spears	21	2.2	22	51	2	725	.08	.11	1.1	18
Fresh	½ c. cut spears	18	2.1	16	47	.9	910	.11	.15	1	20
Beans, fresh:											
Green	½ c.	14	.9	22	15	.5	415	.05	.06	.3	9
Lima	½ c.	76	4	23	61	1.3	230	.11	.07	.9	12
Broccoli	½ c.	22	2.5	98	57	1.0	2,550	.05	.11	.6	56
Carrots, raw	1 med.	21	.6	20	18	.4	6,000	.03	.03	.3	3
Chard, leaves and stalks	½ c.	15	1	76	26	1.8	2,255	.03	.05	.3	13
Corn, sweet	1 ear, med.	84	2.7	5	51	.6	390	.11	.1	1.4	8
Kale	½ c.	22	2.6	124	34	1.2	4,610	.04	.13	.9	28
Lettuce, raw	2 large leaves	7	.6	11	12	.2	270	.02	.04	.1	4
Okra	8 med. pods	28	1.5	70	53	.6	630	.05	.05	.7	17
Peas, English	½ c.	55	3.9	18	98	1.5	575	.2	.11	1.8	12
Rutabaga	½ c.	25	.6	42	32	.3	270	.04	.06	.6	16
Spinach	½ c.	23	2.8	111 *	30	1.8	10,600	.07	.18	.5	27
Squash, winter	½ c.	49	1.9	25	36	.8	6,345	.05	.15	.6	7
Potatoes:											
Irish, baked	1 med.	97	2.4	13	65	.8	20	.11	.05	1.4	17
Irish, boiled	1 med. peeled	105	2.5	14	71	.9	20	.12	.04	1.3	17
Irish, French-fried	8 pieces	157	2.2	12	61	.8	20	.07	.04	1.3	11
Sweet, baked	1 med.	183	2.6	44	72	1.1	11,410 †	.12	.08	.9	28

* May not be available.
** Cooked unless otherwise stated.
† Highly colored.

NUTRIENTS IN AVERAGE SERVINGS OF FOOD (Continued)

Food	*Approximate Measure*	*Calories*	*Protein* (gm.)	*Calcium* (mg.)	*Phosphorus* (mg.)	*Iron* (mg.)	*Vitamin A* (I.U.)	*Thiamine* (mg.)	*Riboflavin* (mg.)	*Niacin* (mg.)	*Ascorbic Acid* (mg.)
Others:											
Beets	½ c. diced	34	.8	18	25	.6	15	.02	.04	.3	6
Cabbage, raw	½ c.	7	.7	23	20	.3	40	.03	.03	.2	25
Celery, raw	3 5-in. stalks	9	.6	25	20	.2	—	.03	.02	.2	4
Cucumber, raw	6 slices, peeled	6	.4	5	10	.2	—	.02	.02	.1	4
Onions, raw	1 med.	49	1.5	35	48	.6	60	.04	.04	.2	10
Squash, summer	½ c.	17	.6	16	16	.4	275	.04	.08	.7	12
Turnips	½ c. diced	21	.6	31	27	.4	tr.	.03	.05	.3	14
EGGS, POULTRY, FISH AND MEAT											
Eggs	1 med.	77	6.1	26	101	1.3	550	.04	.13	tr.	—
Chicken, E.P., roaster	¼ lb.	227	22.9	16	227	1.7	—	.09	.18	9.1	—
Turkey, E.P.	¼ lb.	304	22.8	26	363	4.3	tr.	.10	.16	9.1	—
Fish:											
Cod, E.P.	¼ lb.	84	18.7	11	220	.5	—	.07	.10	2.5	2
Salmon, pink canned	½ c.	122	17.4	159	243	.7	60	.03	.16	6.8	—
Tuna, canned	½ c.	169	24.7	(7)	(299)	1.2	70	.04	.10	10.9	—
Beef, boned:											
Chuck roast	¼ lb.	351	30	13	133	3.5	—	.06	.23	4.7	—
Rib roast	¼ lb.	362	27	11	210	3.4	—	.07	.21	4.9	—
Rump roast	¼ lb.	429	24	9	97	2.9	—	.05	.18	3.5	—
Hamburger	¼ lb.	414	25	10	179	3.2	—	.09	.21	5.5	—
Loin steak	¼ lb.	337	25	11	199	4.4	—	.07	.21	5.3	—
Round steak	¼ lb.	264	31	13	254	3.9	—	.09	.25	6.3	—
Lamb, boned:											
Chops	¼ lb.	475	27	13	227	3.4	—	.16	.29	6.4	—
Leg, roast	¼ lb.	313	27	11	292	3.5	—	.16	.28	5.8	—
Pork, boned:											
Bacon, broiled	2 slices	97	4	4	41	.5	—	.08	.05	.8	—

NUTRIENTS IN AVERAGE SERVINGS OF FOOD (Continued)

Food	*Approximate Measure*	*Calories*	*Protein* (gm.)	*Calcium* (mg.)	*Phosphorus* (mg.)	*Iron* (mg.)	*Vitamin A* (I.U.)	*Thiamine* (mg.)	*Riboflavin* (mg.)	*Niacin* (mg.)	*Ascorbic Acid* (mg.)
Chops, broiled	¼ lb.	377	26	13	267	3.4	—	.94	.27	5.7	—
Ham, smoked	¼ lb.	451	26	11	189	3.3	—	.62	.24	4.7	—
Sausage, links	¼ lb.	510	12.2	7	113	1.8	—	.49	.19	2.6	—
Veal, boned:											
Cutlet	¼ lb.	248	32	14	293	4	—	.09	.32	6.9	—
Shoulder roast	¼ lb.	259	32	14	293	4.1	—	.15	.36	9.0	—
Heart, beef	¼ lb.	115	18	10	216	4.9	37.5	.63	.9	8.3	6
Liver, calf	¼ lb.	150	20.3	6.1	365	11.3	23,913	.23	.31	17.1	37.5
Tongue, beef	¼ lb.	235	18.6	10	212	3.2	—	.14	.33	5.7	—
CEREAL PRODUCTS											
Bread:											
Rye	½ in. slice	57	2.1	17	34	.4	—	.04	.02	.4	—
White, unenriched *	½ in. slice	63	2	18	21	.1	—	.01	.02	.2	—
White, enriched *	½ in. slice	63	2	18	21	.4	—	.06	.04	.5	—
Whole-wheat	½ in. slice	55	2.1	22	60	.5	—	.07	.03	.7	—
Crackers:											
Graham	2 med.	55	1.1	3	28	.3	—	.04	.02	.2	—
Saltines	2, 2-in.	34	.7	2	7	.1	—	tr.	tr.	.1	—
Breakfast cereals:											
Corn flakes	½ c.	48	1	1	7	.1	—	.05	.01	.2	—
Rice, cooked:											
Brown	Approx. 1 c.	187	3.9	20	158	2.1	—	.17	.03	2.4	—
Converted	Approx. 1 c.	169	3.6	11	64	.4	—	.09	.02	1.8	—
White, unenriched	Approx. 1 c.	173	3.6	12	65	.4	—	.03	.01	.8	—
Rice flakes	½ c.	59	.9	3	18	.25	—	.01	.02	.15	—
Rolled oats, cooked	½ c.	74	2.7	10	79	.9	—	.11	.03	.2	—
Shredded wheat	1 lg. biscuit	102	2.9	13	102	1.0	—	.06	.03	1.3	—

* 4 per cent non-fat milk solids.

NUTRIENTS IN AVERAGE SERVINGS OF FOOD (Continued)

Food	*Approximate Measure*	*Calories*	*Protein* (gm.)	*Calcium* (mg.)	*Phosphorus* (mg.)	*Iron* (mg.)	*Vitamin A* (I.U.)	*Thiamine* (mg.)	*Riboflavin* (mg.)	*Niacin* (mg.)	*Ascorbic Acid* (mg.)
Macaroni, enriched, cooked	½ c.	105	3.6	7	46	.7	—	.12	.08	1.0	—
FATS											
Butter	1 tb.	100	.1	3	2	—	460	tr.	tr.	tr.	—
Cream, light	1 tb.	30	.4	15	12	—	120	tr.	.02	tr.	tr.
French dressing	1 tb.	59	.1	—	—	—	—	—	—	—	—
Boiled dressing	1 tb.	28	.8	15	17	.1	80	.01	.03	tr.	tr.
Mayonnaise	1 tb.	92	.2	2	8	.1	30	tr.	tr.	—	—
SWEETS											
Honey	1 tb.	62	.1	1	3	.2	—	tr.	.01	tr.	1
Jams	1 tb.	55	.1	2	2	.1	tr.	tr.	tr.	tr.	1
Jellies	1 tb.	50	—	(2)	(2)	(.1)	(tr.)	(tr.)	(tr.)	(tr.)	1
Molasses, med.	1 tb.	46	—	58	14	1.2	—	—	—	—	—
Sugar:											
Granulated	1 tb.	48	—	—	—	—	—	—	—	—	—
Brown (dark)	1 tb.	51	—	10	5	.4	—	—	—	—	—
Various desserts:											
Cake:											
Cupcake	1 (2¾-in. diameter)	131	2.6	62	55	.2	50	.01	.03	.1	—
Cupcake, iced	1 (2¾-in. diameter)	161	2.6	58	52	.2	50	.01	.04	.1	—
Layer cake, iced	2 in. sector	322	5.2	117	104	.4	90	.02	.07	.2	—
Sponge cake	2 in. sector	117	3.2	11	44	.6	210	.02	.06	.1	—
Cookies, plain	3 in. diam.	109	1.5	6	16	.2	—	.01	.01	.1	—
Ice cream	½ c.	147	2.9	88	71	.05	370	.03	.14	.05	.5
Pie (9-inch):											
Apple	⅙	387	3.3	11	38	.6	252	.05	.03	.4	1.5
Coconut	⅙	310	7.9	189	176	1.8	343	.08	.25	.5	—

APPENDIX C

DESIRABLE WEIGHTS FOR MEN AND WOMEN OF AGES 25 AND OVER IN RELATION TO AGE AND FRAME *

MEN

Height (with shoes on) *Feet*	*Inches*	*Small Frame*	*Medium Frame*	*Large Frame*
5	2	116–125	124–133	131–142
5	3	119–128	127–136	133–144
5	4	122–132	130–140	137–149
5	5	126–136	134–144	141–153
5	6	129–139	137–147	145–157
5	7	133–143	141–151	149–162
5	8	136–147	145–156	153–166
5	9	140–151	149–160	157–170
5	10	144–155	153–164	161–175
5	11	148–159	157–168	165–180
6	0	152–164	161–173	169–185
6	1	157–169	166–178	174–190
6	2	163–175	171–184	179–196
6	3	168–180	176–189	184–202

WOMEN

Height (with shoes on) *Feet*	*Inches*	*Small Frame*	*Medium Frame*	*Large Frame*
4	11	104–111	110–118	117–127
5	0	105–113	112–120	119–129
5	1	107–115	114–122	121–131
5	2	110–118	117–125	124–135
5	3	113–121	120–128	127–138
5	4	116–125	124–132	131–142
5	5	119–128	127–135	133–145
5	6	123–132	130–140	138–150
5	7	126–136	134–144	142–154
5	8	129–139	137–147	145–158
5	9	133–143	141–151	149–162
5	10	136–147	145–155	152–166
5	11	139–150	148–158	155–169

* These tables are based on numerous Medico-Actuarial studies of hundreds of thousands of insured men and women. Weight in pounds is according to frame (as ordinarily dressed).

APPENDIX D

TEMPERATURE TABLES

Comparable Fahrenheit and centigrade temperatures commonly used or referred to in cookery:

a. To convert Fahrenheit to centigrade:
$(F. - 32) \times \frac{5}{9}$ e.g. $212\ F. - 32 = 180$
$\frac{5}{9} \times 180 = 100\ C.$

b. To convert centigrade to Fahrenheit:
$(\frac{9}{5} \times C.) + 32$ e.g. $\frac{9}{5} \times 100\ C. = 180$
$180 + 32 = 212\ F.$

Degrees F.	*Degrees C.*	*Degrees F.*	*Degrees C.*
0	−18	195	91
5	−15	212	100
29	−2	232	111
30	−1	234	112
34	2	236	113
50	10	238	114
60	16	240	116
65	18	242	117
70	21	244	118
80	27	246	119
82	28	265	129
85	29	275	135
86	30	280	138
100	38	300	149
110	43	310	154
120	49	325	163
135	57	340	171
140	60	350	177
143	62	360	182
145	63	365	185
149	65	370	188
150	66	375	191
155	68	380	193
158	70	385	196
160	71	390	199
170	77	395	202
175	79	400	204
180	82	425	218
185	85	450	232

APPENDIX E

MEASURES AND SUBSTITUTIONS FREQUENTLY USED

Measures of Capacity and Weight

3 t.	= 1 tb.	8 fluid oz.	= 1 c.
16 tb.	= 1 c.	16 oz.	= 1 lb.
2 c.	= 1 pt.	1 oz.	= 28.3 gm.
2 pt.	= 1 qt.	1 lb.	= 453.6 gm.

Weight and Measure Equivalents

1 lb. fat	= 2 c.*	1 lb. grated cheese	= 4 c.
1 lb. sugar (granulated)	= 2 c. + 2 tb.	1 oz. chocolate	= 1 square
1 lb. sugar (brown)	= 2⅔ c.	1 egg (medium)	= 3 tb.
1 lb. sugar (powdered)	= 3 c.	1 egg white (med.)	= 2 tb.
1 lb. sifted flour	= 4 c.†	1 egg yolk (med.)	= 1 tb.

* The newer creamed fats—1 lb. = 2⅛ c.
† The accurate equivalent varies with the type of flour.

SUBSTITUTIONS

For fat in terms of 1 c. of butter:

Bacon fat .... ⅘ c.
Chicken fat .... ⅔ c.
Cooking oils .... ⅞ c.
Hydrogenated fats .... ⅞ c.
Lard or compound .... ⅞ c.
Margarine .... 1 c.

For sugar in terms of 1 c. granulated:

In cake, quickbreads, etc.
Honey .... 1 c. .... decrease liquid one-half
Corn sirup .... 1 c. .... decrease liquid one-third

In puddings, custards, and sauces
Corn sirup .... 1½ c. .... decrease liquid one-fourth

For 1 tb. cornstarch: 1½ tb. flour

For 1 c. general utility flour: 1 c. minus 2 tb. bread flour

For 1 square chocolate: 3 tb. cocoa plus ½ tb. butter

For baking powder:

1) ½ t. soda plus 1 c. sour milk or dark molasses are equivalent in leavening power to 2 t. of quick-acting or 1⅓ t. of slow-acting baking powder
2) 1 beaten egg white is equivalent in leavening power to ½ t. of quick-acting or ⅓ t. of slow-acting baking powder.

For 1 c. fluid milk (sweet):

1) ½ c. evaporated milk plus ½ c. water
2) ¼ c. plus 2 t. powdered whole milk plus 1 cup minus 1⅔ tb. water
3) ½ c. plus 1 tb. powdered skim milk plus 1 cup minus 1⅓ tb. water and plus ¾ tb. butter
4) 1 c. skim milk plus ¾ tb. butter
5) 1 c. buttermilk plus ¾ tb. butter.

APPENDIX F

APPROXIMATE BOILING TEMPERATURE OF WATER AT VARIOUS ALTITUDES *

Altitude	*Boiling point of water*	
Feet	Degrees F.	Degrees C.
Sea Level	212.0	100.0
2,000	208.4	98.4
5,000	203.0	95.0
7,500	198.4	92.4
10,000	194.0	90.0
15,000	185.0	85.0
30,000	158.0	70.0

* *Handbook of Food Preparation*, American Home Economics Association, Washington, 1954.

APPENDIX G

This material was adapted from *Prevent Spoilage and Poor Quality in Home-Canned Foods,* a chart by Winifred J. Leverenz and O. B. Williams. This and *Some Important Factors Causing Poor Quality in Home-Canned Foods* are obtainable from Mrs. Winifred Leverenz, Box 35, Wallowa, Oregon.

I: HOW TO PREVENT SPOILAGE IN CANNED FOODS

At least 80 per cent of spoiled food is caused by poor seals. Good seals depend on careful work. Follow directions that come with jar lids or sealer. Replace lost directions from manufacturer of jar lids or sealer or from your home demonstration agent. Check these points carefully when canning:

In Jars Avoid:

1. Nicks or chip on rims of jars.
2. Old or damaged jar rubbers or rubber compound in lid.
3. Rubbers adjusted improperly.
4. Particles of food or grease on sealing surfaces.
5. Insufficient heat to seal lid.
6. Rough handling when processing; inverting or tilting jars while food is hot.
7. Excess fat—deteriorates rubber during storage.
8. Improper storage:
   a. Heat and light deteriorate rubber; may cause spoilage.
   b. Freezing may break seal.

In Tin Cans Avoid:

1. A poorly adjusted sealer. Lids with compound gaskets must have a tighter seal than those with paper gaskets.
2. Letting paper gasket get wet; it often falls out.
3. Using badly bent cans or placing them crooked in sealer.
4. Food particles or grease on rim of can.
5. Too high pressure or a sudden release of steam may cause seam to spread in number 3 cans and larger.
6. Fat on the compound gasket; may cause deterioration.

How to Prevent Underprocessing

1. Use reliable timetables for pressure cooker or water bath.
2. Can low-acid vegetables and meats in pressure cooker only.
3. Use pressure cooker with accurate gauge.
4. Do not close petcock of cooker before air is driven out.
5. Never pack containers too full or too tight; especially shelled beans, corn, greens, mature peas, and pumpkin.
6. Avoid using excess fat in meats or adding fat to vegetables. Bacteria are less readily killed in fat than in water.
7. Have food hot when sealed.

8. Use rack and arrange jars in water bath to allow free circulation of water.
9. When using pressure cooker, count processing time when gauge registers necessary pressure. When using water bath, count time when water begins to boil after containers have been put in.
10. Increase processing time in water bath if water does not completely cover containers; if water does not boil constantly; if kettle is not tightly covered; or if jars have unusually large diameters.

Food	Description of Spoilage	Organism
I *Fruit and Fruit Juices* (not tomatoes).	*Fermentation:* Bubbles; a cheesy, alcoholic odor; a sour taste. Carbon dioxide which accumulates during fermentation may break seal on jar or spread seam of can. Usually there is an outburst of gas and a spurt of liquid when container is opened.	Yeast
II *Fruit, Fruit Juices, and Tomato Products.*	*Swells in Fruit:* Gaseous and frothy in appearance. Has bad odor.	Bacteria: acid-tolerant and usually non-sporeforming.
III *Tomatoes and Tomato Juice (not fruit)*	*Flat Sour in Tomatoes:* A medicinal, sour, or bitter flavor. Sometimes a sour odor. Does not have gas or change of appearance.	Bacteria: mesophilic group; sporeforming.
IV *Fruit, Fruit Juices and Tomato Products.*	*Mold:* A fuzzy, grayish or white growth on surface of food. Usually musty odor. Food often slimy.	Mold
V *Vegetables and Meat.*	Same as IV	Mold
VI *Vegetables and Meat. (This spoilage is common in fat meat, greens, corn, and mature shelled beans and peas.)*	*Putrefactive:* a very foul odor which is more pronounced upon heating. Slimy or soft. Usually darker than normal product. Gas *always* present.	Bacteria: A putrefactive anaerobe which is sporeforming.

PREVENT KINDS OF SPOILAGE

Prevention	Remarks
1. Have good seal. 2. Use water bath for processing; not open kettle. Boiling food in open kettle will destroy yeast; however, more organisms from air or container may get on food as it is being transferred to jar or can; therefore, fruit should be heated in water bath after packing in container.	1. Easiest organism killed by heat. 2. Usually develops within a short time after canning. 3. Foods spoiled by yeast not harmful; usually have very disagreeable flavor; should not be eaten. 4. Yeasts more easily killed in unsweetened fruit or fruit cooked in light sirup.
1. Use fresh food. 2. Have food containers and equipment clean. 3. Process adequately.	1. Spoilage develops within a few days after processing. 2. Food not dangerous to health but not wholesome.
1. Use fresh, clean, sound tomatoes. 2. Have food hot when sealed. 3. Cool quickly after canning. 4. Store in cool place.	1. Not dangerous to health, but unappetizing in flavor.
1. Have good seal. 2. Use water bath for processing; not open kettle. Boiling food in open kettle destroys mold; however, more organisms from air or container may get on food as it is being transferred to jar or can; therefore, fruit should be heated in water bath after packing in container.	1. Not dangerous in small amounts on fruits and tomatoes. Remove mold and part of food near it; boil rest of food 10 min. in open kettle before tasting. 2. Mold may destroy acidity of fruit, affect protein and consume air present; then botulinum organism can develop. Does not apply to preserves and jelly because of high sugar and solids content, nor to pickles because of acid content. With these, remove mold and some of product; not necessary to reheat.
1. Have good seal. 2. Always use pressure cooker for meats and vegetables.	1. *Dangerous.* 2. Discard by burning or burying with lye. 3. Usually due to poor seal.
1. Underprocessing causes this spoilage. Process all vegetables and meats in pressure cooker. Follow processing times in reliable canning books or bulletins. 2. Have food, all utensils, table surface, and containers thoroughly clean. 3. Use clean water for brine.	1. Spoilage develops in a few days or within several weeks. 2. Do not taste unheated food if suspected of putrefactive spoilage. May be *dangerous.* Boil with frequent stirring for 15 to 20 min. before tasting. If odor becomes more pronounced, destroy food and container by burning or burying with lye. 3. In meats, excess fat may make food difficult to process adequately. 4. Never add meat to vegetables before canning.

Food	Description of Spoilage	Organism
VII *Vegetables and meat:* *All vegetables and meat not properly processed are susceptible.*	*Botulinum:* Protein foods may have a cheesy or rancid butter odor, or rotten odor which becomes more pronounced by heating. Gas sometimes but not always present. Liquid sometimes but not always cloudy. Food sometimes soft or slimy but not always. When typical, like putrefactive described above, but *it is not always typical.* In such products as snap beans, greens and asparagus, the spoilage may not be detected by appearance, odor, or even taste.	Bacteria: Clostridium botulinum—a sporeforming putrefactive anaerobe—found in dirt and most *dangerous* of all bacteria which may be present in foods.
VIII *Vegetables:* *Shelled beans, peas and corn are very susceptible. Also common in pumpkin, greens, and mature snap beans.*	*"Flat Sour:"* No gas present and no bulged seam. Disagreeable sour flavor. Unpleasant odor. Usually cloudy liquid and sloppy appearance.	Bacteria: Thermophilic group—very resistant spores.
IX *Vegetables:* *Common in greens, mature peas, shelled beans, and corn.*	*"Swell:"* Gas present. Cans swell, jars burst, crack, or break the seal. If match is lighted as gas escapes when swelled can is opened, a flame will burn. Usually faint odor of rancid butter.	Bacteria: Thermophilic anaerobe—sporeforming.
X *Vegetables:* *Occurs in corn, mature peas, and beans.*	*Sulfide spoilage:* A grayish or black discoloration throughout the product. Rotten egg odor due to hydrogen sulfide. No gas.	Bacteria: Thermophilic group—must have protein present.
XI *Black Beets*	*Black Beets:* No unusual odor or gas. Blackening of beets only indication of spoilage.	Bacteria: Mesophilic—must have iron present.

PREVENT KINDS OF SPOILAGE (Continued)

Prevention	Remarks
1. *Underprocessing* causes this spoilage. Process all vegetables and meats in pressure cooker. Follow processing times in reliable canning books or bulletins. 2. Have food, all utensils, table surface, and containers thoroughly clean. 3. Use clean water for brine.	1. *Deadly poisonous. Toxin so poisonous that death has resulted from merely tasting* a small bite of spoiled food. 2. Usually develops in canned food during storage of 2 or 3 weeks or longer. 3. Boil doubtful food in an open kettle for 15 to 20 min. with frequent stirring before tasting. If a bad odor develops during heating, destroy food and container immediately by burning or burying with lye. 4. Boil all meat or low acid vegetables processed by any method other than pressure cooker before tasting or eating, even if no signs of spoilage are evident. 5. Reheat such food if served at later meal. If organism is present, toxin may develop between meals. 6. Botulinum toxin develops in canned foods only when they have been processed improperly. 7. Does not develop in pickles, preserves or jellies.
1. Speed in gathering, preparing, processing, and cooling is most important. 2. Keep food cool while gathering, preparing for canning, and in storage. 3. Avoid temperature of 100° to 130° F. at all times. Food should be kept higher or lower than this temperature. 4. Cleanliness is essential. 5. Never add sugar to vegetables before canning.	1. Not poisonous, but should not be eaten. 2. Thermophilic bacteria causing flat sour develop best between 100° and 130° F.; avoid letting food stand at this temperature for any length of time, *before*, *during*, or even *after* canning. 3. When bacteria are not all destroyed during canning, if food is cooled quickly and stored in cool place, bacteria remain dormant and cause no trouble. If not cooled quickly and not stored in cool place, bacteria may develop and cause spoilage.
Same as VIII	1. Not poisonous, but should not be eaten. 2. Spoilage usually develops in one to four weeks if stored in warm place.
Same as VIII	1. Too foul to eat. 2. Hydrogen sulfide similar in appearance to iron sulfide or copper sulfide which are not spoilage. Difference is foul odor in hydrogen sulfide spoilage.
1. Process properly. 2. Avoid contact with iron. 3. Cleanliness is essential.	1. Iron must be present for bacteria to develop color. Iron may come from water, iron kettle, or chipped enamel vessel used for precooking. After long storage, iron base of can may cause trouble.

III. HOW TO IDENTIFY AND PREVENT

DESCRIPTION	REMARKS
I *Brownish discoloration of fruit: apples, pears, peaches, apricots,* and *pineapple.*	1. If discolored just on top, fruit was too cool when sealed or was exposed to air too long before heating. May be poor seal. 2. Discolored fruit not harmful to eat if no gas present, no off-odor nor off-flavor, and liquid clear.
II *Pears and apples turning pink or light purple.*	1. Fruit grown in very dry, hot weather often turns pink. 2. An enzymatic and chemical reaction. 3. Takes place in tin cans more often than jars. 4. Found in both commercially and home-canned pears.
III *Grayish to black discoloration. Occurs in meats, corn, mature shelled peas and beans. More noticeable in top of can and along seam. Sometimes scattered throughout contents. Plain can sometimes has purplish splotches on surface.*	1. Small amounts of sulphur compounds are liberated by protein foods during processing. These combine with iron base of tin can, jar lid, or other iron to form iron sulfide which is grayish to black in color. 2. If no bad odor, food may be eaten. In case it might be spoilage, boil at least 15 min. in open kettle before tasting. 3. Unattractive and should be avoided if possible.
IV *Brownish discoloration in tender young corn.*	1. If corn too young or overcooked when very young and tender, sugar caramelizes and causes brownish discoloration. 2. Not harmful but lacks best flavor. 3. Corn at right milk state (not too young nor too old) yields best.
V *Faded food.*	1. Faded food safe to eat if no gas, off-odor, or cloudy liquid present. 2. It is usually considered that the deeper the color, the more food value present, especially Vitamin C.

KINDS OF POOR QUALITY CANNED FOOD

PREVENTION

---

1. Treat with one of following solutions:
   a. 2 T. vinegar or lemon juice and 2 T. salt in 1 gal. cold water. Leave peeled pieces in solution only long enough to prepare enough fruit to precook or pack in jars—not longer than 15 to 25 min. Drain and start canning immediately.
   b. Dissolve 1 level t. thiocarbomide in 1 gal. cool water. Leave peeled fruit in solution 1 min.; drain 30 min. to 1 hour. in cool place before canning.
   c. Dissolve ½ to ¾ oz. sodium bisulfite in 1 gal. water. Leave peeled fruit in solution 1 min. Drain 30 min. to 1 hr. in cool place before canning.
   Note: These two chemicals are inexpensive and harmless. May be ordered through most druggists. Do not increase proportions given. Use enamel, aluminum or crock for holding solution.
2. Handle fruit quickly to prevent unnecessary exposure to air or treat with solution described above.
3. Drop into prepared sirup as fruit is being peeled if not treated with solution described above. Especially good for pineapple.
4. To pack raw and steam, treat with solution described above or cover with hot sirup and start heating as soon as possible.
5. Have food hot when sealed.
6. Do not overcook or underprocess. Either may cause discoloration. Follow directions in reliable publications.
7. Store jars in dark place.

---

1. Keep fruit cool after it is gathered before canning.
2. Avoid overcooking fruit or heating at too high temperature.
3. Store in a cool, dark place.

---

1. Avoid precooking in iron or copper kettle.
2. Avoid water with iron or copper in it.
3. Use stainless steel knives for preparation.
4. Use pure salt such as dairy, cheese, or curing salt, if possible.
5. Use proper kind of can.
6. Use young, tender vegetables.
7. Work quickly; do not let vegetables stand too long.
8. Avoid excess fat in meats. Never add fat to vegetables.
9. Avoid too much head space in can.
10. Have food hot when sealed.
11. Store containers in cool, dark place.

---

1. Avoid overcooking.
2. Use young corn, but not too young.
3. Cool rapidly after canning.

---

1. Store jars in dark place; light destroys color.
2. Use "R" enamel cans for red foods such as berries, beets, or cherries.
3. Use varieties that retain color when canned.
4. Fresh, young, tender products retain color best.
5. Improper preparation and precooking destroy color—e.g., beets and greens.
6. If contents are too cool when sealed, food on top often fades.
7. Avoid loss of liquid when canning in glass.
8. Do not overcook; store in cool place.
9. Use food within 1 to 2 years; age hastens fading.
10. Add 1 t. lemon juice per pint to strawberries canned in glass just before berries are processed.

DESCRIPTION	REMARKS
VI *Floating fruit.*	1. If no gas or off-odor present, food safe to eat. 2. Overcooking causes loss of food value as well as texture.
VII *Mushy food* (*not spoiled*).	1. If no gas or off-odor present, mushy food safe to eat. 2. Overcooking causes loss of food value as well as texture. 3. If overcooking of foods cannot be prevented, use in soups.
VIII *Toughness or hardness in foods.*	1. Do not use soda to soften vegetables; it destroys food value. 2. If vegetables are extremely hard, and if cooking does not tenderize them, grind and use in soups.
IX *Cloudiness in liquid: common in mature peas and beans.*	1. Cloudiness often indicates spoilage; be *cautious*. Flat sour and botulinum spoilage often accompanied by cloudiness. 2. Look for disagreeable odor. Boil food 15 min. before tasting if liquid is very cloudy or if there is question about how food was canned. If food doesn't smell or taste normal after heating, discard. In spoiled foods white deposits and cloudiness of liquid are usually in large amounts.
X *Yellow deposits* (*Called glucoside crystals*) *in snap beans, greens, asparagus.*	1. Little yellow specks or deposits found several weeks to six months after canning. When jar is vigorously shaken or contents heated, deposits dissolve and disappear. 2. No off-odor or unusual flavor; green color not affected. 3. Harmless; may be eaten without danger of poisoning if food is safe otherwise.
XI *White deposits* (*oxalate crystals*).	1. If in large amounts, may be washed off. 2. Not dangerous if eaten. Be sure white deposits do not indicate spoilage as described under cloudiness.
XII *Swelled cans but not spoilage* (*hydrogen springer*). *Often found in prunes, berries, apples and kraut canned in plain tin cans.*	1. Caused by reaction of acid on metal base of can. 2. If no off-odor, cloudy liquid, unusual color, or disagreeable flavor, food may be used without danger.

KINDS OF POOR QUALITY CANNED FOOD (Continued)

PREVENTION

1. Avoid overripe fruit.
2. Fill container full of fruit.
3. Refill after steaming if "pack raw and steam" method is used.
4. Avoid too much sugar.
5. Have food hot when sealed.
6. Do not overcook or overprocess.

---

1. Avoid overripe products.
2. Use good canning varieties.
3. Gather in cool of day; work quickly in preparing for canning.
4. Do not precook food too long or leave it at warm temperature longer than necessary.
5. Avoid much stirring or rough handling in packing.
6. Bring pressure up quickly for vegetables or meats and bring water to a boil quickly for fruits in water bath.
7. Avoid letting pressure go too high.
8. Do not process too long.
9. Cool quickly after canning.
10. Store in cool place but avoid freezing.

---

1. Avoid underripe fruits or too mature vegetables—e.g., shelled beans, peas and corn.
2. Avoid hard water for sirup or brine.
3. Salt containing large amounts of calcium or magnesium causes toughness. May be desirable in tomatoes.
4. Process proper length of time.
5. Some varieties of vegetables not adaptable for canning often become hard or tough.

---

1. Starch content in too mature beans and peas usually causes cloudiness.
2. Poor canning varieties cause cloudiness.
3. Uneven grading results in cloudiness.
4. If peas or beans are shelled too long before canning or if they heat by standing in too deep a container, cloudiness may result.
5. Hard water or salt containing impurities or lump-preventing substances, e.g., magnesium carbonate, may cause cloudiness.
6. In fruit, poor quality sugar or overripe fruit results in cloudiness.
7. In kraut or dill pickles, fermentation causes cloudiness. It is normal and not harmful.

---

1. Cannot be prevented as far as is now known.
2. Probably due to soil and climatic conditions during growth.
3. Yellow deposits caused by chemical reaction of sugar and a complex organic compound.

---

1. Cannot be prevented as far as is now known.
2. Forms from normal constituents of food.

---

1. Use proper type of container.
2. Have food hot when sealed.
3. Fill container full.
4. Process correctly.
5. Cool quickly.
6. Store in cool place.
7. Do not store too long.

APPENDIX H

Equipment That Is Essential for Satisfactory Home Canning

1) Scales for weighing.
2) Accurate measuring utensils, including cups and spoons.
3) A clock for correct timing.
4) Cutting boards.
5) Sharp knives and scissors.
6) Spoons, including at least one with a long handle.
7) Ladles or small dippers.
8) Brushes for cleaning food and equipment.
9) Saucepans and kettles for preparing, scalding, and cooking food.
10) Cheesecloth for straining fruit juice and jelly, and cheesecloth, colander, or wire basket for blanching fruits and vegetables.
11) A utensil large and deep enough to use for the water-bath method of processing. A special canner, fireless cooker utensil, pail, bucket, or well-cleaned wash boiler may be used, depending upon the amount of canning that is done at one time and what is available that is suitable.
12) A rack for the above utensil to raise jars or cans above the bottom of the processing utensil.
13) A pressure cooker if meat, semi-acid, or low-acid vegetables are canned, OR, for small amounts, a pressure pan that operates accurately at 10 pounds pressure.
14) Containers for food—jars, tin cans, bottles, jelly glasses, etc. If tin cans are used, there are three kinds for use in canning various types of food: plain, "C" enamel, and "R" enamel. Newer jars are designed for freezing also.
15) Rubbers for jars. New ones (or self-seal lids) should be used.
16) A sealer if tin cans are used.
17) Labels that will stay on the containers.
18) A wax pencil for marking tin cans before they are labeled.

Equipment That Is Desirable but Not Essential

1) Saccharometer for determining density of sirups.
2) Salinometer for determining density of brines.
3) Thermometer for helping to judge when jellies and preserves are done.
4) Maximum thermometer or master gauge for testing gauge of pressure cooker.
5) Stop watch for accurate timing.
6) Apple corer.
7) Fruit parer and cherry stoner if enough fruit is used to warrant such special equipment.
8) Jar lifter and tongs for removing hot utensils from water and processing utensil. Asbestos gloves are also helpful in this connection.

9) Plate scraper.
10) Wide-mouth funnel.
11) Standard funnel and capper if fruit juice is bottled.
12) Sep-ro-siv for extracting juice.
13) Jel-meter for gauging amount of sugar to use for jelly.

EQUIPMENT FOR PREPARING FOODS FOR FREEZING

1) Items 1–9 and 17 in the first list on page 686.
2) Suitable containers for the food and/or moisture-vapor-proof paper for wrapping.
3) Stand equipped with funnel for filling cartons, adjustable for pint and quart cartons.
4) Adjustable platform for ease in sealing cartons.
5) Iron or curling iron for sealing.
6) Gummed tape for fastening paper-wrapped packages.
7) Insulated case for taking food to locker if locker is some distance from home.

APPENDIX I

SIRUPS * FOR CANNING AND FREEZING

Per Cent Sirup	*Sugar (c)*	*Water (c)*	*Yield (c)*
30	2	4	5
40	3	4	5½
50	4¾	4	6½
60	7	4	7¾

* For a less sweet sirup, some corn sirup—up to ¼ of the sugar—may be used.

APPENDIX J

DENSITY OF BRINE FOR BRINING AND PICKLING

Per Cent Brine	*Water*	*Salt*		*Salinometer Reading*
		Wt.	*Meas.*	
5	1 gal.	½ lb.	1 c.	20°
10	1 gal.	1 lb.	2 c.	40°
20	1 gal.	2 lb.	4 c.	80°

APPENDIX K

DIRECTIONS FOR MAKING LEMON OR ORANGE PECTIN

1) Pare the colored outside skin from Ponderosa lemons *or* thick-skinned oranges, being sure to remove all oil cells.

2) Remove all the white peel, being careful not to remove any of the pulp.

3) Run the peel through a food chopper.

4) Measure the peel and put it into a large saucepan, with 2 c. of water for each cup of peel, and 2 tb. of lemon juice.

5) Let the mixture stand an hour, boil gently for 10 min., and let it stand overnight.

6) Add 4 c. of water, boil 5 min., cool, and strain through a jelly bag.

7) To the remaining pulp add 3 c. of water and 2 tb. of lemon juice, boil 5 min., cool, and strain.

8) Repeat 7.

9) Combine the three extractions, boil 10 min., and fill sterilized jars. Seal.

APPENDIX L

RECORD FOR CANNED FOOD *

Food	*Container*	*Date*	*No. Packages*
Corn (cream style)	No. 2 "C"	6/20/59	1–2–3–4–5– 6–7–8
Corn (whole kernel)	Quart	7/10/59	1–2–3–4–5 6–7
Peaches, ½'s; 30% sir.	No.2	8/10/59	1–2–3–4–5
Peaches, sl.; 40% sir.	Pint	8/10/59	1–2–3–4–5 6–7–8

* Place record on door of storage cupboard or equally handy. Labels on shelves—CORN, PEACHES, etc. Pencil at hand to cross through number of packages removed, starting at last number.

RECORD FOR FROZEN FOOD *

Food	*Size Package*	*Date*	*Place in Freezer*	*No. Package*
Broilers	2 halves	5/8/59	3–R	1–2–3–4–5
Corn (whole kernel)	Pint	6/18/59	1–R	1–2–3–4–5 6–7–8
Peaches (sl.; 40% sir.)	Pint	8/10/59	2–L	1–2–3–4–5 6–7–8–9
T-bone steaks	2	2/4/60	3–M	1–2–3–4
Rolls	8	4/8/60	1–R	1–2–3

* Place record as near as possible to freezer; pencil at hand to cross through number of packages removed, starting at last number.

APPENDIX M

CAKE RECIPE ADJUSTMENT FOR HIGH ALTITUDES *

Adjustment	*3,000 feet*	*5,000 feet*	*7,000 feet*
Reduce baking powder For each teaspoon, decrease	1/8 t.	1/8 to 1/4 t.	1/4 to 1/2 t.
Reduce sugar For each cup, decrease	no change	usually no change	1 to 2 tb.
Increase liquid For each cup, add	1 to 2 tb.	2 to 3 tb.	3 to 4 tb.
Shortening	In very rich cakes, it is sometimes necessary to reduce shortening by 1 to 2 tb.		

* *Handbook of Food Preparation*, American Home Economics Association, 1954.

GLOSSARY

American ice cream (see: Ice cream).

Bake, (a) To cook in an oven or oven-type appliance by means of dry heat. (b) To cook on a hot metal surface, e.g., griddle or waffle baker.

Barbecue, To broil or to roast on a spit, using low heat and basting frequently with a rather highly seasoned sauce.

Baste, To moisten meat or other foods while cooking, thus adding flavor and preventing drying. Melted fat, meat drippings, fruit juice, or a sauce may be the liquid used.

Beat, (a) To mix ingredients, using a motion that lifts the mixture over and over. (b) To incorporate air with a whisk or rotary beater.

Blend, To mix two or more ingredients thoroughly.

Boil, To cook in liquid—usually water—in which bubbles rise continually and break on the surface.

Braise, To cook meat slowly in a covered utensil in a small amount of liquid or in steam. Preceding this cooking, the meat is usually browned in a small amount of fat.

Bread, To coat with fine bread or cracker crumbs, or with crumbs and slightly beaten egg, or with seasoned flour, egg, and crumbs.

Brown, To cook food until the surface has a desirable brown color.

Caramelize, To heat sugar until a brown color and characteristic flavor develop.

Catalyst, A substance that speeds a chemical reaction without entering into the reaction.

Chop, To cut into pieces with a sharp tool, as a knife or chopper.

Coenzyme, A specific nonprotein essential to an enzyme system.

Cream, To soften fat or combine ingredients until soft and creamy, using a spoon, a wooden paddle, or other implement, as the beater of an electric mixer.

Cut, To divide food materials with a knife or scissors.

Cut and fold, To combine ingredients by cutting vertically through the mixture with the edge of a mixing spoon, then moving the spoon along the bottom of the bowl and up to the surface, turning a part of the mixture over with each complete motion.

Cut in, To distribute fat in dry ingredients with knives, a pastry blender, or a blending fork.

Dice, To cut into cubes.

Enzyme, A complex organic substance that acts as a catalyst for a specific metabolic reaction.

Frappé (see: Ices).

French ice cream (see: Ice cream).

Fricassee, To braise—usually applied to chicken.

Fry, To cook in fat—either a small amount or sufficient to submerge the food.

Glaze, To cover with a transparent coating of jelly, juice thickened slightly, or caramel.

Grill, To broil.

Grind, To reduce to particles, by cutting, crushing, or grinding.

Haugh unit, A figure which represents the relationship between the height of the albumin of a broken-out egg and the weight of the egg. It provides a uniform scale of quality as expressed in U.S.D.A. grades. Haugh units may be determined by use of an interior quality calculator for eggs.

Hormone, A chemical compound secreted by the ductless glands into the blood stream.

Ice cream (stirred to freeze). Sweetened, flavored milk and/or cream, with or without thickening. Three general types:

American—A cooked ice cream mixture thickened with eggs and starch.

French—A similar mixture thickened with eggs.

Philadelphia—An uncooked mixture of thin cream, sugar, and flavoring.

Ice Cream (frozen without stirring). Heavy cream base. Three general types are:

Mousse.—Heavy cream sweetened and flavored.

Parfait.—Beaten egg whites into which hot sirup is beaten, combined with whipped cream and flavoring.

Ice cream (above) with heavy cream rather than light and viscosity increased by gelatin, egg white, starch, or a combination of these.

Ices (stirred to freeze). Fruit juice base. Four general types are:

Water ice—Fruit juice and sugar sirup.

Frappé—Fruit juice and sugar syrup frozen to a mush.

Sherbet—Water ice to which egg white or gelatin is added, or in which milk and/or cream is part of the liquid.

International Units, (a) The equivalent of 0.3 microgram of pure vitamin A. (b) The vitamin activity of 0.025 micrograms of vitamin D_3.

Knead, To manipulate with a pressing motion accompanied by folding and stretching.

Lard, To insert strips of fat (lardoons) into or to place strips of fat on uncooked lean meat or fish to give flavor and prevent drying.

Lesion, An injured or diseased region of the body.

Marinade, A liquid, such as French dressing, in which food is allowed to stand before another preparation process.

Marinate, To cover or coat food with a marinade and let it stand to season and tenderize it.

Metabolism, The chemical changes in an organism or in a cell by which food is built up into living protoplasm and protoplasm is broken down into simpler compounds with the liberation of energy.

Microgram, 1/1000 of a gram.

Mince, To cut or chop into very small pieces.

Mousse, (See: Ice cream).

Over-run, The increase in volume, due to incorporation of air, of a dessert frozen with stirring.

Pan-broil, To cook, uncovered, in a hot utensil with little or no fat. As fat accumulates, it is poured off.

Par-boil, To simmer or boil until the food is partially cooked.

Pare, To cut off outside covering.

Parfait (see: Ice cream).

Peel, To strip off outside covering.

Philadelphia ice cream (see: Ice cream).

Poach, To simmer in a hot liquid, being careful to retain the shape of the food as nearly as possible.

Pot-roast, To braise.

Precursor, A substance which is converted into another substance.

Roast, To cook meat in an oven, with no added moisture, or to cook it on a spit. The term may apply to other foods, as corn or potatoes, cooked in ashes or under coals.

Saturated solution, A solution in which no more of the solute will dissolve in the solvent at a given temperature.

Sauté, To cook with only enough fat to keep the food from sticking to the utensil.

Scald, (a) To heat a liquid until bubbles appear where the surface of the liquid touches the utensil. (b) To preheat in boiling water or steam.

Sear, To brown the surface of meat by short application of intense heat.

Sherbet, (See: Ices).

Simmer, To cook in liquid in which bubbles break below the surface—temperature about 185° F. (85° C.).

Sorbet (see: Ices).

Steam, To cook in steam, with or without pressure, in a covered utensil.

Steep, To leave a substance in liquid below the boiling point to extract flavor or color.

Sterilize, To destroy microorganisms by means of boiling water, steam, or dry heat.

Stew, To simmer in a small quantity of water.

Stir, To mix ingredients with a circular motion.

Supersaturated solution, A solution in which the solute remains dissolved instead of being precipitated as the temperature of the solution decreases—e.g., sucrose in water.

Syndrome, Symptoms and signs which, taken together, characterize a disease or lesion.

Toast, To brown by dry heat.

Unsaturated solution, A solution in which more solute can be dissolved in a solvent at a given temperature.

Water ice (see: Ices).

Whip, To beat rapidly to incorporate air and thus increase volume.

GENERAL INDEX

Table of Abbreviations: *ff.*: following *q.v.*: see also *passim*: frequent references *s.v.*: under